Solutions Manual for

Algebra 1

An Incremental Development

Second Edition

JOHN H. SAXON, JR.

SAXON PUBLISHERS, INC.

Algebra 1: An Incremental Development
Second Edition
Solutions Manual

Printed in the United States of America

ISBN: 0-939798-98-0

Production supervisor: David Pond
Production coordinator: Joan Coleman

Third printing: February 1995

This manual contains solutions to every problem in the *Algebra 1*, Second Edition, textbook by John Saxon. Early solutions of a problem of a particular type contain every step. Later solutions omit steps considered unnecessary.

The following people were instrumental in the development of this solutions manual, and we gratefully acknowledge their contributions: Mikki Hunter, Jonathan Maltz, Kevin McKeown, and Smith Richardson for working the solutions and proofing the various revisions; Tim Maltz and Letha Steinbron for typesetting the manual; and Tim Maltz and John Chitwood for creating the artwork.

Saxon Publishers, Inc.
1320 W. Lindsey, Suite 100
Norman, Oklahoma 73069

Problem Set A

1. $\dfrac{1}{5} + \dfrac{2}{5} = \dfrac{3}{5}$

2. $\dfrac{3}{8} - \dfrac{2}{8} = \dfrac{1}{8}$

3. $\dfrac{4}{3} - \dfrac{1}{3} + \dfrac{8}{3} = \dfrac{3}{3} + \dfrac{8}{3} = \dfrac{11}{3} = 3\dfrac{2}{3}$

4. $\dfrac{1}{3} + \dfrac{1}{5} = \dfrac{5}{15} + \dfrac{3}{15} = \dfrac{8}{15}$

5. $\dfrac{3}{8} - \dfrac{1}{5} = \dfrac{15}{40} - \dfrac{8}{40} = \dfrac{7}{40}$

6. $\dfrac{2}{3} - \dfrac{1}{8} = \dfrac{16}{24} - \dfrac{3}{24} = \dfrac{13}{24}$

7. $\dfrac{1}{13} + \dfrac{1}{5} = \dfrac{5}{65} + \dfrac{13}{65} = \dfrac{18}{65}$

8. $\dfrac{17}{15} - \dfrac{2}{3} = \dfrac{17}{15} - \dfrac{10}{15} = \dfrac{7}{15}$

9. $\dfrac{5}{9} + \dfrac{2}{5} = \dfrac{25}{45} + \dfrac{18}{45} = \dfrac{43}{45}$

10. $\dfrac{14}{17} - \dfrac{6}{34} = \dfrac{28}{34} - \dfrac{6}{34} = \dfrac{22}{34} = \dfrac{11}{17}$

11. $\dfrac{5}{13} + \dfrac{1}{26} = \dfrac{10}{26} + \dfrac{1}{26} = \dfrac{11}{26}$

12. $\dfrac{4}{7} - \dfrac{2}{5} = \dfrac{20}{35} - \dfrac{14}{35} = \dfrac{6}{35}$

13. $\dfrac{4}{7} + \dfrac{1}{8} + \dfrac{1}{2} = \dfrac{32}{56} + \dfrac{7}{56} + \dfrac{28}{56} = \dfrac{67}{56}$
    $= 1\dfrac{11}{56}$

14. $\dfrac{3}{5} + \dfrac{1}{8} + \dfrac{1}{8} = \dfrac{24}{40} + \dfrac{5}{40} + \dfrac{5}{40} = \dfrac{34}{40} = \dfrac{17}{20}$

15. $\dfrac{5}{11} - \dfrac{1}{6} + \dfrac{2}{3} = \dfrac{30}{66} - \dfrac{11}{66} + \dfrac{44}{66} = \dfrac{63}{66} = \dfrac{21}{22}$

16. $2\dfrac{1}{2} + 3\dfrac{1}{5} = 2\dfrac{5}{10} + 3\dfrac{2}{10} = 5\dfrac{7}{10}$

17. $7\dfrac{3}{8} + 4\dfrac{7}{3} = 7\dfrac{9}{24} + 4\dfrac{56}{24} = 11\dfrac{65}{24} = 13\dfrac{17}{24}$

18. $1\dfrac{1}{8} + 7\dfrac{2}{5} = 1\dfrac{5}{40} + 7\dfrac{16}{40} = 8\dfrac{21}{40}$

19. $15\dfrac{1}{3} - 7\dfrac{4}{5} = 15\dfrac{5}{15} - 7\dfrac{12}{15} = 14\dfrac{20}{15} - 7\dfrac{12}{15}$
    $= 7\dfrac{8}{15}$

20. $42\dfrac{3}{8} - 21\dfrac{3}{4} = 42\dfrac{3}{8} - 21\dfrac{6}{8} = 41\dfrac{11}{8} - 21\dfrac{6}{8}$
    $= 20\dfrac{5}{8}$

21. $22\dfrac{2}{5} - 13\dfrac{7}{15} = 22\dfrac{6}{15} - 13\dfrac{7}{15}$
    $= 21\dfrac{21}{15} - 13\dfrac{7}{15} = 8\dfrac{14}{15}$

22. $421\dfrac{1}{11} - 17\dfrac{4}{3} = 421\dfrac{3}{33} - 17\dfrac{44}{33}$
    $= 419\dfrac{69}{33} - 17\dfrac{44}{33} = 402\dfrac{25}{33}$

23. $78\dfrac{2}{5} - 14\dfrac{7}{10} = 78\dfrac{4}{10} - 14\dfrac{7}{10}$
    $= 77\dfrac{14}{10} - 14\dfrac{7}{10} = 63\dfrac{7}{10}$

24. $43\dfrac{1}{13} - 6\dfrac{5}{8} = 43\dfrac{8}{104} - 6\dfrac{65}{104}$
    $= 42\dfrac{112}{104} - 6\dfrac{65}{104} = 36\dfrac{47}{104}$

25. $21\dfrac{1}{5} - 15\dfrac{7}{13} = 21\dfrac{13}{65} - 15\dfrac{35}{65}$
    $= 20\dfrac{78}{65} - 15\dfrac{35}{65} = 5\dfrac{43}{65}$

26. $21\dfrac{2}{19} - 7\dfrac{7}{10} = 21\dfrac{20}{190} - 7\dfrac{133}{190}$
    $= 20\dfrac{210}{190} - 7\dfrac{133}{190} = 13\dfrac{77}{190}$

27. $43\dfrac{3}{17} - 21\dfrac{9}{10} = 43\dfrac{30}{170} - 21\dfrac{153}{170}$
    $= 42\dfrac{200}{170} - 21\dfrac{153}{170} = 21\dfrac{47}{170}$

28. $AC = AB + BC$
    $= 7\dfrac{1}{8} + 5\dfrac{2}{7}$
    $= 7\dfrac{7}{56} + 5\dfrac{16}{56}$
    $= 12\dfrac{23}{56}$ units

29. $CX = XL - LC$

$= 42\frac{1}{7} - 24\frac{2}{11}$

$= 42\frac{11}{77} - 24\frac{14}{77}$

$= 41\frac{88}{77} - 24\frac{14}{77}$

$= 17\frac{74}{77}$ **units**

30. $YX = KX - YZ - KZ$

$= 74\frac{1}{11} - 22\frac{1}{3} - 44\frac{2}{3}$

$= 74\frac{3}{33} - 22\frac{11}{33} - 44\frac{22}{33}$

$= 73\frac{36}{33} - 22\frac{11}{33} - 44\frac{22}{33}$

$= 7\frac{3}{33}$

$= 7\frac{1}{11}$ **units**

PROBLEM SET B

1. $\frac{3}{5} + \frac{2}{7} = \frac{21}{35} + \frac{10}{35} = \frac{31}{35}$

2. $\frac{7}{2} + \frac{13}{4} = \frac{14}{4} + \frac{13}{4} = \frac{27}{4} = 6\frac{3}{4}$

3. $\frac{8}{3} + \frac{1}{15} = \frac{40}{15} + \frac{1}{15} = \frac{41}{15} = 2\frac{11}{15}$

4. $5\frac{2}{5} + 7\frac{11}{10} = 5\frac{4}{10} + 7\frac{11}{10} = 12\frac{15}{10} = 13\frac{5}{10}$

$= 13\frac{1}{2}$

5. $8\frac{1}{3} + 3\frac{7}{5} = 8\frac{5}{15} + 3\frac{21}{15} = 11\frac{26}{15} = 12\frac{11}{15}$

6. $9\frac{3}{5} + 5\frac{8}{3} = 9\frac{9}{15} + 5\frac{40}{15} = 14\frac{49}{15} = 17\frac{4}{15}$

7. $23\frac{7}{10} - 14\frac{6}{7} = 23\frac{49}{70} - 14\frac{60}{70}$

$= 22\frac{119}{70} - 14\frac{60}{70} = 8\frac{59}{70}$

8. $42\frac{3}{8} - 14\frac{3}{4} = 42\frac{3}{8} - 14\frac{6}{8} = 41\frac{11}{8} - 14\frac{6}{8}$

$= 27\frac{5}{8}$

9. $22\frac{2}{5} - 14\frac{8}{15} = 22\frac{6}{15} - 14\frac{8}{15}$

$= 21\frac{21}{15} - 14\frac{8}{15} = 7\frac{13}{15}$

10. $426\frac{1}{11} - 16\frac{5}{3} = 426\frac{3}{33} - 16\frac{55}{33}$

$= 424\frac{69}{33} - 16\frac{55}{33} = 408\frac{14}{33}$

11. $8\frac{2}{5} - 3\frac{7}{3} = 8\frac{6}{15} - 3\frac{35}{15} = 6\frac{36}{15} - 3\frac{35}{15}$

$= 3\frac{1}{15}$

12. $42\frac{3}{13} - 5\frac{2}{5} = 42\frac{15}{65} - 5\frac{26}{65} = 41\frac{80}{65} - 5\frac{26}{65}$

$= 36\frac{54}{65}$

13. $CB = BD - CD$

$= 10\frac{3}{7} - 3\frac{1}{5}$

$= 10\frac{15}{35} - 3\frac{7}{35}$

$= 7\frac{8}{35}$ **in.**

14. $r = \frac{d}{2} = \frac{4\text{ cm}}{2} = 2$ cm

$A = \pi r^2$

$= 3.14(2\text{ cm})^2$

≈ 12.56 **cm²**

15. $A = s^2$

$36\text{ in.}^2 = s^2$

$s = \sqrt{36\text{ in.}^2}$

$s = 6$ **in.**

16. $C = 2\pi r$

$42\text{ m} = 2\pi r$

$r = \frac{42\text{ m}}{2(3.14)} \approx 6.69$ **m**

17. $P = (8 + 4 + 4 + 4 + 8 + 12)$ cm

$= 40$ **cm**

18. $P = (16 + 6 + 16 + 6)$ cm

$= 44$ **cm**

19. $A = A_{\text{Square}} + A_{\text{Semicircle}}$

$= (6)^2 + \frac{\pi(3)^2}{2}$

$= \left(36 + \frac{9\pi}{2}\right) \approx 50.13$ **m²**

20. $A = A_{\text{Triangle}} + A_{\text{Rectangle}}$

$= \frac{(10 \times 5)}{2} + (10 \times 5)$

$= 25 + 50 = 75$ **m²**

21. $A_{\text{Shaded}} = A_{\text{Parallelogram}} - A_{\text{Circle}}$
$= (24 \times 8) - \pi(2)^2$
$= 192 - 4\pi \approx \textbf{179.44 cm}^2$

22. $4\frac{2}{3} - 1\frac{8}{3} = 2\frac{8}{3} - 1\frac{8}{3} = \textbf{1}$

23. $16\frac{1}{4} - 5\frac{17}{2} = 15\frac{5}{4} - 13\frac{2}{4} = \textbf{2}\frac{\textbf{3}}{\textbf{4}}$

24. $14\frac{9}{2} - 12\frac{4}{3} = 14\frac{27}{6} - 12\frac{8}{6} = 2\frac{19}{6} = \textbf{5}\frac{\textbf{1}}{\textbf{6}}$

25. $121\frac{5}{8} - 6\frac{21}{3} = 121\frac{15}{24} - 6\frac{168}{24}$
$= 114\frac{183}{24} - 6\frac{168}{24} = 108\frac{15}{24} = \textbf{108}\frac{\textbf{5}}{\textbf{8}}$

26. $26\frac{5}{7} - 4\frac{8}{5} = 26\frac{25}{35} - 4\frac{56}{35} = 25\frac{60}{35} - 4\frac{56}{35}$
$= \textbf{21}\frac{\textbf{4}}{\textbf{35}}$

27. $93\frac{2}{7} - 12\frac{14}{5} = 93\frac{10}{35} - 12\frac{98}{35}$
$= 90\frac{115}{35} - 12\frac{98}{35} = \textbf{78}\frac{\textbf{17}}{\textbf{35}}$

28. $14\frac{7}{3} - 7\frac{14}{5} = 14\frac{35}{15} - 7\frac{42}{15} = 13\frac{50}{15} - 7\frac{42}{15}$
$= \textbf{6}\frac{\textbf{8}}{\textbf{15}}$

29. $15\frac{2}{11} - 3\frac{11}{2} = 15\frac{4}{22} - 3\frac{121}{22}$
$= 9\frac{136}{22} - 3\frac{121}{22} = \textbf{6}\frac{\textbf{15}}{\textbf{22}}$

30. $93\frac{1}{5} - 6\frac{8}{3} = 93\frac{3}{15} - 6\frac{40}{15} = 90\frac{48}{15} - 6\frac{40}{15}$
$= \textbf{84}\frac{\textbf{8}}{\textbf{15}}$

Problem Set C

1. $12\frac{1}{5} - 3\frac{1}{7} = 12\frac{7}{35} - 3\frac{5}{35} = \textbf{9}\frac{\textbf{2}}{\textbf{35}}$

2. $5\frac{2}{3} + 1\frac{3}{11} = 5\frac{22}{33} + 1\frac{9}{33} = \textbf{6}\frac{\textbf{31}}{\textbf{33}}$

3. $5\frac{1}{8} + 8\frac{3}{7} = 5\frac{7}{56} + 8\frac{24}{56} = \textbf{13}\frac{\textbf{31}}{\textbf{56}}$

4. $2\frac{3}{8} - 1\frac{2}{11} = 2\frac{33}{88} - 1\frac{16}{88} = \textbf{1}\frac{\textbf{17}}{\textbf{88}}$

5. $6\frac{2}{5} - 4\frac{3}{8} = 6\frac{16}{40} - 4\frac{15}{40} = \textbf{2}\frac{\textbf{1}}{\textbf{40}}$

6. $14\frac{8}{3} - 4\frac{7}{11} = 14\frac{88}{33} - 4\frac{21}{33} = 10\frac{67}{33} = \textbf{12}\frac{\textbf{1}}{\textbf{33}}$

7. $8\frac{7}{8} + 14\frac{8}{5} = 8\frac{35}{40} + 14\frac{64}{40} = 22\frac{99}{40} = \textbf{24}\frac{\textbf{19}}{\textbf{40}}$

8. $93\frac{7}{13} - 5\frac{1}{5} = 93\frac{35}{65} - 5\frac{13}{65} = \textbf{88}\frac{\textbf{22}}{\textbf{65}}$

9. $9\frac{3}{8} - 5\frac{7}{13} = 9\frac{39}{104} - 5\frac{56}{104} = 8\frac{143}{104} - 5\frac{56}{104}$
$= \textbf{3}\frac{\textbf{87}}{\textbf{104}}$

10. $V = \pi r^2 h$
$= \pi(5)^2(10) \approx \textbf{785 ft}^3$

11. $V = A_{\text{Triangle}} \times h$
$= \frac{(4 \times 14)}{2}(10) = \textbf{280 in.}^3$

12. A **rectangle** is a parallelogram with four right angles. A **square** is a rhombus with four right angles. Yes, every square is a rectangle.

13. $AM = KA + MK$
$= 14\frac{1}{3} + 12\frac{2}{5}$
$= 14\frac{5}{15} + 12\frac{6}{15} = \textbf{26}\frac{\textbf{11}}{\textbf{15}} \textbf{ cm}$

14. $C = \pi D$
$10 \text{ cm} = \pi D$
$D = \frac{10 \text{ cm}}{\pi} \approx \textbf{3.18 cm}$

15. $P = 2l + 2w$
$2l + 2w = 140 \text{ ft}$
$2l + 2(10 \text{ ft}) = 140 \text{ ft}$
$2l = 120 \text{ ft}$
$l = \textbf{60 ft}$

16. $P = (50 + 62 + 50 + 62) \text{ mi}$
$= \textbf{224 mi}$

17. $P = (500 + 620 + 400 + 210 + 100 + 410) \text{ mi}$
$= \textbf{2240 mi}$

18. $A = \frac{1}{2}b_1 h + \frac{1}{2}b_2 h$
$= \frac{1}{2}(13)(8) \text{ m}^2 + \frac{1}{2}(10)(8) \text{ m}^2 = \textbf{92 m}^2$

19. $A = A_{\text{Square}} + A_{\text{Semicircle}}$
$= (4 \text{ m})^2 + \frac{\pi(2 \text{ m})^2}{2}$
$= (16 + 2\pi) \text{ m}^2 \approx \textbf{22.28 m}^2$

20. $A_{Shaded} = A_{Big\ triangle} - A_{Circle} - A_{Small\ triangle}$

$$= \left(\frac{16(8)}{2} - \pi(3)^2 - \frac{4(2)}{2}\right) km^2$$

$$= (64 - 9\pi - 4)\ km^2$$

$$= (60 - 9\pi)\ km^2 \approx \mathbf{31.74\ km^2}$$

21. $5\frac{7}{8} - 4\frac{11}{12} = 5\frac{21}{24} - 4\frac{22}{24} = 4\frac{45}{24} - 4\frac{22}{24}$

$$= \mathbf{\frac{23}{24}}$$

22. $6\frac{8}{5} + 14\frac{9}{10} = 6\frac{16}{10} + 14\frac{9}{10} = 20\frac{25}{10} = 22\frac{5}{10}$

$$= \mathbf{22\frac{1}{2}}$$

23. $33\frac{5}{8} - 7\frac{2}{5} = 33\frac{25}{40} - 7\frac{16}{40} = \mathbf{26\frac{9}{40}}$

24. $5\frac{11}{12} - 4\frac{12}{13} = 5\frac{143}{156} - 4\frac{144}{156}$

$$= 4\frac{299}{156} - 4\frac{144}{156} = \mathbf{\frac{155}{156}}$$

25. $7\frac{1}{8} + 2\frac{3}{11} = 7\frac{11}{88} + 2\frac{24}{88} = \mathbf{9\frac{35}{88}}$

26. $93\frac{2}{5} - 1\frac{11}{12} = 93\frac{24}{60} - 1\frac{55}{60} = 92\frac{84}{60} - 1\frac{55}{60}$

$$= \mathbf{91\frac{29}{60}}$$

27. $4\frac{9}{13} - 2\frac{1}{11} = 4\frac{99}{143} - 2\frac{13}{143} = \mathbf{2\frac{86}{143}}$

28. $9\frac{2}{5} - 7\frac{1}{8} = 9\frac{16}{40} - 7\frac{5}{40} = \mathbf{2\frac{11}{40}}$

29. $35\frac{1}{7} - 6\frac{2}{3} = 35\frac{3}{21} - 6\frac{14}{21} = 34\frac{24}{21} - 6\frac{14}{21}$

$$= \mathbf{28\frac{10}{21}}$$

30.

```
    41
   163
    97.5
     0.072
    94.32
 +   0.05
 ─────────
   395.942
```

PROBLEM SET 1

1. A **number** is an idea. A **numeral** is a single symbol or a collection of symbols used to express the idea of a particular number.

2. The decimal system

3. The Hindus of India

4. 0, 1, 2, 3, 4, 5, 6, 7, 8, 9

5. 1, 2, 3, . . .

6. 1, 2, 3, . . .

7. Those numbers which can be used to describe a physical distance greater than zero.

8. The origin

9. (a) $C = 2\pi r$

$$= 2\pi(4\ cm) = 8\pi\ cm \approx \mathbf{25.12\ cm}$$

(b) $A = \pi r^2$

$$= \pi(4\ cm)^2 = 16\pi\ cm^2 \approx \mathbf{50.24\ cm^2}$$

10. $$A = \frac{b \times h}{2}$$

$$\frac{b \times h}{2} = 40\ in.^2$$

$$\frac{b(10\ in.)}{2} = 40\ in.^2$$

$$b = \frac{40\ in.^2\ (2)}{10\ in.} = \mathbf{8\ in.}$$

11. $C = 2\pi r$

$628\ cm = 2\pi r$

$$r = \frac{628\ cm}{2(\pi)} = \frac{314\ cm}{\pi} \approx \mathbf{100\ cm}$$

12. $C = 2\pi r$

$314\ ft = 2\pi r$

$$r = \frac{314\ ft}{2(\pi)} = \frac{157}{\pi}\ ft \approx \mathbf{50\ ft}$$

13. $P = (10 + 14 + 10 + 11 + 3)\ in.$

$$= \mathbf{48\ in.}$$

14. $A_S = A_{Parallelogram} - A_{Circle}$

$$= ((7 \times 5) - \pi(2)^2)\ cm^2$$

$$= (35 - 4\pi)\ cm^2 \approx \mathbf{22.44\ cm^2}$$

15. $A = A_{Rectangle} + A_{Semicircle}$

$$= \left((8 \times 4) + \frac{\pi(2)^2}{2}\right) in.^2$$

$$= (32 + 2\pi)\ in.^2 \approx \mathbf{38.28\ in.^2}$$

16. $4\frac{1}{2} \times 6\frac{2}{3} = \frac{\cancel{9}^3}{\cancel{2}} \times \frac{\cancel{20}^{10}}{\cancel{3}} = \mathbf{30}$

17. $4\frac{1}{2} \div 6\frac{2}{3} = \frac{9}{2} \times \frac{3}{20} = \mathbf{\frac{27}{40}}$

18. $\dfrac{14\frac{2}{3}}{3\frac{1}{4}} = \frac{44}{3} \times \frac{4}{13} = \frac{176}{39} = \mathbf{4\frac{20}{39}}$

19. Multiply:

$$\frac{8}{5} \times \frac{25}{2} = \frac{\overset{4}{\cancel{8}}}{\cancel{5}} \times \frac{\overset{5}{\cancel{25}}}{\cancel{2}} = \mathbf{20}$$

20. $\frac{4}{5} \div 2\frac{1}{3} = \frac{4}{5} \times \frac{3}{7} = \dfrac{\mathbf{12}}{\mathbf{35}}$

21. $7\frac{1}{8} \times 5\frac{1}{16} = \frac{57}{8} \times \frac{81}{16} = \frac{4617}{128} = \mathbf{36\frac{9}{128}}$

22. $\frac{4}{7} \times 5\frac{2}{5} = \frac{4}{7} \times \frac{27}{5} = \frac{108}{35} = \mathbf{3\frac{3}{35}}$

23. $\frac{4}{3} \times \frac{7}{2} \times \frac{9}{5} = \frac{\overset{2}{\cancel{4}}}{\cancel{3}} \times \frac{7}{\cancel{2}} \times \frac{\overset{3}{\cancel{9}}}{5} = \frac{42}{5} = \mathbf{8\frac{2}{5}}$

24. $4\frac{1}{2} \times 5\frac{1}{16} = \frac{9}{2} \times \frac{81}{16} = \frac{729}{32} = \mathbf{22\frac{25}{32}}$

25. $146\frac{1}{2} - 13\frac{2}{3} = 146\frac{3}{6} - 13\frac{4}{6} = 145\frac{9}{6} - 13\frac{4}{6}$

$= \mathbf{132\frac{5}{6}}$

26. $7\frac{4}{5} + 19\frac{5}{3} = 7\frac{12}{15} + 19\frac{25}{15} = 26\frac{37}{15} = \mathbf{28\frac{7}{15}}$

27. $18\frac{3}{5} - 6\frac{4}{9} = 18\frac{27}{45} - 6\frac{20}{45} = \mathbf{12\frac{7}{45}}$

28. $MC = XM - CX$

$= 10\frac{1}{5} - 4\frac{2}{3}$

$= 10\frac{3}{15} - 4\frac{10}{15}$

$= 9\frac{18}{15} - 4\frac{10}{15} = \mathbf{5\frac{8}{15}}$ miles

29. $800 \, \cancel{ft} \times \dfrac{12 \, \cancel{in.}}{1 \, \cancel{ft}} \times \dfrac{2.54 \text{ cm}}{1 \, \cancel{in.}} = \mathbf{800(12)(2.54)}$ **cm**

30. $V = A_{Base} \times \text{height}$

$= 426 \text{ cm}^2 \times 10 \text{ cm}$

$= \mathbf{4260 \text{ cm}^3}$

PROBLEM SET 2

1. The surface area of the solid

2.

```
      75.45
  2 ) 150.90
      14
      ──
      10
      10
      ──
       9
       8
      ──
      10
```

3. Multiply:

```
    64.09
  ×  1.3
  ───────
   19227
   6409
  ───────
  83.317
```

4. $\{1, 2, 3, \ldots\}$

5. $90°$

6. Members of the set

7. The numbers are addends; the answer is the sum.

8. A number which can be used to describe a physical distance greater than zero.

9. $180°$

10. If its graph is farther to the right on the number line.

11. $4000 \, \cancel{ft} \times \dfrac{12 \, \cancel{in.}}{1 \, \cancel{ft}} \times \dfrac{2.54 \text{ cm}}{1 \, \cancel{in.}} = \mathbf{4000(12)(2.54)}$ **cm**

12. The quotient

13. $4 + 0 = 4$; The sum of zero and any number is the number itself.

$4 \cdot 0 = 0$; The product of any number and zero is zero.

14. (a) $\quad C = 2\pi r$

$40 \text{ cm} = 2\pi r$

$r = \frac{40}{2\pi} \text{ cm} = \frac{20}{\pi} \text{ cm} \approx \mathbf{6.37 \text{ cm}}$

(b) $D = 2r \approx 2(6.37 \text{ cm}) \approx \mathbf{12.74 \text{ cm}}$

15. $P = \left(\left(\dfrac{2\pi(3)}{2} \right) + 2 + 2 + 1 + 2 + 3 + 4 \right) \text{ft}$

$= (3\pi + 14) \text{ ft} \approx \mathbf{23.42 \text{ ft}}$

16. $A = A_{Semicircle} + A_{Rectangle} + A_{Triangle}$

$= \left(\dfrac{\pi(3)^2}{2} + 8(6) + \dfrac{4(6)}{2} \right) \text{cm}^2$

$= \left(\dfrac{9}{2}\pi + 60 \right) \text{cm}^2 \approx \mathbf{74.13 \text{ cm}^2}$

17. $A_S = A_{Circle} - A_{Rectangle} - A_{Triangle}$

$= \left(\pi(4)^2 - 3(2) - \dfrac{2(2)}{2} \right) \text{in.}^2$

$= (16\pi - 8) \text{ in.}^2 \approx \mathbf{42.24 \text{ in.}^2}$

18. Convert 42.6 inches to centimeters:

$42.6 \, \cancel{in.} \times \dfrac{2.54 \text{ cm}}{1 \, \cancel{in.}} = \mathbf{42.6(2.54)}$ **cm**

19. Convert 5.6 miles to inches:

$$5.6 \text{ mi} \times \frac{5280 \text{ ft}}{1 \text{ mi}} \times \frac{12 \text{ in.}}{1 \text{ ft}} = \mathbf{5.6(5280)(12) \text{ in.}}$$

20. $V_{Cylinder} = A_{Circle} \times \text{length}$
$$= \pi(6 \text{ ft})^2 \times 18 \text{ ft}$$
$$= 648\pi \text{ ft}^3 \approx \mathbf{2034.72 \text{ ft}^3}$$

21. $4\frac{1}{2} \times 7\frac{3}{3} = \frac{\cancel{9}^{3}}{\cancel{2}} \times \frac{\cancel{24}^{12}}{\cancel{3}} = \mathbf{36}$

22. $4\frac{1}{2} \div 7\frac{2}{3} = \frac{9}{2} \div \frac{23}{3} = \frac{9}{2} \times \frac{3}{23} = \mathbf{\frac{27}{46}}$

23. $\dfrac{7\frac{1}{8}}{4\frac{2}{5}} = \frac{57}{8} \div \frac{22}{5} = \frac{57}{8} \times \frac{5}{22} = \frac{285}{176}$
$$= \mathbf{1\frac{109}{176}}$$

24. $47\frac{3}{4} - 14\frac{7}{8} = 47\frac{6}{8} - 14\frac{7}{8} = 46\frac{14}{8} - 14\frac{7}{8}$
$$= \mathbf{32\frac{7}{8}}$$

25. $95\frac{1}{8} - 4\frac{13}{16} = 95\frac{2}{16} - 4\frac{13}{16} = 94\frac{18}{16} - 4\frac{13}{16}$
$$= \mathbf{90\frac{5}{16}}$$

26. $94\frac{2}{5} - 7\frac{3}{6} = 94\frac{12}{30} - 7\frac{15}{30} = 93\frac{42}{30} - 7\frac{15}{30}$
$$= 86\frac{27}{30} = \mathbf{86\frac{9}{10}}$$

27. $MX = XK - KM$
$$= 7\frac{2}{3} - 4\frac{1}{2}$$
$$= 7\frac{4}{6} - 4\frac{3}{6}$$
$$= \mathbf{3\frac{1}{6}}$$

28. $A = \text{length} \times \text{width}$
$$\begin{array}{r} 4.27 \text{ ft} \\ \times\ 0.046 \text{ ft} \\ \hline 2562 \\ 1708 \\ \hline \mathbf{0.19642 \text{ ft}^2} \end{array}$$

29. $15\frac{3}{8} - 2\frac{1}{7} = 15\frac{21}{56} - 2\frac{8}{56} = \mathbf{13\frac{13}{56}}$

30. $15\frac{3}{8} \times 2\frac{1}{7} = \frac{123}{8} \times \frac{15}{7} = \frac{1845}{56} = \mathbf{32\frac{53}{56}}$

31. $15\frac{3}{8} \div 2\frac{1}{7} = \frac{123}{8} \div \frac{15}{7} = \frac{123}{8} \div \frac{7}{15}$
$$= \frac{287}{40} = \mathbf{7\frac{7}{40}}$$

32. Surface Area:

Area of front	$= 4 \text{ m} \times 8 \text{ m} =$	32 m^2
Area of back	$= 4 \text{ m} \times 8 \text{ m} =$	32 m^2
Area of top	$= 6 \text{ m} \times 8 \text{ m} =$	48 m^2
Area of bottom	$= 6 \text{ m} \times 8 \text{ m} =$	48 m^2
Area of side	$= 4 \text{ m} \times 6 \text{ m} =$	24 m^2
Area of side	$= 4 \text{ m} \times 6 \text{ m} =$	$\underline{24 \text{ m}^2}$
Surface Area	$=$ total $=$	$\mathbf{208 \text{ m}^2}$

33. Surface Area:

Area of front	$= \dfrac{4 \text{ in.} \times 3 \text{ in.}}{2} =$	6 in.^2
Area of back	$= \dfrac{4 \text{ in.} \times 3 \text{ in.}}{2} =$	6 in.^2
Area of top	$= 5 \text{ in.} \times 8 \text{ in.} =$	40 in.^2
Area of bottom	$= 4 \text{ in.} \times 8 \text{ in.} =$	32 in.^2
Area of side	$= 3 \text{ in.} \times 8 \text{ in.} =$	$\underline{24 \text{ in.}^2}$
Surface Area	$=$ total $=$	$\mathbf{108 \text{ in.}^2}$

PROBLEM SET 3

1. $|-8| = \mathbf{8}$

2. $|+8| = \mathbf{8}$

3. $|-12| = \mathbf{12}$

4. $-|30 - 12| = -|18| = \mathbf{-18}$

5. $-|15 - 5| = -|10| = \mathbf{-10}$

6. The sum is **−5**.

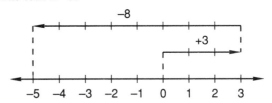

7. The sum is **1**.

8. The sum is **7**.

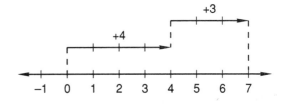

9. The sum is **2**.

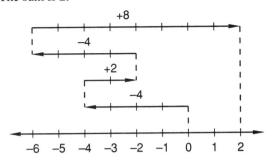

10. The sum is **4**.

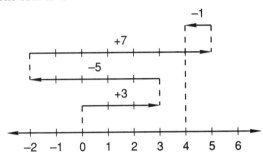

11. The sum is **–5**.

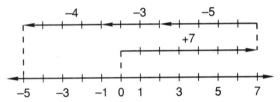

12. $\{1, 2, 3, 4, 5, \ldots\}$

13. $\{\ldots, -3, -2, -1, 0, 1, 2, 3, \ldots\}$

14. The quotient

15. The number that is associated with the point

16. The mark made on the number line to indicate the numbers' location

17. The product

18. One of two or more numbers to be multiplied

19. 10 is the dividend; 5 is the divisor

20. All real numbers can be graphed on the number line.

21. $1472\frac{1}{2} - 1432\frac{15}{16} = 1472\frac{8}{16} - 1432\frac{15}{16}$

$= 1471\frac{24}{16} - 1432\frac{15}{16} = \mathbf{39\frac{9}{16}}$

22. $\frac{1}{2} + \frac{7}{4} + \frac{9}{8} - \frac{1}{16} = \frac{8}{16} + \frac{28}{16} + \frac{18}{16} - \frac{1}{16}$

$= \frac{53}{16} = \mathbf{3\frac{5}{16}}$

23. Multiply:

$$\frac{\overset{2}{\cancel{14}}}{\underset{4}{\cancel{32}}} \times \frac{\overset{1}{\cancel{8}}}{\underset{3}{\cancel{21}}} = \frac{2}{12} = \frac{1}{6}$$

24. $5\frac{1}{3} + 7\frac{3}{8} - 1\frac{1}{4} = 5\frac{8}{24} + 7\frac{9}{24} - 1\frac{6}{24}$

$= \mathbf{11\frac{11}{24}}$

25.
$$212 \overline{)\begin{array}{l} 4.003 \\ 848.636 \end{array}}$$
$\begin{array}{r} 848 \\ \hline \quad 636 \\ \quad 636 \\ \hline \end{array}$

26. $P = (31 + 26 + 10 + 18 + 11 + 18 + 10$
$\qquad + 26)$ in.
$\quad = \mathbf{150\ in.}$

27. $V = A_{Base} \times height$
$\quad = (6\,cm(4\,cm) + 8\,cm(2\,cm)) \times 6\,cm$
$\quad = 40\,cm^2 \times 6\,cm = \mathbf{240\ cm^3}$

$S.A. = 2A_{Base} + (P \times height)$
$\quad = 2[6(4) + 8(2)]\,cm^2$
$\qquad + [12 + 6 + 4 + 4 + 8 + 2](6)\,cm^2$
$\quad = 2[40] + [36](6)\,cm^2 = \mathbf{296\ cm^2}$

28. $2\frac{1}{4} \div 3\frac{1}{8} = \frac{9}{4} \div \frac{25}{8} = \frac{9}{\cancel{4}} \times \frac{\overset{2}{\cancel{8}}}{25} = \frac{18}{25}$

29. $7\frac{2}{5} \times 3\frac{5}{7} = \frac{37}{5} \times \frac{26}{7} = \frac{962}{35} = \mathbf{27\frac{17}{35}}$

30. $7\frac{3}{8} + 7\frac{3}{5} - 3\frac{3}{10} = 7\frac{15}{40} + 7\frac{24}{40} - 3\frac{12}{40}$

$= \mathbf{11\frac{27}{40}}$

31.
$$304 \overline{)\begin{array}{l} 4.002 \\ 1216.608 \end{array}}$$
$\begin{array}{r} 1216 \\ \hline \quad 608 \\ \quad 608 \\ \hline \end{array}$

32.
$\begin{array}{r} 0.00143 \\ 0.012 \\ 443.6 \\ +\quad 0.0007 \\ \hline \mathbf{443.61413} \end{array}$

33. Multiply:

$$\begin{array}{r} 3.628 \\ \times\ 0.0404 \\ \hline 14512 \\ 14512 \\ \hline \mathbf{0.1465712} \end{array}$$

34. $4\dfrac{1}{4} \div 3\dfrac{2}{5} = \dfrac{17}{4} \div \dfrac{17}{5} = \dfrac{17}{4} \times \dfrac{5}{17} = \dfrac{5}{4}$

$= \mathbf{1\dfrac{1}{4}}$

35. $\dfrac{2\dfrac{1}{8}}{3\dfrac{4}{3}} = \dfrac{17}{8} \div \dfrac{13}{3} = \dfrac{17}{8} \times \dfrac{3}{13} = \dfrac{\mathbf{51}}{\mathbf{104}}$

36. $100\ \cancel{ft} \times \dfrac{12\ \cancel{in.}}{1\ \cancel{ft}} \times \dfrac{2.54\ cm}{1\ \cancel{in.}} = \mathbf{100(12)(2.54)\ cm}$

PROBLEM SET 4

1. We add the absolute values of both numbers and give the result the same sign as the numbers' sign.

2. We take the difference in the absolute values of the numbers and give the result the sign of the greater.

3. (a) A number that is to be multiplied
(b) The answer to a division problem
(c) The answer to a multiplication problem

4. S.A. $= 2(A_{Top}) + 2(A_{Front}) + 2(A_{Side})$
$= 2(20\ m(21\ m)) + 2(21\ m(10\ m))$
$\quad + 2(20\ m(10\ m))$
$= 840\ m^2 + 420\ m^2 + 400\ m^2$
$= \mathbf{1660\ m^2}$

5. P $= (31 + 26 + 16 + 18 + 9 + 18 + 6$
$\quad + 26)\ km$
$= \mathbf{150\ km}$

6. V $= A_{Base} \times$ height
$= (20\ m(21\ m)) \times 10\ m$
$= \mathbf{4200\ m^3}$

7. S.A. $= (C \times$ height$) + 2(A_{Base})$
$= (\pi(4\ cm) \times 12\ cm) + 2(\pi(2\ cm)^2)$
$= 48\pi\ cm^2 + 8\pi\ cm^2$
$= 56\pi\ cm^2 \approx \mathbf{175.84\ cm^2}$

8. Convert 3000 inches to miles:

$3000\ \cancel{in.} \times \dfrac{1\ \cancel{ft}}{12\ \cancel{in.}} \times \dfrac{1\ mi}{5280\ \cancel{ft}} = \dfrac{\mathbf{3000}}{\mathbf{(12)(5280)}}\ \mathbf{mi}$

9. $(+3) + (-14) = \mathbf{-11}$

10. $(-3) + (-14) = \mathbf{-17}$

11. $(-14) + (-21) = \mathbf{-35}$

12. $(-32) + (+4) = \mathbf{-28}$

13. $(-7) + (-24) = \mathbf{-31}$

14. $(-5) + (4) + (-3) + (+8) = \mathbf{4}$

15. $(-3) + (+2) + (-2) + |-2| = \mathbf{-1}$

16. $(-2) + (-5) + (3) + (-5) = \mathbf{-9}$

17. $(+2) + (-5) + (-3) + (-7) = \mathbf{-13}$

18. $(-5) + (-3) + (11) + (-2) = \mathbf{1}$

19. $(-14) + (-3) + (-7) + (-14) = \mathbf{-38}$

20. $-4 - 3 + 2 - 4 - 3 - 8 = \mathbf{-20}$

21. $-2 + 11 - 4 + 3 - 8 = \mathbf{0}$

22. $-11 - 3 + 14 - 2 - 5 + 7 = \mathbf{0}$

23. $-5 - 11 + 20 - 14 + 5 = \mathbf{-5}$

24. $-2 - 8 + 3 - 2 + 5 - 7 = \mathbf{-11}$

25. $7 - 3 - 2 - 11 + 4 - 5 + 3 = \mathbf{-7}$

26. $-7 - 4 - 13 + 4 - 2 + 7 = \mathbf{-15}$

27. $-8 + 13 - 4 + 13 - 2 - 5 - 7 = \mathbf{0}$

28. $-7 + (-8) + 3 = \mathbf{-12}$

29. $+|-2| + (-5) = \mathbf{-3}$

30. $|-2 - 3| + (-5) = \mathbf{0}$

31. $-7 + (-3) + 4 - 3 + (-2) = \mathbf{-11}$

32. $-6 + |-2| + (-3) - 1 = \mathbf{-8}$

33. $(-8) + (5) + (-10) - 4 - |-2| = \mathbf{-19}$

34. $|-2 - 3| - 2 = \mathbf{3}$

35. $-4 - 2 + (-8) + |-5| = \mathbf{-9}$

36. $+|-2 - 3| - 4 + (-8) = \mathbf{-7}$

37. $|-2| + (-2) - 2 = \mathbf{-2}$

38. $YZ = XZ - XY$

$\quad = 17\dfrac{3}{8} - 9\dfrac{4}{5}$

$\quad = 17\dfrac{15}{40} - 9\dfrac{32}{40}$

$\quad = 16\dfrac{55}{40} - 9\dfrac{32}{40}$

$\quad = \mathbf{7\dfrac{23}{40}}$ **in.**

39.
$$4\,\overline{)\,370.0}\quad \substack{92.5}$$

$$\begin{array}{r} 92.5 \\ 4\,\overline{)\,370.0} \\ \underline{36} \\ 10 \\ \underline{8} \\ 2\,0 \\ \underline{2\,0} \end{array}$$

Problem Set 5

1. **45,654**

2. **0**

3. $-(+4) = \mathbf{-4}$

4. $-(-4) = \mathbf{4}$

5. $-[-(-4)] = \mathbf{-4}$

6. $-\{-[-(-4)]\} = \mathbf{4}$

7. $P = (30 + 30 + 30 + 20 + 11 + 21)\ \text{ft}$
$\quad = \mathbf{142\ ft}$

8. $A_{\text{Total}} = A_{\text{Semicircle}} + A_{\text{Triangle}}$

$\quad = \left(\dfrac{\pi(12)^2}{2} + \dfrac{25 \times 12}{2}\right) \text{m}^2$

$\quad = (72\pi + 150)\ \text{m}^2 \approx \mathbf{376.08\ m^2}$

9. $444\ \cancel{\text{ft}} \times \dfrac{12\ \cancel{\text{in.}}}{1\ \cancel{\text{ft}}} \times \dfrac{2.54\ \text{cm}}{1\ \cancel{\text{in.}}} = \mathbf{444(12)(2.54)\ cm}$

10. $+7 - (-3) + (-2) = (+7) + (+3) + (-2) = \mathbf{8}$

11. $-3 + (-2) - (-3) = (-3) + (-2) + (+3) = \mathbf{-2}$

12. $4 - (-3) - 7 + (-2)$
$\quad = (+4) + (+3) + (-7) + (-2) = \mathbf{-2}$

13. $3 - (+4) - (-2) = (+3) + (-4) + (+2) = \mathbf{1}$

14. $-6 - (-8) - (-6) = (-6) + (+8) + (+6) = \mathbf{8}$

15. $-2 - |-2| = (-2) + (-2) = \mathbf{-4}$

16. $6 + |-2| = (+6) + (+2) = \mathbf{8}$

17. $-3 - (-3) + |-3| = (-3) + (+3) + (+3) = \mathbf{3}$

18. $-2 - (-3) - \{-[-(-4)]\} = (-2) + (+3) + (+4)$
$\quad = \mathbf{5}$

19. $-2 + 5 - (-3) + |-3|$
$\quad = (-2) + (+5) + (+3) + (+3) = \mathbf{9}$

20. $-|-10| - (-10) = (-10) + (+10) = \mathbf{0}$

21. $-2 - (-(-6)) + |-5| = (-2) + (-6) + (+5)$
$\quad = \mathbf{-3}$

22. $-7 + (-5) - (+5) - |2|$
$\quad = (-7) + (-5) + (-5) + (-2) = \mathbf{-19}$

23. $|-2 - 5 - 7| - |-4| = (+14) + (-4) = \mathbf{10}$

24. $-8 - 3 - 4 - (-10) + |12|$
$\quad = (-8) + (-3) + (-4) + (+10) + (+12) = \mathbf{7}$

25. $|7 - 3| - (-2) + 7 - 4 + |-11|$
$\quad = (+4) + (+2) + (+7) + (-4) + (+11) = \mathbf{20}$

26. $-4 - (-3) - 7 + (-3)$
$\quad = (-4) + (+3) + (-7) + (-3) = \mathbf{-11}$

27. $-(-5) + (-2) - 3 - |-14|$
$\quad = (+5) + (-2) + (-3) + (-14) = \mathbf{-14}$

28. $-(-2) - (+2) - 3 - (-3)$
$\quad = (+2) + (-2) + (-3) + (+3) = \mathbf{0}$

29. $-|-3 - 2| - (-3) - 2 - 5$
$\quad = (-5) + (+3) + (-2) + (-5) = \mathbf{-9}$

30. $-(-3) - [-(-4)] - 2 + 7$
$\quad = (+3) + (-4) + (-2) + (+7) = \mathbf{4}$

31. $31\dfrac{3}{8} - 4\dfrac{7}{15} = 31\dfrac{45}{120} - 4\dfrac{56}{120}$

$\quad = 30\dfrac{165}{120} - 4\dfrac{56}{120} = \mathbf{26\dfrac{109}{120}}$

32. $3\dfrac{2}{5} \div 3\dfrac{1}{4} = \dfrac{17}{5} \div \dfrac{13}{4} = \dfrac{17}{5} \times \dfrac{4}{13} = \dfrac{68}{65}$

$\quad = \mathbf{1\dfrac{3}{65}}$

33. $\dfrac{22}{3} \div \dfrac{30}{7} = \dfrac{\overset{11}{\cancel{22}}}{3} \times \dfrac{7}{\underset{15}{\cancel{30}}} = \dfrac{77}{45} = \mathbf{1\dfrac{32}{45}}$

34.
$$\begin{array}{r} 0.416 \\ +\ 5.007 \\ \hline \mathbf{5.423} \end{array}$$

35.
$$\begin{array}{r} \mathbf{0.402} \\ 1\,\overline{)\,0.402} \end{array}$$

36. Multiply:

$$
\begin{array}{r}
21.02 \\
\times\ 0.3004 \\
\hline
8408 \\
6306 \\
\hline
\mathbf{6.314408}
\end{array}
$$

37. Divide:

$$
\begin{array}{r}
\mathbf{0.06} \\
102\ \overline{)\ 6.12} \\
\underline{6.12}
\end{array}
$$

PROBLEM SET 6

1. The number that is associated with the point

2. +2

3. If its graph is farther to the right on the number line

4. The product

5. The quotient

6. $\{\ldots, -3, -2, -1, 0, 1, 2, 3, \ldots\}$

7. P = (46 + 29 + 46 + 21 + 11 + 19) m
   = **172 m**

8. $A_{Shaded} = A_{Rectangle} - A_{Trapezoid}$

$$= \left(12(6)\ -\ \frac{10(2)}{2}\ -\ \frac{8(2)}{2}\right) cm^2$$

$$= \mathbf{54\ cm^2}$$

9. S.A. $= 2(A_{Top}) + 2(A_{Front}) + 2(A_{Side})$

$$= 2(15(30))m^2 + 2(5(30))m^2 + 2(5(15))m^2$$

$$= 900\ m^2 + 300\ m^2 + 150\ m^2$$

$$= \mathbf{1350\ m^2}$$

10. V $= A_{Triangle} \times$ length

$$= \frac{6\ ft(4\ ft)}{2} \times 23\ ft$$

$$= \mathbf{276\ ft^3}$$

S.A. $= 2(A_{End}) + 2(A_{Side}) + A_{Bottom}$

$$= 2\left(\frac{6\ ft(4\ ft)}{2}\right) + 2(5\ ft(23\ ft)) + 6\ ft(23\ ft)$$

$$= 24\ ft^2 + 230\ ft^2 + 138\ ft^2$$

$$= \mathbf{392\ ft^2}$$

11. $(-3)(-5) = \mathbf{15}$

12. $5(-2) = \mathbf{-10}$

13. $-5(2) = \mathbf{-10}$

14. $-[-(-4)] = \mathbf{-4}$

15. $-|-2| - (-2) = (-2) + (+2) = \mathbf{0}$

16. $4 + (-2) + (-4) = (+4) + (-2) + (-4) = \mathbf{-2}$

17. $-(-4) + (-2) - (-3) = (+4) + (-2) + (+3)$
   $= \mathbf{5}$

18. $|-4| + 5 - 6 - |-2 - 4|$
   $= (+4) + (+5) + (-6) + (-6) = \mathbf{-3}$

19. $-3 + 7 - 8 - 5 - (4)$
   $= (-3) + (+7) + (-8) + (-5) + (-4) = \mathbf{-13}$

20. $-|-2| + |2| - (-2) = (-2) + (+2) + (+2) = \mathbf{2}$

21. $-7 + 3 - 2 - 5 + (-6)$
   $= (-7) + (+3) + (-2) + (-5) + (-6) = \mathbf{-17}$

22. $-3 + (-3) + (-6) - 2$
   $= (-3) + (-3) + (-6) + (-2) = \mathbf{-14}$

23. $-5 + 3 - 2 - 5 - (-2)$
   $= (-5) + (+3) + (-2) + (-5) + (+2) = \mathbf{-7}$

24. $5 - 3 - (-2) - (-(-3))$
   $= (+5) + (-3) + (+2) + (-3) = \mathbf{1}$

25. $-3 - (-3) + (-2) - (3)$
   $= (-3) + (+3) + (-2) + (-3) = \mathbf{-5}$

26. $|-4 - 3| - 2 + 7 - (-3)$
   $= (+7) + (-2) + (+7) + (+3) = \mathbf{15}$

27. $7 - 4 - 5 + 12 - 2 - |-2|$
   $= (+7) + (-4) + (-5) + (+12) + (-2) + (-2)$
   $= \mathbf{6}$

28. $|-3 - 2| - (-3) - 4 - 6$
   $= (+5) + (+3) + (-4) + (-6) = \mathbf{-2}$

29. $5 - |-2 + 5| - (-3) + 2$
   $= (+5) + (-3) + (+3) + (+2) = \mathbf{7}$

30. $-8 + 5 - 3 - (-2) + (-3)$
   $= (-8) + (+5) + (-3) + (+2) + (-3) = \mathbf{-7}$

31. $-3 + 7 - (-2) + (-3) - 2$
   $= (-3) + (+7) + (+2) + (-3) + (-2) = \mathbf{1}$

32. $4 - 3 - (-2) - |12 - 3 + 4|$
   $= (+4) + (-3) + (+2) + (-13) = \mathbf{-10}$

33.
$$
\begin{array}{r}
41.263 \\
+\ 0.002 \\
\hline
\mathbf{41.265}
\end{array}
$$

34. $21\frac{2}{5} - 7\frac{7}{8} = 21\frac{16}{40} - 7\frac{35}{40} = 20\frac{56}{40} - 7\frac{35}{40}$

   $= \mathbf{13\frac{21}{40}}$

35. Divide:

$$\begin{array}{r} 8100 \\ 5\overline{)40500} \\ 40 \\ \hline 5 \\ 5 \\ \hline 00 \\ 00 \\ \hline \end{array}$$

36. $\dfrac{5\frac{1}{2}}{6\frac{2}{3}} = 5\frac{1}{2} \div 6\frac{2}{3} = \frac{11}{2} \div \frac{20}{3} = \frac{11}{2} \times \frac{3}{20}$

$= \dfrac{33}{40}$

37. $-3\frac{1}{5} + 2\frac{1}{8} = -3\frac{8}{40} + 2\frac{5}{40} = \mathbf{-1\frac{3}{40}}$

38. $\dfrac{\cancel{15}^{3}}{\cancel{7}} \times \dfrac{\cancel{21}^{3}}{\cancel{5}} \times \dfrac{2}{49} = \mathbf{\dfrac{18}{49}}$

39. $620\,\cancel{cm} \times \dfrac{1\,\cancel{in.}}{2.54\,\cancel{cm}} \times \dfrac{1\,ft}{12\,\cancel{in.}} = \mathbf{\dfrac{620}{(2.54)(12)}}\,ft$

PROBLEM SET 7

1. Division

2. Multiplication

3. $4000\,\cancel{cm} \times \dfrac{1\,\cancel{in.}}{2.54\,\cancel{cm}} \times \dfrac{1\,ft}{12\,\cancel{in.}} = \mathbf{\dfrac{4000}{(2.54)(12)}}\,ft$

4. $-4(-3) = \mathbf{12}$

5. $4(-12) = \mathbf{-48}$

6. $-3(8) = \mathbf{-24}$

7. $\dfrac{-16}{-2} = \mathbf{8}$

8. $V = A_{Base} \times height$
$= 20\,ft(30\,ft) \times 10\,ft$
$= \mathbf{6000\,ft^3}$

9. $P = (40 + 20 + 40 + 5 + 10 + 5)\,m = \mathbf{120\,m}$

10. S.A. $= 2(A_{Front}) + 2(A_{Top}) + 2(A_{Side})$
$= 2(21(10)) + 2(21(20)) + 2(20(10))$
$= 420 + 840 + 400$
$= \mathbf{1660\,cm^2}$

11. $BX = XM - MB$
$= 7\frac{6}{15} - 3\frac{2}{5}$
$= 7\frac{6}{15} - 3\frac{6}{15}$
$= \mathbf{4}$

12. $-|-5 + 3 - 2| + 2 = (-4) + (+2) = \mathbf{-2}$

13. $-4 + 5 - 7 + (-3) - 2 + 7$
$= (-4) + (+5) + (-7) + (-3) + (-2) + (+7)$
$= \mathbf{-4}$

14. $-[-3(-2)] + (-5) = (-6) + (-5) = \mathbf{-11}$

15. $-3 - (+6) + (-6) - 2$
$= (-3) + (-6) + (-6) + (-2) = \mathbf{-17}$

16. $-|-6| - [-(-2)] + 5$
$= (-6) + (-2) + (+5) = \mathbf{-3}$

17. $-5 - (3) - 2 + (-3)$
$= (-5) + (-3) + (-2) + (-3) = \mathbf{-13}$

18. $-7 - 4 - (-3) + |-3|$
$= (-7) + (-4) + (+3) + (+3) = \mathbf{-5}$

19. $-2 + (-3) - (-4) + 2$
$= (-2) + (-3) + (+4) + (+2) = \mathbf{1}$

20. $-|-3 - 3| - 2 = (-6) + (-2) = \mathbf{-8}$

21. $-3 + (-3) - (-5) - |7|$
$= (-3) + (-3) + (+5) + (-7) = \mathbf{-8}$

22. $-4 - (6) - (-3) - 2$
$= (-4) + (-6) + (+3) + (-2) = \mathbf{-9}$

23. $-|-2 - 5 + 7| - (-3) = (0) + (+3) = \mathbf{3}$

24. $7 - |-3 - 5 + 1| - (-2)$
$= (+7) + (-7) + (+2) = \mathbf{2}$

25. $-6 - 4 - (3) - (-3) + 3$
$= (-6) + (-4) + (-3) + (+3) + (+3) = \mathbf{-7}$

26. $5 - |-2 - 3| + |+7 - 3|$
$= (+5) + (-5) + (+4) = \mathbf{4}$

27. $-6 + (-3) - [-(-2)] + 7$
$= (-6) + (-3) + (-2) + (+7) = \mathbf{-4}$

28. $|-3| + (-2) - 4 + 7$
$= (+3) + (-2) + (-4) + (+7) = \mathbf{4}$

29. $-6 - (-6) - 4 + (-2) - 1$
$= (-6) + (+6) + (-4) + (-2) + (-1) = \mathbf{-7}$

30. $-5 + (-2) - (-7) - 4$
$= (-5) + (-2) + (+7) + (-4) = \mathbf{-4}$

31. $8 - 7 + (-6) - 3 + (-5) - |-2|$
$= (+8) + (-7) + (-6) + (-3) + (-5) + (-2)$
$= -15$

32. $4\frac{2}{3} \div 3\frac{1}{9} = \frac{14}{3} \div \frac{28}{9} = \frac{\overset{1}{\cancel{14}}}{\cancel{3}} \times \frac{\overset{3}{\cancel{9}}}{\underset{2}{\cancel{28}}} = \frac{3}{2} = 1\frac{1}{2}$

33. $3\frac{2}{5} \div 7\frac{6}{15} = \frac{17}{5} \div \frac{111}{15} = \frac{17}{\cancel{5}} \times \frac{\overset{3}{\cancel{15}}}{111}$
$= \frac{51}{111} = \frac{17}{37}$

34. $416 \overline{)8.32} \overset{0.02}{}$
$\underline{8.32}$

PROBLEM SET 8

1. Yes

2. No

3. Because we are trying to undo a multiplication that was never performed.

4. $-4(3)(-2) = -12(-2) = \mathbf{24}$

5. $4(-3)(-4) = -12(-4) = \mathbf{48}$

6. $-2(3)(4) = -6(4) = \mathbf{-24}$

7. $\frac{-15}{-3} = \mathbf{5}$

8. $\frac{-4}{2} = \mathbf{-2}$

9. $\frac{4}{-2} = \mathbf{-2}$

10. $-3(2)(-1)(3) = -6(-1)(3) = 6(3) = \mathbf{18}$

11. $-2(-3)(-2)(2) = 6(-2)(2) = -12(2) = \mathbf{-24}$

12. $-4(-2)(-3) = 8(-3) = \mathbf{-24}$

13. $4(-2)(-3)(2) = -8(-3)(2) = 24(2) = \mathbf{48}$

14. $-3 - 6 + 5 - 2 + 4 - 3$
$= (-3) + (-6) + (+5) + (-2) + (+4) + (-3)$
$= \mathbf{-5}$

15. $-3 + (-2) + 3 - (-4)$
$= (-3) + (-2) + (+3) + (+4) = \mathbf{2}$

16. $|-2| + |-4 - 5| + 2$
$= (+2) + (+9) + (+2) = \mathbf{13}$

17. $-2 - (-3) + (-4) - |-3|$
$= (-2) + (+3) + (-4) + (-3) = \mathbf{-6}$

18. $-|-2 + 3 - 5| - |-3 - 6|$
$= (-4) + (-9) = \mathbf{-13}$

19. $-2 - (-3) - |-4 - 3| + 2$
$= (-2) + (+3) + (-7) + (+2) = \mathbf{-4}$

20. $-\{-[-(-2)]\} - |-4 - 2| = (+2) + (-6) = \mathbf{-4}$

21. $-5 + (-3) - (-2) + 2$
$= (-5) + (-3) + (+2) + (+2) = \mathbf{-4}$

22. $-|-3 - 2| + (-5) = (-5) + (-5) = \mathbf{-10}$

23. $7 + 5 - 3 - 2 + (-5)$
$= (+7) + (+5) + (-3) + (-2) + (-5) = \mathbf{2}$

24. $-[-(-4)] - (-3) + 2$
$= (-4) + (+3) + (+2) = \mathbf{1}$

25. $|-6| + |-3| - 5 + (-3)$
$= (+6) + (+3) + (-5) + (-3) = \mathbf{1}$

26. $-4 - 3 - (+3) + (-3)$
$= (-4) + (-3) + (-3) + (-3) = \mathbf{-13}$

27. $|-2 - 5 + 7| - (-3) + 2$
$= (0) + (+3) + (+2) = \mathbf{5}$

28. $3 - (-4) + (-3) - (-4)$
$= (+3) + (+4) + (-3) + (+4) = \mathbf{8}$

29. $3 - |-2 - 3| + (-6) - (-3)$
$= (+3) + (-5) + (-6) + (+3) = \mathbf{-5}$

30. $147 \, \cancel{m^3} \times \frac{100 \text{ cm}}{1 \, \cancel{m}} \times \frac{100 \text{ cm}}{1 \, \cancel{m}} \times \frac{100 \text{ cm}}{1 \, \cancel{m}}$

$= \mathbf{147(100)(100)(100) \text{ cm}^3}$

31. S.A. $= 2(A_{\text{Base}}) + (C \times \text{length})$
$= 2(\pi(4 \text{ cm})^2) + [\pi(8 \text{ cm}) \times 10 \text{ cm}]$
$= 32\pi \text{ cm}^2 + 80\pi \text{ cm}^2$
$= 112\pi \text{ cm}^2 \approx \mathbf{351.68 \text{ cm}^2}$

32. V $= A_{\text{Triangle}} \times \text{length}$
$= \frac{20 \text{ cm} \times 10 \text{ cm}}{2} \times 41 \text{ cm}$
$= 100 \text{ cm}^2 \times 41 \text{ cm}$
$= 4100 \text{ cm}^3 = \mathbf{4100 \text{ one-centimeter cubes}}$

S.A. $= 2(A_{\text{End}}) + 2(A_{\text{Side}}) + A_{\text{Bottom}}$
$= 2\left(\frac{20(10)}{2}\right) + 2(41(14.1)) + 20(41)$
$= 200 + 1156.2 + 820$
$= \mathbf{2176.2 \text{ cm}^2}$

33. $3\frac{2}{5} \div 7\frac{1}{3} = \frac{17}{5} \div \frac{22}{3} = \frac{17}{5} \times \frac{3}{22} = \frac{51}{110}$

34. $7\frac{1}{3} \div 3\frac{2}{5} = \frac{22}{3} \div \frac{17}{5} = \frac{22}{3} \times \frac{5}{17} = \frac{110}{51}$

$= \mathbf{2\frac{8}{51}}$

35.
$$\begin{array}{r} 4.00165 \\ -\ 1.00072 \\ \hline \mathbf{3.00093} \end{array}$$

36.
$$\begin{array}{r} 3.03 \\ 28\overline{)84.84} \\ 84 \\ \hline 84 \\ 84 \\ \hline \end{array}$$

37. $-2\frac{3}{5} + 1\frac{2}{3} = -2\frac{9}{15} + 1\frac{10}{15} = -\frac{39}{15} + \frac{25}{15}$

$= -\mathbf{\frac{14}{15}}$

38. $-7\frac{4}{11} + 2\frac{7}{8} = -7\frac{32}{88} + 2\frac{77}{88}$

$= -6\frac{120}{88} + 2\frac{77}{88} = -\mathbf{4\frac{43}{88}}$

PROBLEM SET 9

1. Zero; if we try to write the reciprocal, we get a meaningless statement.

2. (a) 1
(b) No

3. (a) The answer to a division problem
(b) The answer to a multiplication problem

4. 8; $-8 + 8 = 0$

5. $420\ \mathrm{ft}^3 \times \frac{12\ \text{in.}}{1\ \mathrm{ft}} \times \frac{12\ \text{in.}}{1\ \mathrm{ft}} \times \frac{12\ \text{in.}}{1\ \mathrm{ft}}$

$= \mathbf{420(12)(12)(12)\ in.^3}$

6. $465\ \mathrm{m} \times \frac{100\ \text{cm}}{1\ \mathrm{m}} \times \frac{1\ \text{in.}}{2.54\ \text{cm}} = \mathbf{\frac{465(100)}{2.54}}$ **in.**

7. $V = A_{\text{Base}} \times \text{length}$

$= (\pi(8\ \mathrm{m})^2) \times 12\ \mathrm{m}$

$= 64\pi\ \mathrm{m}^2 \times 12\ \mathrm{m}$

$= 768\pi\ \mathrm{m}^3 \approx \mathbf{2411.52\ m^3}$

8. $A_{\text{Total}} = A_{\text{Triangle}} + A_{\text{Rectangle}}$

$= \frac{4\ \mathrm{m} \times 3\ \mathrm{m}}{2} + 6\ \mathrm{m}(3\ \mathrm{m})$

$= 6\ \mathrm{m}^2 + 18\ \mathrm{m}^2 = \mathbf{24\ m^2}$

9. $6 - 8 + 2(3) = 6 - 8 + 6 = \mathbf{4}$

10. $3 - 2 \cdot 4 + 3 \cdot 2 = 3 - 8 + 6 = \mathbf{1}$

11. $-5 - 7 - 3 \cdot 2 = -5 - 7 - 6 = \mathbf{-18}$

12. $4 - 5(-5) + 3 = 4 + 25 + 3 = \mathbf{32}$

13. $-2(-2) - 2 - 2 = 4 - 2 - 2 = \mathbf{0}$

14. $-3(-2)(-3) - 2 = -18 - 2 = \mathbf{-20}$

15. $-3 - 6 + 2 \cdot 5 = -3 - 6 + 10 = \mathbf{1}$

16. $-6(-2) - 3(-2) = 12 + 6 = \mathbf{18}$

17. $-4(-3) + (-2)(-5) = 12 + 10 = \mathbf{22}$

18. $-2 - 3(+6) = -2 - 18 = \mathbf{-20}$

19. $\frac{-18}{-9} = \mathbf{2}$

20. $(-2)(-2) - 2 = 4 - 2 = \mathbf{2}$

21. $-3 + (-2) - (+2)(2) = -3 + (-2) - 4 = \mathbf{-9}$

22. $-2 - 2(-2) + (-2)(-2) = -2 + 4 + 4 = \mathbf{6}$

23. $(-2)(-2)(-2) - |-8| = -8 - 8 = \mathbf{-16}$

24. $-(-5) + (-2) + (-5)|-3|$
$= 5 + (-2) - 15 = \mathbf{-12}$

25. $(-7)(2) - 2(-3) + 6 = -14 + 6 + 6 = \mathbf{-2}$

26. $(-5) - (-5) + 2(-2) + 4$
$= -5 + 5 - 4 + 4 = \mathbf{0}$

27. $-3 - (-2) + (-3) - 2(-2)$
$= -3 + 2 + (-3) + 4 = \mathbf{0}$

28. $3(-2) - |(-3)(+3)| + 9 - 7(-2)$
$= -6 - 9 + 9 + 14 = \mathbf{8}$

29. $(-5)(-5) - 5(2) + 3 = 25 - 10 + 3 = \mathbf{18}$

30. $(-3)(-3) - 3 - 2|(-3)(2) + 5|$
$= 9 - 3 - 2 = \mathbf{4}$

31. $3\frac{2}{7} - 7\frac{6}{15} = 3\frac{30}{105} - 7\frac{42}{105} = \frac{345}{105} - \frac{777}{105}$

$= -\frac{432}{105} = -4\frac{12}{105} = -\mathbf{4\frac{4}{35}}$

32. $3\frac{1}{5} \div 7\frac{6}{15} = \frac{16}{5} \div \frac{111}{15} = \frac{16}{\cancel{5}} \times \frac{\cancel{15}^3}{111}$

$= \frac{48}{111} = \mathbf{\frac{16}{37}}$

33. Divide:

$$52 \overline{)\, \begin{array}{r} 8 \\ 416 \\ 416 \end{array}}$$

34. $\dfrac{19}{\underset{2}{\cancel{8}}} \times \dfrac{\overset{7}{\cancel{28}}}{5} = \dfrac{133}{10} = 13\dfrac{3}{10}$

PROBLEM SET 10

1. $\{0, 1, 2, 3, \ldots\}$

2. $\{\ldots, -3, -2, -1, 0, 1, 2, 3, \ldots\}$

3. (a) One of the quantities multiplied to form a product
(b) The answer to a division problem
(c) The answer to an addition problem

4. $(-2 - 2)(-3 - 4) = (-4)(-7) = \mathbf{28}$

5. $-3(-6 - 2) + 3(-2 + 5)$
$= -3(-8) + 3(3) = 24 + 9 = \mathbf{33}$

6. $(-3 - 2) - (-6 + 2) = (-5) + (+4) = \mathbf{-1}$

7. $(-4 + 7) + (-3 - 2) = 3 + (-5) = \mathbf{-2}$

8. $5(9 + 2) - (-4)(5 + 1)$
$= 5(11) + 4(6) = 55 + 24 = \mathbf{79}$

9. $(-3 - 2)(-2)(-2 - 2) = (-5)(-2)(-4) = \mathbf{-40}$

10. $420 \,\cancel{cm} \times \dfrac{1 \,\cancel{in.}}{2.54 \,\cancel{cm}} \times \dfrac{1 \text{ ft}}{12 \,\cancel{in.}} = \dfrac{420}{(2.54)(12)} \text{ ft}$

11. $420 \,\cancel{in.^3} \times \dfrac{1 \text{ ft}}{12 \,\cancel{in.}} \times \dfrac{1 \text{ ft}}{12 \,\cancel{in.}} \times \dfrac{1 \text{ ft}}{12 \,\cancel{in.}}$

$= \dfrac{420}{(12)(12)(12)} \text{ ft}^3$

12. $A_{\text{Total}} = A_{\text{Rectangle}} - A_{\text{Semicircle}}$

$= \left(6(4) - \dfrac{\pi(2)^2}{2} \right) \text{m}^2$

$= (24 - 2\pi) \text{ m}^2 \approx \mathbf{17.72 \text{ m}^2}$

13. S.A. $= 2(2 \text{ in.} \times 2 \text{ in.}) + 2(2 \text{ in.} \times 2 \text{ in.})$
$\qquad + 2(2 \text{ in.} \times 2 \text{ in.})$
$= 8 \text{ in.}^2 + 8 \text{ in.}^2 + 8 \text{ in.}^2$
$= \mathbf{24 \text{ in.}^2}$

14. $\dfrac{-150}{-25} = \mathbf{6}$

15. $\dfrac{75}{-3} = \mathbf{-25}$

16. $-2(-5 - 7) - 3(-8 + 2)$
$= -2(-12) - 3(-6) = 24 + 18 = \mathbf{42}$

17. $(-2 - 7 + 4) - (-3 - 2) = (-5) + (+5) = \mathbf{0}$

18. $(2 - 3)(-8 + 2) + |-3 + 5|$
$= (-1)(-6) + 2 = 6 + 2 = \mathbf{8}$

19. $-4 - 6 - (-3) - (-3 - 8)$
$= (-4) + (-6) + (+3) + (+11) = \mathbf{4}$

20. $\dfrac{1}{4}(8 - 4) - 5(8 - 2) - 2$

$= \dfrac{1}{4}(4) - 5(6) - 2 = 1 - 30 - 2 = \mathbf{-31}$

21. $(6 - 2)(-3 - 5) - (-5)$
$= (4)(-8) + 5 = -32 + 5 = \mathbf{-27}$

22. $-|-2 - 5 + 3|(5 - 2) = (-4)(3) = \mathbf{-12}$

23. $2(2 - 4) - 8 - 6(7 + 3) - |-2|$
$= 2(-2) - 8 - 6(10) - 2 = -4 - 8 - 60 - 2$
$= \mathbf{-74}$

24. $4(8 + 4) + 7(10 - 8)$
$= 4(12) + 7(2) = 48 + 14 = \mathbf{62}$

25. $-8 - 4 - (-2) - (+2)(-3)$
$= (-8) - 4 + 2 + 6 = \mathbf{-4}$

26. $6(10 + 3) + 2(-3 - 2)(-2 - 2)$
$= 6(13) + 2(-5)(-4) = 78 + 40 = \mathbf{118}$

27. $5(12 + 2) - 6(-3 + 8) - (2 + 3)$
$= 5(14) - 6(5) - 5 = 70 - 30 - 5 = \mathbf{35}$

28. $-6 - (+3) + (-3) - 5(4 - 3)$
$= -6 - 3 - 3 - 5(1) = \mathbf{-17}$

29. $4 - 6 - 2(-3) - 5(6) + 7$
$= 4 - 6 + 6 - 30 + 7 = \mathbf{-19}$

30. $7(14 - 7) - 6(-12 - 4)$
$= 7(7) - 6(-16) = 49 + 96 = \mathbf{145}$

31. $2 - 4 - 5(-2) + 5(-2) - 4$
$= 2 - 4 + 10 - 10 - 4 = \mathbf{-6}$

32. $-8(+2) + 3(-2)(4 - 3)$
$= -16 + (-6)(1) = -16 - 6 = \mathbf{-22}$

33.

$$-4 \overline{)\, \begin{array}{r} -4.02 \\ 16.08 \\ 16 \\ \hline 8 \\ 8 \end{array}}$$

34. $3\frac{2}{3} \div -5\frac{1}{6} = \frac{11}{3} \div -\frac{31}{6} = \frac{11}{3} \times \left(-\frac{6}{31}\right)$

$= -\frac{22}{31}$

35. $-4\frac{1}{5} + 2\frac{1}{3} = -4\frac{3}{15} + 2\frac{5}{15} = -\frac{63}{15} + \frac{35}{15}$

$= -\frac{28}{15} = -1\frac{13}{15}$

PROBLEM SET 11

1. $\{0, 1, 2, 3, \ldots\}$

2. Any number that can be graphed on a number line

3. (a) One of the quantities multiplied to form a product
   (b) The answer to a multiplication problem
   (c) The answer to a division problem

4. $-2(-6 - 3) + \frac{0}{5} = -2(-9) + 0 = 18 + 0$
   $= \mathbf{18}$

5. $(-7) - [-(-2)]5 = -7 - (2)(5) = -7 - 10$
   $= \mathbf{-17}$

6. $-2 + 3|-4| = -2 + 12 = \mathbf{10}$

7. $(-3 + 2)(-6) = (-1)(-6) = \mathbf{6}$

8. $(-3 - 2) - (5 + 2) = (-5) - 7 = \mathbf{-12}$

9. $(-3 + 5)(2 - 3) = (2)(-1) = \mathbf{-2}$

10. $(5 - 3)(-3) + (-2)7 = (2)(-3) - 14$
   $= -6 - 14 = \mathbf{-20}$

11. $-2 - 3 - (-2) + (-3)$
   $= -2 - 3 + 2 - 3 = \mathbf{-6}$

12. $-2 - (-2) - |-2|(2) = -2 + 2 - 4 = \mathbf{-4}$

13. $-|-4 - 2|(-2) + 3 = (-6)(-2) + 3 = 12 + 3$
   $= \mathbf{15}$

14. $-3(-3)\big(-2 - 5 + |-11|\big) = (-3)(-3)(4) = \mathbf{36}$

15. $-2 + 3 - 2(-2)3 = -2 + 3 + 4(3)$
   $= -2 + 3 + 12 = \mathbf{13}$

16. $-|-11| + (-3)|-3 + 5| = (-11) + (-3)(2)$
   $= -11 - 6 = \mathbf{-17}$

17. $-3\big\{[(-5 - 2)](-1)\big\} = -3(-7)(-1) = \mathbf{-21}$

18. (a) $P = \left(\frac{2\pi(10)}{2} + 30 + 20 + 30\right) m$
   $= (10\pi + 80) \, m \approx \mathbf{111.4 \, m}$

   (b) $A = A_{Semicircle} + A_{Rectangle}$
   $= \left(\frac{\pi(10)^2}{2} + 30(20)\right) m^2$
   $= (50\pi + 600) \, m^2 \approx \mathbf{757 \, m^2}$

19. $A_{Shaded} = A_{Parallelogram} - A_{Circle}$
   $= (44(18) - \pi(5)^2) \, in.^2$
   $= (792 - 25\pi) \, in.^2 \approx \mathbf{713.5 \, in.^2}$

20. $\frac{-3(4 - 2) - (-5)}{4 - (3)(-3)} = \frac{-3(2) + 5}{4 + 9}$
   $= \frac{-6 + 5}{13} = -\frac{1}{13}$

21. $\frac{-(-2 - 6)}{(-2)(-1 - 3) + 8} = \frac{-(-8)}{(-2)(-4) + 8}$
   $= \frac{8}{16} = \frac{1}{2}$

22. $\frac{-(-3 + 5) + 7}{4 - (-3)} = \frac{-(2) + 7}{4 + 3} = \frac{5}{7}$

23. $-3 - (-2) + (3 - 5)(-2) - 5$
   $= -3 + 2 + (-2)(-2) - 5 = -3 + 2 + 4 - 5$
   $= \mathbf{-2}$

24. $\frac{3(-4 - 2)}{2(-3)(-4)} = \frac{3(-6)}{2(12)} = \frac{-18}{24} = -\frac{3}{4}$

25. $-3 - [-(-2)] + (-3)(5) = -3 - [2] + (-15)$
   $= \mathbf{-20}$

26. $-6 - 2 - (-3) + 2 - 6$
   $= -6 - 2 + 3 + 2 - 6 = \mathbf{-9}$

27. $\frac{-6(2)(-2)}{-(-5 - 3)} = \frac{(-12)(-2)}{-(-8)} = \frac{24}{8} = \mathbf{3}$

28. $\frac{-4(-2 - 2)}{-3 - (-2)} = \frac{-4(-4)}{-3 + 2} = \frac{16}{-1} = \mathbf{-16}$

29. $\frac{-3(-2 + 5)}{-5(-6 + 4)} = \frac{-3(3)}{-5(-2)} = \frac{-9}{10} = -\frac{9}{10}$

30.
$$3006 \overline{\smash{)}\begin{array}{r} 1.05 \\ 3156.30 \\ \underline{3006} \\ 150\,30 \\ \underline{150\,30} \end{array}}$$

31. Convert 485 inches to meters:

$$485 \text{ in.} \times \frac{2.54 \text{ cm}}{1 \text{ in.}} \times \frac{1 \text{ m}}{100 \text{ cm}} = \frac{485(2.54)}{100} \text{ m}$$

32. $476 \text{ mi}^2 \times \dfrac{5280 \text{ ft}}{1 \text{ mi}} \times \dfrac{5280 \text{ ft}}{1 \text{ mi}}$

$= \mathbf{476(5280)(5280) \text{ ft}^2}$

PROBLEM SET 12

1. Negative number

2. Negative number

3. $-\dfrac{1}{5}$

4. Multiplicative inverse

5. $V = A_{\text{Base}} \times \text{height}$

$= (A_{\text{Semicircle}} + A_{\text{Triangle}}) \times \text{height}$

$= \left(\dfrac{\pi(10)^2}{2} + \dfrac{27 \times 20}{2} \right) \text{cm}^2 \times 100 \text{ cm}$

$= (50\pi + 270) \text{ cm}^2 \times 100 \text{ cm}$

$= (5000\pi + 27{,}000) \text{ cm}^3 \approx \mathbf{42{,}700 \text{ cm}^3}$

6. $\text{S.A.} = 2(A_{\text{Front}}) + 2(A_{\text{Top}}) + 2(A_{\text{Side}})$

$= 2[6(4)] \text{ in.}^2 + 2[4(2)] \text{ in.}^2 + 2[6(2)] \text{ in.}^2$

$= 48 \text{ in.}^2 + 16 \text{ in.}^2 + 24 \text{ in.}^2$

$= \mathbf{88 \text{ in.}^2}$

7. $60 \text{ m} \times \dfrac{100 \text{ cm}}{1 \text{ m}} \times \dfrac{1 \text{ in.}}{2.54 \text{ cm}} = \dfrac{\mathbf{60(100)}}{\mathbf{2.54}} \text{ in.}$

8. $48{,}700 \text{ ft}^3 \times \dfrac{1 \text{ mi}}{5280 \text{ ft}} \times \dfrac{1 \text{ mi}}{5280 \text{ ft}} \times \dfrac{1 \text{ mi}}{5280 \text{ ft}}$

$= \dfrac{\mathbf{48{,}700}}{\mathbf{(5280)(5280)(5280)}} \text{ mi}^3$

9. $4 - \dfrac{(+12)}{(-3)} + 2 = 4 - (-4) + 2 = \mathbf{10}$

10. $\dfrac{-6}{-1} + (-3)(-2) + 3|-4 - 2|$

$= 6 + 6 + 3(6) = 6 + 6 + 18 = \mathbf{30}$

11. $-3(-2 - 5)4 = -3(-7)(4) = 21(4) = \mathbf{84}$

12. $-5(-3 - 2) + (-2) - (-3 - 4)$

$= -5(-5) - 2 - (-7) = 25 - 2 + 7 = \mathbf{30}$

13. $\dfrac{-6 - 3}{-4 + (4 - 3)} = \dfrac{-9}{-4 + (1)} = \dfrac{-9}{-3} = \mathbf{3}$

14. $\dfrac{-5(-2) - 4}{(-2 - 1)(-1)} = \dfrac{10 - 4}{(-3)(-1)} = \dfrac{6}{3} = \mathbf{2}$

15. $\dfrac{-2(-6) - 2}{-3 + (-7 + 2)} = \dfrac{12 - 2}{-3 + (-5)} = \dfrac{10}{-8} = -\dfrac{\mathbf{5}}{\mathbf{4}}$

16. $\dfrac{-2 - 4(-3 - 2)}{3 + (-2)(+7)} = \dfrac{-2 - 4(-5)}{3 + (-14)}$

$= \dfrac{-2 + 20}{-11} = \dfrac{18}{-11} = -\dfrac{\mathbf{18}}{\mathbf{11}}$

17. $-3 - (2) + (-2) - (-3)(-2) = -3 - 2 - 2 - 6$

$= \mathbf{-13}$

18. $\dfrac{(-3)|-1 - 4|}{-3 - |-2|} = \dfrac{(-3)(5)}{-3 - 2} = \dfrac{-15}{-5} = \mathbf{3}$

19. $\dfrac{(-8 - 2)(-2)}{-2 - 6(2)} = \dfrac{(-10)(-2)}{-2 - 12} = \dfrac{20}{-14} = -\dfrac{\mathbf{10}}{\mathbf{7}}$

20. $-2 + (-2) - (-4)5 = -2 - 2 - (-20) = \mathbf{16}$

21. $-2(-6 - 1 - 2) - (-2 + 7) = -2(-9) - (5)$

$= 18 - 5 = \mathbf{13}$

22. $-3 - (-2 - 6)(-2 + 4) = -3 - (-8)(2)$

$= -3 + 16 = \mathbf{13}$

23. $(-5 - 6) - 2(3 - 6) + |-4|$

$= (-11) - 2(-3) + (4) = -11 + 6 + 4 = \mathbf{-1}$

24. $-2 - 3 - (2)(-2) + (-1)(-3)$

$= -2 - 3 - (-4) + (3)$

$= -2 - 3 + 4 + 3 = \mathbf{2}$

25. $-2[3 - 2 - (-3)] - [(3 - 2)(-2)]$

$= -2[3 - 2 + 3] - [(1)(-2)] = -2[4] + 2$

$= -8 + 2 = \mathbf{-6}$

26. $(-2)(-3)(-4 + 2) - (3 + 1)$

$= (6)(-2) - (4) = -12 - 4 = \mathbf{-16}$

27. $-7 - (2) + (-2) - 3|-4| = -7 - 2 - 2 - 3(4)$

$= -7 - 2 - 2 - 12 = \mathbf{-23}$

28. $5 - 6 - 4 + 3 - (-2)(-3 - 2)$

$= 5 - 6 - 4 + 3 + 2(-5) = -2 - 10 = \mathbf{-12}$

29. $-3(-2|-11|) + 5(-3 + 2) = -3(-22) + 5(-1)$

$= 66 - 5 = \mathbf{61}$

30. $3 - 6 - 2 - (-3)(-4) + 2$

$= 3 - 6 - 2 - 12 + 2 = \mathbf{-15}$

31. $-3\dfrac{1}{5} + 2\dfrac{1}{6} = -3\dfrac{6}{30} + 2\dfrac{5}{30} = -1\dfrac{1}{30}$

32.
$$63 \overline{)\,-138.6\,}^{\,-2.2}$$
$$\underline{-126}$$
$$-12\,6$$
$$\underline{-12\,6}$$

33. $-3\dfrac{1}{5} \div 2\dfrac{1}{6} = -\dfrac{16}{5} \div \dfrac{13}{6} = -\dfrac{16}{5} \times \dfrac{6}{13}$

$= -\dfrac{96}{65} = -1\dfrac{31}{65}$

PROBLEM SET 13

1. A numerical expression contains only numbers, and an algebraic expression contains only numbers or only letters or both.

2. The value of an expression is the one number being represented.

3. (a) A letter that represents an unspecified number
(b) A variable

4. $75 \text{ ft} \times \dfrac{12 \text{ in.}}{1 \text{ ft}} \times \dfrac{2.54 \text{ cm}}{1 \text{ in.}} = \textbf{75(12)(2.54) cm}$

5. $7000 \text{ mi}^2 \times \dfrac{5280 \text{ ft}}{1 \text{ mi}} \times \dfrac{5280 \text{ ft}}{1 \text{ mi}}$

$= \textbf{7000(5280)(5280) ft}^2$

6. $V = A_{\text{Base}} \times \text{height}$
$= (\pi(22)^2) \text{ m}^2 \times 8 \text{ m}$
$= 484\pi \text{ m}^2 \times 8 \text{ m}$
$= 3872\pi \text{ m}^3 \approx \textbf{12,158.08 m}^3$

7. $A = \dfrac{1}{2}b_1 h + \dfrac{1}{2}b_2 h$

$= \dfrac{1}{2}(60 \text{ cm})(20 \text{ cm}) + \dfrac{1}{2}(20 \text{ cm})(20 \text{ cm})$

$= 600 \text{ cm}^2 + 200 \text{ cm}^2$

$= \textbf{800 cm}^2$

8. $xm - 2m = [(-2)(-3)] - [2(-3)] = 6 - (-6)$
$= \textbf{12}$

9. $ma - m - a = [(-2)(-4)] - (-2) - (-4)$
$= 8 + 2 + 4 = \textbf{14}$

10. $2abc - 3ab = [2(2)(-3)(4)] - [3(2)(-3)]$
$= -48 + 18 = \textbf{-30}$

11. $xy - 3y = [(2)(4)] - [3(4)] = 8 - 12 = \textbf{-4}$

12. $-x(a + b) = -(4)[(-3) + (-5)] = -4(-8) = \textbf{32}$

13. $-a + b + ab = -(-5) + (-2) + [(-5)(-2)]$
$= 5 - 2 + 10 = \textbf{13}$

14. $x - y(a - x) = (-3) - (4)[(4) - (-3)]$
$= -3 - 4(7) = -3 - 28 = \textbf{-31}$

15. $-(m - x)(a - mx)$
$= -[(3) - (-4)][(-2) - (3)(-4)] = -(7)(10)$
$= \textbf{-70}$

16. $-xa(x + a) - a$
$= -[(2)(-4)][(2) + (-4)] - (-4)$
$= -(-8)(-2) + 4 = \textbf{-12}$

17. $|-b - a| + a = |-(2) - (-4)| + (-4)$
$= |2| - 4 = \textbf{-2}$

18. $-a + (-a + b) = -(-3) + [-(-3) + (-5)]$
$= 3 + (-2) = \textbf{1}$

19. $-xy - (-x + y)$
$= -[(-3)(-4)] - [-(-3) + (-4)] = -12 - (-1)$
$= \textbf{-11}$

20. $-c - (p - c) = -(2) - [(-5) - (2)]$
$= -2 - (-7) = -2 + 7 = \textbf{5}$

21. $-xy - x(x - y)$
$= -[(-4)(-1)] - (-4)[(-4) - (-1)]$
$= -4 + 4(-3) = \textbf{-16}$

22. $-2[-3(-2 - 5)(3)] = -2[-3(-7)(3)]$
$= -2[63] = \textbf{-126}$

23. $-3 - (-2) - 3(-2 + 5) + 2|-3|$
$= -3 + 2 - 3(3) + 6 = \textbf{-4}$

24. $-|-3|(2 - 5) - [-(-3)] = -3(-3) - (3)$
$= 9 - 3 = \textbf{6}$

25. $-4 - 2(3 - 2) - (-2 - 5) = -4 - 2(1) - (-7)$
$= -4 - 2 + 7 = \textbf{1}$

26. $-3(-2 - 3)(5 - 7) - 2 = -3(-5)(-2) - 2$
$= -30 - 2 = \textbf{-32}$

27. $5 - 3(-2 + 6) - (5 - 7) - 2$
$= 5 - 3(4) - (-2) - 2$
$= 5 - 12 + 2 - 2 = \textbf{-7}$

28. $-5(-3 + 7)(-2)(-3 + 2) = -5(4)(-2)(-1) = \textbf{-40}$

29. $-3(5 - 3) - (-2)(-6 - 1) = -3(2) + 2(-7)$
$= -6 - 14 = \textbf{-20}$

30. $\dfrac{(-5 - 2) + (-3 - 2)}{-3 - (-2)} = \dfrac{(-7) + (-5)}{-3 + 2}$

$= \dfrac{-12}{-1} = \textbf{12}$

31. $\dfrac{-2[-(-3)]}{(-2)(-4 + 3)} = \dfrac{-2(3)}{-2(-1)} = \dfrac{-6}{2} = \mathbf{-3}$

32. $-3\dfrac{1}{4} + 2\dfrac{3}{11} = -3\dfrac{11}{44} + 2\dfrac{12}{44} = -\dfrac{143}{44} + \dfrac{100}{44}$

$= -\dfrac{43}{44}$

33. $-\dfrac{16}{3} \div \dfrac{20}{3} = -\dfrac{\overset{4}{\cancel{16}}}{\cancel{3}} \times \dfrac{\cancel{3}}{\underset{5}{\cancel{20}}} = -\dfrac{4}{5}$

PROBLEM SET 14

1. (a) A **factor** is one of the quantities multiplied to form a product.
(b) A **quotient** is the answer to a division problem.
(c) A **sum** is the answer to an addition problem.

2. $x - xy = (-2) - [(-2)(-3)] = (-2) - [6] = \mathbf{-8}$

3. $x(x - y) = (-2)[(-2) - (-3)] = (-2)[1] = \mathbf{-2}$

4. $(x - y)(y - x) = [(2) - (-3)][(-3) - (2)]$
$= [5][-5] = \mathbf{-25}$

5. $(x - y) - (x - y)$
$= [(-2) - (3)] - [(-2) - (3)]$
$= [-5] - [-5] = \mathbf{0}$

6. $(-x) + (-y) = [-(-2)] + [-(3)]$
$= [2] + [-3] = \mathbf{-1}$

7. $-xa(x - a) = [-(4)(-2)][(4) - (-2)]$
$= [8][6] = \mathbf{48}$

8. $(-x + a) - (x - a)$
$= [-(-4) + (5)] - [(-4) - (5)] = [9] - [-9]$
$= \mathbf{18}$

9. $-x(a - xa) = [-(3)]\{(-5) - [(3)(-5)]\}$
$= [-3]\{-5 + 15\} = [-3]\{10\} = \mathbf{-30}$

10. $-mp(p - m) = [-(-5)(2)][(2) - (-5)]$
$= [10][7] = \mathbf{70}$

11. $(p - x)(a - px)$
$= [(2) - (-4)]\{(-3) - [(2)(-4)]\}$
$= [6]\{5\} = \mathbf{30}$

12. $(p - px) + (a + p)$
$= \{(2) - [(2)(-4)]\} + [(-3) + (2)]$
$= \{10\} + [-1] = \mathbf{9}$

13. $(p - px) + (a + p)$
$= \{(-3) - [(-3)(4)]\} + [(-5) + (-3)]$
$= \{9\} + [-8] = \mathbf{1}$

14. $-a[(-x - a) - (x - y)]$
$= -(-3)\{[-(4) - (-3)] - [(4) - (-5)]\}$
$= 3\{[-1] - [9]\} = 3\{-10\} = \mathbf{-30}$

15. $V = A_{Triangle} \times length$

$= \left(\dfrac{4 \times 6}{2}\right) m^2 \times 12\ m$

$= 12\ m^2 \times 12\ m = \mathbf{144\ m^3}$

$S.A. = 2(A_{End}) + A_{Bottom} + A_{Side\ 1} + A_{Side\ 2}$

$= \left(2\left(\dfrac{4 \times 6}{2}\right) + (4 \times 12)\right) m^2$

$+ ((7.2 \times 12) + (6 \times 12))\ m^2$

$= (24 + 48 + 86.4 + 72)\ m^2$

$= \mathbf{230.4\ m^2}$

16. $P = (12 + 10 + 10 + 6 + 6 + 2 + 10)\ ft$
$= \mathbf{56\ ft}$

17. $4700\ ft^3 \times \dfrac{1\ yd}{3\ ft} \times \dfrac{1\ yd}{3\ ft} \times \dfrac{1\ yd}{3\ ft} = \dfrac{4700}{(3)(3)(3)}\ yd^3$

18. $-3[-2 - 5(3 - 7)] = -3[-2 - 5(-4)]$
$= -3[18] = \mathbf{-54}$

19. $-3 - (-2) - \{-[-(5)]\} = -3 + 2 - \{5\} = \mathbf{-6}$

20. $-2 + (-3) - |-5 + 2|3 = -2 - 3 - 3(3)$
$= -2 - 3 - 9 = \mathbf{-14}$

21. $-8 - 6(-2 - 1) + (-5) = -8 - 6(-3) - 5$
$= -8 + 18 - 5 = \mathbf{5}$

22. $-3[(2 - 5) - (3 - 1)] = -3[(-3) - (2)]$
$= -3\{-5\} = \mathbf{15}$

23. $\dfrac{-3(-6 - 2) + 5}{-3(-2 + 1)} = \dfrac{-3(-8) + 5}{-3(-1)}$

$= \dfrac{24 + 5}{3} = \dfrac{29}{3} = \mathbf{9\dfrac{2}{3}}$

24. $\dfrac{3(-2 - 1)}{-7(2 - 4)} = \dfrac{3(-3)}{-7(-2)} = \dfrac{-9}{14} = \mathbf{-\dfrac{9}{14}}$

25. $\dfrac{3(-2) - 5}{-3(-2)} = \dfrac{-6 - 5}{6} = \dfrac{-11}{6} = -\dfrac{11}{6}$

$= \mathbf{-1\dfrac{5}{6}}$

26. $-2(-4) - \{-[-(-6)]\} = 8 - \{-6\} = 8 + \{6\}$
$= \mathbf{14}$

27. $-3 - 2[(5 - 3)2 - (2 - 3)]$
$= -3 - 2[(2)2 - (-1)] = -3 - 2[5] = -3 - 10$
$= \mathbf{-13}$

28. $-2(-5 - 2) + (-3)(-6) - 2 = -2(-7) + 18 - 2$
    $= 14 + 18 - 2 = \mathbf{30}$

29. $5(-2 - 3) - 3(-2 + 5) = 5(-5) - 3(3)$
    $= -25 - 9 = \mathbf{-34}$

30. $-3 - 2 - 5(-2 - 1) + (-3)$
    $= -3 - 2 - 5(-3) + (-3) = -3 - 2 + 15 - 3$
    $= \mathbf{7}$

31. $4[2(3 - 2) - (6 - 4)] = 4[2(1) - (2)] = 4[0]$
    $= \mathbf{0}$

32. $-2 - |-2 - 5| + (-3)(-6 - 2)$
    $= -2 - |-7| - 3(-8) = -2 - 7 + 24 = \mathbf{15}$

PROBLEM SET 15

1. A **coefficient** is a factor. Usually this word is reserved for the numerical factor of a term.

2. A **literal coefficient** is a factor made up of letters.

3. $A = A_{\text{Trapezoid}} - A_{\text{Triangle}}$
    $= \dfrac{1}{2}[(40)(10) + (20)(10) - (10)(10)] \text{ ft}^2$
    $= [200 + 100 - 50] \text{ ft}^2$
    $= \mathbf{250 \text{ ft}^2}$

4. $V = A_{\text{Base}} \times \text{length}$
    $= (\pi(4)^2) \text{ cm}^2 \times 14 \text{ cm}$
    $= 16\pi \text{ cm}^2 \times 14 \text{ cm}$
    $= 224\pi \text{ cm}^3 \approx \mathbf{703.36 \text{ cm}^3}$

5. $280 \text{ in.}^3 \times \dfrac{1 \text{ ft}}{12 \text{ in.}} \times \dfrac{1 \text{ ft}}{12 \text{ in.}} \times \dfrac{1 \text{ ft}}{12 \text{ in.}}$
    $= \dfrac{280}{(12)(12)(12)} \text{ ft}^3$

6. $-7(-8 + 3) = (-7)(-8) + (-7)(3) = 56 - 21$
    $= \mathbf{35}$

7. $5(-3 - 6) = 5(-3) + 5(-6) = -15 - 30 = \mathbf{-45}$

8. $mx(ab - b) = \mathbf{mxab - mxb}$

9. $-4y(d + cx) = \mathbf{-4yd - 4ycx}$

10. $(a + bc)2x = \mathbf{2ax + 2bcx}$

11. $3a(x + 2y) = \mathbf{3ax + 6ay}$

12. $-a(a - b) = -(-2)[(-2) - (-7)] = 2[5] = \mathbf{10}$

13. $(-a + b) + (-a) = [-(-2) + (5)] + [-(-2)]$
    $= [7] + [2] = \mathbf{9}$

14. $(a - x)(-x) = [(2) - (-5)][-(-5)] = [7][5]$
    $= \mathbf{35}$

15. $(x - y) - (y - x)$
    $= [(-2) - (-4)] - [(-4) - (-2)] = [2] - [-2]$
    $= \mathbf{4}$

16. $x - 2a(-a) = (4) - 2(-3)[-(-3)] = 4 + 6[3]$
    $= 4 + 18 = \mathbf{22}$

17. $-x(a - xa) = -(-4)\{(-3) - [(-4)(-3)]\}$
    $= 4\{-3 - [12]\} = 4\{-15\} = \mathbf{-60}$

18. $-y[-ay - (xy)]$
    $= -(-3)\{[-(-2)(-3)] - [(2)(-3)]\}$
    $= 3\{[-6] - [-6]\} = 3\{0\} = \mathbf{0}$

19. $-|-2| + (-3) - 3 - (-4 - 2)$
    $= -2 - 3 - 3 - (-6) = -2 - 3 - 3 + 6 = \mathbf{-2}$

20. $4[(2 - 4) - (6 - 3)] = 4[(-2) - (3)] = 4[-5]$
    $= \mathbf{-20}$

21. $5[(3 - 2)(-5 - 3)] = 5[(1)(-8)] = 5[-8]$
    $= \mathbf{-40}$

22. $-3 - 5(-2) - 4 + (-6)(3)$
    $= -3 + 10 - 4 - 18 = \mathbf{-15}$

23. $-2[-5 - 3(-2)][(-4) + 2] = -2[-5 + 6][-2]$
    $= -2[1][-2] = \mathbf{4}$

24. $-5(-2)(-2 - 3) - (-|-2|) = 10(-5) - (-2)$
    $= -50 + 2 = \mathbf{-48}$

25. $-[-(-3)] - 2(-2) + (-3) = -3 + 4 - 3 = \mathbf{-2}$

26. $3(-2)(-3 - 2) - (-4 - 2) = -6(-5) - (-6)$
    $= 30 + 6 = \mathbf{36}$

27. $\dfrac{3 - (-2)(4)}{5 - (-3)} = \dfrac{3 + 8}{5 + 3} = \dfrac{11}{8} = \mathbf{1\dfrac{3}{8}}$

28. $-|-3| - 2(-3) + (-3) - 5 - 2$
    $= -3 + 6 - 3 - 5 - 2 = \mathbf{-7}$

29. $\dfrac{3 + 7(-3)}{-6 - 2(-4)} = \dfrac{3 - 21}{-6 + 8} = \dfrac{-18}{2} = \mathbf{-9}$

30. $(-2 - 5 + 3)(-2) - [-6 + 3(-2)]$
$= (-4)(-2) - [-6 - 6] = 8 + 12 = \mathbf{20}$

31.
$$
\begin{array}{r}
-0.0162 \\
405 \overline{)-6.5610} \\
\underline{-4\,05} \\
-2\,511 \\
\underline{-2\,430} \\
-810 \\
\underline{-810} \\
\end{array}
$$

32. $-3\dfrac{1}{3} \div 2\dfrac{1}{5} = -\dfrac{10}{3} \div \dfrac{11}{5} = -\dfrac{10}{3} \times \dfrac{5}{11}$

$= -\dfrac{50}{33} = -1\dfrac{17}{33}$

33. $-3\dfrac{1}{5} + 1\dfrac{3}{8} = -3\dfrac{8}{40} + 1\dfrac{15}{40} = -\dfrac{128}{40} + \dfrac{55}{40}$

$= -\dfrac{73}{40} = -1\dfrac{33}{40}$

PROBLEM SET 16

1. A **term** is a single symbol, a product, or a quotient.

2. **Like terms**, ones that have the same variables in the same form or in equivalent form, may be added.

3. (a) A **factor** is one of the quantities that is multiplied to form a product.
(b) A **product** is the answer to a multiplication problem.
(c) A **quotient** is the answer to a division problem.

4. $A = A_{\text{Large semicircle}} + 2A_{\text{Small semicircle}}$

$= \left(\dfrac{\pi(12)^2}{2} + 2\left(\dfrac{\pi(6)^2}{2} \right) \right) \text{ft}^2$

$= (72\pi + 36\pi) \text{ft}^2$

$= 108\pi \text{ ft}^2 \approx \mathbf{339.12 \text{ ft}^2}$

5. S.A. $= 2A_{\text{Front}} + 2A_{\text{Top}} + 2A_{\text{Side}}$

$= (2(4 \times 3) + 2(4 \times 3) + 2(3 \times 3)) \text{ in.}^2$

$= (24 + 24 + 18) \text{ in.}^2$

$= \mathbf{66 \text{ in.}^2}$

6. $6 \, \cancel{\text{ft}} \times \dfrac{12 \, \cancel{\text{in.}}}{1 \, \cancel{\text{ft}}} \times \dfrac{2.54 \, \cancel{\text{cm}}}{1 \, \cancel{\text{in.}}} \times \dfrac{1 \text{ m}}{100 \, \cancel{\text{cm}}}$

$= \dfrac{6(12)(2.54)}{100} \text{ m}$

7. $42{,}000 \, \cancel{\text{in.}^2} \times \dfrac{1 \, \cancel{\text{ft}}}{12 \, \cancel{\text{in.}}} \times \dfrac{1 \, \cancel{\text{ft}}}{12 \, \cancel{\text{in.}}} \times \dfrac{1 \text{ mi}}{5280 \, \cancel{\text{ft}}} \times \dfrac{1 \text{ mi}}{5280 \, \cancel{\text{ft}}}$

$= \dfrac{42{,}000}{(12)(12)(5280)(5280)} \text{ mi}^2$

8. $3xyz + 2zxy - 7zyx + 2xy = \mathbf{2xy - 2xyz}$

9. $4x + 3 - 2xy - 5x - 7 + 4xy = \mathbf{2xy - x - 4}$

10. $(4 + 2y)x = \mathbf{4x + 2xy}$

11. $3x(y - 2m) = \mathbf{3xy - 6mx}$

12. $2p(xy - 3k) = \mathbf{2pxy - 6kp}$

13. $-a(x - a) = -(-3)[(6) - (-3)] = 3[9] = \mathbf{27}$

14. $-x - (-a)(a - x) = -(-2) - [-(4)][(4) - (-2)]$
$= 2 + 4[6] = 2 + 24 = \mathbf{26}$

15. $(m - p)p = [(3) - (-2)](-2) = [5](-2) = \mathbf{-10}$

16. $-p(-x) - px = -(-3)[-(4)] - [(-3)(4)]$
$= 3[-4] + [12] = -12 + 12 = \mathbf{0}$

17. $(x - y) - (y - x)$
$= [(-3) - (-2)] - [(-2) - (-3)] = [-1] - [1]$
$= \mathbf{-2}$

18. $-x(-y) - xy = -(3)[-(-2)] - [(3)(-2)]$
$= -3[2] - [-6] = -6 + 6 = \mathbf{0}$

19. $-px(x - p) = [-(5)(-4)][(-4) - (5)]$
$= [20][-9] = \mathbf{-180}$

20. $(-a)(b)(-a + b) = (-6)(-3)[-(6) + (-3)]$
$= 18[-9] = \mathbf{-162}$

21. $-3 - 2(-4 + 7) - 5 - |-2 - 5|$
$= -3 - 2(3) - 5 - 7 = -3 - 6 - 5 - 7$
$= \mathbf{-21}$

22. $-\{3(-2)(-4 + 2) - [3 - (-2)]\}$
$= -\{-6(-2) - [3 + 2]\} = -\{12 - [5]\} = -\{7\}$
$= \mathbf{-7}$

23. $-4 - (-2) - [-(-2)] - |-3|$
$= -4 + 2 - [2] - 3 = \mathbf{-7}$

24. $-6 - 2(-3)(-1) - 5(3 - 2 - 2)$
$= -6 - 6 - 5(-1) = -6 - 6 + 5 = \mathbf{-7}$

25. $3 - (-6 + 8)2 - 4(-3) + (-3)$
$= 3 - (2)2 + 12 - 3 = 3 - 4 + 12 - 3 = \mathbf{8}$

26. $-5 - 2 - 6(-3 + 7)2 - 2(-3)$
$= -5 - 2 - 6(4)2 + 6 = -5 - 2 - 48 + 6$
$= \mathbf{-49}$

27. $-2[(-3 + 5)(-2) - (3 - 2)]$
$= -2[(2)(-2) - (1)] = -2[-4 - 1] = -2[-5]$
$= \mathbf{10}$

28. $\dfrac{-2(-3 + 7)}{(-2)(-3)} = \dfrac{-2(4)}{6} = -\dfrac{8}{6} = -\dfrac{4}{3} = \mathbf{-1\dfrac{1}{3}}$

29. $\dfrac{-7(-2 + 3)}{-2(-3)} = \dfrac{-7(1)}{6} = -\dfrac{7}{6} = -1\dfrac{1}{6}$

30. $-\dfrac{16}{\cancel{8}} \times \dfrac{\cancel{10}^{\;2}}{57} = -\dfrac{32}{57}$

31. $-5\dfrac{1}{5} + 7\dfrac{2}{3} = 7\dfrac{10}{15} - 5\dfrac{3}{15} = 2\dfrac{7}{15}$

32.
$$
\begin{array}{r}
-2.03 \\
-46\,\overline{)\,93.38} \\
\underline{92} \\
1\,38 \\
\underline{1\,38} \\
\end{array}
$$

PROBLEM SET 17

1. One solution is: $2(3 + 4) = 2(3) + 2(4)$

2. All integers are real numbers.

3. $A = A_{Triangle} + A_{Square} - A_{Semicircle}$

$= \left(\dfrac{10 \times 10}{2} + 10 \times 10 - \dfrac{\pi(5)^2}{2} \right)$ in.^{2}

$= \left(150 - \dfrac{25\pi}{2} \right)$ in.^{2}

$\approx$ **111 one-inch-square tiles**

4. $V = A_{End} \times$ length

$= \left(\dfrac{12(9)}{2} \right)$ ft^2 $\times$ 12 ft

$=$ **648 ft^3**

S.A. $= 2(A_{End}) + A_{Side\,1} + A_{Side\,2} + A_{Bottom}$

$= 2\left(\dfrac{12(9)}{2} \right) + 12(9) + 15(12) + 12(12)$

$= 108 + 108 + 180 + 144$

$=$ **540 ft^2**

5. $42\,\cancel{ft} \times \dfrac{12\,\cancel{in.}}{1\,\cancel{ft}} \times \dfrac{2.54\,\cancel{cm}}{1\,\cancel{in.}} \times \dfrac{1\,m}{100\,\cancel{cm}}$

$= \dfrac{42(12)(2.54)}{100}$ m

6. $170\,\cancel{in.^2} \times \dfrac{1\,\cancel{ft}}{12\,\cancel{in.}} \times \dfrac{1\,\cancel{ft}}{12\,\cancel{in.}} \times \dfrac{1\,yd}{3\,\cancel{ft}} \times \dfrac{1\,yd}{3\,\cancel{ft}}$

$= \dfrac{170}{(12)(12)(3)(3)}$ yd^2

7. $42\,\cancel{m^3} \times \dfrac{100\,cm}{1\,\cancel{m}} \times \dfrac{100\,cm}{1\,\cancel{m}} \times \dfrac{100\,cm}{1\,\cancel{m}}$

$=$ **42(100)(100)(100) cm^3**

8. $xym - 3ymx - 4xmy - 3my + 2ym$
$=$ **$-6mxy - my$**

9. $-3pxk + pkx - 3kpx - kp - 3kx$
$=$ **$-5kpx - kp - 3kx$**

10. $m + 4 + 3m - 6 - 2m + mc - 4mc$
$=$ **$2m - 3mc - 2$**

11. $a - 3 - 7a + 2a - 6ax + 4xa - 5$
$=$ **$-4a - 2ax - 8$**

12. $-p - 5 - 3p - 6 - 2p + 7 - ax + 3xa$
$=$ **$2ax - 6p - 4$**

13. $x(4 - ap) =$ **$4x - apx$**

14. $(5p - 2c)4xy =$ **$20pxy - 8cxy$**

15. $4k(2c - a + 3m) =$ **$8ck - 4ak + 12km$**

16. $|x - a| - a(-x) = |(4) - (-3)| - (-3)(-4)$
$= 7 - 12 =$ **-5**

17. $(-x - a) - a(x - a)$
$= [-(-4) - (-3)] - (-3)[(-4) - (-3)]$
$= [7] + 3[-1] = 7 - 3 =$ **4**

18. $-a(b - a) = -(-4)[(-3) - (-4)] = 4[1] =$ **4**

19. $-(a - x)(x - a) = -[(-5) - (3)][(3) - (-5)]$
$= -[-8][8] =$ **64**

20. $(-p) - a(p - a) = [-(5)] - (-4)[(5) - (-4)]$
$= [-5] + 4[9] = -5 + 36 =$ **31**

21. $-a[(x - a) + (2x + a)]$
$= -(-4)\{[(3) - (-4)] + [2(3) + (-4)]\}$
$= 4\{[7] + [2]\} = 4\{9\} =$ **36**

22. $-(x + xy) = -[(-3) + (-3)(2)] = -[-3 - 6]$
$= -[-9] =$ **9**

23. $m[(x + 2xm) - (3x - mx)]$
$= (2)\{[(-4) + 2(-4)(2)] - [3(-4) - (2)(-4)]\}$
$= 2\{[-4 - 16] - [-12 + 8]\}$
$= 2\{[-20] - [-4]\} = 2\{-16\} =$ **-32**

24. $-3(4 - 3) - 3 - |-3| = -3(1) - 3 - 3$
$= -3 - 3 - 3 =$ **-9**

25. $-2^2 + (-3 - 5) - (-2) = -(2)(2) - 8 + 2$
$= -4 - 8 + 2 =$ **-10**

26. $-4(-3 + 7) - (-2) - 3 = -4(4) + 2 - 3$
$= -16 + 2 - 3 =$ **-17**

27. $-2(-5 - 2)(-2)(-2 - 3) = -2(-7)(-2)(-5)$
$= (14)(10) =$ **140**

28. $-5 + (-5) - (3) + (2) = -5 - 5 - 3 + 2$
$=$ **-11**

29. $\dfrac{-4(2 - 4)}{(-2)(-4)} = \dfrac{-4(-2)}{8} = \dfrac{8}{8} = 1$

30. $-2(-4) - 3^2 + 2 - 5 = 8 - (3)(3) + 2 - 5$
$= 8 - 9 - 3 = -4$

31. $(-2)^3 - 2(2) - 3(-5) = (-2)(-2)(-2) - 4 + 15$
$= -8 - 4 + 15 = 3$

32. $-7 + (6) - (-3) + (-2)^2$
$= -7 + 6 + 3 + (-2)(-2) = 2 + 4 = 6$

PROBLEM SET 18

1. (a) $\{0, 1, 2, 3, \ldots\}$
(b) $\{\ldots, -3, -2, -1, 0, 1, 2, 3, \ldots\}$

2. **Reciprocal**

3. The product is a **positive number** because it has an even number of negative factors.

4. $3^2 + (-3)^2 = (3)(3) + (-3)(-3) = 9 + 9 = 18$

5. $-2^3 + (-2)^3 = -(2)(2)(2) + (-2)(-2)(-2)$
$= -8 - 8 = -16$

6. $-2^2 + (-4)^2 = -(2)(2) + (-4)(-4) = -4 + 16$
$= 12$

7. $-(-3)^2 - (-2)^3 = -(-3)(-3) - (-2)(-2)(-2)$
$= -9 + 8 = -1$

8. $-3^2(-2)^2 - 2 = -(3)(3)(-2)(-2) - 2 = -36 - 2$
$= -38$

9. $-3 - 2^3 - (-3)^3 + \sqrt[6]{64}$
$= -3 - (2)(2)(2) - (-3)(-3)(-3) + 2$
$= -3 - 8 + 27 + 2 = 18$

10. $V = [A_{\text{Rect 1}} + A_{\text{Square}} + A_{\text{Rect 2}}] \times \text{height}$
$= [8(6) + 4(4) + 4(8)] \text{ ft}^2 \times 8 \text{ ft}$
$= 96 \text{ ft}^2 \times 8 \text{ ft} = 768 \text{ ft}^3$
The solid will hold **768 one-ft-square sugar cubes**

S.A. $= 2(A_{\text{Base}}) + (P \times \text{height})$
$= \left[2(8(6) + 4(4) + 4(8)) + (52 \times 8)\right]$
$= (192 + 416)$
$= \mathbf{608 \ ft^2}$

11. $A = \dfrac{1}{2}b_1h + \dfrac{1}{2}b_2h$
$= \left(\dfrac{1}{2}(15 \times 6) + \dfrac{1}{2}(2 \times 6)\right) \text{in.}^2$
$= 51 \text{ in.}^2$
It will take **51 one-in.-square tiles** to cover the trapezoid.

12. Convert 49 meters to feet:

$49 \ \cancel{\text{m}} \times \dfrac{100 \ \cancel{\text{cm}}}{1 \ \cancel{\text{m}}} \times \dfrac{1 \ \cancel{\text{in.}}}{2.54 \ \cancel{\text{cm}}} \times \dfrac{1 \text{ ft}}{12 \ \cancel{\text{in.}}}$

$= \dfrac{49(100)}{(2.54)(12)} \text{ ft}$

13. $-x^2 - y^3 = -(-3)(-3) - (-2)(-2)(-2) = -9 + 8$
$= -1$

14. $a^2 - b^2a = (-2)(-2) - (3)(3)(-2) = 4 + 18$
$= 22$

15. $-3^2 - 2(-3 - 4) = -(3)(3) - 2(-7) = -9 + 14$
$= 5$

16. $-2^2 - 4(-3) = -(2)(2) + 12 = -4 + 12 = 8$

17. $-2(-2)(-2 - 3) = 4(-5) = -20$

18. $-|-2| - 3 + (-3 - 2) = -2 - 3 - 5 = -10$

19. $5(3 - 4)(-2) + (-5 - 2) = 5(-1)(-2) - 7$
$= 10 - 7 = 3$

20. $2[-3(-2 - 4)(3 - 2)] = 2[-3(-6)(1)] = 2[18]$
$= 36$

21. $5 - x + xy - 3yx - 2 + 2x = \mathbf{x - 2xy + 3}$

22. $-3bpx - 3bp - 3 + 5pb = \mathbf{-3bpx + 2bp - 3}$

23. $7 - 3k - 2k + 2kx - xk + 8 = \mathbf{kx - 5k + 15}$

24. $-8 - py + 2yp + 4 - y = \mathbf{py - y - 4}$

25. $(4 - 2p)4x = \mathbf{16x - 8px}$

26. $-3(-x - 4) = \mathbf{3x + 12}$

27. $-2x(a - 3p) = \mathbf{-2ax + 6px}$

28. $-x(a - 3x) + x = -(4)[(3) - 3(4)] + (4)$
$= -4[-9] + 4 = 36 + 4 = 40$

29. $-p(-a + 2p) + p$
$= -(-3)[-(2) + 2(-3)] + (-3) = 3[-8] - 3$
$= -24 - 3 = -27$

30. $k(ak - 4a) + k = (-3)[(2)(-3) - 4(2)] + (-3)$
$= -3[-14] - 3 = 42 - 3 = 39$

31. $2\dfrac{3}{5} \div -4\dfrac{7}{8} = \dfrac{13}{5} \div -\dfrac{39}{8} = \dfrac{13}{5} \times \left(-\dfrac{8}{39}\right)$
$= -\dfrac{8}{15}$

32. $-1\frac{1}{8} + 2\frac{7}{16} = -1\frac{2}{16} + 2\frac{7}{16} = 1\frac{5}{16}$

33.

$$3\overline{)\begin{array}{r} -0.004 \\ -0.012 \end{array}}$$
$$\underline{-0.012}$$

PROBLEM SET 19

1. A **variable** is a letter that stands for an unspecified number.

2. Terms can be called like terms when their letters represent the same number no matter what numbers are used to replace the letters.

3. A = $A_{\text{Rectangle 1}}$ + $A_{\text{Rectangle 2}}$ + $A_{\text{Rectangle 3}}$
   = $(4 \times 2 + 4 \times 2 + 4 \times 2)$ in.^{2}
   = 24 in.^{2}
   24 one-in.-square tiles would cover the figure.

4. A_{Shaded} = $A_{\text{Parallelogram}}$ − A_{Circle}
   = $(8 \times 6 - \pi(2)^2)$ cm^2
   = $(48 - 4\pi)$ cm^2 ≈ **35.44 cm^2**

5. $x^2yyyx^3yx = \boldsymbol{x^6y^4}$

6. $xm^2xm^3x^3m = \boldsymbol{x^5m^6}$

7. $ky^2k^3k^2y^5 = \boldsymbol{k^6y^7}$

8. $a^2ba^2b^3ab^4 = \boldsymbol{a^5b^8}$

9. $40 \, \text{m} \times \dfrac{100 \, \text{cm}}{1 \, \text{m}} \times \dfrac{1 \, \text{in.}}{2.54 \, \text{cm}} \times \dfrac{1 \, \text{ft}}{12 \, \text{in.}}$
   = $\dfrac{40(100)}{(2.54)(12)}$ ft

10. $400 \, \text{m}^3 \times \dfrac{1 \, \text{km}}{1000 \, \text{m}} \times \dfrac{1 \, \text{km}}{1000 \, \text{m}} \times \dfrac{1 \, \text{km}}{1000 \, \text{m}}$
    = $\dfrac{400}{(1000)(1000)(1000)}$ km^3

11. $3ab^2 - 2ab + 5b^2a - ba = \boldsymbol{8ab^2 - 3ab}$

12. $x^2 - 3yx + 2yx^2 - 2xy + yx$
    = $\boldsymbol{x^2 - 4xy + 2yx^2}$

13. $xym^2p - 3m^2yxp + 7pm^2xy - 3y^2mxp$
    = $\boldsymbol{5xym^2p - 3y^2mxp}$

14. $x(3p - 2y) = \boldsymbol{3px - 2xy}$

15. $(3 - 2b)a^2 = \boldsymbol{3a^2 - 2a^2b}$

16. $5(2 - 4p) = \boldsymbol{10 - 20p}$

17. $x^2 - y^2 = (-3)(-3) - (-2)(-2) = 9 - 4 = \boldsymbol{5}$

18. $x(y^2 - x^2) = (-3)[(2)(2) - (-3)(-3)]$
    = $-3[4 - 9] = \boldsymbol{15}$

19. $a^3 - y^3 = (-3)(-3)(-3) - (2)(2)(2) = -27 - 8$
    = $\boldsymbol{-35}$

20. $a(b^3 - a) = (-2)[(-4)(-4)(-4) - (-2)]$
    = $-2[-62] = \boldsymbol{124}$

21. $(a - x)(x - a) = [(-3) - (4)][(4) - (-3)]$
    = $[-7][7] = \boldsymbol{-49}$

22. $x^2(a - x) = (3)(3)[(-5) - (3)] = 9[-8] = \boldsymbol{-72}$

23. $m(x - m) + x = (-3)[(-4) - (-3)] + (-4)$
    = $-3[-1] - 4 = 3 - 4 = \boldsymbol{-1}$

24. $|-p + a| - a^2 = |-(4) + (-2)| - (-2)(-2)$
    = $6 - 4 = \boldsymbol{2}$

25. $-4 - (-2)(-2 + 5) - 3 + \sqrt[3]{-27}$
    = $-4 + 2(3) - 3 + (-3) = -4 + 6 - 3 - 3$
    = $\boldsymbol{-4}$

26. $\dfrac{-3 - [-(-3)]}{-(-2)} = \dfrac{-3 - 3}{2} = -\dfrac{6}{2} = \boldsymbol{-3}$

27. $-6 - [-3 + 5(-2)] - 2 = -6 - [-3 - 10] - 2$
    = $-6 + 13 - 2 = \boldsymbol{5}$

28. $-3^2 - 2^2 - (-3)^3 - \sqrt[3]{-8}$
    = $-(3)(3) - (2)(2) - (-3)(-3)(-3) - (-2)$
    = $-9 - 4 + 27 + 2 = \boldsymbol{16}$

29. $-5 - (-5)^2 - 3 + (-2)$
    = $-5 - (-5)(-5) - 3 - 2 = -5 - 25 - 3 - 2$
    = $\boldsymbol{-35}$

30. $-2[(-3 - 5) + (-7 + 2)] = -2[(-8) + (-5)]$
    = $-2[-13] = \boldsymbol{26}$

31. $1\frac{3}{4} \div -2\frac{1}{3} = \frac{7}{4} \div -\frac{7}{3} = \frac{\cancel{7}}{4} \times -\frac{3}{\cancel{7}} = \boldsymbol{-\frac{3}{4}}$

32. $5\frac{2}{3} - 7\frac{9}{10} = 5\frac{20}{30} - 7\frac{27}{30} = \boldsymbol{-2\frac{7}{30}}$

33.

$$\begin{array}{r} 0.004 \\ \times \, 0.012 \\ \hline 0008 \\ 0004 \\ \hline \boldsymbol{0.000048} \end{array}$$

PROBLEM SET 20

1. Although possible solutions are given, answers will vary. Refer to Lesson 20.C, if necessary.
   (a) $6 = 4 + 1 + 1$
   (b) $x + 2 = x$
   (c) $x + 2 = 4$

2. $P = (30 + 30 + 30 + 20 + 11 + 21)$ ft
   $= \textbf{142 ft}$

3. S.A. $= 2(A_{Base}) + (C \times height)$
   $= (2\pi(24)^2) + (2\pi(24) \times 20)$ in.^{2}
   $= (1152\pi + 960\pi)$ in.^{2}
   $= 2112\pi$ in.$^2 \approx \textbf{6631.68 in.}^2$

4. $12 \ \cancel{ft^3} \times \dfrac{1 \text{ yd}}{3 \ \cancel{ft}} \times \dfrac{1 \text{ yd}}{3 \ \cancel{ft}} \times \dfrac{1 \text{ yd}}{3 \ \cancel{ft}} = \dfrac{12}{(3)(3)(3)} \textbf{yd}^3$

5. $x^2xxy^2xy^3 = \textbf{\textit{x}}^5\textbf{\textit{y}}^5$

6. $p^2m^5ypp^3my^2 = \textbf{\textit{p}}^6\textbf{\textit{m}}^6\textbf{\textit{y}}^3$

7. $8k^5nn^2kn^3k^5k = \textbf{8\textit{k}}^{12}\textbf{\textit{n}}^6$

8. $a^2aba^3b^2a^5 = \textbf{\textit{a}}^{11}\textbf{\textit{b}}^3$

9. $m^2pap^2ma^2aa^3 = \textbf{\textit{a}}^7\textbf{\textit{m}}^3\textbf{\textit{p}}^3$

10. $4p^2x^2kpx^3k^2k = \textbf{4\textit{k}}^4\textbf{\textit{p}}^3\textbf{\textit{x}}^5$

11. $3x + 2 - x^2 + 2x^2 - 4 = \textbf{\textit{x}}^2 + \textbf{3\textit{x}} - \textbf{2}$

12. $xy - 3xy^2 + 5y^2x - 4xy = \textbf{2\textit{xy}}^2 - \textbf{3\textit{xy}}$

13. $-3x^2ym + 7x - 5ymx^2 + 16x = \textbf{23\textit{x}} - \textbf{8\textit{x}}^2\textbf{\textit{ym}}$

14. $5mp^2y - 6myp^2 + 3ymp^2 - 2p^2my = \textbf{0}$

15. $x + 2x^2 - 3 + 5x - 6x^2 - 10$
    $= -\textbf{4\textit{x}}^2 + \textbf{6\textit{x}} - \textbf{13}$

16. $m^2y - 6ym^2 + 2y - 3m^2y + 4y = \textbf{6\textit{y}} - \textbf{8\textit{m}}^2\textbf{\textit{y}}$

17. $5 - 3x + 7 - 4 + 4x^2 - 2x - x^2$
    $= \textbf{3\textit{x}}^2 - \textbf{5\textit{x}} + \textbf{8}$

18. $a(3x - 2) = \textbf{3\textit{ax}} - \textbf{2\textit{a}}$

19. $4xy(5 - 2a) = \textbf{20\textit{xy}} - \textbf{8\textit{axy}}$

20. $(3a - 4)6x = \textbf{18\textit{ax}} - \textbf{24\textit{x}}$

21. $(-3)^2 - 2^3 = (-3)(-3) - (2)(2)(2) = 9 - 8 = \textbf{1}$

22. $-3^2 - (-2)^2 + \sqrt[3]{-27}$
    $= -(3)(3) - (-2)(-2) + (-3) = -9 - 4 - 3$
    $= -\textbf{16}$

23. $(-3)^3 + (-2)^3 - |-2|$
    $= (-3)(-3)(-3) + (-2)(-2)(-2) - 2$
    $= -27 - 8 - 2 = -\textbf{37}$

24. $-3[(-3 + 5)(-2 - 6)] - 3 = -3[(2)(-8)] - 3$
    $= -3[-16] - 3 = 48 - 3 = \textbf{45}$

25. $-2[(5 - 3) - (5 - 8)] = -2[(2) - (-3)]$
    $= -2[5] = -\textbf{10}$

26. $a^3 - b^3 = (-2)(-2)(-2) - (3)(3)(3) = -8 - 27$
    $= -\textbf{35}$

27. $a - b(a^2 - b) = (-2) - (3)[(-2)(-2) - (3)]$
    $= -2 - 3[1] = -2 - 3 = -\textbf{5}$

28. $cy[(cx - y)] = (-2)(3)[(-2)(-3) - (3)]$
    $= -6[6 - 3] = -6[3] = -\textbf{18}$

29. $-b^2a(a - b) = -(2)(2)(-3)[(-3) - (2)]$
    $= 12[-5] = -\textbf{60}$

30. $b(b^2) - a^2 = (-2)(-2)(-2) - (3)(3) = -8 - 9$
    $= -\textbf{17}$

31. $\dfrac{13}{4} \times -\dfrac{7}{19} = -\dfrac{91}{76} = -\textbf{1}\dfrac{\textbf{15}}{\textbf{76}}$

32. $-3\dfrac{1}{4} + 2\dfrac{5}{7} = -3\dfrac{7}{28} + 2\dfrac{20}{28} = -\dfrac{91}{28} + \dfrac{76}{28}$
    $= -\dfrac{\textbf{15}}{\textbf{28}}$

33.
```
           0.12
     303 ) 36.36
           30 3
           ────
            6 06
            6 06
```

PROBLEM SET 21

1. To solve an equation means to find the value(s) of the variable that will make the equation a true equation.

2. **Equivalent equations** are equations that have the same answers or solution set.

3. $30 \ \cancel{m^2} \times \dfrac{100 \ \cancel{cm}}{1 \ \cancel{m}} \times \dfrac{100 \ \cancel{cm}}{1 \ \cancel{m}} \times \dfrac{1 \text{ in.}}{2.54 \ \cancel{cm}} \times \dfrac{1 \text{ in.}}{2.54 \ \cancel{cm}}$
   $= \dfrac{\textbf{30(100)(100)}}{\textbf{(2.54)(2.54)}}$ in.^{2}

4. $x - 15 = \quad 30$
   $\underline{+15 \quad +15}$
   $x \qquad = \quad \textbf{45}$

5. Solve:

$$y - 13 = 23$$
$$\underline{+13 \quad +13}$$
$$y \quad = 36$$

6. $x + 1\frac{1}{4} = -\frac{9}{10}$

$$\underline{-1\frac{1}{4} \quad -1\frac{1}{4}}$$
$$x \quad = -\frac{36}{40} - \frac{50}{40}$$
$$x = -2\frac{3}{20}$$

7. $k + 7 = 93$

$$\underline{-7 \quad -7}$$
$$k \quad = 86$$

8. $m - 2 = 17$

$$\underline{+2 \quad +2}$$
$$m \quad = 19$$

9. $4 + k = -7$

$$\underline{-4 \qquad -4}$$
$$k = -11$$

10. $A_{\text{Shaded}} = A_{\text{Parallelogram}} - A_{\text{Circle}} - A_{\text{Circle}}$
$$= ((49 \times 24) - \pi(5)^2 - \pi(5)^2)\ \text{cm}^2$$
$$= (1176 - 50\pi)\ \text{cm}^2 \approx \mathbf{1019\ cm^2}$$

11. $P = \left(8 + \dfrac{2\pi(2)}{2} + 8 + 2 + 2 + \dfrac{2\pi(2)}{2}\right)$ yd
$$= (20 + 4\pi)\ \text{yd} \approx \mathbf{32.56\ yd}$$

12. $x^2ym^5x^2y^4 = \mathbf{x^4y^5m^5}$

13. $x^3y^2myxm = \mathbf{x^4y^3m^2}$

14. $xxx^2yyy^3xy = \mathbf{x^5y^6}$

15. $x^2y + 3yx - 2y^2x - 4yx^2 = \mathbf{3yx - 3x^2y - 2y^2x}$

16. $3x - 3 - x^2 - 2x^3 + 7 - 2x + 6x^2$
$$= \mathbf{-2x^3 + 5x^2 + x + 4}$$

17. $p^2xy - 3yp^2x + 2xp^2y - 5 = \mathbf{-5}$

18. $-4 + 7x - 3x - 5 + 2x - 4x^2$
$$= \mathbf{-4x^2 + 6x - 9}$$

19. $4x(a + 2b) = \mathbf{4ax + 8bx}$

20. $(2x + 4)3 = \mathbf{6x + 12}$

21. $4px(my - 3ab^2) = \mathbf{4pxmy - 12pxab^2}$

22. $a^3 - b^3 = (-2)(-2)(-2) - (3)(3)(3) = -8 - 27$
$$= \mathbf{-35}$$

23. $(a - b)(b - x) = [(3) - (-3)][(-3) - (2)]$
$$= [6][-5] = \mathbf{-30}$$

24. $x^3 - a(a - b) = (-2)(-2)(-2) - (3)[(3) - (-3)]$
$$= -8 - 3[6] = -8 - 18 = \mathbf{-26}$$

25. $x(x - y) - y = (-2)[(-2) - (3)] - (3)$
$$= -2[-5] - 3 = 10 - 3 = \mathbf{7}$$

26. $(-2)^3 - 2^3 = (-2)(-2)(-2) - (2)(2)(2)$
$$= -8 - 8 = \mathbf{-16}$$

27. $-3^2 - (-3)^2 + \sqrt[5]{32} = -(3)(3) - (-3)(-3) + (2)$
$$= -9 - 9 + 2 = \mathbf{-16}$$

28. $-4(-3 - 2) - 5(-2) - 2|-4|$
$$= -4(-5) + 10 - 8 = 20 + 10 - 8 = \mathbf{22}$$

29. $\dfrac{5(-2^2 - 4)}{-4 - 6(-2)} = \dfrac{5(-(2)(2) - 4)}{-4 + 12} = \dfrac{5(-8)}{8}$
$$= \dfrac{-40}{8} = \mathbf{-5}$$

30. $\dfrac{-3[5(-2 - 1) - (6 - 2)]}{2(-3 - 2)}$

$$= \dfrac{-3[5(-3) - (4)]}{2(-5)} = \dfrac{-3[-19]}{-10} = \dfrac{57}{-10}$$

$$= \mathbf{-5\dfrac{7}{10}}$$

PROBLEM SET 22

1. Reciprocal

2. 1

3. $\dfrac{1\frac{5}{8}\,y}{1\frac{5}{8}} = \dfrac{26}{1\frac{5}{8}}$

$$y = \dfrac{26}{\frac{13}{8}}$$
$$y = \mathbf{16}$$

4. $\dfrac{3\frac{4}{5}\,x}{3\frac{4}{5}} = \dfrac{-38}{3\frac{4}{5}}$

$$x = \dfrac{-38}{\frac{19}{5}}$$
$$x = \mathbf{-10}$$

5. $\dfrac{7x}{7} = \dfrac{49}{7}$

$\quad x = \dfrac{49}{7} = \mathbf{7}$

6. $\dfrac{7x}{7} = 5 \cdot 7$

$\quad x = \mathbf{35}$

7. $\dfrac{2x}{2} = \dfrac{20}{2}$

$\quad x = \dfrac{20}{2} = \mathbf{10}$

8. $\dfrac{3x}{3} = 5 \cdot 3$

$\quad x = \mathbf{15}$

9. $16{,}000 \ \cancel{cm} \times \dfrac{1 \ \cancel{in.}}{2.54 \ \cancel{cm}} \times \dfrac{1 \ \cancel{ft}}{12 \ \cancel{in.}} \times \dfrac{1 \ mi}{5280 \ \cancel{ft}}$

$\quad = \dfrac{\mathbf{16{,}000}}{\mathbf{(2.54)(12)(5280)}} \ \mathbf{mi}$

10. $A_{Shaded} = \dfrac{1}{2}b_1 h + \dfrac{1}{2}b_2 h - A_{Circle}$

$\quad = \left(\dfrac{24(10)}{2} + \dfrac{20(10)}{2} \right) m^2 - \pi(5)^2 \ m^2$

$\quad = (120 + 100 - 25\pi) \ m^2$

$\quad = (220 - 25\pi) \ m^2 \approx \mathbf{141.5 \ m^2}$

11. $S.A. = 2(A_{End}) + (C \times length)$

$\quad = \left(2(\pi(5)^2) + (2\pi(5) \times 16) \right) cm^2$

$\quad = (50\pi + 160\pi) \ cm^2$

$\quad = 210\pi \ cm^2 \approx \mathbf{659.4 \ cm^2}$

12. $\begin{aligned} x + 5 &= 7 \\ \underline{-5} \ \ &\ \underline{-5} \\ x \ \ &= \mathbf{2} \end{aligned}$

13. $x + \dfrac{1}{2} = 2\dfrac{1}{5}$

$\quad \underline{-\dfrac{1}{2} \qquad -\dfrac{1}{2}}$

$\quad x \ \ = \dfrac{22}{10} - \dfrac{5}{10}$

$\quad\quad x = \dfrac{\mathbf{17}}{\mathbf{10}}$

14. $\begin{aligned} y - 3 &= 2 \\ \underline{+3} \ \ &\ \underline{+3} \\ y \ \ &= \mathbf{5} \end{aligned}$

15. $y - \dfrac{1}{2} = -2\dfrac{1}{2}$

$\quad \underline{+\dfrac{1}{2} \qquad +\dfrac{1}{2}}$

$\quad y \ \ = \mathbf{-2}$

16. $\dfrac{3x}{3} = 19 \cdot 3$

$\quad x = \mathbf{57}$

17. $\dfrac{\frac{1}{2}x}{\frac{1}{2}} = 4 \cdot \dfrac{1}{2}$

$\quad x = \mathbf{2}$

18. $\dfrac{3x}{3} = \dfrac{4\frac{1}{2}}{3}$

$\quad x = \dfrac{\frac{9}{2}}{3}$

$\quad x = \dfrac{\mathbf{3}}{\mathbf{2}}$

19. $x - \dfrac{1}{4} = \dfrac{7}{8}$

$\quad \underline{+\dfrac{1}{4} \qquad +\dfrac{1}{4}}$

$\quad x \ \ = \dfrac{7}{8} + \dfrac{2}{8}$

$\quad\quad x = \dfrac{\mathbf{9}}{\mathbf{8}}$

20. $k - \dfrac{2}{3} = 3\dfrac{1}{3}$

$\quad \underline{+\dfrac{2}{3} \qquad +\dfrac{2}{3}}$

$\quad k \ \ = \dfrac{10}{3} + \dfrac{2}{3}$

$\quad\quad k = \mathbf{4}$

21. $\dfrac{3\frac{2}{5}m}{3\frac{2}{5}} = \dfrac{\frac{1}{2}}{3\frac{2}{5}}$

$\quad m = \dfrac{\frac{1}{2}}{\frac{17}{5}}$

$\quad m = \dfrac{\mathbf{5}}{\mathbf{34}}$

22. $m^2 xyp^2 x^3 y^5 = \mathbf{m^2 x^4 y^6 p^2}$

23. $3p^2 xxypp^3 xy^2 = \mathbf{3p^6 x^3 y^3}$

24. $a + 3 - 2a - 5a^2 + 5 - a = \mathbf{-5a^2 - 2a + 8}$

25. $-3x^2 ym + 5myx^2 - 2my^2 x = \mathbf{2x^2 ym - 2my^2 x}$

26. $(3a - 5p)xy = \mathbf{3axy - 5pxy}$

27. $a^3 - (a - b) - |-a^3|$
$= (-2)(-2)(-2) - [(-2) - (3)] - |-(-2)(-2)(-2)|$
$= -8 - [-5] - |8| = -8 + 5 - 8 = \mathbf{-11}$

28. $(-x)^3 - y = (2)(2)(2) - (4) = \mathbf{4}$

29. $(-2)^3 - (-2)^2 - 5 + \sqrt[3]{-64}$
$= (-2)(-2)(-2) - (4) - 5 + (-4)$
$= -8 - 4 - 5 - 4 = \mathbf{-21}$

30. $-2\{-5(-3 + 4) - [3 - (-4)]\}$
$= -2\{-5(1) - [3 + 4]\} = -2\{-5 - 7\}$
$= -2\{-12\} = \mathbf{24}$

PROBLEM SET 23

1. $\dfrac{3x}{3} = \dfrac{4\frac{1}{2}}{3}$

$x = \dfrac{\frac{9}{2}}{3}$

$x = \dfrac{\mathbf{3}}{\mathbf{2}}$

2. $x + \dfrac{1}{2} = \dfrac{2}{3}$

$\dfrac{-\dfrac{1}{2} \qquad -\dfrac{1}{2}}{}$

$x \qquad = \dfrac{4}{6} - \dfrac{3}{6}$

$x = \dfrac{\mathbf{1}}{\mathbf{6}}$

3. $3x - 4 = 10$

$\dfrac{+4 \qquad +4}{3x \qquad = 14}$

$\dfrac{3x}{3} = \dfrac{14}{3}$

$x = \dfrac{\mathbf{14}}{\mathbf{3}}$

4. $5k - 4 = -30$

$\dfrac{+4 \qquad +4}{5k \qquad = -26}$

$\dfrac{5k}{5} = \dfrac{-26}{5}$

$k = -\dfrac{\mathbf{26}}{\mathbf{5}}$

5. $-2p + 3 = -29$

$\dfrac{-3 \qquad -3}{-2p \qquad = -32}$

$\dfrac{-2p}{-2} = \dfrac{-32}{-2}$

$p = \mathbf{16}$

6. $\dfrac{\frac{2}{3}y}{\frac{2}{3}} = \dfrac{5\frac{1}{2}}{\frac{2}{3}}$

$y = \dfrac{\frac{11}{2}}{\frac{2}{3}} = \dfrac{\mathbf{33}}{\mathbf{4}}$

7. $-2x - 2 = 5$

$\dfrac{+2 \qquad +2}{-2x \qquad = 7}$

$\dfrac{-2x}{-2} = \dfrac{7}{-2}$

$x = -\dfrac{\mathbf{7}}{\mathbf{2}}$

8. $\dfrac{3\frac{1}{2}x}{3\frac{1}{2}} = 3\frac{1}{2} \cdot 5$

$x = \dfrac{7}{2} \cdot 5 = \dfrac{\mathbf{35}}{\mathbf{2}}$

9. $\dfrac{1}{8}m - \dfrac{1}{3} = \dfrac{3}{4}$

$\dfrac{+\dfrac{1}{3} \qquad +\dfrac{1}{3}}{}$

$\dfrac{1}{8}m \qquad = \dfrac{9}{12} + \dfrac{4}{12}$

$\dfrac{1}{8}m = \dfrac{13}{12}$

$\dfrac{\frac{1}{8}m}{\frac{1}{8}} = \dfrac{\frac{13}{12}}{\frac{1}{8}}$

$m = \dfrac{\mathbf{26}}{\mathbf{3}}$

10. $x + 3\dfrac{1}{3} = 5$

$\dfrac{-3\dfrac{1}{3} \qquad -3\dfrac{1}{3}}{}$

$x \qquad = \dfrac{15}{3} - \dfrac{10}{3}$

$x = \dfrac{\mathbf{5}}{\mathbf{3}}$

11. $y - \dfrac{1}{4} = \dfrac{5}{7}$

$\dfrac{+\dfrac{1}{4} \qquad +\dfrac{1}{4}}{}$

$y \qquad = \dfrac{20}{28} + \dfrac{7}{28}$

$y = \dfrac{\mathbf{27}}{\mathbf{28}}$

12. Solve:

$$-3y + \frac{1}{2} = \frac{5}{7}$$
$$\quad\;\; -\frac{1}{2} \quad\; -\frac{1}{2}$$

$$-3y \quad\;\; = \frac{10}{14} - \frac{7}{14}$$

$$-3y = \frac{3}{14}$$

$$\frac{-3y}{-3} = \frac{\frac{3}{14}}{-3}$$

$$y = -\frac{1}{14}$$

13. $300 \text{ km} \times \dfrac{1000 \text{ m}}{1 \text{ km}} \times \dfrac{100 \text{ cm}}{1 \text{ m}} \times \dfrac{1 \text{ in.}}{2.54 \text{ cm}}$

$$= \frac{300(1000)(100)}{2.54} \text{ in.}$$

14. $V = A_{Base} \times \text{height}$

$= (A_{Rectangle} + A_{Triangle}) \times \text{height}$

$= \left(30(10) + \left(\dfrac{30(12)}{2} \right) \right) \text{in.}^2 \times 10 \text{ in.}$

$= 480 \text{ in.}^2 \times 10 \text{ in.}$

$= \mathbf{4800 \text{ in.}^3}$

S.A. $= 2(A_{Base}) + (P \times \text{height})$

$= 2\left(30(10) + \dfrac{30(12)}{2} \right) + 88.6(10)$

$= (960 + 886)$

$= \mathbf{1846 \text{ in.}^2}$

15. $x^2 k x k^2 x^2 y k x^2 = \mathbf{k^4 x^7 y}$

16. $aaa^3 bx a^2 b^3 ab x^4 = \mathbf{a^8 b^5 x^5}$

17. $3a^2 xy + 5xa^2 y - 2ya^2 x = \mathbf{6a^2 xy}$

18. $6c - 6 - 2c - 5 - 3c + 7 = \mathbf{c - 4}$

19. $a^2 xx + a^2 x^2 - 3x^2 aa = a^2 x^2 + a^2 x^2 - 3a^2 x^2$
$= \mathbf{-a^2 x^2}$

20. $4x(2y - 3 + 2a) = \mathbf{8xy - 12x + 8ax}$

21. $(x - 4)3 = \mathbf{3x - 12}$

22. $a(a^3 - b) - b = (-2)[(-2)(-2)(-2) - (3)] - (3)$
$= -2[-11] - 3 = 22 - 3 = \mathbf{19}$

23. $x(y - a) + a(y - x)$
$= (-3)[(2) - (-1)] + (-1)[(2) - (-3)]$
$= -3[3] - 1[5] = -9 - 5 = \mathbf{-14}$

24. $-b(b - a) = -(1)[(1) - (-2)] = -1[3] = \mathbf{-3}$

25. $(-d)(d - c) = [-(-5)][(-5) - (-3)]$
$= 5[-2] = \mathbf{-10}$

26. $-4[(-5 + 2) - 3(-2 - 1)] = -4[(-3) - 3(-3)]$
$= -4[6] = \mathbf{-24}$

27. $-3^2 + (-3)^3 - 4 - \sqrt[3]{27}$
$= -(3)(3) + (-3)(-3)(-3) - 4 - (3)$
$= -9 - 27 - 4 - 3 = \mathbf{-43}$

28. $\dfrac{2^2 - 3^3 - 4^2}{(-2)^3}$

$= \dfrac{(2)(2) - (3)(3)(3) - (4)(4)}{(-2)(-2)(-2)}$

$= \dfrac{4 - 27 - 16}{-8} = \dfrac{-39}{-8} = \mathbf{\dfrac{39}{8}}$

29. $(-2)^2 - 3^3 - (-4)^2 - |-2 - 3|$
$= (-2)(-2) - (3)(3)(3) - (-4)(-4) - |-5|$
$= 4 - 27 - 16 - 5 = \mathbf{-44}$

PROBLEM SET 24

1. **Equivalent equations** are equations that have the same answers or solution set.

2. **Yes;** the number 4 satisfies both equations.

3. $120 \text{ mi}^2 \times \dfrac{5280 \text{ ft}}{1 \text{ mi}} \times \dfrac{5280 \text{ ft}}{1 \text{ mi}} \times \dfrac{12 \text{ in.}}{1 \text{ ft}} \times \dfrac{12 \text{ in.}}{1 \text{ ft}}$
$= \mathbf{120(5280)(5280)(12)(12) \text{ in.}^2}$

4. $200 \text{ m}^3 \times \dfrac{100 \text{ cm}}{1 \text{ m}} \times \dfrac{100 \text{ cm}}{1 \text{ m}} \times \dfrac{100 \text{ cm}}{1 \text{ m}}$
$= \mathbf{200(100)(100)(100) \text{ cm}^3}$

5. $A = A_{Rect\,1} + A_{Rect\,2} + A_{Rect\,3} + A_{Semicircle}$

$= (8(6) + 8(4) + 2(8)) \text{ yd}^2 + \left(\dfrac{\pi(4)^2}{2} \right) \text{ yd}^2$

$= (48 + 32 + 16 + 8\pi) \text{ yd}^2$

$= (96 + 8\pi) \text{ yd}^2 \approx 121.12 \text{ yd}^2$

It would take **121.12 one-yd-square tiles** to cover the area.

6. $V = A_{End} \times \text{length}$
$= \pi(2)^2 \text{ cm}^2 \times 12 \text{ cm}$
$= 48\pi \text{ cm}^3 \approx \mathbf{150.72 \text{ cm}^3}$

7. $\dfrac{2\frac{1}{2}x}{2\frac{1}{2}} = \dfrac{\frac{3}{7}}{2\frac{1}{2}}$

$$x = \dfrac{\frac{3}{7}}{\frac{5}{2}} = \mathbf{\dfrac{6}{35}}$$

8. $\dfrac{-x}{-1} = \dfrac{3}{-1}$

$\qquad x = \mathbf{-3}$

9. $3x - 4 = 7$

$\qquad \underline{+4 \quad +4}$

$\qquad 3x = 11$

$\qquad \dfrac{3x}{3} = \dfrac{11}{3}$

$\qquad x = \mathbf{\dfrac{11}{3}}$

10. $0.02p - 2.4 = 0.006$

$\qquad \underline{+2.4 \quad +2.4}$

$\qquad 0.02p = 2.406$

$\qquad \dfrac{0.02p}{0.02} = \dfrac{2.406}{0.02}$

$\qquad p = \mathbf{120.3}$

11. $2x + x + 3 = x + 2 - 5$

$\qquad 3x + 3 = x - 3$

$\qquad \underline{-x \qquad\quad -x}$

$\qquad 2x + 3 = -3$

$\qquad \underline{-3 \qquad -3}$

$\qquad 2x = -6$

$\qquad \dfrac{2x}{2} = \dfrac{-6}{2}$

$\qquad x = \mathbf{-3}$

12. $5x - 3 - 2 = 3x - 2 + x$

$\qquad 5x - 5 = 4x - 2$

$\qquad \underline{-4x \qquad -4x}$

$\qquad x - 5 = -2$

$\qquad \underline{+5 \qquad +5}$

$\qquad x = \mathbf{3}$

13. $m + 4m - 2 - 2m = 2m + 2 - 3$

$\qquad 3m - 2 = 2m - 1$

$\qquad \underline{-2m \qquad -2m}$

$\qquad m - 2 = -1$

$\qquad \underline{+2 \qquad +2}$

$\qquad m = \mathbf{1}$

14. $-m - 6m + 4 = -2m - 5$

$\qquad -7m + 4 = -2m - 5$

$\qquad \underline{+2m \qquad +2m}$

$\qquad -5m + 4 = -5$

$\qquad \underline{-4 \qquad -4}$

$\qquad -5m = -9$

$\qquad \dfrac{-5m}{-5} = \dfrac{-9}{-5}$

$\qquad m = \mathbf{\dfrac{9}{5}}$

15. $y + 2y - 4 - y = 3y - 2 + y$

$\qquad 2y - 4 = 4y - 2$

$\qquad \underline{-4y \qquad -4y}$

$\qquad -2y - 4 = -2$

$\qquad \underline{+4 \qquad +4}$

$\qquad -2y = 2$

$\qquad \dfrac{-2y}{-2} = \dfrac{2}{-2}$

$\qquad y = \mathbf{-1}$

16. $m^2 y^5 m y y^3 m^3 = \mathbf{m^6 y^9}$

17. $k^5 m m m^2 k^2 m^2 k^3 a a^2 = \mathbf{a^3 k^{10} m^6}$

18. $xym^2z - 3m^2zxy + 2xm^2yz - 5xym^2z = \mathbf{-5xym^2z}$

19. $a^2bc + 2bc - bca^2 + 5ca^2b - 3cb$

$\quad = \mathbf{5a^2bc - bc}$

20. $a - ax + 2xa - 3a - 3 = \mathbf{ax - 2a - 3}$

21. $4(7 - 3x) = \mathbf{28 - 12x}$

22. $(m + 2p)3axy = \mathbf{3axym + 6axyp}$

23. $a(-a^2 + b) = (-2)\big[-(-2)(-2) + (4)\big]$

$\quad = -2[-4 + 4] = -2[0] = \mathbf{0}$

24. $x(x - y) = (-3)\big[(-3) - (5)\big] = -3[-8] = \mathbf{24}$

25. $p(a - 2p^2) = (-4)\big[(-2) - 2(-4)(-4)\big]$

$\quad = -4[-2 - 32] = -4[-34] = \mathbf{136}$

26. $(y - m^2) - m = \big[(-3) - (2)(2)\big] - (2)$

$\quad = [-7] - 2 = \mathbf{-9}$

27. $-3^2 - (-3)^3 + (-2) - \sqrt[3]{-125}$

$\quad = -(3)(3) - (-3)(-3)(-3) - 2 - (-5)$

$\quad = -9 + 27 - 2 + 5 = \mathbf{21}$

28. $-4(-3 + 2) - 3 - (-4) - |-3 + 2|$

$\quad = -4(-1) - 3 + 4 - |-1| = 4 - 3 + 4 - 1$

$\quad = \mathbf{4}$

29. $\dfrac{-3(-2 - 3 - 4)}{-(-3 + 2)} = \dfrac{-3(-9)}{-(-1)} = \dfrac{27}{1} = \mathbf{27}$

30. $\dfrac{-2(-3) + (-6)}{-4(-2)} = \dfrac{6 - 6}{8} = \dfrac{0}{8} = \mathbf{0}$

PROBLEM SET 25

1. $a(b + c) = ab + ac$

2. -4

3. $430 \, \cancel{ft} \times \dfrac{12 \, \cancel{in.}}{1 \, \cancel{ft}} \times \dfrac{2.54 \, \cancel{cm}}{1 \, \cancel{in.}} \times \dfrac{1 \, m}{100 \, \cancel{cm}}$

$= \dfrac{\mathbf{430(12)(2.54)}}{\mathbf{100}} \, \mathbf{m}$

4. $6500 \, \cancel{ft^2} \times \dfrac{1 \, yd}{3 \, \cancel{ft}} \times \dfrac{1 \, yd}{3 \, \cancel{ft}} = \dfrac{\mathbf{6500}}{\mathbf{(3)(3)}} \, \mathbf{yd^2}$

5.
$$3x + 2 = 7$$
$$\underline{\quad -2 \quad\quad -2}$$
$$3x \quad = 5$$
$$\frac{3x}{3} = \frac{5}{3}$$
$$x = \frac{\mathbf{5}}{\mathbf{3}}$$

6.
$$\frac{1}{2}x + \frac{3}{4} = -\frac{3}{7}$$
$$\underline{\quad -\frac{3}{4} \quad\quad -\frac{3}{4}}$$
$$\frac{1}{2}x \quad = -\frac{12}{28} - \frac{21}{28}$$
$$\frac{1}{2}x = -\frac{33}{28}$$
$$\frac{\frac{1}{2}x}{\frac{1}{2}} = \frac{-\frac{33}{28}}{\frac{1}{2}}$$
$$x = -\frac{\mathbf{33}}{\mathbf{14}}$$

7.
$$3\frac{1}{3}x - \frac{1}{2} = 5$$
$$\underline{\quad +\frac{1}{2} \quad\quad +\frac{1}{2}}$$
$$3\frac{1}{3}x \quad = \frac{10}{2} + \frac{1}{2}$$
$$3\frac{1}{3}x = \frac{11}{2}$$
$$\frac{3\frac{1}{3}x}{3\frac{1}{3}} = \frac{\frac{11}{2}}{3\frac{1}{3}}$$
$$x = \frac{\frac{11}{2}}{\frac{10}{3}} = \frac{\mathbf{33}}{\mathbf{20}}$$

8. Solve:
$$-\frac{1}{7} + \frac{4}{3}x = \frac{1}{5}$$
$$\underline{+\frac{1}{7} \quad\quad\quad +\frac{1}{7}}$$
$$\frac{4}{3}x = \frac{7}{35} + \frac{5}{35}$$
$$\frac{4}{3}x = \frac{12}{35}$$
$$\frac{\frac{4}{3}x}{\frac{4}{3}} = \frac{\frac{12}{35}}{\frac{4}{3}}$$
$$x = \frac{\mathbf{9}}{\mathbf{35}}$$

9.
$$x + 3 - 5 - 2x = x - 3 - 7x$$
$$-x - 2 = -6x - 3$$
$$\underline{+6x \quad\quad\quad +6x}$$
$$5x - 2 = -3$$
$$\underline{\quad +2 \quad\quad\quad +2}$$
$$5x \quad = -1$$
$$\frac{5x}{5} = \frac{-1}{5}$$
$$x = -\frac{\mathbf{1}}{\mathbf{5}}$$

10.
$$4x - 5 + 2x = 3x - 4 + x$$
$$6x - 5 = 4x - 4$$
$$\underline{-4x \quad\quad\quad -4x}$$
$$2x - 5 = -4$$
$$\underline{\quad +5 \quad\quad\quad +5}$$
$$2x \quad = 1$$
$$\frac{2x}{2} = \frac{1}{2}$$
$$x = \frac{\mathbf{1}}{\mathbf{2}}$$

11.
$$-2y - 4 - y = -y + 2 + 3y$$
$$-3y - 4 = 2y + 2$$
$$\underline{-2y \quad\quad\quad -2y}$$
$$-5y - 4 = 2$$
$$\underline{\quad +4 \quad\quad\quad +4}$$
$$-5y \quad = 6$$
$$\frac{-5y}{-5} = \frac{6}{-5}$$
$$y = -\frac{\mathbf{6}}{\mathbf{5}}$$

12. $-5 - x - 2 + 7x = 3 - 4x$

$$6x - 7 = -4x + 3$$
$$\underline{+4x \qquad\qquad +4x}$$
$$10x - 7 = \qquad 3$$
$$\underline{\qquad +7 \qquad +7}$$
$$10x = \qquad 10$$
$$\frac{10x}{10} = \frac{10}{10}$$
$$x = \mathbf{1}$$

13. $-a - 2a + 4 - 4a = 7 - 3a$

$$-7a + 4 = -3a + 7$$
$$\underline{+3a \qquad\qquad +3a}$$
$$-4a + 4 = \qquad 7$$
$$\underline{\qquad -4 \qquad -4}$$
$$-4a = \qquad 3$$
$$\frac{-4a}{-4} = \frac{3}{-4}$$
$$a = \mathbf{-\frac{3}{4}}$$

14. $p - 2p - 5 + 7p = 3 - 2p$

$$6p - 5 = -2p + 3$$
$$\underline{+2p \qquad\qquad +2p}$$
$$8p - 5 = \qquad 3$$
$$\underline{\qquad +5 \qquad +5}$$
$$8p = \qquad 8$$
$$\frac{8p}{8} = \frac{8}{8}$$
$$p = \mathbf{1}$$

15. $p^2xyy^2x^2yx^2x = \mathbf{p^2x^6y^4}$

16. $3p^2x^4yp^5xxyy^2 = \mathbf{3p^7x^6y^4}$

17. $-3x^2y + 5 - yx^2 - 13 + xy = \mathbf{xy - 4x^2y - 8}$

18. $-4x + x^2 - 3x - 5 + 7x^2 = \mathbf{8x^2 - 7x - 5}$

19. $xyp^2 - 4p^2xy + 5xp^2y - 7yxp^2 = \mathbf{-5xyp^2}$

20. $x^2y(x^3 - xyz^3) = (x^2y)(x^3) - (x^2y)(xyz^3)$
$= \mathbf{x^5y - x^3y^2z^3}$

21. $4x^2(ax - 2) = (4x^2)(ax) - (4x^2)(2)$
$= \mathbf{4ax^3 - 8x^2}$

22. $A_S = A_{22} - A_{16} - A_6$
$= (\pi(22)^2 - \pi(16)^2 - \pi(6)^2)$ cm^2
$= (484\pi - 256\pi - 36\pi)$ cm^2
$= 192\pi$ cm$^2 \approx 602.88$ cm^2

It will take **602.88 one-cm-square floor tiles** to cover the area.

23. $V = A_{Base} \times$ height

$= \left(\frac{6(8)}{2} + 8(8) + \frac{\pi(4)^2}{2} \right)$ in.$^2 \times 3$ in.

$= (88 + 8\pi)$ in.$^2 \times 3$ in.

$= (264 + 24\pi)$ in.$^3 \approx 339.36$ in.^{3}

The solid will hold **339.36 one-in. sugar cubes.**

S.A. $= 2(A_{Base}) + (P \times$ height$)$

$= 2(88 + 8\pi)$ in.^{2}

$+ \left(\left(32 + \frac{2\pi(4)}{2} \right) \times 3 \right)$ in.^{2}

$= (176 + 16\pi)$ in.$^2 + (96 + 12\pi)$ in.^{2}

$= (272 + 28\pi)$ in.$^2 \approx \mathbf{359.92}$ **in.**^{2}

24. $(ay - 4y^5)2x^2y$
$= [(-2)(-1) - 4(-1)(-1)(-1)(-1)(-1)][2(2)(2)(-1)]$
$= [2 + 4][-8] = [6][-8] = \mathbf{-48}$

25. $-(-a - x) - x^2 = -[-(4) - (-3)] - (-3)(-3)$
$= -[-1] - (9) = 1 - 9 = \mathbf{-8}$

26. $-y^2(y - 2x) = -(-2)(-2)[(-2) - 2(3)] = -4[-8]$
$= \mathbf{32}$

27. $-(-p)^2 + (p - x) = -(2)(2) + [(-2) - (5)]$
$= -4 + [-7] = \mathbf{-11}$

28. $(a - b) + (-a)^2 = [(-3) - (6)] + (3)(3)$
$= [-9] + 9 = \mathbf{0}$

29. $-3^2 - 3(3^2 - 4) - \sqrt[4]{16} - |-7 + 2|$
$= -(3)(3) - 3[(3)(3) - 4] - (2) - |-5|$
$= -9 - 3[5] - 2 - 5 = -9 - 15 - 2 - 5$
$= \mathbf{-31}$

30. $\dfrac{-6 - (-2 - 3)}{4 - (-3)} = \dfrac{-6 - (-5)}{7} = \dfrac{-1}{7}$

$= \mathbf{-\dfrac{1}{7}}$

PROBLEM SET 26

1. $50 \cancel{ft} \times \dfrac{12 \cancel{in.}}{1 \cancel{ft}} \times \dfrac{2.54 \cancel{cm}}{1 \cancel{in.}} \times \dfrac{1 \text{ m}}{100 \cancel{cm}}$

$= \dfrac{50(12)(2.54)}{100} \text{ m}$

2. $50 \cancel{m^3} \times \dfrac{100 \text{ cm}}{1 \cancel{m}} \times \dfrac{100 \text{ cm}}{1 \cancel{m}} \times \dfrac{100 \text{ cm}}{1 \cancel{m}}$

$= \mathbf{50(100)(100)(100) \text{ cm}^3}$

3. S.A. $= 2(A_{\text{Front}}) + A_{\text{Top}} + A_{\text{Bottom}}$
$\qquad + A_{\text{Side 1}} + A_{\text{Side 2}}$

$= 2\left(4(20) + \dfrac{26(20)}{2} \right) + 4(10) + 30(10)$

$\qquad + 33(10) + 20(10)$

$= (680 + 40 + 300 + 330 + 200)$

$= \mathbf{1550 \text{ cm}^2}$

4. A $= A_{\text{Triangle 1}} + A_{\text{Triangle 2}}$

$= \left(\dfrac{22 \times 19}{2} + \dfrac{24 \times 18}{2} \right) \text{ ft}^2$

$= (209 + 216) \text{ ft}^2$

$= \mathbf{425 \text{ ft}^2}$

5. $(F) \times (\text{of}) = (\text{is})$
$(WF)(324) = (270)$

$\dfrac{WF \cdot 324}{324} = \dfrac{270}{324}$

$\qquad WF = \dfrac{\mathbf{5}}{\mathbf{6}}$

6. $(F) \times (\text{of}) = (\text{is})$
$\left(\dfrac{7}{3} \right) \times (42) = (WN)$

$\qquad \mathbf{98} = WN$

7. $\dfrac{1}{2}x + \dfrac{1}{2} = 2\dfrac{1}{5}$

$\qquad -\dfrac{1}{2} \qquad -\dfrac{1}{2}$

$\rule{2cm}{0.4pt}$

$\dfrac{1}{2}x \qquad = 1\dfrac{7}{10}$

$\dfrac{\frac{1}{2}x}{\frac{1}{2}} = \dfrac{1\frac{7}{10}}{\frac{1}{2}}$

$\qquad x = \dfrac{\mathbf{17}}{\mathbf{5}}$

8. Solve:

$-\dfrac{7}{8} + \dfrac{1}{2}x = \dfrac{3}{4}$

$+\dfrac{7}{8} \qquad\qquad +\dfrac{7}{8}$

$\rule{3cm}{0.4pt}$

$\qquad \dfrac{1}{2}x = \dfrac{13}{8}$

$\dfrac{\frac{1}{2}x}{\frac{1}{2}} = \dfrac{\frac{13}{8}}{\frac{1}{2}}$

$\qquad x = \dfrac{\mathbf{13}}{\mathbf{4}}$

9. $0.005p + 1.4 = 0.005$

$\quad 5p + 1400 = \qquad 5$

$\qquad -1400 \quad -1400$

$\rule{4cm}{0.4pt}$

$\quad 5p \qquad\quad = -1395$

$\qquad \dfrac{5p}{5} = \dfrac{-1395}{5}$

$\qquad\quad p = \mathbf{-279}$

10. $x - 2 - 2x = 3 - x + 4x$

$\quad -x - 2 = \quad 3x + 3$

$\quad -3x \qquad\qquad -3x$

$\rule{4cm}{0.4pt}$

$\quad -4x - 2 = \qquad 3$

$\qquad +2 \qquad\qquad +2$

$\rule{4cm}{0.4pt}$

$\quad -4x \qquad = \qquad 5$

$\qquad \dfrac{-4x}{-4} = \dfrac{5}{-4}$

$\qquad\quad x = -\dfrac{\mathbf{5}}{\mathbf{4}}$

11. $3y - y + 2y - 5 = 7 - 2y + 5$

$\qquad 4y - 5 = -2y + 12$

$\qquad +2y \qquad\quad +2y$

$\rule{4cm}{0.4pt}$

$\qquad 6y - 5 = \qquad\quad 12$

$\qquad +5 \qquad\qquad +5$

$\rule{4cm}{0.4pt}$

$\qquad 6y \qquad = \qquad\quad 17$

$\qquad\quad \dfrac{6y}{6} = \dfrac{17}{6}$

$\qquad\qquad y = \dfrac{\mathbf{17}}{\mathbf{6}}$

12. $p - 2p + 4 - 7 = p + 2$

$\qquad -p - 3 = \quad p + 2$

$\qquad -p \qquad\quad -p$

$\rule{4cm}{0.4pt}$

$\qquad -2p - 3 = \qquad 2$

$\qquad +3 \qquad\qquad +3$

$\rule{4cm}{0.4pt}$

$\qquad -2p \qquad = \qquad 5$

$\qquad \dfrac{-2p}{-2} = \dfrac{5}{-2}$

$\qquad\qquad p = -\dfrac{\mathbf{5}}{\mathbf{2}}$

13. $k - 4 - 2k = 7 + 3k - k + 5$

$$-k - 4 = 2k + 12$$
$$\underline{-2k \qquad\qquad -2k}$$
$$\overline{-3k - 4 = \qquad\quad 12}$$
$$\underline{\qquad +4 \qquad\qquad +4}$$
$$\overline{-3k = \qquad\qquad 16}$$
$$\frac{-3k}{-3} = \frac{16}{-3}$$
$$k = -\frac{16}{3}$$

14. $x - 5 - (-2) + 2x = 7$

$$3x - 3 = 7$$
$$\underline{\qquad +3 \quad +3}$$
$$\overline{3x = 10}$$
$$\frac{3x}{3} = \frac{10}{3}$$
$$x = \frac{10}{3}$$

15. $3x - 4x + 7 = 5 + x - 6$

$$-x + 7 = x - 1$$
$$\underline{-x \qquad\qquad -x}$$
$$\overline{-2x + 7 = \qquad -1}$$
$$\underline{\quad -7 \qquad\qquad -7}$$
$$\overline{-2x = \qquad\qquad -8}$$
$$\frac{-2x}{-2} = \frac{-8}{-2}$$
$$x = 4$$

16. $y^5x^2y^3yxy^2 = \mathbf{y^{11}x^3}$

17. $m^2myy^2m^3ym = \mathbf{m^7y^4}$

18. $xym^2 + 3xy^2m - 4m^2xy + 5mxy^2$
$= \mathbf{-3xym^2 + 8mxy^2}$

19. $pc - 4cp + c - p + 7pc - 7c$
$= \mathbf{4pc - 6c - p}$

20. $a^2xy + 4xa^2y - yxa^2 + 3yx^2a = \mathbf{4a^2xy + 3yx^2a}$

21. $x^2y^3(3xy - 5y) = (x^2y^3)(3xy) - (x^2y^3)(5y)$
$= \mathbf{3x^3y^4 - 5x^2y^4}$

22. $3x^4a(x^3 - 2x^4a^3) = (3x^4a)(x^3) - (3x^4a)(2x^4a^3)$
$= \mathbf{3x^7a - 6x^8a^4}$

23. $(xyp - 3xp)p^2xy = (xyp)(p^2xy) - (3xp)(p^2xy)$
$= \mathbf{p^3x^2y^2 - 3p^3x^2y}$

24. $x^3y(x - y) = (-3)(-3)(-3)(1)[(-3) - (1)]$
$= -27[-4] = \mathbf{108}$

25. $p^2 - a^2(p - a) = (3)(3) - (5)(5)[(3) - (5)]$
$= 9 - 25[-2] = 9 + 50 = \mathbf{59}$

26. $ka(-a) - k + a = (4)(-3)(3) - (4) + (-3)$
$= -36 - 4 - 3 = \mathbf{-43}$

27. $p(a) - xp(-a) = (-2)(3) - (4)(-2)(-3)$
$= -6 - 24 = \mathbf{-30}$

28. $-3^2 + (-2)^3 - \sqrt[4]{81}$
$= -(3)(3) + (-2)(-2)(-2) - (3) = -9 - 8 - 3$
$= \mathbf{-20}$

29. $-4(-7 + 5)(-2) - |-2 - 5|$
$= -4(-2)(-2) - |-7| = -16 - 7 = \mathbf{-23}$

30. $\dfrac{-5(-3 + 7)}{-5 + (-2)} = \dfrac{-5(4)}{-7} = \dfrac{-20}{-7} = \dfrac{20}{7}$

PROBLEM SET 27

1. (a) $\{\ldots, -3, -2, -1, 0, 1, 2, 3, \ldots\}$
(b) $\{0, 1, 2, 3, \ldots\}$

2. $(F) \times (\text{of}) = (\text{is})$

$$\left(\frac{9}{4}\right) \times (WN) = (750)$$
$$\frac{\frac{9}{4} \times WN}{\frac{9}{4}} = \frac{750}{\frac{9}{4}}$$
$$WN = \frac{1000}{3}$$

3. $(F) \times (\text{of}) = (\text{is})$
$(WF) \times (72) = (63)$
$$\frac{WF \times 72}{72} = \frac{63}{72}$$
$$WF = \frac{7}{8}$$

4. $(F) \times (\text{of}) = (\text{is})$

$$\left(\frac{25}{8}\right) \times (72) = (WN)$$
$$\mathbf{225} = WN$$

5. $-5 + 2\frac{1}{2}x = 17$

$$\underline{+5 \qquad\qquad +5}$$
$$\overline{2\frac{1}{2}x = 22}$$
$$\frac{2\frac{1}{2}x}{2\frac{1}{2}} = \frac{22}{2\frac{1}{2}}$$
$$x = \frac{22}{\frac{5}{2}} = \frac{44}{5}$$

6. Solve:

$$3\frac{1}{2}x + 2 = 9$$

$$\underline{\quad -2 \quad -2 \quad}$$

$$3\frac{1}{2}x \quad = 7$$

$$\frac{3\frac{1}{2}x}{3\frac{1}{2}} = \frac{7}{3\frac{1}{2}}$$

$$x = \frac{7}{\frac{7}{2}} = 2$$

7.

$$\frac{1}{4}x + \frac{1}{2} = \frac{7}{8}$$

$$\underline{\quad -\frac{1}{2} \quad -\frac{1}{2} \quad}$$

$$\frac{1}{4}x \quad = \frac{3}{8}$$

$$\frac{\frac{1}{4}x}{\frac{1}{4}} = \frac{\frac{3}{8}}{\frac{1}{4}}$$

$$x = \frac{3}{2}$$

8.

$$3x + 5 - x = x + 5$$

$$2x + 5 = x + 5$$

$$\underline{\quad -5 \quad\quad -5 \quad}$$

$$2x = x$$

$$\underline{\quad -x \quad\quad -x \quad}$$

$$x = 0$$

9.

$$3y - 5 = 7 - 2y + 8$$

$$3y - 5 = -2y + 15$$

$$\underline{\quad +5 \quad\quad\quad +5 \quad}$$

$$3y = -2y + 20$$

$$\underline{+2y \quad\quad +2y \quad}$$

$$5y = 20$$

$$\frac{5y}{5} = \frac{20}{5}$$

$$y = 4$$

10.

$$7p - 14 = 4p - 5 + p$$

$$7p - 14 = 5p - 5$$

$$\underline{\quad +14 \quad\quad\quad +14 \quad}$$

$$7p = 5p + 9$$

$$\underline{-5p \quad\quad -5p \quad}$$

$$2p = 9$$

$$\frac{2p}{2} = \frac{9}{2}$$

$$p = \frac{9}{2}$$

11.

$$0.0025k + 0.06 = 4.003$$

$$25k + 600 = 40030$$

$$\underline{\quad -600 \quad\quad -600 \quad}$$

$$25k \quad = 39430$$

$$\frac{25k}{25} = \frac{39430}{25}$$

$$k = \frac{7886}{5} = \mathbf{1577.2}$$

12.

$$3m - 2 - m = -2 + m - 5$$

$$2m - 2 = m - 7$$

$$\underline{\quad +2 \quad\quad\quad +2 \quad}$$

$$2m = m - 5$$

$$\underline{-m \quad\quad\quad -m \quad}$$

$$m = \mathbf{-5}$$

13.

$$x - 3x - 5 - 2x = 7x + 3 - 5 + 2x$$

$$-4x - 5 = 9x - 2$$

$$\underline{\quad +5 \quad\quad\quad +5 \quad}$$

$$-4x = 9x + 3$$

$$\underline{-9x \quad\quad -9x \quad}$$

$$-13x = 3$$

$$\frac{-13x}{-13} = \frac{3}{-13}$$

$$x = -\frac{3}{13}$$

14.

$$7200 \,\cancel{\text{in.}} \times \frac{2.54 \,\cancel{\text{cm}}}{1 \,\cancel{\text{in.}}} \times \frac{1 \text{ m}}{100 \,\cancel{\text{cm}}} = \frac{\mathbf{7200(2.54)}}{\mathbf{100}} \text{ m}$$

15.

$$V = A_{\text{Base}} \times \text{height}$$

$$= \left(\frac{\pi(4)^2}{2} + \frac{8(12)}{2} - \frac{\pi(2)^2}{2} \right) \text{in.} \times 48 \text{ in.}$$

$$= (8\pi + 48 - 2\pi) \text{ in.}^2 \times 48 \text{ in.}$$

$$= (6\pi + 48) \text{ in.}^2 \times 48 \text{ in.}$$

$$= (288\pi + 2304) \text{ in.}^3 \approx \mathbf{3208.32 \text{ in.}^3}$$

$$\text{S.A.} = 2(A_{\text{Base}}) + (P \times \text{height})$$

$$= 2(6\pi + 48) \text{ in.}^2 + \left(\frac{2\pi(4)}{2} \times 48 \right) \text{in.}^2$$

$$+ \left(\left(14.4 + 8 + \frac{2\pi(2)}{2} \right) \times 48 \right) \text{in.}^2$$

$$= (12\pi + 96) \text{ in.}^2 + (6\pi + 22.4)(48) \text{ in.}^2$$

$$= (12\pi + 96 + 288\pi + 1075.2) \text{ in.}^2$$

$$= (300\pi + 1171.2) \text{ in.}^2 \approx \mathbf{2113.2 \text{ in.}^2}$$

Algebra 1 Solutions Manual

16. $\text{S.A.} = 2(A_{\text{Front}}) + 2(A_{\text{Side}}) + A_{\text{Bottom}}$

$$= 2\left(\frac{10(12)}{2}\right) + 2(22)(13) + (22)(10)$$

$$= (120 + 572 + 220)$$

$$= \mathbf{912\ ft^2}$$

17. $\dfrac{1}{(-2)^{-2}} = (-2)^2 = (-2)(-2) = \mathbf{4}$

18. $2^{-4} = \dfrac{1}{2^4} = \dfrac{1}{(2)(2)(2)(2)} = \mathbf{\dfrac{1}{16}}$

19. $\dfrac{1}{2^{-2}} - \sqrt[5]{243} = 2^2 - (3) = 4 - 3 = \mathbf{1}$

20. $x^{-5}y^5axy^5y^{-8}a^{-4} = aa^{-4}x^{-5}xy^5y^5y^{-8} = \mathbf{a^{-3}x^{-4}y^2}$

21. $m^2p^{-4}m^{-2}p^6m^4m^{-5} = m^2m^{-2}m^4m^{-5}p^{-4}p^6$
$= \mathbf{m^{-1}p^2}$

22. $4x^2yp - px^2y + 3ypx^2 - 4 = \mathbf{6x^2yp - 4}$

23. $5m^2x^2y - 2x^2m^2y + 8m^2y^2x = \mathbf{3m^2x^2y + 8m^2xy^2}$

24. $(6x^2yp - 4p + 2)x^2y^3p$
$= (6x^2yp)(x^2y^3p) - (4p)(x^2y^3p) + (2)(x^2y^3p)$
$= \mathbf{6x^4y^4p^2 - 4p^2x^2y^3 + 2x^2y^3p}$

25. $4mz(m^3cz^2 - 5mz^5)$
$= (4mz)(m^3cz^2) - (4mz)(5mz^5)$
$= \mathbf{4m^4cz^3 - 20m^2z^6}$

26. $-xa^2(a + x) = -(-2)(3)(3)[(3) + (-2)]$
$= 18[1] = \mathbf{18}$

27. $m^2p - p(m - p)$
$= (-3)(-3)(5) - (5)[(-3) - (5)] = 45 - 5[-8]$
$= 45 + 40 = \mathbf{85}$

28. $4x(a + x)(-x) = 4(-3)[(2) + (-3)][-(-3)]$
$= -12[-1][3] = \mathbf{36}$

29. $m(k^2 - m^3) = (-1)[(-2)(-2) - (-1)(-1)(-1)]$
$= -1[4 + 1] = -1[5] = \mathbf{-5}$

30. $\dfrac{4(2 - 5)}{-2(4 - 2) - (-2)} = \dfrac{4(-3)}{-2(2) + 2}$

$= \dfrac{-12}{-4 + 2} = \dfrac{-12}{-2} = \mathbf{6}$

PROBLEM SET 28

1. $80\ \text{yd}^3 \times \dfrac{3\ \text{ft}}{1\ \text{yd}} \times \dfrac{3\ \text{ft}}{1\ \text{yd}} \times \dfrac{3\ \text{ft}}{1\ \text{yd}} \times \dfrac{12\ \text{in.}}{1\ \text{ft}}$

$\times \dfrac{12\ \text{in.}}{1\ \text{ft}} \times \dfrac{12\ \text{in.}}{1\ \text{ft}}$

$= \mathbf{80(3)(3)(3)(12)(12)(12)\ in.^3}$

2. $42\ \text{cm}^3 \times \dfrac{1\ \text{in.}}{2.54\ \text{cm}} \times \dfrac{1\ \text{in.}}{2.54\ \text{cm}} \times \dfrac{1\ \text{in.}}{2.54\ \text{cm}}$

$= \mathbf{\dfrac{42}{(2.54)(2.54)(2.54)}\ in.^3}$

3. $(D) \times (\text{of}) = (\text{is})$

$\dfrac{0.8WN}{0.8} = \dfrac{7.68}{0.8}$

$WN = \mathbf{9.6}$

4. $3x - 7 = 42$

$\underline{+7 \quad +7}$

$3x \quad = 49$

$\dfrac{3x}{3} = \dfrac{49}{3}$

$x = \mathbf{\dfrac{49}{3}}$

5. $2\frac{1}{2}x - 5 = 17$

$\underline{\phantom{2\frac{1}{2}x}+5 \quad +5}$

$2\frac{1}{2}x \quad = 22$

$\dfrac{\frac{5}{2}x}{\frac{5}{2}} = \dfrac{22}{\frac{5}{2}}$

$x = \mathbf{\dfrac{44}{5}}$

6. $\dfrac{3}{4} + \dfrac{1}{2}x + 2 = 0$

$\underline{-\dfrac{3}{4} \qquad -2 \quad -\dfrac{3}{4} - 2}$

$\dfrac{1}{2}x \quad = -2\dfrac{3}{4}$

$\dfrac{\frac{1}{2}x}{\frac{1}{2}} = \dfrac{-\frac{11}{4}}{\frac{1}{2}}$

$x = \mathbf{-\dfrac{11}{2}}$

7. $0.4k + 0.4k - 0.02 = 4.02$

$40k + 40k - 2 = 402$

$\underline{\qquad +2 \qquad +2}$

$80k \qquad = 404$

$\dfrac{80k}{80} = \dfrac{404}{80}$

$k = \dfrac{101}{20} = \mathbf{5.05}$

8. $-2x - 5 - x - 8 - 5x - 3 = 0$

$-8x - 16 = \quad 0$

$\underline{\qquad +16 \quad +16}$

$-8x \qquad = \quad 16$

$\dfrac{-8x}{-8} = \dfrac{16}{-8}$

$x = \mathbf{-2}$

9. $5m - m - 2m + 5 = -3m - 2$

$2m + 5 = -3m - 2$

$\underline{\quad -5 \qquad \qquad -5}$

$2m \qquad = -3m - 7$

$\underline{+3m \qquad \quad +3m}$

$5m \qquad = \qquad -7$

$\dfrac{5m}{5} = \dfrac{-7}{5}$

$m = -\dfrac{\mathbf{7}}{\mathbf{5}}$

10. $-3x - 2 = 3x - 5 + 8$

$-3x - 2 = \quad 3x + 3$

$\underline{-3x \qquad \quad -3x}$

$-6x - 2 = \qquad \quad 3$

$\underline{\quad +2 \qquad \qquad +2}$

$-6x \qquad = \qquad \quad 5$

$\dfrac{-6x}{-6} = \dfrac{5}{-6}$

$x = -\dfrac{\mathbf{5}}{\mathbf{6}}$

11. $-p - 2p - 4 + 7p = 5 + 2p - 6$

$4p - 4 = \quad 2p - 1$

$\underline{-2p \qquad \quad -2p}$

$2p - 4 = \qquad \quad -1$

$\underline{\quad +4 \qquad \qquad +4}$

$2p \qquad = \qquad \quad 3$

$\dfrac{2p}{2} = \dfrac{3}{2}$

$p = \dfrac{\mathbf{3}}{\mathbf{2}}$

12. $-2k + k - 3k = 7 + 2k - 2$

$-4k = \quad 2k + 5$

$\underline{-2k \qquad -2k}$

$-6k = \qquad \quad 5$

$\dfrac{-6k}{-6} = \dfrac{5}{-6}$

$k = -\dfrac{\mathbf{5}}{\mathbf{6}}$

13. $(-3)^{-2} = \dfrac{1}{(-3)^2} = \dfrac{1}{(-3)(-3)} = \dfrac{\mathbf{1}}{\mathbf{9}}$

14. $\dfrac{1}{4^{-2}} - \sqrt[3]{-27} = 4^2 - (-3) = (4)(4) + 3$

$= 16 + 3 = \mathbf{19}$

15. $\dfrac{1}{(-4)^{-3}} = (-4)^3 = (-4)(-4)(-4) = \mathbf{-64}$

16. $\dfrac{1}{2^{-3}} = 2^3 = (2)(2)(2) = \mathbf{8}$

17. $(-5)^{-3} = \dfrac{1}{(-5)^3} = \dfrac{1}{(-5)(-5)(-5)} = -\dfrac{\mathbf{1}}{\mathbf{125}}$

18. $A = \dfrac{1}{2}b_1 h + \dfrac{1}{2}b_2 h$

$= \left(\dfrac{1}{2}(11)(4) + \dfrac{1}{2}(5)(4)\right) \text{cm}^2$

$= (22 + 10) \text{ cm}^2$

$= \mathbf{32 \text{ cm}^2}$

19. $V = A_{\text{Base}} \times \text{height}$

$= \left(\dfrac{\pi(4)^2}{2} + 10(8)\right) \text{ft}^2 \times 6 \text{ ft}$

$= (8\pi + 80) \text{ ft}^2 \times 6 \text{ ft}$

$= (48\pi + 480) \text{ ft}^3 \approx \mathbf{630.72 \text{ ft}^3}$

$\text{S.A.} = 2(A_{\text{Base}}) + (P \times \text{height})$

$= 2\left(\dfrac{\pi(4)^2}{2} + 10(8)\right) \text{ft}^2$

$+ \left(\left(\dfrac{2\pi(4)}{2} + 28\right) \times 6\right) \text{ft}^2$

$= (16\pi + 160) \text{ ft}^2 + (24\pi + 168) \text{ ft}^2$

$= (40\pi + 328) \text{ ft}^2 \approx \mathbf{453.6 \text{ ft}^2}$

20. $(x^2 - 4x^5 y^{-5})3p^0 x^{-2} = 3x^0 - 12x^3 y^{-5}$

$= \mathbf{3 - 12x^3 y^{-5}}$

21. $2x^{-2}y^0(x^2 y^0 - 4x^{-6}y^4) = 2x^0 - 8x^{-8}y^4$

$= \mathbf{2 - 8x^{-8}y^4}$

22. $x^{-4}y^0(x^4 - 3y^2 x^5 p^0) = x^0 - 3y^2 x = \mathbf{1 - 3y^2 x}$

23. $m^0x(x^{-1}y^0 - y^2m^0) = x^0 - xy^2 = \mathbf{1 - xy^2}$

24. $x^2ym^3 - 3x^2y + 6ym^3x^2 + yx^2 = \mathbf{7x^2ym^3 - 2x^2y}$

25. $abc^2 - 2ab^2c + 6c^2ab - 4b^2ac$
$= \mathbf{7abc^2 - 6ab^2c}$

26. $-a^3(a^0 - b) = -(-2)(-2)(-2)[(-2)^0 - (4)]$
$= 8[1 - 4] = 8[-3] = \mathbf{-24}$

27. $-c(c - b) = -(-2)[(-2) - (4)] = 2[-6] = \mathbf{-12}$

28. $x(x^0 - y)(y - 2x)$
$= (-3)[(-3)^0 - (5)][(5) - 2(-3)]$
$= -3[1 - 5][5 + 6] = -3[-4][11] = \mathbf{132}$

29. $-3^2 + (-3)^3 - 3^0 - |-3 - 3|$
$= -(3)(3) + (-3)(-3)(-3) - 3^0 - |-6|$
$= -9 - 27 - 1 - 6 = \mathbf{-43}$

30. $\dfrac{-4[2 - (-2)]}{-7(5 - 2)} = \dfrac{-4[2 + 2]}{-7(3)} = \dfrac{-4[4]}{-21}$
$= \dfrac{-16}{-21} = \dfrac{\mathbf{16}}{\mathbf{21}}$

PROBLEM SET 29

1. $(D) \times (\text{of}) = (\text{is})$
$1.6WN = 3200$
$\dfrac{1.6WN}{1.6} = \dfrac{3200}{1.6}$
$WN = \mathbf{2000}$

2. $(D) \times (\text{of}) = (\text{is})$
$WD80 = 8400$
$\dfrac{80WD}{80} = \dfrac{8400}{80}$
$WD = \mathbf{105}$

3. $(F) \times (\text{of}) = (\text{is})$
$\dfrac{29}{6}(4596) = WN$
$\mathbf{22,214} = WN$

4. $4200 \text{ in.}^3 \times \dfrac{2.54 \text{ cm}}{1 \text{ in.}} \times \dfrac{2.54 \text{ cm}}{1 \text{ in.}} \times \dfrac{2.54 \text{ cm}}{1 \text{ in.}}$
$\times \dfrac{1 \text{ m}}{100 \text{ cm}} \times \dfrac{1 \text{ m}}{100 \text{ cm}} \times \dfrac{1 \text{ m}}{100 \text{ cm}}$
$= \dfrac{\mathbf{4200(2.54)(2.54)(2.54)}}{\mathbf{(100)(100)(100)}} \text{ m}^3$

5. $A = A_{\text{Rectangle}} - A_{\text{Semicircle}}$
$= \left(12(8) - \dfrac{\pi(4)^2}{2}\right) \text{ m}^2$
$= (96 - 8\pi) \text{ m}^2 \approx \mathbf{70.88 \text{ m}^2}$

6. $\mathbf{5N - 8}$

7. $\mathbf{3(-N - 7)}$

8. $\dfrac{1}{2}x + 2 = -\dfrac{3}{4}$
$\phantom{\dfrac{1}{2}x} \underline{-2 \qquad -2}$
$\dfrac{1}{2}x \qquad = -2\dfrac{3}{4}$

$\dfrac{\frac{1}{2}x}{\frac{1}{2}} = \dfrac{-\frac{11}{4}}{\frac{1}{2}}$
$x = -\dfrac{\mathbf{11}}{\mathbf{2}}$

9. $0.3k + 0.85k - 2 = 2.6$
$115k - 200 = 260$
$\underline{+200 \qquad +200}$
$115k = 460$
$\dfrac{115k}{115} = \dfrac{460}{115}$
$k = \mathbf{4}$

10. $\dfrac{1}{7}k - \dfrac{4}{7} = -7$
$\underline{\phantom{\dfrac{1}{7}k}+\dfrac{4}{7} \qquad +\dfrac{4}{7}}$
$\dfrac{1}{7}k \phantom{+\dfrac{4}{7}} = -\dfrac{45}{7}$
$\dfrac{\frac{1}{7}k}{\frac{1}{7}} = \dfrac{-\frac{45}{7}}{\frac{1}{7}}$
$k = \mathbf{-45}$

11. $2k - 5 + k - 3 = 2 + 2k + 5$
$3k - 8 = 2k + 7$
$\underline{-2k \qquad\quad -2k}$
$k - 8 = 7$
$\underline{+8 \qquad\qquad +8}$
$k = \mathbf{15}$

12. $-2 - 6p + p - 2 = 7 - p$
$-5p - 4 = -p + 7$
$\underline{+p \qquad\qquad +p}$
$-4p - 4 = 7$
$\underline{+4 \qquad\qquad +4}$
$-4p = 11$
$\dfrac{-4p}{-4} = \dfrac{11}{-4}$
$p = -\dfrac{\mathbf{11}}{\mathbf{4}}$

13. $3m - m = 5 - 4 + 2m + 5 - 5m$

$ 2m = -3m + 6$

$ \underline{+3m +3m}$

$ 5m = 6$

$ \dfrac{5m}{5} = \dfrac{6}{5}$

$ m = \dfrac{\mathbf{6}}{\mathbf{5}}$

14. $(-6)^{-2} = \dfrac{1}{(-6)^2} = \dfrac{1}{(-6)(-6)} = \dfrac{\mathbf{1}}{\mathbf{36}}$

15. $3^{-3} = \dfrac{1}{3^3} = \dfrac{1}{(3)(3)(3)} = \dfrac{\mathbf{1}}{\mathbf{27}}$

16. $\dfrac{1}{(-4)^{-2}} = (-4)^2 = (-4)(-4) = \mathbf{16}$

17. $\dfrac{1}{5^{-3}} - \sqrt[3]{-125} = (5)^3 - (-5) = (5)(5)(5) + 5$

$= 125 + 5 = \mathbf{130}$

18. $p^0 x^{-1}(x - 2x^0) = x^0 - 2x^{-1} = \mathbf{1 - 2x^{-1}}$

19. $4x^2 p^0(3xp^5 - 2x^{-2}) = 12x^3 p^5 - 8x^0$

$= \mathbf{12x^3 p^5 - 8}$

20. $(y^{-2}x^{-1} + 3p^2 y^{-2}k^0)xp^0 y^2 = x^0 y^0 + 3p^2 xy^0$

$= \mathbf{1 + 3p^2 x}$

21. $4m^2 x^{-5}(2m^{-2}x^{-5} - 3m^{-2}k^0)$

$= 8m^0 x^{-10} - 12m^0 x^{-5} = \mathbf{8x^{-10} - 12x^{-5}}$

22. $2p^{-4}x^2 y^{-2}(p^4 x^2 y^2 k^0 - 3p^2 x)$

$= 2p^0 x^4 y^0 - 6p^{-2}x^3 y^{-2} = \mathbf{2x^4 - 6p^{-2}x^3 y^{-2}}$

23. $4x^2 yp^{-3}(x^{-2}y^4 p^6 - 5x^4 yp^{-3})$

$= 4x^0 y^5 p^3 - 20x^6 y^2 p^{-6} = \mathbf{4y^5 p^3 - 20x^6 y^2 p^{-6}}$

24. $xmp^{-2} - 4p^{-2}xm + 6p^{-2}mx - 5mx$

$= \mathbf{3xmp^{-2} - 5mx}$

25. $k^2 p^{-4}y - 5k^2 yp^{-4} + 2yk^2 p^{-4} - 5k^2 yp^{-4}$

$= \mathbf{-7k^2 p^{-4}y}$

26. $a^3 - (b^0 - a) = (-3)(-3)(-3) - [(4)^0 - (-3)]$

$= -27 - [1 + 3] = -27 - 4 = \mathbf{-31}$

27. $p - a(p - ap) = (-3) - (-2)[(-3) - (-2)(-3)]$

$= -3 + 2[-3 - 6] = -3 + 2[-9]$

$= -3 - 18 = \mathbf{-21}$

28. $-k^0 - (-km) = -(-5)^0 - [-(-5)(3)]$

$= -1 - [15] = \mathbf{-16}$

29. $-2(-3) - (-4)^0(-3)|-5 - 2| = 6 - 1(-3)(7)$

$= 6 + 21 = \mathbf{27}$

30. $\dfrac{-7(-4 - 6)}{-(-4) - [-(-6)]} = \dfrac{-7(-10)}{4 - [6]} = \dfrac{70}{-2} = \mathbf{-35}$

PROBLEM SET 30

1. $\mathbf{7(N - 5)}$

2. $2(-N) - 7 = \mathbf{-2N - 7}$

3. $\mathbf{7N - 51}$

4. $\mathbf{4N - 15}$

5. $(D) \times (\text{of}) = (\text{is})$

$3.25WN = 585$

$\dfrac{3.25WN}{3.25} = \dfrac{585}{3.25}$

$WN = \mathbf{180}$

6. $(F) \times (\text{of}) = (\text{is})$

$WF \cdot 6\dfrac{7}{8} = \dfrac{1}{4}$

$\dfrac{\frac{55}{8}WF}{\frac{55}{8}} = \dfrac{\frac{1}{4}}{\frac{55}{8}}$

$WF = \dfrac{\mathbf{2}}{\mathbf{55}}$

7. $(F) \times (\text{of}) = (\text{is})$

$\dfrac{21}{8}(21) = WN$

$\dfrac{\mathbf{441}}{\mathbf{8}} = WN$

8. $70 \text{ ft}^2 \times \dfrac{12 \text{ in.}}{1 \text{ ft}} \times \dfrac{12 \text{ in.}}{1 \text{ ft}} \times \dfrac{2.54 \text{ cm}}{1 \text{ in.}} \times \dfrac{2.54 \text{ cm}}{1 \text{ in.}}$

$\times \dfrac{1 \text{ m}}{100 \text{ cm}} \times \dfrac{1 \text{ m}}{100 \text{ cm}} = \dfrac{\mathbf{70(12)(12)(2.54)(2.54)}}{\mathbf{(100)(100)}} \text{ m}^2$

9. $10{,}000 \text{ km} \times \dfrac{1000 \text{ m}}{1 \text{ km}} \times \dfrac{100 \text{ cm}}{1 \text{ m}} \times \dfrac{1 \text{ in.}}{2.54 \text{ cm}}$

$\times \dfrac{1 \text{ ft}}{12 \text{ in.}} = \dfrac{\mathbf{10{,}000(1000)(100)}}{\mathbf{(2.54)(12)}} \text{ ft}$

10. S.A. $= 2(A_{\text{Base}}) + (C \times \text{length})$

$= (2(\pi(20)^2) + (2\pi(20) \times 100)) \text{ cm}^2$

$= (800\pi + 4000\pi) \text{ cm}^2$

$= 4800\pi \text{ cm}^2 \approx \mathbf{15{,}072 \text{ cm}^2}$

11. $A = \frac{1}{2}b_1h_1 + \frac{1}{2}b_2h_2 + \frac{1}{2}\pi r^2$

$= \left(\frac{1}{2}(10)(10) + \frac{1}{2}(10)(12) + \frac{1}{2}\pi(6)^2\right) \text{ft}^2$

$= (50 + 60 + 18\pi) \text{ft}^2$

$= (110 + 18\pi) \text{ft}^2 \approx \mathbf{166.52 \ ft^2}$

12. $0.1p - 0.2p + 2 = -4.6$

$\quad -p + 20 = -46$

$\quad \underline{-20 \qquad -20}$

$\quad -p \quad\ = -66$

$\qquad p = \mathbf{66}$

13. $\frac{1}{4} + 4\frac{1}{2}k = \frac{1}{8}$

$-\frac{1}{4} \qquad\quad -\frac{1}{4}$

$\overline{\qquad\qquad\qquad}$

$4\frac{1}{2}k = -\frac{1}{8}$

$\dfrac{\frac{9}{2}k}{\frac{9}{2}} = \dfrac{-\frac{1}{8}}{\frac{9}{2}}$

$k = -\dfrac{1}{36}$

14. $12 - 2x + 5 = -2 + (x - 3)$

$\quad -2x + 17 = \quad x - 5$

$\quad \underline{-x \qquad\qquad -x}$

$\quad -3x + 17 = \qquad -5$

$\quad \underline{\quad -17 \qquad\quad -17}$

$\quad -3x \qquad = \qquad -22$

$\qquad x = \dfrac{22}{3}$

15. $-4(4y - 17) + (-y) = (2y - 1) - (-y)$

$\quad -17y + 68 = \quad 3y - 1$

$\quad \underline{-3y \qquad\qquad -3y}$

$\quad -20y + 68 = \qquad -1$

$\quad \underline{\qquad -68 \qquad\quad -68}$

$\quad -20y \qquad = \qquad -69$

$\qquad y = \dfrac{69}{20}$

16. $\dfrac{1}{(-4)^{-3}} - \sqrt{4} = (-4)^3 - 2$

$= (-4)(-4)(-4) - 2 = -64 - 2 = \mathbf{-66}$

17. $4^{-3} = \dfrac{1}{4^3} = \dfrac{1}{(4)(4)(4)} = \dfrac{\mathbf{1}}{\mathbf{64}}$

18. $y^0x^{-4}(x^4 - 5y^4x^4) = x^0 - 5y^4x^0 = \mathbf{1 - 5y^4}$

19. $(y^{-5} + 3x^5y^2)x^0y^5 = y^0 + 3x^5y^7 = \mathbf{1 + 3x^5y^7}$

20. $-2x^2(3x^4 - 6x^{-2}y^0p) = -6x^6 + 12x^0p$

$= \mathbf{-6x^6 + 12p}$

21. $5x^0y^2(y^4x^6 - 5x^0y^{-4}) = \mathbf{5y^6x^6 - 25y^{-2}}$

22. $3m^2n^2(p^0m^4n - m^{-2}n^{-2}) = 3m^6n^3 - 3m^0n^0$

$= \mathbf{3m^6n^3 - 3}$

23. $(x^0p^5 - 3x^0p^{-5})2p^0x^5 = \mathbf{2x^5p^5 - 6p^{-5}x^5}$

24. $3xym^2z^3 + 2x^2xy^2y^{-1}m^2z^2 - xym^5m^{-3}z^2x^2$

$= 3xym^2z^3 + 2x^3ym^2z^2 - x^3ym^2z^2$

$= \mathbf{3xym^2z^3 + x^3ym^2z^2}$

25. $3xy - 2x^2yx^{-1} + 5x^3x^{-2}y^3y^{-2} + 5xxxx^{-2}y$

$= 3xy - 2xy + 5xy + 5xy = \mathbf{11xy}$

26. $-a^2 - 3a(a - b)$

$= -(-2)(-2) - 3(-2)[(-2) - (-1)]$

$= -4 + 6[-1] = -4 - 6 = \mathbf{-10}$

27. $-c(ac - a^0) = -(4)[(-3)(4) - (-3)^0]$

$= -4[-12 - 1] = -4[-13] = \mathbf{52}$

28. $-n(n^0 - m) - |m^2|$

$= -(-4)[(-4)^0 - (6)] - |(6)^2| = 4[1 - 6] - 36$

$= 4[-5] - 36 = -20 - 36 = \mathbf{-56}$

29. $-2^0 - 2^2 - (-2)^3 = -1 - (2)(2) - (-2)(-2)(-2)$

$= -1 - 4 + 8 = \mathbf{3}$

30. $-3 + (-3)(-3)^2 + (-3)^3$

$= -3 - 3(-3)(-3) + (-3)(-3)(-3)$

$= -3 - 27 - 27 = \mathbf{-57}$

Problem Set 31

1. $800 \text{ cm}^3 \times \dfrac{1 \text{ in.}}{2.54 \text{ cm}} \times \dfrac{1 \text{ in.}}{2.54 \text{ cm}} \times \dfrac{1 \text{ in.}}{2.54 \text{ cm}}$

$\times \dfrac{1 \text{ ft}}{12 \text{ in.}} \times \dfrac{1 \text{ ft}}{12 \text{ in.}} \times \dfrac{1 \text{ ft}}{12 \text{ in.}}$

$= \dfrac{800}{(2.54)(2.54)(2.54)(12)(12)(12)} \text{ ft}^3$

2. $N - 21 = 2(-N)$

$N - 21 = -2N$

$\underline{\quad + 21 \qquad\qquad + 21}$

$N \qquad = -2N + 21$

$\underline{+ 2N \qquad\qquad +2N}$

$3N \qquad = \qquad 21$

$N = \mathbf{7}$

3. Solve:

$$3N + 7 = N + 23$$
$$\underline{-N \qquad\quad -N}$$
$$2N + 7 = \qquad 23$$
$$\underline{\quad -7 \qquad\qquad -7}$$
$$2N \quad = \qquad 16$$
$$N = \mathbf{8}$$

4. $V = A_{Base} \times height$

$$= \left(\frac{1}{2}(16)(6) + \frac{1}{2}(8)(6)\right)(10) \text{ in.}^3$$
$$= (72)(10) \text{ in.}^3$$
$$= \mathbf{720 \text{ in.}^3}$$

$$\text{S.A.} = 2(A_{Base}) + (P \times height)$$
$$= 2(72) \text{ in.}^2 + (37.8)(10) \text{ in.}^2$$
$$= (144 + 378) \text{ in.}^2$$
$$= \mathbf{522 \text{ in.}^2}$$

5. $A = \frac{1}{2}bh$

$$= \frac{1}{2}(48 \text{ in.})(20 \text{ in.})$$
$$= \mathbf{480 \text{ in.}^2}$$

6. $(F) \times (of) = (is)$

$$2\frac{1}{9} \cdot WN = 3\frac{4}{5}$$
$$\frac{\frac{19}{9}WN}{\frac{19}{9}} = \frac{\frac{19}{5}}{\frac{19}{9}}$$
$$WN = \mathbf{\frac{9}{5}}$$

7. $(D) \times (of) = (is)$

$$D \cdot 0.05 = 1.25$$
$$\frac{0.05D}{0.05} = \frac{1.25}{0.05}$$
$$D = \mathbf{25}$$

8.

$$\frac{p}{7} - 2 = \frac{15}{3}$$
$$\underline{\quad +2 \qquad +2}$$
$$\frac{p}{7} = \frac{21}{3}$$
$$\frac{\frac{1}{7}p}{\frac{1}{7}} = \frac{\frac{21}{3}}{\frac{1}{7}}$$
$$p = \mathbf{49}$$

9. Solve:

$$2\frac{1}{4}k + \frac{1}{4} = \frac{1}{8}$$
$$\underline{\qquad -\frac{1}{4} \quad -\frac{1}{4}}$$
$$2\frac{1}{4}k \qquad = -\frac{1}{8}$$
$$\frac{\frac{9}{4}k}{\frac{9}{4}} = \frac{-\frac{1}{8}}{\frac{9}{4}}$$
$$k = -\mathbf{\frac{1}{18}}$$

10.

$$1.3p + 0.3p - 2 = 1.2$$
$$16p - 20 = 12$$
$$\underline{\quad +20 \qquad +20}$$
$$16p \qquad = 32$$
$$p = \mathbf{2}$$

11.

$$3(p - 2) = p + 7$$
$$3p - 6 = p + 7$$
$$\underline{-p \qquad\quad -p}$$
$$2p - 6 = \qquad 7$$
$$\underline{\quad +6 \qquad\qquad +6}$$
$$2p \quad = \qquad 13$$
$$p = \mathbf{\frac{13}{2}}$$

12.

$$+2(3x - 5) = 7x + 2$$
$$6x - 10 = 7x + 2$$
$$\underline{-7x \qquad\quad -7x}$$
$$-x - 10 = \qquad 2$$
$$\underline{\quad +10 \qquad\qquad +10}$$
$$-x \quad = \qquad 12$$
$$x = \mathbf{-12}$$

13.

$$-(x - 3) - 2(x - 4) = 7$$
$$-3x + 11 = 7$$
$$\underline{\qquad -11 \quad -11}$$
$$-3x \quad = -4$$
$$x = \mathbf{\frac{4}{3}}$$

14.

$$-5(p - 4) - 3(-2 - p) = p - 2$$
$$-2p + 26 = p - 2$$
$$\underline{-p \qquad\qquad -p}$$
$$-3p + 26 = \qquad -2$$
$$\underline{\qquad -26 \qquad\qquad -26}$$
$$-3p \qquad = -28$$
$$p = \mathbf{\frac{28}{3}}$$

15. $2(3p - 2) - (p + 4) = 3p$

$$5p - 8 = 3p$$
$$\underline{-5p \qquad\quad -5p}$$
$$-8 = -2p$$
$$4 = p$$

16. $6^{-2} = \dfrac{1}{6^2} = \dfrac{1}{(6)(6)} = \mathbf{\dfrac{1}{36}}$

17. $\dfrac{1}{(-3)^{-3}} = (-3)^3 = (-3)(-3)(-3) = \mathbf{-27}$

18. $(-2)^{-2} - 2^2 = \dfrac{1}{(-2)^2} - 2^2$

$\quad = \dfrac{1}{(-2)(-2)} - (2)(2) = \dfrac{1}{4} - 4 = -\mathbf{\dfrac{15}{4}}$

19. $\dfrac{1}{(-4)^{-3}} = (-4)^3 = (-4)(-4)(-4) = \mathbf{-64}$

20. $-3x^0p(-5xp^0 - 2p^{-1}) = 15px + 6p^0 = \mathbf{15px + 6}$

21. $2xp^{-4}(x^{-4}p - 3x^2p^{-2}) = \mathbf{2x^{-3}p^{-3} - 6x^3p^{-6}}$

22. $2p^4x^0y(p^5m^4x - 5x^{-2}y^{-4})$
$\quad = \mathbf{2p^9m^4xy - 10p^4y^{-3}x^{-2}}$

23. $(x^4 - 2p^2)3x^0p^{-4} = \mathbf{3p^{-4}x^4 - 6p^{-2}}$

24. $-3x^2x^0xy^2 + 2x^3y^{-3}y^5 + 5x^{-3}x^{-6}yy^2y^{-5}$
$\quad = -3x^3y^2 + 2x^3y^2 + 5x^{-9}y^{-2} = \mathbf{-x^3y^2 + 5x^{-9}y^{-2}}$

25. $2xym^2 + 3x^2ym - 4y^2my^{-1}m^0x^4x^{-2}$
$\quad = 2xym^2 + 3x^2ym - 4x^2ym = \mathbf{2xym^2 - x^2ym}$

26. $a - a(b^0 - a) = (-2) - (-2)[(5)^0 - (-2)]$
$\quad = -2 + 2[1 + 2] = -2 + 6 = \mathbf{4}$

27. $x^2 - xy^2(x - y)$
$\quad = (-3)(-3) - (-3)(4)(4)[(-3) - (4)]$
$\quad = 9 + 48[-7] = \mathbf{-327}$

28. $m - m^2 - (m - n)$
$\quad = (-3) - (-3)(-3) - [(-3) - (-5)]$
$\quad = -3 - 9 - [2] = \mathbf{-14}$

29. $-3^3 - 3^2 - (-3)^4 - |-3^2 - 3|$
$\quad = -(3)(3)(3) - (3)(3) - (-3)(-3)(-3)(-3)$
$\quad\quad - |-(3)(3) - 3|$
$\quad = -27 - 9 - 81 - |-12| = -117 - 12 = \mathbf{-129}$

30. $\dfrac{-5(-5 - 4)}{-2^0(-8 - 1)} = \dfrac{-5(-9)}{-1(-9)} = \dfrac{45}{9} = \mathbf{5}$

PROBLEM SET 32

1. $120\ \cancel{ft^3} \times \dfrac{12\ \cancel{in.}}{1\ \cancel{ft}} \times \dfrac{12\ \cancel{in.}}{1\ \cancel{ft}} \times \dfrac{12\ \cancel{in.}}{1\ \cancel{ft}}$

$\quad \times \dfrac{2.54\ cm}{1\ \cancel{in.}} \times \dfrac{2.54\ cm}{1\ \cancel{in.}} \times \dfrac{2.54\ cm}{1\ \cancel{in.}}$

$\quad = \mathbf{120(12)(12)(12)(2.54)(2.54)(2.54)\ cm^3}$

2. S.A. $= 2(A_{Top}) + 2(A_{Side}) + 2(A_{Front})$
$\quad = (2(6)(3) + 2(2)(3) + 2(6)(2))\ cm^2$
$\quad = (36 + 12 + 24)\ cm^2$
$\quad = \mathbf{72\ cm^2}$

3. A $= \dfrac{1}{2}bh$
$\quad = \dfrac{1}{2}(5)(12)(80)\ in.^2$
$\quad = \mathbf{2400\ in.^2}$

4. $(F) \times (of) = (is)$

$\quad \dfrac{3}{7}WN = 2\dfrac{1}{5}$

$\quad \dfrac{\frac{3}{7}WN}{\frac{3}{7}} = \dfrac{\frac{11}{5}}{\frac{3}{7}}$

$\quad\quad WN = \mathbf{\dfrac{77}{15}}$

5. $(F) \times (of) = (is)$

$\quad F \cdot 40 = 90$

$\quad \dfrac{40F}{40} = \dfrac{90}{40}$

$\quad\quad F = \mathbf{\dfrac{9}{4}}$

6. $(D) \times (of) = (is)$

$\quad 1.025 \times 50 = WN$

$\quad\quad \mathbf{51.25 = WN}$

7. $\dfrac{5}{8}x - 3 = \dfrac{1}{2}$

$\quad \underline{\qquad +3 \qquad +3}$

$\quad \dfrac{5}{8}x \qquad = 3\dfrac{1}{2}$

$\quad \dfrac{\frac{5}{8}x}{\frac{5}{8}} = \dfrac{\frac{7}{2}}{\frac{5}{8}}$

$\quad\quad x = \mathbf{\dfrac{28}{5}}$

8. Solve:

$$\frac{1}{7}y + 10 = 14\frac{1}{4}$$

$$\underline{\quad -10 \qquad -10 \quad}$$

$$\frac{1}{7}y \qquad = 4\frac{1}{4}$$

$$\frac{\frac{1}{7}y}{\frac{1}{7}} = \frac{\frac{17}{4}}{\frac{1}{7}}$$

$$y = \mathbf{\frac{119}{4}}$$

9. $0.3 + 0.06p + 0.02 - 0.02p = 4$

$$4p + 32 = 400$$

$$\underline{\qquad -32 \quad -32\quad}$$

$$4p \quad = 368$$

$$p = \mathbf{92}$$

10. $3p - 4 - 6 = -2(p - 5)$

$$3p - 10 = -2p + 10$$

$$\underline{+2p \qquad +2p\quad}$$

$$5p - 10 = \qquad 10$$

$$\underline{\quad +10 \qquad +10\quad}$$

$$5p \quad = \qquad 20$$

$$p = \mathbf{4}$$

11. $k + 4 - 5(k + 2) = 3k - 2$

$$-4k - 6 = 3k - 2$$

$$\underline{-3k \qquad\quad -3k\quad}$$

$$-7k - 6 = \qquad -2$$

$$\underline{\quad +6 \qquad\quad +6\quad}$$

$$-7k \quad = \qquad 4$$

$$k = \mathbf{-\frac{4}{7}}$$

12. $x - 4(x - 3) + 7 = 6 - (x - 4)$

$$-3x + 19 = -x + 10$$

$$\underline{+x \qquad\quad +x\quad}$$

$$-2x + 19 = \qquad 10$$

$$\underline{\quad -19 \qquad -19\quad}$$

$$-2x \quad = \qquad -9$$

$$x = \mathbf{\frac{9}{2}}$$

13. $p - 3(p + 4) = 2(p + 1)$

$$-2p - 12 = 2p + 2$$

$$\underline{-2p \qquad\quad -2p\quad}$$

$$-4p - 12 = \qquad 2$$

$$\underline{\quad +12 \qquad +12\quad}$$

$$-4p \quad = \qquad 14$$

$$p = \mathbf{-\frac{7}{2}}$$

14. $\dfrac{160}{5} = 32$, $\dfrac{32}{2} = 16$, $\dfrac{16}{2} = 8$, $\dfrac{8}{2} = 4$, $\dfrac{4}{2} = 2$

$\mathbf{160 = 2 \cdot 2 \cdot 2 \cdot 2 \cdot 2 \cdot 5}$

15. $\dfrac{294}{2} = 147$, $\dfrac{147}{3} = 49$, $\dfrac{49}{7} = 7$

$\mathbf{294 = 2 \cdot 3 \cdot 7 \cdot 7}$

16. $\dfrac{250}{5} = 50$, $\dfrac{50}{5} = 10$, $\dfrac{10}{5} = 2$

$\mathbf{250 = 2 \cdot 5 \cdot 5 \cdot 5}$

17. $\dfrac{450}{5} = 90$, $\dfrac{90}{5} = 18$, $\dfrac{18}{3} = 6$, $\dfrac{6}{3} = 2$

$\mathbf{450 = 2 \cdot 3 \cdot 3 \cdot 5 \cdot 5}$

18. $(-3)^{-3} = \dfrac{1}{(-3)^3} = \dfrac{1}{(-3)(-3)(-3)} = \mathbf{-\dfrac{1}{27}}$

19. $2^{-3} = \dfrac{1}{2^3} = \dfrac{1}{(2)(2)(2)} = \mathbf{\dfrac{1}{8}}$

20. $2x^{-2}(x^{-2}y^0 + x^2y^5p^0) = 2x^{-2}x^{-2} + 2x^{-2}x^2y^5$

$= \mathbf{2x^{-4} + 2y^5}$

21. $x^{-3}p^0(x^6p^5 - 3x^3p^0) = x^{-3}x^6p^5 - x^{-3}3x^3$

$= \mathbf{x^3p^5 - 3}$

22. $4x^2y^0(x^0y^2 - 3x^2y^{-2}) = 4x^2y^2 - 4x^23x^2y^{-2}$

$= \mathbf{4x^2y^2 - 12x^4y^{-2}}$

23. $(4p^{-2} - 3x^{-3}p^5)p^2x^0 = 4p^{-2}p^2 - 3x^{-3}p^5p^2$

$= \mathbf{4 - 3x^{-3}p^7}$

24. $-3x^{-2}y^2x^5 + 6x^3y^{-2}y^4 - 3x^3y^2 + 5x^2y^3$

$= -3x^3y^2 + 6x^3y^2 - 3x^3y^2 + 5x^2y^3 = \mathbf{5x^2y^3}$

25. $-xyz^5z^{-4} + 5xy^{-4}y^5z - 3zxy^7y^{-6}$

$= -xyz + 5xyz - 3xyz = \mathbf{xyz}$

26. $m - (-m)(m^0 - a) = -2 - (-(-2))((-2)^0 - 3)$

$= -2 - 2(1 - 3) = -2 - 2(-2) = \mathbf{2}$

27. $k^2 - k^3(km^0) = (-3)^2 - (-3)^3((-3)(2)^0)$

$= 9 - (-27)(-3) = \mathbf{-72}$

28. $a^3x - x^3 = (-3)^3(-2) - (-2)^3$

$= (-27)(-2) - (-8) = 54 + 8 = \mathbf{62}$

29. $-3^3 - 2^2 - 4^3 - |-2^2 - 2|$

$= -27 - 4 - 64 - |-4 - 2| = -95 - 6$

$= \mathbf{-101}$

30. $\dfrac{-(-3 + 7) - 4^0}{(-2)(-3 + 5)} = \dfrac{-(4) - 1}{(-2)(2)} = \dfrac{-5}{-4} = \mathbf{\dfrac{5}{4}}$

PROBLEM SET 33

1. $3N + 60 = -50$
$3N = -110$
$N = -\dfrac{110}{3}$

2. $2(3N + 60) = -N + 155$
$6N + 120 = -N + 155$
$7N = 35$
$N = \mathbf{5}$

3. $0.125(WN) = 5.25$
$WN = \dfrac{5.25}{0.125}$
$WN = \mathbf{42}$

4. $WF(4) = \dfrac{1}{4}$
$WF = \dfrac{1}{4}\left(\dfrac{1}{4}\right)$
$WF = \dfrac{1}{16}$

5. $\dfrac{3}{5}\left(6\dfrac{2}{3}\right) = WN$
$\dfrac{\cancel{3}}{\cancel{5}}\left(\dfrac{\overset{4}{\cancel{20}}}{\cancel{3}}\right) = WN$
$\mathbf{4} = WN$

6. $3\dfrac{1}{2} + 2\dfrac{1}{4}x = \dfrac{5}{4}$
$\dfrac{7}{2} + \dfrac{9}{4}x = \dfrac{5}{4}$
$\dfrac{9}{4}x = -\dfrac{9}{4}$
$x = \mathbf{-1}$

7. $3(x - 2) + (2x + 5) = x + 7$
$3x - 6 + 2x + 5 = x + 7$
$4x = 8$
$x = \mathbf{2}$

8. $-4.2 + 0.02x - 0.4 = 0.03x$
$-420 + 2x - 40 = 3x$
$\mathbf{-460} = x$

9. $-p - 4 - (2p - 5) = 4 + 2(p + 3)$
$-p - 4 - 2p + 5 = 4 + 2p + 6$
$-9 = 5p$
$p = -\dfrac{9}{5}$

10. $8 - k + 2(4 - 2k) = k + 2k$
$8 - k + 8 - 4k = 3k$
$16 = 8k$
$k = \mathbf{2}$

11. Convert 500 cubic inches to cubic centimeters:
$500 \text{ in.}^3 \times \dfrac{2.54 \text{ cm}}{1 \text{ in.}} \times \dfrac{2.54 \text{ cm}}{1 \text{ in.}} \times \dfrac{2.54 \text{ cm}}{1 \text{ in.}}$
$= \mathbf{500(2.54)(2.54)(2.54) \text{ cm}^3}$

12. Convert 500 cubic inches to cubic meters:
$500 \text{ in.}^3 \times \dfrac{2.54 \text{ cm}}{1 \text{ in.}} \times \dfrac{2.54 \text{ cm}}{1 \text{ in.}} \times \dfrac{2.54 \text{ cm}}{1 \text{ in.}}$
$\times \dfrac{1 \text{ m}}{100 \text{ cm}} \times \dfrac{1 \text{ m}}{100 \text{ cm}} \times \dfrac{1 \text{ m}}{100 \text{ cm}}$
$= \dfrac{\mathbf{500(2.54)(2.54)(2.54)}}{\mathbf{100(100)(100)}} \mathbf{m^3}$

13. $A = (32 \text{ in.})(12 \text{ in.}) = \mathbf{384 \text{ in.}^2}$

14. $4ab^2c^4 - 2a^2b^3c^2 + 6a^3b^4c$
$= 2ab^2c(2c^3 - abc + 3a^2b^2)$
The GCF is $\mathbf{2ab^2c}$.

15. $5x^2y^5m^2 - 10xy^2m^2 + 15x^2y^4m^2$
$= 5xy^2m^2(xy^3 - 2 + 3xy^2)$
The GCF is $\mathbf{5xy^2m^2}$.

16. $\dfrac{630}{5} = 126, \dfrac{126}{3} = 42, \dfrac{42}{3} = 14, \dfrac{14}{2} = 7$
$\mathbf{630 = 2 \cdot 3 \cdot 3 \cdot 5 \cdot 7}$

17. $\dfrac{600}{2} = 300, \dfrac{300}{2} = 150, \dfrac{150}{2} = 75, \dfrac{75}{3} = 25,$
$\dfrac{25}{5} = 5$
$\mathbf{600 = 2 \cdot 2 \cdot 2 \cdot 3 \cdot 5 \cdot 5}$

18. $2^{-4} = \dfrac{1}{2^4} = \dfrac{1}{(2)(2)(2)(2)} = \dfrac{1}{16}$

19. $\dfrac{1}{4^{-3}} - \sqrt[5]{-32} = 4^3 - \sqrt[5]{(-2)^5} = 64 - (-2)$
$= \mathbf{66}$

20. $3x^2y^0(x^{-2} - 3y^2x^4) = 3x^2x^{-2} - 3x^2 3y^2 x^4$
$= \mathbf{3 - 9x^6y^2}$

21. $2p^{-5}(p^2x^5 - 3x^0p^5) = 2p^{-5}p^2x^5 - 2p^{-5}3p^5$
$= \mathbf{2x^5p^{-3} - 6}$

22. $4x^{-3}y^2(x^{-3}y^{-2} - 2x^4y^4)$
$= 4x^{-3}y^2x^{-3}y^{-2} - 4x^{-3}y^2 2x^4y^4 = \mathbf{4x^{-6} - 8xy^6}$

23. $(y^{-5} - 2y^7x^5)x^0y^5 = y^{-5}y^5 - 2y^7x^5y^5$
$= \mathbf{1 - 2y^{12}x^5}$

24. $3xyz^2 - 4z^2xy + 7yx^2z - 5zx^2y$
$= 3xyz^2 - 4xyz^2 + 7x^2yz - 5x^2yz$
$= \mathbf{-xyz^2 + 2x^2yz}$

25. $3x^2xyy^3y^{-1} + 2x^2xyyy - 4x^{-2}yx^5y^2 + 7x^2$
$= 3x^3y^3 + 2x^3y^3 - 4x^3y^3 + 7x^2 = \boldsymbol{x^3y^3 + 7x^2}$

26. $-x^0 - a(x - 2a) = -(-5)^0 - 3((-5) - 2(3))$
$= -1 - 3(-11) = \boldsymbol{32}$

27. $p^3 - a^2 + ap = (-3)^3 - (2)^2 + (2)(-3)$
$= -27 - 4 - 6 = \boldsymbol{-37}$

28. $a^2 - a^3 - a^4 = (-2)^2 - (-2)^3 - (-2)^4$
$= 4 - (-8) - (16) = \boldsymbol{-4}$

29. $-3^3 - 3^2 - (-3)^2 - |-2^2|$
$= -27 - 9 - 9 - |-4| = \boldsymbol{-49}$

30. $\dfrac{-4(3^0 - 6)(-2)}{-4 - (-3)(-2) - 3} = \dfrac{-4(-5)(-2)}{-4 - 6 - 3}$
$= \dfrac{-40}{-13} = \boldsymbol{\dfrac{40}{13}}$

PROBLEM SET 34

1. $5N + 7 = -42$
$5N = -49$
$N = -\boldsymbol{\dfrac{49}{5}}$

2. $(5N + 7)(3) = -N + 11$
$15N + 21 = -N + 11$
$16N = -10$
$N = -\boldsymbol{\dfrac{5}{8}}$

3. $4\dfrac{1}{3}(WN) = 3\dfrac{5}{8}$
$\dfrac{\cancel{3}}{\cancel{13}}\left(\dfrac{\cancel{13}}{\cancel{3}}\right)WN = \dfrac{29}{8}\left(\dfrac{3}{13}\right)$
$WN = \boldsymbol{\dfrac{87}{104}}$

4. $WD(0.42) = 0.00504$
$WD = \dfrac{0.504}{42}$
$WD = \boldsymbol{0.012}$

5. $WN = 3\dfrac{2}{5}\left(3\dfrac{1}{8}\right)$
$WN = \dfrac{17}{\cancel{5}}\left(\dfrac{\cancel{25}^{5}}{8}\right)$
$WN = \boldsymbol{\dfrac{85}{8}}$

6. $3\dfrac{1}{2}n - \dfrac{1}{2} = \dfrac{4}{3}$
$\dfrac{7}{2}n = \dfrac{8}{6} + \dfrac{3}{6}$
$n = \dfrac{11}{6} \cdot \dfrac{2}{7} = \boldsymbol{\dfrac{11}{21}}$

7. $x - 4 - 2x + 5 = 3(2x - 4)$
$-x + 1 = 6x - 12$
$13 = 7x$
$\boldsymbol{\dfrac{13}{7}} = x$

8. $0.2m + 4.34 - m = 2.3$
$20m + 434 - 100m = 230$
$-80m = -204$
$m = \boldsymbol{2.55}$

9. $3(-k - 4) + 6 = k + 7$
$-3k - 12 = k + 1$
$-13 = 4k$
$-\boldsymbol{\dfrac{13}{4}} = k$

10. Average $= \dfrac{473.11 + 742.8 + 947.61}{3}$
$= \dfrac{2163.52}{3} = \boldsymbol{721.17}$

11. $20 \, \cancel{mi}^2 \cdot \dfrac{5280 \, \cancel{ft}}{1 \, \cancel{mi}} \cdot \dfrac{5280 \, \cancel{ft}}{1 \, \cancel{mi}} \cdot \dfrac{12 \, \cancel{in.}}{1 \, \cancel{ft}}$
$\cdot \dfrac{12 \, \cancel{in.}}{1 \, \cancel{ft}} \cdot \dfrac{2.54 \, cm}{1 \, \cancel{in.}} \cdot \dfrac{2.54 \, cm}{1 \, \cancel{in.}}$
$= \boldsymbol{20(5280)(5280)(12)(12)(2.54)(2.54) \, cm^2}$

12. $P = 0.1 \, m + 0.5 \, m + 0.1 \, m + 0.5 \, m + 0.15 \, m$
$+ 0.15 \, m = \boldsymbol{1.5 \, m}$

13. $A_{Shaded} = A_{Parallelogram} - A_{Triangle}$
$= 90(20) \, m^2 - \dfrac{1}{2}(10)(10) \, m^2$
$= \boldsymbol{1750 \, m^2}$

14. $3x^4y^2p - 6x^2y^5p^4 = \boldsymbol{3x^2y^2p(x^2 - 2y^3p^3)}$

15. $6a^3x^2m^5 + 2a^4x^5m^5 + 4a^2x^2m$
$= \boldsymbol{2a^2x^2m(3am^4 + a^2x^3m^4 + 2)}$

16. $\dfrac{250}{5} = 50; \dfrac{50}{5} = 10; \dfrac{10}{5} = 2$
$\boldsymbol{250 = 2 \cdot 5 \cdot 5 \cdot 5}$

17. $\dfrac{360}{5} = 72; \dfrac{72}{3} = 24; \dfrac{24}{3} = 8; \dfrac{8}{2} = 4; \dfrac{4}{2} = 2$
$\boldsymbol{360 = 2 \cdot 2 \cdot 2 \cdot 3 \cdot 3 \cdot 5}$

18. $3^{-4} = \dfrac{1}{3^4} = \dfrac{1}{(3)(3)(3)(3)} = \boldsymbol{\dfrac{1}{81}}$

19. $\dfrac{1}{4^{-3}} = 4^3 = (4)(4)(4) = \mathbf{64}$

20. $y^0x^{-2}(x^2 - 4x^4y^6) = x^{-2}x^2 - x^{-2}4x^4y^6$
$= \mathbf{1 - 4x^2y^6}$

21. $(p^5y^5 - y^{-5})p^0y^5 = p^5y^5y^5 - y^{-5}y^5 = \mathbf{p^5y^{10} - 1}$

22. $p^0x^2y(x^3y^{-1} - 3x^5y^{-2}) = x^2yx^3y^{-1} - x^2y3x^5y^{-2}$
$= \mathbf{x^5 - 3x^7y^{-1}}$

23. $x^2(2x^{-2} - 4x^0p^5y^5) = x^22x^{-2} - x^24p^5y^5$
$= \mathbf{2 - 4x^2p^5y^5}$

24. $4x^2y^{-2}p^4 - 3y^{-2}x^2p^4 + 7yyx^2p^4$
$= \mathbf{x^2y^{-2}p^4 + 7x^2y^2p^4}$

25. $3xxy^2x^{-2} - 2x^0yy + 5y^2 - 6x^2 - 4x^3x^{-1}$
$= 3y^2 - 2y^2 + 5y^2 - 6x^2 - 4x^2 = \mathbf{6y^2 - 10x^2}$

26. $-p(x - px) = -(-3)(4 - (-3)4) = 3(4 + 12)$
$= \mathbf{48}$

27. $x^3 - x^2 + 2x = (-2)^3 - (-2)^2 + 2(-2)$
$= -8 - 4 - 4 = \mathbf{-16}$

28. $x(y - xy^0) = (-2)(4 - (-2)4^0) = -2(4 + 2)$
$= \mathbf{-12}$

29. $3^2 - 3^3 - 3^0 + |-3^0| = 9 - 27 - 1 + |-1|$
$= -19 + 1 = \mathbf{-18}$

30. $\dfrac{4(-2 - 3) - 4^0}{-2(-4 + 6) - 3} = \dfrac{4(-5) - 1}{-2(2) - 3} = \dfrac{-21}{-7}$
$= \mathbf{3}$

PROBLEM SET 35

1. $4(N - 6) = 20$
$N - 6 = 5$
$N = \mathbf{11}$

2. $(4N + 6)3 = -N + 5$
$12N + 18 = -N + 5$
$13N = -13$
$N = \mathbf{-1}$

3. $5\dfrac{7}{10}(WN) = 9\dfrac{1}{2}$

$\left(\dfrac{\cancel{10}}{\cancel{57}}\right)\dfrac{\cancel{57}}{\cancel{10}}WN = \dfrac{\cancel{19}}{\cancel{2}}\left(\dfrac{\cancel{10}^5}{\cancel{57}_3}\right)$

$WN = \dfrac{\mathbf{5}}{\mathbf{3}}$

4. $WF\left(2\dfrac{1}{4}\right) = 7\dfrac{1}{8}$

$\left(\dfrac{\cancel{4}}{\cancel{9}}\right)WF\left(\dfrac{\cancel{9}}{\cancel{4}}\right) = \dfrac{\overset{19}{\cancel{57}}}{\underset{2}{\cancel{8}}}\left(\dfrac{\cancel{4}}{\cancel{9}}\right)_3$

$WF = \dfrac{\mathbf{19}}{\mathbf{6}}$

5. $WN = 1.05(0.043)$
$WN = \mathbf{0.04515}$

6. $-5\dfrac{1}{2} + 2\dfrac{2}{5}p = 6\dfrac{1}{4}$

$\dfrac{12}{5}p = \dfrac{25}{4} + \dfrac{11}{2}$

$\dfrac{12}{5}p = \dfrac{25}{4} + \dfrac{22}{4}$

$p = \dfrac{47}{4} \cdot \dfrac{5}{12} = \dfrac{\mathbf{235}}{\mathbf{48}}$

7. $-n + 0.4n + 1.8 = -3$
$-10n + 4n + 18 = -30$
$-6n = -48$
$n = \mathbf{8}$

8. $x - (3x - 2) + 5 = 2x + 4$
$-2x + 7 = 2x + 4$
$3 = 4x$
$\dfrac{\mathbf{3}}{\mathbf{4}} = x$

9. $5(x - 2) - (-x + 3) = 7$
$6x - 13 = 7$
$6x = 20$
$x = \dfrac{\mathbf{10}}{\mathbf{3}}$

10. $4a^2xy^4p - 6a^2x^4 = \mathbf{2a^2x(2y^4p - 3x^3)}$

11. $3a^2x^4y^6 + 9ax^2y^4 - 6x^4a^2y^5z$
$= \mathbf{3ax^2y^4(ax^2y^2 + 3 - 2ax^2yz)}$

12. $3000\,\cancel{m^3} \cdot \dfrac{100\,\cancel{cm}}{1\,\cancel{m}} \cdot \dfrac{100\,\cancel{cm}}{1\,\cancel{m}} \cdot \dfrac{100\,\cancel{cm}}{1\,\cancel{m}}$

$\cdot \dfrac{1\text{ in.}}{2.54\,\cancel{cm}} \cdot \dfrac{1\text{ in.}}{2.54\,\cancel{cm}} \cdot \dfrac{1\text{ in.}}{2.54\,\cancel{cm}}$

$= \dfrac{3000(100)(100)(100)}{(2.54)(2.54)(2.54)}\text{ in.}^3$

13. $A = A_{\text{Rectangle}} + A_{\text{Triangle}}$

$= 15(0.4)(100)\text{ cm}^2 + \dfrac{1}{2}(0.4)(100)(7)\text{ cm}^2$

$= \mathbf{740\text{ cm}^2}$

14. $V = A_{Base} \times height$

$$= \left[(40)(3) + (10)(2) + \frac{(17)(28)}{2}\right](2)$$

$$= [378](2)$$

$$= \textbf{756 ft}^3$$

$S.A. = 2A_{Base} + (P \times height)$

$$= [2(378) + (127.8)(2)] = \textbf{1011.6 ft}^2$$

15. $\dfrac{2x + 6}{2} = \dfrac{2(x + 3)}{2} = \textbf{\textit{x} + 3}$

16. $\dfrac{k^2x - k^3x}{k^2xy} = \dfrac{k^2x(1 - k)}{k^2xy} = \dfrac{\textbf{1} - \textbf{\textit{k}}}{\textbf{\textit{y}}}$

17. Avg. $= \dfrac{648.32 + 475.61 + 983.56 + 811.4}{4}$

$$= \dfrac{2918.89}{4} = \textbf{729.72}$$

18. $\dfrac{270}{5} = 54; \dfrac{54}{3} = 18; \dfrac{18}{3} = 6; \dfrac{6}{3} = 2$

$\textbf{270} = \textbf{2} \cdot \textbf{3} \cdot \textbf{3} \cdot \textbf{3} \cdot \textbf{5}$

19. $\dfrac{1}{4^{-4}} - \sqrt[3]{125} = 4^4 - \sqrt[3]{5^3} = 256 - 5 = \textbf{251}$

20. $(x^3y^0 - p^0x^2y^4)x^{-3} = x^3x^{-3} - x^2y^4x^{-3}$

$$= \textbf{1} - \textbf{\textit{x}}^{-1}\textbf{\textit{y}}^4$$

21. $3x^0y^{-3}(4y^3z - 7x^2) = 3y^{-3}4y^3z - 3y^{-3}7x^2$

$$= \textbf{12\textit{z}} - \textbf{21\textit{x}}^2\textbf{\textit{y}}^{-3}$$

22. $3x^4y^2(xy^{-4} - 3x^{-4}y^5) = 3x^4y^2xy^{-4} - 3x^4y^23x^{-4}y^5$

$$= \textbf{3\textit{x}}^5\textbf{\textit{y}}^{-2} - \textbf{9\textit{y}}^7$$

23. $2x^0y^{-5}(4xyy^5 - 3x^5y^4) = 2y^{-5}4xyy^5 - 2y^{-5}3x^5y^4$

$$= \textbf{8\textit{xy}} - \textbf{6\textit{x}}^5\textbf{\textit{y}}^{-1}$$

24. $3x^2ym^5 - 2xym^5 + 4m^5yx^2 - 6m^5yx$

$$= \textbf{7\textit{x}}^2\textbf{\textit{ym}}^5 - \textbf{8\textit{xym}}^5$$

25. $2x^4y^{-3} - 3x^2x^2y^{-7}y^4 + 6x^3xy^{-1}y^{-3} + xxy^{-3}$

$$= 2x^4y^{-3} - 3x^4y^{-3} + 6x^4y^{-4} + x^2y^{-3}$$

$$= \textbf{6\textit{x}}^4\textbf{\textit{y}}^{-4} - \textbf{\textit{x}}^4\textbf{\textit{y}}^{-3} + \textbf{\textit{x}}^2\textbf{\textit{y}}^{-3}$$

26. $a^2 - a^0(a - ab) = (-3)^2 - (-3)^0((-3) - (-3)5)$

$$= 9 - 1(-3 + 15) = \textbf{-3}$$

27. $b - ab(b - a) = 5 - (-3)(5)(5 - (-3))$

$$= 5 + 15(5 + 3) = \textbf{125}$$

28. $-k - kp^0 - (-pk^2)$

$$= -(-3) - (-3)(2)^0 - (-2(-3)^2)$$

$$= 3 + 3 - (-18) = \textbf{24}$$

29. $2^2 - 2^3 - (-3)^2 + \sqrt[4]{81} = 4 - 8 - 9 + 3$

$$= \textbf{-10}$$

30. $\dfrac{-3^2 + 4^2 + 3^3}{2(-5 + 2) - 3^0} = \dfrac{-9 + 16 + 27}{-6 - 1}$

$$= -\dfrac{\textbf{34}}{\textbf{7}}$$

Problem Set 36

1. $(2N - 3)4 = 28$

$8N - 12 = 28$

$8N = 40$

$N = \textbf{5}$

2. $-3N - 5 = -2N - 25$

$\textbf{20} = N$

3. $2\dfrac{5}{8}(WN) = 14$

$$\left(\dfrac{8}{21}\right)\dfrac{21}{8}WN = \dfrac{\overset{2}{\cancel{14}}}{1}\left(\dfrac{8}{\underset{3}{\cancel{21}}}\right)$$

$$WN = \dfrac{\textbf{16}}{\textbf{3}}$$

4. $WF\left(3\dfrac{3}{4}\right) = 22\dfrac{1}{2}$

$$WF\left(\dfrac{\cancel{15}}{\cancel{4}}\right)\left(\dfrac{\cancel{4}}{\cancel{15}}\right) = \dfrac{\overset{3}{\cancel{45}}}{\underset{2}{\cancel{2}}}\left(\dfrac{\cancel{4}}{\cancel{15}}\right)$$

$$WF = \textbf{6}$$

5. $2.625(WN) = 8.00625$

$$WN = \dfrac{8006.25}{2625}$$

$$WN = \textbf{3.05}$$

6. $3\dfrac{1}{4}n - \dfrac{2}{5} = 3$

$$\dfrac{13}{4}n = 3 + \dfrac{2}{5}$$

$$\dfrac{13}{4}n = \dfrac{15}{5} + \dfrac{2}{5}$$

$$n = \dfrac{17}{5} \times \dfrac{4}{13}$$

$$n = \dfrac{\textbf{68}}{\textbf{65}}$$

7. $x - 3(x - 2) = 7x - (2x + 5)$

$-2x + 6 = 5x - 5$

$11 = 7x$

$$\dfrac{\textbf{11}}{\textbf{7}} = x$$

8. $-3m - 3 + 5m - 2 = -(2m + 3)$
$\quad\quad\quad 2m - 5 = -2m - 3$
$\quad\quad\quad\quad\quad 4m = 2$
$\quad\quad\quad\quad\quad\quad m = \dfrac{1}{2}$

9. $0.2k - 4.21 - 0.8k = 2(-k + 0.1)$
$\quad\quad -0.6k - 4.21 = -2k + 0.2$
$\quad\quad\quad\quad\quad 1.4k = 4.41$
$\quad\quad\quad\quad\quad\quad\quad k = \mathbf{3.15}$

10. $12a^2x^5y^7 - 3ax^2y^2 = \mathbf{3ax^2y^2(4ax^3y^5 - 1)}$

11. $15a^5x^4y^6 + 3a^4x^3y^7 - 9a^2x^6y$
$\quad = \mathbf{3a^2x^3y(5a^3xy^5 + a^2y^6 - 3x^3)}$

12. $\dfrac{4x^2 - 4x}{4x} = \dfrac{4x(x - 1)}{4x} = \mathbf{x - 1}$

13. $\dfrac{2 - 6x}{2} = \dfrac{2(1 - 3x)}{2} = \mathbf{1 - 3x}$

14. $\dfrac{x^2ym + xym}{xym} = \dfrac{xym(x + 1)}{xym} = \mathbf{x + 1}$

15. $\dfrac{x^2y - xy}{xym} = \dfrac{xy(x - 1)}{xym} = \mathbf{\dfrac{x - 1}{m}}$

16. $\dfrac{750}{5} = 150; \ \dfrac{150}{5} = 30; \ \dfrac{30}{5} = 6; \ \dfrac{6}{3} = 2$
$\mathbf{750 = 2 \cdot 3 \cdot 5 \cdot 5 \cdot 5}$

17. $-3^{-2} = -\dfrac{1}{3^2} = -\dfrac{1}{(3)(3)} = \mathbf{-\dfrac{1}{9}}$

18. $(-3)^{-2} = \dfrac{1}{(-3)^2} = \dfrac{1}{(-3)(-3)} = \mathbf{\dfrac{1}{9}}$

19. $\dfrac{1}{-3^{-2}} - \sqrt[3]{8} = -3^2 - \sqrt[3]{2^3} = -9 - 2 = \mathbf{-11}$

20. $\dfrac{1}{(-3)^2} = \mathbf{\dfrac{1}{9}}$

21. $500 \text{ in.}^3 \times \dfrac{2.54 \text{ cm}}{1 \text{ in.}} \times \dfrac{2.54 \text{ cm}}{1 \text{ in.}} \times \dfrac{2.54 \text{ cm}}{1 \text{ in.}}$
$\quad \times \dfrac{1 \text{ m}}{100 \text{ cm}} \times \dfrac{1 \text{ m}}{100 \text{ cm}} \times \dfrac{1 \text{ m}}{100 \text{ cm}}$
$\quad = \mathbf{\dfrac{500(2.54)(2.54)(2.54)}{(100)(100)(100)} \ m^3}$

22. S.A. $= 2A_{\text{Top}} + 2A_{\text{Side}} + 2A_{\text{Front}}$
$\quad = \left[2(48)\left(\dfrac{1}{12}\right)(2) + 2(3)(2) \right] \text{ft}^2$
$\quad\quad + \left[2(3)(48)\left(\dfrac{1}{12}\right) \right] \text{ft}^2$
$\quad = \mathbf{52 \ ft^2}$

23. $\dfrac{ax}{c^2}\left(\dfrac{b^4}{xk} - 2b^2 \right) = \dfrac{axb^4}{c^2xk} - \dfrac{ax2b^2}{c^2}$
$\quad = \mathbf{\dfrac{ab^4}{c^2k} - \dfrac{2axb^2}{c^2}}$

24. $(p^0x^2 - 4p^{-6}xy^5)x^{-2} = x^2x^{-2} - 4p^{-6}xy^5x^{-2}$
$\quad = \mathbf{1 - 4p^{-6}x^{-1}y^5}$

25. $-xym^2 + 6ym^2x - 3x^2ym^2 - 9yx^2m^2$
$\quad = \mathbf{5xym^2 - 12x^2ym^2}$

26. $3x^4x^{-3}y^0 + xy^0y^{-2}y^2 - 7x^4x^{-3}p^0 = 3x + x - 7x$
$\quad = \mathbf{-3x}$

27. $m(a^0 - ma)(-m) + |m^2 - 2|$
$\quad = 2((-4)^0 - 2(-4))(-2) + |2^2 - 2|$
$\quad = 2(1 + 8)(-2) + |2| = \mathbf{-34}$

28. $k^3 - k(a)^2 = (-3)^3 - (-3)(2)^2 = -27 + 12$
$\quad = \mathbf{-15}$

29. $-mx(a - x) - a = -(-3)(2)(2 - 2) - 2 = \mathbf{-2}$

30. $\dfrac{-3^2 + 4^2 - 5(4 - 2)}{3^0(5 - 2)} = \dfrac{-9 + 16 - 10}{3}$
$\quad = \mathbf{-1}$

PROBLEM SET 37

1. $3N - 5 = 40$
$\quad\quad 3N = 45$
$\quad\quad\quad N = \mathbf{15}$

2. $7N + 7 = 9N - 1$
$\quad\quad\quad 8 = 2N$
$\quad\quad\quad 4 = \mathbf{N}$

3. $\left(\dfrac{\cancel{4}}{\cancel{X}} \right)\dfrac{\cancel{X}}{\cancel{4}}(WN) = \dfrac{3}{\cancel{8}_2}\left(\dfrac{\cancel{4}}{1} \right)$
$\quad\quad\quad\quad WN = \mathbf{\dfrac{3}{2}}$

4. $WD(41.25) = 2.475$
$\quad\quad\quad WD = \mathbf{0.06}$

5. $WN = \dfrac{1}{3}\left(7\dfrac{1}{6} \right)$
$\quad WN = \dfrac{1}{3}\left(\dfrac{43}{6} \right)$
$\quad WN = \mathbf{\dfrac{43}{18}}$

6. $-\dfrac{1}{5} + 2\dfrac{1}{2}p = 2$

$\qquad \dfrac{5}{2}p = 2 + \dfrac{1}{5}$

$\qquad \dfrac{5}{2}p = \dfrac{10}{5} + \dfrac{1}{5}$

$\qquad p = \dfrac{11}{5} \times \dfrac{2}{5}$

$\qquad p = \dfrac{22}{25}$

7. $3(x - 2) - (2x + 5) = -2x + 10$

$\qquad x - 11 = -2x + 10$

$\qquad 3x = 21$

$\qquad x = 7$

8. $4x - 3(x + 2) = 2x - 5$

$\qquad x - 6 = 2x - 5$

$\qquad -1 = x$

9. $0.004m - 0.001m + 0.002 = -0.004$

$\qquad 4m - m + 2 = -4$

$\qquad 3m = -6$

$\qquad m = -2$

10. $4a^2x^3y^5 - 8a^4x^2y^4 = 4a^2x^2y^4(xy - 2a^2)$

11. $6a^2xm^5 + 2ax^4m^6 - 18a^5x^3m^5$
$= 2axm^5(3a + x^3m - 9a^4x^2)$

12. $\dfrac{3x - 9}{3} = \dfrac{3(x - 3)}{3} = x - 3$

13. $\dfrac{4px^2 - 8px}{px^2} = \dfrac{px(4x - 8)}{px^2} = \dfrac{4x - 8}{x}$

14. $100 \ \cancel{\text{km}} \times \dfrac{1000 \ \cancel{\text{m}}}{1 \ \cancel{\text{km}}} \times \dfrac{100 \ \cancel{\text{cm}}}{1 \ \cancel{\text{m}}} \times \dfrac{1 \ \cancel{\text{in.}}}{2.54 \ \cancel{\text{cm}}}$

$\times \dfrac{1 \ \cancel{\text{ft}}}{12 \ \cancel{\text{in.}}} \times \dfrac{1 \ \text{mi}}{5280 \ \cancel{\text{ft}}} = \dfrac{100(1000)(100)}{(2.54)(12)(5280)} \ \text{mi}$

15. $V = A_{\text{Base}} \times \text{height}$

$= \left[27(20) + \dfrac{(10)^2\pi}{2} + \dfrac{21(20)}{2} \right](50) \ \text{cm}^3$

$\approx [907](50) \ \text{cm}^3$

$\approx 45{,}350 \ \text{cm}^3$

S.A. $= 2A_{\text{Base}} + (P \times \text{height})$

$= \left[2(907) + (104 + 10\pi)(50) \right] \ \text{cm}^2$

$\approx 8584 \ \text{cm}^2$

16. $x < 2$

17. $x \geq 2$

18. $-3^{-3} = -\dfrac{1}{3^3} = -\dfrac{1}{27}$

19. $(-3)^{-3} = \dfrac{1}{(-3)^3} = -\dfrac{1}{27}$

20. $\dfrac{1}{-5^{-2}} - \sqrt[3]{125} = -5^2 - \sqrt[3]{5^3} = -25 - 5$

$= -30$

21. $\dfrac{p^2}{x}\left(\dfrac{k^2p}{x^2} - \dfrac{p^2}{x} \right) = \dfrac{p^2k^2p}{xx^2} - \dfrac{p^2p^2}{xx}$

$= \dfrac{p^3k^2}{x^3} - \dfrac{p^4}{x^2}$

22. $\left(\dfrac{a^2}{x} - \dfrac{2x}{a} \right)\dfrac{4x^2}{a} = \dfrac{a^2 4x^2}{xa} - \dfrac{2x4x^2}{aa}$

$= 4ax - \dfrac{8x^3}{a^2}$

23. $\dfrac{ax}{c^2}\left(\dfrac{ax2}{c} - \dfrac{3c^2a}{x^3} \right) = \dfrac{axax2}{c^2c} - \dfrac{ax3c^2a}{c^2x^3}$

$= \dfrac{a^2x^3}{c^3} - \dfrac{3a^2}{x^2}$

24. $x^{-2}(x^2p^0 - 5x^4p^7) = x^{-2}x^2 - x^{-2}5x^4p^7$

$= 1 - 5x^2p^7$

25. $x^3y^3p + px^3y^3 - 4x^2xyy^2p^2p^{-1}$

$= x^3y^3p + x^3y^3p - 4x^3y^3p = -2x^3y^3p$

26. $5a^2x + 7xa^2 + aax^2x^{-1} - 2ax^3x^{-1}$

$= 5a^2x + 7a^2x + a^2x - 2ax^2 = 13a^2x - 2ax^2$

27. $m^2 - (m - p) = 2^2 - (2 - (-2))$

$= 4 - (2 + 2) = 0$

28. $a^2 - y^3(y - a) = (-2)^2 - (-3)^3((-3) - (-2))$

$= 4 + 27(-3 + 2) = -23$

29. $k(x - ka) = 3((-3) - 3(-2)) = 3(-3 + 6) = 9$

30. $\dfrac{-3^2 - (-3)^3 - 3}{-3(-3)(+3)} = \dfrac{-9 + 27 - 3}{27} = \dfrac{15}{27}$

$= \dfrac{5}{9}$

PROBLEM SET 38

1. $17 \, \cancel{mi} \times \dfrac{5280 \, \cancel{ft}}{1 \, \cancel{mi}} \times \dfrac{12 \, \cancel{in.}}{1 \, \cancel{ft}} \times \dfrac{2.54 \, cm}{1 \, \cancel{in.}}$

$= \mathbf{17(5280)(12)(2.54) \ cm}$

2. S.A. $= 2A_{Base} + (C \times length)$

$= 2(\pi)(6)^2 \ cm^2 + (2\pi)(6)(12) \ cm^2$

$\approx \mathbf{678.24 \ cm^2}$

3. $\dfrac{R}{G} = \dfrac{13}{5}$

$\dfrac{R}{600} = \dfrac{13}{5}$

$\dfrac{5R}{5} = \dfrac{13 \cdot 600}{5}$

$R = \mathbf{1560}$

4. $(2N - 7) + 8 = -N + 16$

$2N + 1 = -N + 16$

$3N = 15$

$N = \mathbf{5}$

5. $2.125(WN) = 0.1275$

$WN = \dfrac{0.1275}{2.125}$

$WN = \mathbf{0.06}$

6. $WF\left(\dfrac{7}{8}\right) = 2\dfrac{5}{11}$

$WF\left(\dfrac{\cancel{7}}{\cancel{8}}\right)\left(\dfrac{\cancel{8}}{\cancel{7}}\right) = \dfrac{27}{11}\left(\dfrac{8}{7}\right)$

$WF = \dfrac{27}{11}\left(\dfrac{8}{7}\right)$

$WF = \mathbf{\dfrac{216}{77}}$

7. $0.06 + 0.06x = -0.042$

$60 + 60x = -42$

$60x = -102$

$x = \mathbf{-1.7}$

8. $3\dfrac{1}{2}k + \dfrac{3}{4} = -\dfrac{7}{8}$

$\dfrac{7}{2}k = -\dfrac{7}{8} - \dfrac{6}{8}$

$k = -\dfrac{13}{8} \times \dfrac{2}{7}$

$k = \mathbf{-\dfrac{13}{28}}$

9. $2(5 - x) - (-2)(x - 3) = -(3x - 4)$

$10 - 2x + 2x - 6 = -3x + 4$

$3x = 0$

$x = \mathbf{0}$

10. $3(-2x - 2 - 3) - (-x + 2) = -2(x + 1)$

$-6x - 15 + x - 2 = -2x - 2$

$-15 = 3x$

$\mathbf{-5} = x$

11. $-x - 2(-x - 3) = -4 - x$

$-x + 2x + 6 = -4 - x$

$2x = -10$

$x = \mathbf{-5}$

12. $3x^2y^3z^5 - 9xy^6z^6 = \mathbf{3xy^3z^5(x - 3y^3z)}$

13. $4x^2y - 12xy^2 + 24x^3y^3 = \mathbf{4xy(x - 3y + 6x^2y^2)}$

14. $\dfrac{7x + 7}{7} = \dfrac{7(x + 1)}{7} = \mathbf{x + 1}$

15. $\dfrac{k^4p - 2k^5p^2}{k^4p} = \dfrac{k^4p(1 - 2kp)}{k^4p} = \mathbf{1 - 2kp}$

16. $x \geq -2$

17. $x > 4$

18. $(-2)^{-2} = \dfrac{1}{(-2)^2} = \mathbf{\dfrac{1}{4}}$

19. $-2^{-2} = -\dfrac{1}{2^2} = \mathbf{-\dfrac{1}{4}}$

20. $(-2)^{-3} = \dfrac{1}{(-2)^3} = \mathbf{-\dfrac{1}{8}}$

21. $\dfrac{p^2}{x}\left(\dfrac{4x}{p^2} - \dfrac{p^4}{p^2x}\right) = \dfrac{p^2 4x}{xp^2} - \dfrac{p^2 p^4}{xp^2 x}$

$= \mathbf{4 - \dfrac{p^4}{x^2}}$

22. $\dfrac{4a^2}{x}\left(\dfrac{ax}{x} - \dfrac{3x}{a}\right) = \dfrac{4a^2 ax}{xx} - \dfrac{4a^2 3x}{xa}$

$= \mathbf{\dfrac{4a^3}{x} - 12a}$

23. $\dfrac{mp}{k}\left(\dfrac{mp}{k} - \dfrac{k}{mp}\right) = \dfrac{mpmp}{kk} - \dfrac{mpk}{kmp}$

$= \mathbf{\dfrac{m^2 p^2}{k^2} - 1}$

24. $x^{-3}(y^{-2}k^0 - 3xk^5) = x^{-3}y^{-2} - x^{-3}3xk^5$

$= \mathbf{x^{-3}y^{-2} - 3x^{-2}k^5}$

25. $3p^3x^{-4}xp^4 - 2pp^2p^3x^{-1}x^{-2} - 4x^2x^{-2}x^{-3}pp^6$

$= 3x^{-3}p^7 - 2x^{-3}p^6 - 4x^{-3}p^7 = \mathbf{-2x^{-3}p^6 - x^{-3}p^7}$

26. $xy - 3yx + 7x^3y^2x^{-2}y^{-1} - 2x^2yy^5y^{-4}y^{-1}x^{-1}$
$= xy - 3xy + 7xy - 2xy = \mathbf{3xy}$

27. $(m - x^2)x - (-m)$
$= ((-3) - (-2)^2)(-2) - (-(-3))$
$= (-3 - 4)(-2) - 3 = \mathbf{11}$

28. $(a^3 - y^2)(a - y) = ((-3)^3 - (4)^2)((-3) - 4)$
$= (-27 - 16)(-3 - 4) = \mathbf{301}$

29. $x(x - y)(3 - 2xy)$
$= (-2)((-2) - 5)(3 - 2(-2)(5))$
$= -2(-7)(3 + 20) = \mathbf{322}$

30. $-2^2 + (-2)^3 - 2(-2 - 2) - 2$
$= -4 - 8 - 2(-4) - 2 = \mathbf{-6}$

PROBLEM SET 39

1. $3N + 5 = -55$
$3N = -60$
$N = \mathbf{-20}$

2. $(-2N + 5)2 = N + 22$
$-4N + 10 = N + 22$
$-5N = 12$
$N = \mathbf{-\dfrac{12}{5}}$

3. $28{,}000 \text{ in.}^2 \times \dfrac{1\,\cancel{\text{ft}}}{12\,\cancel{\text{in.}}} \times \dfrac{1\,\cancel{\text{ft}}}{12\,\cancel{\text{in.}}} \times \dfrac{1 \text{ mi}}{5280\,\cancel{\text{ft}}}$
$\times \dfrac{1 \text{ mi}}{5280\,\cancel{\text{ft}}} = \mathbf{\dfrac{28{,}000}{(12)(12)(5280)(5280)}}\ \mathbf{mi}^2$

4. $\text{Average} = \dfrac{(740 + 832 + 804 + 760) \text{ kg}}{4}$
$= \dfrac{3136 \text{ kg}}{4} = \mathbf{784 \ kg}$

5. $WN = \dfrac{2}{5}\left(23\dfrac{1}{3}\right)$
$WN = \dfrac{2}{\cancel{5}}\left(\dfrac{\cancel{70}^{14}}{3}\right)$
$WN = \mathbf{\dfrac{28}{3}}$

6. $2\dfrac{1}{3}k - 4 = 7$
$\dfrac{7}{3}k = 11$
$k = \mathbf{\dfrac{33}{7}}$

7. $p - 3(p - 4) = 2 + (2p + 5)$
$-2p + 12 = 2p + 7$
$5 = 4p$
$\mathbf{\dfrac{5}{4}} = \mathbf{p}$

8. $5x - 4(2x - 2) = 5 - x$
$-3x + 8 = 5 - x$
$3 = 2x$
$\mathbf{\dfrac{3}{2}} = \mathbf{x}$

9. $0.02x - 4 - 0.01x - 2 = -6.3$
$2x - 400 - x - 200 = -630$
$x - 600 = -630$
$x = \mathbf{-30}$

10. $12a^2x + 4ax^4 = \mathbf{4ax(3a + x^3)}$

11. $2x^2a^3y - xay + 4ay^2 = \mathbf{ay(2x^2a^2 - x + 4y)}$

12. $\dfrac{3x - 9}{3} = \dfrac{3(x - 3)}{3} = \mathbf{x - 3}$

13. $\dfrac{5xy + 20xy^2}{5xy} = \dfrac{5xy(1 + 4y)}{5xy} = \mathbf{1 + 4y}$

14. $V = A_{\text{Base}} \times \text{height}$
$= \left[\pi(10)^2 + \dfrac{1}{2}(20)(20)\right](5)(12) \text{ in.}^3$
$\approx [514](60) \text{ in.}^3$
$\approx \mathbf{30{,}840}$ **one-inch sugar cubes**

$\text{S.A.} = 2A_{\text{Base}} + (P \times \text{height})$
$= 2(514) \text{ in.}^2 + [(20\pi) + 28.3](5)(12) \text{ in.}^2$
$\approx \mathbf{6{,}494 \ in.}^2$

15. $P = (300 \text{ cm})(2) + 2(1)(100) \text{ cm} = \mathbf{800 \ cm}$

16. $x \ngtr 3$

17. $y \geq 3$

18. $-2^{-2} = -\dfrac{1}{2^2} = -\dfrac{1}{4}$

19. $(-2)^{-2} = \dfrac{1}{(-2)^2} = \dfrac{1}{4}$

20. $-(-2)^{-2} = -\dfrac{1}{(-2)^2} = -\dfrac{1}{4}$

21. $\left(\dfrac{p}{a} - \dfrac{p}{xa}\right)\dfrac{p^2}{a} = \dfrac{pp^2}{aa} - \dfrac{pp^2}{xaa} = \dfrac{p^3}{a^2} - \dfrac{p^3}{xa^2}$

22. $\dfrac{4x^2y}{m}\left(\dfrac{x^3}{m^2} - \dfrac{y}{m}\right) = \dfrac{4x^2yx^3}{mm^2} - \dfrac{4x^2yy}{mm}$
$= \dfrac{4x^5y}{m^3} - \dfrac{4x^2y^2}{m^2}$

        Algebra 1 Solutions Manual

23. $\dfrac{mp}{x}\left(\dfrac{a}{x} - \dfrac{1}{x^2}\right) = \dfrac{mpa}{xx} - \dfrac{mp}{xx^2}$

$= \dfrac{\boldsymbol{mpa}}{\boldsymbol{x^2}} - \dfrac{\boldsymbol{mp}}{\boldsymbol{x^3}}$

24. $p^{-2}x^0(p^2 - 3p^5x^5) = p^{-2}p^2 - p^{-2}3p^5x^5$

$= \boldsymbol{1 - 3p^3x^5}$

25. $5yxp^2 - p^2yx + 2ppyx - 3p^2y^2y^{-1}x$

$= 5p^2xy - p^2xy + 2p^2xy - 3p^2xy = \boldsymbol{3p^2xy}$

26. $3ay - 5ya - 6y^{-2}y^3a - 4a^3ay$

$= 3ay - 5ay - 6ay - 4a^4y = \boldsymbol{-8ay - 4a^4y}$

27. $kp^0 - (k - p) = (-4)(1)^0 - ((-4) - 1)$

$= -4 - (-5) = \boldsymbol{1}$

28. $m^2 - m^{-3}(p) = (-2)^2 - (-2)^{-3}(3) = 4 + \dfrac{3}{8}$

$= \dfrac{\boldsymbol{35}}{\boldsymbol{8}}$

29. $a^2b - (a - b) = (-2)^2(-1) - ((-2) - (-1))$

$= -4 - (-1) = \boldsymbol{-3}$

30. $\dfrac{-4(3 - 5) - 2^0}{(-2)^3 - 2(-2)} = \dfrac{8 - 1}{-8 + 4} = \boldsymbol{-\dfrac{7}{4}}$

PROBLEM SET 40

1. $7N - 4 = -25$

$7N = -21$

$N = \boldsymbol{-3}$

2. $-3N + 16 = N + 26$

$-4N = 10$

$N = \boldsymbol{-\dfrac{5}{2}}$

3. $G = 7, T = 11$; Total $= 18$

$\dfrac{7}{18} = \dfrac{G}{2520}$

$G = \dfrac{7 \cdot 2520}{18}$

$G = \boldsymbol{980}$

4. $WF\left(2\dfrac{1}{8}\right) = 6$

$WF\left(\dfrac{\cancel{17}}{\cancel{8}}\right)\left(\dfrac{\cancel{8}}{\cancel{17}}\right) = 6\left(\dfrac{8}{17}\right)$

$WF = \dfrac{\boldsymbol{48}}{\boldsymbol{17}}$

5. $1.205(3.2) = WN$

$\boldsymbol{3.856 = WN}$

6. $\dfrac{2}{3}k + 5 = 12$

$\dfrac{2}{3}k = 7$

$k = \dfrac{\boldsymbol{21}}{\boldsymbol{2}}$

7. $x - 5x + 4(x - 2) = 3x - 8$

$-8 = 3x - 8$

$\boldsymbol{0} = x$

8. $2p - 5(p - 4) = 2p + 12$

$-3p + 20 = 2p + 12$

$8 = 5p$

$\dfrac{\boldsymbol{8}}{\boldsymbol{5}} = p$

9. $0.4x - 0.02x + 1.396 = 0.598$

$400x - 20x + 1396 = 598$

$380x = -798$

$x = \boldsymbol{-2.1}$

10. $3x^2y^5p^6 - 9x^2y^4p^3 + 12x^2yp^4$

$= \boldsymbol{3x^2yp^3(y^4p^3 - 3y^3 + 4p)}$

11. $2x^2y^2 - 6y^2x^4 - 12xy^5 = \boldsymbol{2xy^2(x - 3x^3 - 6y^3)}$

12. $\dfrac{5x^2 - 25x}{5x} = \dfrac{5x(x - 5)}{5x} = \boldsymbol{x - 5}$

13. $\dfrac{4xy + 16x^2y^2}{4xy} = \dfrac{4xy(1 + 4xy)}{4xy} = \boldsymbol{1 + 4xy}$

14. $x \ngtr -2$

$x < -2$

15. $\dfrac{360}{5} = 72; \dfrac{72}{3} = 24; \dfrac{24}{3} = 8; \dfrac{8}{2} = 4; \dfrac{4}{2} = 2$

$\boldsymbol{360 = 2 \cdot 2 \cdot 2 \cdot 3 \cdot 3 \cdot 5}$

16. $-2^{-4} = -\dfrac{1}{2^4} = \boldsymbol{-\dfrac{1}{16}}$

17. $\dfrac{1}{-(-3)^{-3}} - \sqrt[3]{-27} = -(-3)^3 - \sqrt[3]{(-3)^3}$

$= 27 - (-3) = \boldsymbol{30}$

18. Convert 200 square miles to square inches:

$200\ \cancel{mi}^2 \times \dfrac{5280\ \cancel{ft}}{1\ \cancel{mi}} \times \dfrac{5280\ \cancel{ft}}{1\ \cancel{mi}} \times \dfrac{12\ \text{in.}}{1\ \cancel{ft}} \times \dfrac{12\ \text{in.}}{1\ \cancel{ft}}$

$= \boldsymbol{200(5280)(5280)(12)(12)\ \text{in.}^2}$

19. $V = A_{Base} \times \text{height}$

$= (A_{Square} - A_{Semicircle} + A_{Triangle}) \times \text{height}$

$= \left[8(8) - \dfrac{\pi(4)^2}{2} + \dfrac{(7)(8)}{2} \right] \text{in.}^2 \times 12 \text{ in.}$

$\approx [66.88](12) \text{ in.}^3$

$\approx$ **802.56 one-inch sugar cubes**

$\text{S.A.} = 2A_{Base} + (P \times \text{height})$

$= 2(66.88) + \left[\dfrac{2\pi(4)}{2} + 33.6 \right](12)$

$\approx$ **687.68 in.²**

20. $\dfrac{m^5 z x^2 y^{-5}}{y^4 z^2 x^{-3}} = m^5 z^{1-2} x^{2-(-3)} y^{-5-4} = \mathbf{m^5 z^{-1} x^5 y^{-9}}$

21. $\dfrac{p^2}{x}\left(\dfrac{a}{bc} - \dfrac{1}{c} \right) = \dfrac{p^2 a}{xbc} - \dfrac{p^2}{xc}$

22. $\left(\dfrac{x}{m^2} - \dfrac{2x}{m} \right)\dfrac{3x^2 y}{m} = \dfrac{x3x^2 y}{m^2 m} - \dfrac{2x3x^2 y}{mm}$

$= \dfrac{3x^3 y}{m^3} - \dfrac{6x^3 y}{m^2}$

23. $p^{-2}k^0(p^2 - 4p^4 k^5) = p^{-2}p^2 - p^{-2}4p^4 k^5$

$= \mathbf{1 - 4p^2 k^5}$

24. $3x^2 y^{-4}(x^4 y^{-2} - 2x^{-2} y^2)$

$= 3x^2 y^{-4} x^4 y^{-2} - 3x^2 y^{-4} 2x^{-2} y^2 = \mathbf{3x^6 y^{-6} - 6y^{-2}}$

25. $\text{Average} = \dfrac{78.6 + 314.2 + 90 + 116.85}{4}$

$= \dfrac{599.65}{4} = \mathbf{149.9125}$

26. $xa - a(x^{-2} - xa)$

$= (3)(-1) - (-1)((3)^{-2} - 3(-1))$

$= -3 + \left(\dfrac{1}{9} + 3 \right) = \dfrac{1}{9}$

27. $m(-a^0 - m) = (-4)(-(1)^0 - (-4))$

$= -4(-1 + 4) = \mathbf{-12}$

28. $p - (m - pm) = (-3) - (4 - (-3)4)$

$= -3 - (4 + 12) = \mathbf{-19}$

29. $\dfrac{-2^0(-5 - 7)(-3) - |-4|}{-2(-(-6))} = \dfrac{-36 - 4}{-12}$

$= \dfrac{10}{3}$

1. $3 + 5N = -27$

$5N = -30$

$N = \mathbf{-6}$

2. $(7N - 5)2 = 2N - 14$

$14N - 10 = 2N - 14$

$12N = -4$

$N = -\dfrac{1}{3}$

3. $A = 9,\ W = 5,\ T = 14$

$\dfrac{9}{14} = \dfrac{A}{1428}$

$A = \dfrac{9 \cdot 1428}{14}$

$A = \mathbf{918}$

4. $WF(72) = 16$

$WF = \dfrac{2}{9}$

5. $\dfrac{130}{5} = 26;\ \dfrac{26}{2} = 13$

$\mathbf{130 = 2 \cdot 5 \cdot 13}$

6. $\dfrac{3}{5}p + 7 = 22$

$\dfrac{3}{5}p = 15$

$p = \mathbf{25}$

7. $3x - (x - 2) + 5 = 4x + 6$

$2x + 7 = 4x + 6$

$1 = 2x$

$\dfrac{1}{2} = x$

8. $3p - 2(p - 4) = 7p + 6$

$p + 8 = 7p + 6$

$2 = 6p$

$\dfrac{1}{3} = p$

9. $0.004k - 0.002 + 0.002k = 4$

$4k - 2 + 2k = 4000$

$6k = 4002$

$k = \mathbf{667}$

10. $4x^2 m^5 y - 2x^4 m^3 y^3 = \mathbf{2x^2 m^3 y(2m^2 - x^2 y^2)}$

11. $4m^2 x^5 - 2m^2 x^2 + 6m^5 x^2$

$= \mathbf{2m^2 x^2(2x^3 - 1 + 3m^3)}$

12. $\dfrac{4 - 4x}{4} = \dfrac{4(1 - x)}{4} = \mathbf{1 - x}$

13. $\dfrac{9x - 3x^2}{3x} = \dfrac{3x(3 - x)}{3x} = \mathbf{3 - x}$

14. $x \le -5$

$$-7 \quad -6 \quad -5 \quad -4 \quad -3$$

15. $x > -2; \ x \nleq -2$

16. $-3^{-2} = -\dfrac{1}{3^2} = -\dfrac{1}{9}$

17. $\dfrac{1}{(-3)^2} = \dfrac{1}{9}$

18. $\dfrac{x^3 y^2}{xy^4} = \dfrac{x^{3-1}}{y^{4-2}} = \dfrac{x^2}{y^2}$

19. $\dfrac{x^3 y^{-3} z}{z^5 x^2 y} = \dfrac{x^{3-2}}{z^{5-1} y^{1-(-3)}} = \dfrac{x}{z^4 y^4}$

20. $\dfrac{x^{-4} y^{-3} p^2}{x^{-5} y p^4} = \dfrac{x^{-4-(-5)}}{y^{1-(-3)} p^{4-2}} = \dfrac{x}{y^4 p^2}$

21. $390 \, \text{mi} \times \dfrac{5280 \, \text{ft}}{1 \, \text{mi}} \times \dfrac{12 \, \text{in.}}{1 \, \text{ft}} \times \dfrac{2.54 \, \text{cm}}{1 \, \text{in.}}$

$\times \dfrac{1 \, \text{m}}{100 \, \text{cm}} \times \dfrac{1 \, \text{km}}{1000 \, \text{m}} = \dfrac{390(5280)(12)(2.54)}{(100)(1000)} \, \text{km}$

22. $A = A_{\text{Rectangle}} + A_{\text{Triangle}}$

$= 30(26) \, \text{cm}^2 + \dfrac{1}{2}(26)(18) \, \text{cm}^2 = \mathbf{1014 \, cm^2}$

23. $\left(\dfrac{x^{-4}}{a^3} - \dfrac{a^3}{x} \right) \dfrac{a^{-3}}{x} = \dfrac{x^{-4} a^{-3}}{a^3 x} - \dfrac{a^3 a^{-3}}{xx}$

$= \dfrac{1}{a^6 x^5} - \dfrac{1}{x^2}$

24. $\dfrac{m^{-2}}{b} \left(\dfrac{b^2}{m^3} - \dfrac{4am^2}{b^4} \right) = \dfrac{m^{-2} b^2}{bm^3} - \dfrac{m^{-2} 4am^2}{bb^4}$

$= \dfrac{b}{m^5} - \dfrac{4a}{b^5}$

25. $x^2 yp - 4xxyp - 3x^2 py$

$= x^2 yp - 4x^2 yp - 3x^2 yp = \mathbf{-6x^2 py}$

26. $3x^2 ym - 2m^2 x^2 y - 5x^2 my + 4ym^2 x^2$

$= 3x^2 ym - 2x^2 m^2 y - 5x^2 ym + 4x^2 m^2 y$

$= \mathbf{2x^2 m^2 y - 2x^2 my}$

27. $m - 3m^{-3} = (-3) - 3(-3)^{-3} = -3 + \dfrac{3}{27}$

$= -\dfrac{81}{27} + \dfrac{3}{27} = -\dfrac{78}{27} = -\dfrac{\mathbf{26}}{\mathbf{9}}$

28. $a(b^0 - ab) = 3((-5)^0 - 3(-5)) = 3(1 + 15)$

$= \mathbf{48}$

29. $x - (-y) - y^2 = (-2) - (-3) - (3)^2$

$= -2 + 3 - 9 = \mathbf{-8}$

30. $-3 - 2^0 |-4 - 3| - 2(-2) = -3 - |-7| + 4$

$= \mathbf{-6}$

PROBLEM SET 42

1. $7N - 3 = -31$

$7N = -28$

$N = \mathbf{-4}$

2. $(7N - 3)2 = -N + 114$

$14N - 6 = -N + 114$

$15N = 120$

$N = \mathbf{8}$

3. $P = 14, \ F = 3, \ T = 17$

$\dfrac{14}{17} = \dfrac{P}{2244}$

$P = \dfrac{14 \cdot 2244}{17}$

$P = \mathbf{1848}$

4. $WD(7) = 14.14$

$WD = \mathbf{2.02}$

5. $2\dfrac{1}{4} \left(3\dfrac{5}{8} \right) = WN$

$\dfrac{9}{4} \left(\dfrac{29}{8} \right) = WN$

$\dfrac{\mathbf{261}}{\mathbf{32}} = WN$

6. $\dfrac{1}{2} + \dfrac{1}{8}x - 5 = 10\dfrac{1}{2}$

$\dfrac{1}{8}x = 5 + \dfrac{21}{2} - \dfrac{1}{2}$

$\dfrac{1}{8}x = \dfrac{10}{2} + \dfrac{21}{2} - \dfrac{1}{2}$

$x = 15 \cdot \dfrac{8}{1}$

$x = \mathbf{120}$

7. $4(x - 2) - 4x = -(3x + 2)$

$-8 = -3x - 2$

$-6 = -3x$

$\mathbf{2} = x$

8. $-5x + 2 = -2(x - 5)$

$-3x = 8$

$x = -\dfrac{\mathbf{8}}{\mathbf{3}}$

9. $0.3z - 0.02z + 0.2 = 1.18$

$30z - 2z + 20 = 118$

$28z = 98$

$z = \mathbf{3.5}$

10. $6k^5m^2 - 2mk^3 - mk = \textbf{mk(6mk}^4 - \textbf{2k}^2 - \textbf{1)}$

11. $x^4y^2m - x^3y^3m^2 + 5x^6y^2m^2$
    $= \textbf{x}^3\textbf{y}^2\textbf{m(x} - \textbf{ym} + \textbf{5x}^3\textbf{m)}$

12. $\dfrac{3x - 9x^2}{3x} = \dfrac{3x(1 - 3x)}{3x} = \textbf{1} - \textbf{3x}$

13. $\dfrac{4xy - 4x}{4x^2} = \dfrac{4x(y - 1)}{4x^2} = \dfrac{\textbf{y} - \textbf{1}}{\textbf{x}}$

14. $x \not> 5$
    $x \le 5$

$\qquad 3 \quad 4 \quad 5 \quad 6 \quad 7$

15. $x > 2$

16. $\dfrac{280}{5} = 56; \ \dfrac{56}{7} = 8; \ \dfrac{8}{2} = 4; \ \dfrac{4}{2} = 2$
    $\textbf{280} = \textbf{2} \cdot \textbf{2} \cdot \textbf{2} \cdot \textbf{5} \cdot \textbf{7}$

17. $\dfrac{x^2y^5}{x^4y^{-3}m^2} = x^{2-4}y^{5-(-3)}m^{-2} = \textbf{x}^{-2}\textbf{y}^8\textbf{m}^{-2}$

18. $\dfrac{x^5y^5mm^{-2}}{xx^3y^{-3}m^4} = x^{5-1-3}y^{5-(-3)}m^{1-2-4} = \textbf{xy}^8\textbf{m}^{-5}$

19. $\dfrac{x^2xyp^{-5}}{p^{-3}p^{-4}y^{-4}} = x^{2+1}y^{1-(-4)}p^{-5-(-3)-(-4)} = \textbf{x}^3\textbf{y}^5\textbf{p}^2$

20. $\dfrac{x^{-2}}{y}\left(\dfrac{xz}{y} - \dfrac{1}{y^{-4}}\right) = \dfrac{x^{-2}xz}{yy} - \dfrac{x^{-2}}{yy^{-4}}$
    $= \dfrac{z}{xy^2} - \dfrac{y^3}{x^2}$

21. $\left(\dfrac{a}{b} - \dfrac{2b}{a}\right)\dfrac{a^{-2}}{b^{-2}} = \dfrac{aa^{-2}}{bb^{-2}} - \dfrac{2ba^{-2}}{ab^{-2}}$
    $= \dfrac{b}{a} - \dfrac{2b^3}{a^3}$

22. $80 \text{ km} \times \dfrac{1000 \text{ m}}{1 \text{ km}} \times \dfrac{100 \text{ cm}}{1 \text{ m}} \times \dfrac{1 \text{ in.}}{2.54 \text{ cm}}$
    $= \dfrac{\textbf{80(1000)(100)}}{\textbf{2.54}} \text{ in.}$

23. $x - 9 = 4$
    $\quad x = 13$

    $x - 19 = (13) - 19 = \textbf{-6}$

24. $V = A_{End} \times length$
    $= \dfrac{1}{2}(10)(7)(20) \text{ m}^3 = \textbf{700 m}^3$

    S.A. $= 2A_{End} + 2A_{Top} + A_{Bottom}$
    $= 2\left(\dfrac{10(7)}{2}\right) + 2[8.6(20)] + 20(10)$
    $= 70 + 344 + 200$
    $= \textbf{614 m}^2$

25. $\dfrac{m^2}{y^2} - \dfrac{3y^{-2}}{m^{-2}} = \dfrac{m^2}{y^2} - \dfrac{3m^2}{y^2} = -\dfrac{\textbf{2m}^2}{\textbf{y}^2}$

26. $-a^{-3}(a - a^2x) = -(-2)^{-3}((-2) - (-2)^2 4)$
    $= \dfrac{1}{8}(-18) = -\dfrac{\textbf{9}}{\textbf{4}}$

27. $b - (-c^0) = -2 - (-4^0) = -2 + 1 = \textbf{-1}$

28. $k^3 - (k - c) = (-2)^3 - ((-2) - 4)$
    $= -8 - (-6) = \textbf{-2}$

29. $\left|-3^{-3}\right| = \left|-\dfrac{1}{3^3}\right| = \left|-\dfrac{1}{27}\right| = \dfrac{\textbf{1}}{\textbf{27}}$

30. $\dfrac{-(-2 - 5) - (-3 - 6)}{-2^0(-4)(-2)} = \dfrac{7 + 9}{-8} = \textbf{-2}$

PROBLEM SET 43

1. $(2N - 10)(-4) = -N + 61$
   $\quad -8N + 40 = -N + 61$
   $\quad\quad\quad -7N = 21$
   $\quad\quad\quad\quad N = \textbf{-3}$

2. $H = 2, \ O = 19, \ T = 21$
   $\dfrac{2}{21} = \dfrac{H}{84,000}$
   $H = \dfrac{2 \cdot 84,000}{21}$
   $H = \textbf{8000 farthings}$

3. $WF(30) = 18$
   $WF = \dfrac{\textbf{3}}{\textbf{5}}$

4. $2\dfrac{1}{3}x + 5 = 19$
   $\dfrac{7}{3}x = 14$
   $x = 14 \cdot \dfrac{3}{7}$
   $x = \textbf{6}$

5. $3(-x - 4) = 2x + 3(x - 5)$
$-3x - 12 = 5x - 15$
$3 = 8x$
$\dfrac{3}{8} = x$

6. $-(5 - 2x) + x = 7(x - 2)$
$-5 + 3x = 7x - 14$
$9 = 4x$
$\dfrac{9}{4} = x$

7. $-(0.2 - 0.4z) - 0.4 = z - 1.47$
$-20 + 40z - 40 = 100z - 147$
$87 = 60z$
$\mathbf{1.45 = z}$

8. $400\,\text{km} \times \dfrac{1000\,\text{m}}{1\,\text{km}} \times \dfrac{100\,\text{cm}}{1\,\text{m}} \times \dfrac{1\,\text{in.}}{2.54\,\text{cm}}$
$\times \dfrac{1\,\text{ft}}{12\,\text{in.}} \times \dfrac{1\,\text{mi}}{5280\,\text{ft}} = \dfrac{400(1000)(100)}{(2.54)(12)(5280)}$ **miles**

9. $V = A_{\text{Base}} \times \text{height}$
$= (A_{\text{Semicircle }10} + A_{\text{Semicircle }5}) \times \text{height}$
$= \left(\left(\dfrac{1}{2}\right)(10)^2\pi + \left(\dfrac{1}{2}\right)(5)^2\pi\right)(2)(3)\ \text{ft}^3$
$\approx \mathbf{1177.50\ ft^3}$

S.A. $= 2A_{\text{Base}} + (P \times \text{height})$
$= 2\left(\dfrac{125}{2}\pi\right)\text{ft}^2 + (10 + 15\pi)(2)(3)\ \text{ft}^2$
$\approx \mathbf{735.10\ ft^2}$

10. $(60.6 + 90.08 + 56.92) + x = 58.8(4)$
$x = \mathbf{27.6}$

11. $x - 4 + 2x - 5 = 6$
$3x = 15$
$x = 5$

$3x - 2 = 3(5) - 2 = 15 - 2 = \mathbf{13}$

12. $3x + 2y = 5 - y$
$3y = -3x + 5$
$\dfrac{3y}{3} = -\dfrac{3x}{3} + \dfrac{5}{3}$
$y = -x + \dfrac{5}{3}$

13. $-2y + 6y - x - 4 = 0$
$4y = x + 4$
$\dfrac{4y}{4} = \dfrac{x}{4} + \dfrac{4}{4}$
$y = \dfrac{1}{4}x + 1$

14. $6x^4y^2 - 4zx^2y^2 = 2x^2y^2(3x^2 - 2z)$

15. $8x^5y^2z - 16x^2y^2z^2 - xyz$
$= xyz(8x^4y - 16xyz - 1)$

16. $\dfrac{4x - 8xy}{4x} = \dfrac{4x(1 - 2y)}{4x} = 1 - 2y$

17. $\dfrac{5x^2y^2 - 25x^3y^3}{x^2y^2} = \dfrac{x^2y^2(5 - 25xy)}{x^2y^2}$
$= \mathbf{5 - 25xy}$

18. $x \not\le 2$
$x > 2$

19. $\dfrac{1125}{5} = 225;\ \dfrac{225}{5} = 45;\ \dfrac{45}{5} = 9;\ \dfrac{9}{3} = 3$
$\mathbf{1125 = 3 \cdot 3 \cdot 5 \cdot 5 \cdot 5}$

20. $\dfrac{x^5yx^{-7}y^2}{x^4yy^3x^3} = \dfrac{1}{x^{7-(-2)}y^{4-3}} = \dfrac{1}{x^9y}$

21. $\dfrac{4x^{-2}y^{-6}m}{x^5y^5m^{-4}} = \dfrac{4m^{1-(-4)}}{x^{5-(-2)}y^{5-(-6)}} = \dfrac{4m^5}{x^7y^{11}}$

22. $x^2z^{-2}\left(\dfrac{x^4z^{-4}}{x} - \dfrac{3z^2}{x^2}\right)$
$= x^2z^{-2}x^3z^{-4} - \dfrac{x^2z^{-2}3z^2}{x^2} = x^5z^{-6} - 3$

23. $\dfrac{3x^{-2}x^3y}{y^{-4}} - 2xy^5 = 3xy^5 - 2xy^5 = xy^5$

24. $\dfrac{3x^{-2}y^2}{m^{-2}} - \dfrac{5m^2y^2}{x^2} + \dfrac{2my^2}{m^{-1}x^2}$
$= 3x^{-2}y^2m^2 - 5x^{-2}y^2m^2 + 2x^{-2}y^2m^2 = \mathbf{0}$

25. $xy^2 - \dfrac{3xy}{y^{-1}} + \dfrac{2x^0y^2}{x^{-1}} - \dfrac{4x^2}{y^2} + 2x^2y^{-2}$
$= xy^2 - 3xy^2 + 2xy^2 - 4x^2y^{-2} + 2x^2y^{-2}$
$= \mathbf{-2x^2y^{-2}}$

26. $|x| - x(y)(-x) = |-2| - (-2)(4)(-(-2))$
$= 2 + 16 = \mathbf{18}$

27. $cx - c^3x = (-3)(5) - (-3)^3(5) = -15 + 135$
$= \mathbf{120}$

28. $ab^0(a^{-3} - b^{-2}) = (-2)(3)^0((-2)^{-3} - (3)^{-2})$

$= -2\left(-\dfrac{1}{8} - \dfrac{1}{9}\right) = -2\left(-\dfrac{17}{72}\right) = \dfrac{\mathbf{17}}{\mathbf{36}}$

29. $-3 - \dfrac{1}{3^{-2}} = -3 - 9 = \mathbf{-12}$

30. $\dfrac{-4\left[(-2 + 5) - (-3 + 8)\right]}{-2^0|5 - 1|} = \dfrac{-4(-2)}{-4}$

$= \mathbf{-2}$

PROBLEM SET 44

1. $(2N + 5)(-3) = -57$

$-6N - 15 = -57$

$-6N = -42$

$N = \mathbf{7}$

2. $B = 14,\ Tr = 3,\ T = 17$

$\dfrac{3}{17} = \dfrac{Tr}{3400}$

$Tr = \dfrac{3 \cdot 3400}{17}$

$Tr = \mathbf{600}$

3. $WF\left(2\dfrac{1}{8}\right) = \dfrac{1}{5}$

$WF\left(\dfrac{\cancel{17}}{\cancel{8}}\right)\left(\dfrac{\cancel{8}}{\cancel{17}}\right) = \dfrac{1}{5}\left(\dfrac{8}{17}\right)$

$WF = \dfrac{\mathbf{8}}{\mathbf{85}}$

4. $-4\dfrac{3}{4} + 8\dfrac{1}{3}x = 13\dfrac{1}{4}$

$\dfrac{25}{3}x = \dfrac{53}{4} + \dfrac{19}{4}$

$x = \dfrac{72}{4} \cdot \dfrac{3}{25}$

$x = \dfrac{\mathbf{54}}{\mathbf{25}}$

5. $-2 - |-3| - 2^2 - (3 - x) = -(-3)^3$

$-12 + x = 27$

$x = \mathbf{39}$

6. $-3x - 2(5 - 7x) = 14$

$11x - 10 = 14$

$11x = 24$

$x = \dfrac{\mathbf{24}}{\mathbf{11}}$

7. $5p - 6(2p + 1) = -4p - 2$

$-7p - 6 = -4p - 2$

$-3p = 4$

$p = -\dfrac{\mathbf{4}}{\mathbf{3}}$

8. $x + 3y - 4 = 0$

$\dfrac{3y}{3} = \dfrac{-x}{3} + \dfrac{4}{3}$

$y = -\dfrac{1}{3}x + \dfrac{4}{3}$

9. $4y - x = 7$

$\dfrac{4y}{4} = \dfrac{x}{4} + \dfrac{7}{4}$

$y = \dfrac{1}{4}x + \dfrac{7}{4}$

10. $2y + 2k + 4x - 4 = 0$

$\dfrac{2y}{2} = \dfrac{-2k}{2} - \dfrac{4x}{2} + \dfrac{4}{2}$

$y = -k - 2x + 2$

11. $3y - 2x - 7 = 0$

$\dfrac{3y}{3} = \dfrac{2x}{3} + \dfrac{7}{3}$

$y = \dfrac{2}{3}x + \dfrac{7}{3}$

12. $3a^2b^4c^5 - 6a^2b^6c^6 = \mathbf{3a^2b^4c^5(1 - 2b^2c)}$

13. $8x^2a - 4x^2a^2 + 2xa^2 = \mathbf{2xa(4x - 2xa + a)}$

14. $\dfrac{3xyz - 3xy}{3xy} = \dfrac{3xy(z - 1)}{3xy} = \mathbf{z - 1}$

15. $\dfrac{2xy - 2x}{y - 1} = \dfrac{2x(y - 1)}{y - 1} = \mathbf{2x}$

16. $\mathbf{x \geq -2;\ x \nless -2}$

17. $(4.3 + 5.2 + 7 + 6.8) + x = 34$

$x = \mathbf{10.7}$

18. $80\,\cancel{yd} \times \dfrac{3\,\cancel{ft}}{1\,\cancel{yd}} \times \dfrac{12\,\cancel{in.}}{1\,\cancel{ft}} \times \dfrac{2.54\,\text{cm}}{1\,\cancel{in.}}$

$= \mathbf{80(3)(12)(2.54)\ cm}$

19. $16:\ 2 \cdot 2 \cdot 2 \cdot 2;$

$12:\ 2 \cdot 2 \cdot 3;$

$50:\ 2 \cdot 5 \cdot 5$

$2 \cdot 2 \cdot 2 \cdot 2 \cdot 3 \cdot 5 \cdot 5 = \mathbf{1200}$

20. $\dfrac{p^5 p^{-4} z^2}{z^{-5} z p^3} = p^{1-3} z^{2-(-4)} = \mathbf{p^{-2} z^6}$

21. $\dfrac{akp^2 p^4}{a^{-3} a^5 p^5 k^4} = a^{1-2} k^{1-4} p^{6-5} = \mathbf{a^{-1} k^{-3} p}$

22. $\dfrac{m m^{-4} p p^5}{m^{-3} p p^6} = m^{-3-(-3)} p^{6-7} = \mathbf{p^{-1}}$

23. $m^{-2}z^4\left(m^2z^{-4} - \dfrac{3m^6z}{z^4}\right)$

$= m^{-2}z^4 m^2 z^{-4} - m^{-2}z^4 3m^6 z^{-3} = \mathbf{1 - 3m^4 z}$

24. $aaxxy^{-3} + \dfrac{2a^2x^2}{y^3} - \dfrac{4axxx}{y^3}$

$= a^2x^2y^{-3} + 2a^2x^2y^{-3} - 4ax^3y^{-3}$

$= \mathbf{3a^2x^2y^{-3} - 4ax^3y^{-3}}$

25. $m^2xy^{-2} - 3mmxy^{-2} + \dfrac{4m^2x}{y^2} - 3mmx^{-1}y^2$

$= m^2xy^{-2} - 3m^2xy^{-2} + 4m^2xy^{-2} - 3m^2x^{-1}y^2$

$= \mathbf{2m^2xy^{-2} - 3m^2x^{-1}y^2}$

26. $a^2 - b^{-3}c = 3^2 - (-2)^{-3}(-1) = 9 - \dfrac{1}{8} = \dfrac{\mathbf{71}}{\mathbf{8}}$

27. $ab(b^0 - bc) = 3(-1)\left((-1)^0 - (-1)(-4)\right)$

$= -3(1 - 4) = \mathbf{9}$

28. $m - (m - x) = -5 - (-5 - 3) = -5 + 8 = \mathbf{3}$

29. $-2^4 + \dfrac{1}{-(-2)^3} + \sqrt[3]{64} = -16 + \dfrac{1}{8} + 4$

$= -\dfrac{\mathbf{95}}{\mathbf{8}}$

30. $\dfrac{-2\left[(-3 + 2)(-3 + 5^0)\right]}{-2 - |-3 - 1|} = \dfrac{-2(-1)(-2)}{-2 - 4} = \dfrac{\mathbf{2}}{\mathbf{3}}$

PROBLEM SET 45

1. $(2N - 10)4 = N - 2$

$8N - 40 = N - 2$

$7N = 38$

$N = \dfrac{\mathbf{38}}{\mathbf{7}}$

2. $R = 7,\ r = 5,\ T = 12$

$\dfrac{5}{12} = \dfrac{r}{1080}$

$r = \dfrac{5 \cdot 1080}{12}$

$r = \mathbf{450}$

3. $WD(2.25) = 1.3995$

$WD = \mathbf{0.622}$

4. $3\dfrac{1}{4}x - 4 = 21$

$\dfrac{13}{4}x = 25$

$x = \dfrac{\mathbf{100}}{\mathbf{13}}$

5. $7(x - 3) - 6x + 4 = 2 - (x + 3)$

$7x - 21 - 6x + 4 = 2 - x - 3$

$x - 17 = -x - 1$

$2x = 16$

$x = \mathbf{8}$

6. $-2x + 3(-5 - x) = x$

$-5x - 15 = x$

$-15 = 6x$

$-\dfrac{\mathbf{5}}{\mathbf{2}} = x$

7. $0.04x + 0.2 - 0.4x = 0.38$

$4x + 20 - 40x = 38$

$-36x = 18$

$x = \mathbf{-0.5}$

8. $2x - 5y + 4 = 0$

$\dfrac{2x}{5} + \dfrac{4}{5} = \dfrac{5y}{5}$

$y = \dfrac{\mathbf{2}}{\mathbf{5}}x + \dfrac{\mathbf{4}}{\mathbf{5}}$

9. $4 + 2x + 2y - 3 = 5$

$\dfrac{2y}{2} = -\dfrac{2x}{2} + \dfrac{4}{2}$

$y = \mathbf{-x + 2}$

10. $5x^2y^5m^2 - 10x^4y^2m^3 = \mathbf{5x^2y^2m^2(y^3 - 2x^2m)}$

11. $3x^2yz - 4zyx^2 + 2xyz^2 = -x^2yz + 2xyz^2$

$= \mathbf{xyz(-x + 2z)}$

12. $\dfrac{2x + 2}{2} = \dfrac{2(x + 1)}{2} = \mathbf{x + 1}$

13. $\dfrac{4xy + 4x}{4x} = \dfrac{4x(y + 1)}{4x} = \mathbf{y + 1}$

14. $x \nleq 2$

$x > 2$

15. 75: $3 \cdot 5 \cdot 5$;

8: $2 \cdot 2 \cdot 2$;

30: $2 \cdot 3 \cdot 5$

$2 \cdot 2 \cdot 2 \cdot 3 \cdot 5 \cdot 5 = \mathbf{600}$

16. 18: $2 \cdot 3 \cdot 3$;

27: $3 \cdot 3 \cdot 3$;

45: $3 \cdot 3 \cdot 5$

$2 \cdot 3 \cdot 3 \cdot 3 \cdot 5 = \mathbf{270}$

17. V = A$_{Base}$ × height

= [A$_{Rectangle}$ + A$_{Triangle}$] × height

= $\left[(1)(12)(40) + \frac{1}{2}(40)(7)\right](10)$ in.^{3}

= [620](10) in.^{3}

= **6200 in.^{3}**

S.A. = 2A$_{Base}$ + (P × height)

= [2(620) + 107(10)] in.^{2}

= **2310 in.^{2}**

18. 200 cm^2 × $\frac{1 \text{ in.}}{2.54 \text{ cm}}$ × $\frac{1 \text{ in.}}{2.54 \text{ cm}}$

× $\frac{1 \text{ ft}}{12 \text{ in.}}$ × $\frac{1 \text{ ft}}{12 \text{ in.}}$ × $\frac{1 \text{ yd}}{3 \text{ ft}}$ × $\frac{1 \text{ yd}}{3 \text{ ft}}$

= $\frac{200}{(2.54)(2.54)(12)(12)(3)(3)}$ yd^2

19. $x + 3 = 4$

$x = 1$

$x^2 - 19 = (1)^2 - 19 = \mathbf{-18}$

20. $\frac{x^{-4}}{y^2 p^{-4}} = \frac{\mathbf{p^4}}{\mathbf{x^4 y^2}}$

21. $\frac{k^5 m^2}{k^7 m^{-5}} = \frac{\mathbf{m^7}}{\mathbf{k^2}}$

22. $\frac{a^2 bc^{-2} c^5}{a^2 b^{-3} a^2 c^3} = \frac{\mathbf{b^4}}{\mathbf{a^2}}$

23. $\left(\frac{m^2}{y^{-1}} + 4m^5 y^6\right)m^{-2}y$

= $\frac{m^2 m^{-2} y}{y^{-1}} + 4m^5 y^6 m^{-2} y = \mathbf{y^2 + 4m^3 y^7}$

24. $axy^2 + \frac{2ax}{y^{-2}} - \frac{3ay^2}{x^{-1}} + 5ay^2 x^{-1}$

= $axy^2 + 2axy^2 - 3axy^2 + 5ay^2 x^{-1} = \mathbf{5ay^2 x^{-1}}$

25. $3m^2 k^5 - \frac{2m^3 k^6}{mk} + 4mmk^6 k^{-1} - 3mk^5$

= $3m^2 k^5 - 2m^2 k^5 + 4m^2 k^5 - 3mk^5$

= $\mathbf{5m^2 k^5 - 3mk^5}$

26. $-|-a|(a - x) = -|-(-2)|(-2 - 4) = -2(-6)$

= **12**

27. $-xy(y - x^0) = -3(-2)(-2 - 3^0) = 6(-3) = \mathbf{-18}$

28. $p^{-2}(a^{-5} - y) = 2^{-2}((-1)^{-5} - (-4))$

= $\frac{1}{4}(-1 + 4) = \frac{\mathbf{3}}{\mathbf{4}}$

29. $-3^{-3} = -\frac{1}{3^3} = -\frac{\mathbf{1}}{\mathbf{27}}$

30. $\frac{4(-3 + 2) - |-5 + 2^0|}{3(-2)^2} = \frac{-4 - 4}{12}$

= $-\frac{\mathbf{2}}{\mathbf{3}}$

PROBLEM SET 46

1. $2N - 5 = -N + 35$

$3N = 40$

$N = \frac{\mathbf{40}}{\mathbf{3}}$

2. $P = 3$, $A = 10$, $T = 13$

$\frac{10}{13} = \frac{A}{27,989}$

$A = \frac{10 \cdot 27,989}{13}$

$A = \mathbf{21,530}$

3. $-2x - 4(x - 2) = 3x + 5$

$-6x + 8 = 3x + 5$

$3 = 9x$

$\frac{\mathbf{1}}{\mathbf{3}} = x$

4. $-2(x - 4) + 8 = 4 - (x + 2)$

$-2x + 16 = 2 - x$

$\mathbf{14} = x$

5. $(-2)^3(-x - 4) - |-2| - 3^2 = -2(x - 4) - x$

$8x + 32 - 2 - 9 = -3x + 8$

$11x = -13$

$x = -\frac{\mathbf{13}}{\mathbf{11}}$

6. $3x + 2y = 5$

$\frac{2y}{2} = \frac{-3x}{2} + \frac{5}{2}$

$y = -\frac{\mathbf{3}}{\mathbf{2}}x + \frac{\mathbf{5}}{\mathbf{2}}$

7. $x - 3y + 7 = 0$

$\frac{x}{3} + \frac{7}{3} = \frac{3y}{3}$

$y = \frac{\mathbf{1}}{\mathbf{3}}x + \frac{\mathbf{7}}{\mathbf{3}}$

8. 50.8 cm^2 × $\frac{1 \text{ in.}}{2.54 \text{ cm}}$ × $\frac{1 \text{ in.}}{2.54 \text{ cm}}$

× $\frac{1 \text{ ft}}{12 \text{ in.}}$ × $\frac{1 \text{ ft}}{12 \text{ in.}}$ = $\frac{50.8}{(2.54)(2.54)(12)(12)}$ ft^2

9. $x + 9 = 3$

$x = -6$

$-x^2 + 4 = -(-6)^2 + 4 = -36 + 4 = \mathbf{-32}$

10. $(58.8 + 11.4 + 73 + 62.2) + x = (60.12)(5)$
$$x = \mathbf{95.2}$$

11. S.A. $= 2A_{End} + 2A_{Top} + A_{Bottom}$

$$= 2\left(\frac{(6)(4)}{2}\right)m^2 + 2(20)(5)\,m^2 + (20)(6)\,m^2$$

$$= (24 + 200 + 120)(100)(100)\ cm^2$$

$$= \mathbf{3{,}440{,}000\ cm^2}$$

$V = A_{End} \times$ length

$$= \left(\frac{(6)(4)}{2}\right)m^2 \times 20\ m$$

$$= (12)(20)(100)(100)(100)\ cm^3$$

$$= \mathbf{240{,}000{,}000\ cm^3}$$

12. $\dfrac{a}{b} + \dfrac{c^2 - a}{b} + \dfrac{4}{b} = \dfrac{a + c^2 - a + 4}{b}$

$$= \mathbf{\dfrac{c^2 + 4}{b}}$$

13. $x \le -4;\ x \not> -4$

14. 125: $5 \cdot 5 \cdot 5$;
75: $3 \cdot 5 \cdot 5$;
45: $3 \cdot 3 \cdot 5$
$5 \cdot 5 \cdot 5 \cdot 3 \cdot 3 = \mathbf{1125}$

15. c^3: $c \cdot c \cdot c$;
c^2: $c \cdot c$;
2: $2 \cdot 1$
$1 \cdot 2 \cdot c \cdot c \cdot c = \mathbf{2c^3}$

16. $4c^3$: $2 \cdot 2 \cdot c \cdot c \cdot c$;
c^2: $c \cdot c$;
$3c^4$: $3 \cdot c \cdot c \cdot c \cdot c$
$2 \cdot 2 \cdot 3 \cdot c \cdot c \cdot c \cdot c = \mathbf{12c^4}$

17. b^3: $b \cdot b \cdot b$;
b^2c: $b \cdot b \cdot c$;
b^2c^2: $b \cdot b \cdot c \cdot c$
$b \cdot b \cdot b \cdot c \cdot c = \mathbf{b^3c^2}$

18. $4x^2y^5p^2 - 3x^5y^4p^2 = \mathbf{x^2y^4p^2(4y - 3x^3)}$

19. $\dfrac{4x^2 - 4x}{4x} = \dfrac{4x(x - 1)}{4x} = \mathbf{x - 1}$

20. $\dfrac{x^5y^2}{x^3y^5} = \mathbf{\dfrac{1}{x^{-2}y^3}}$

21. $\dfrac{m^4p^5}{p^{-3}m^6} = \mathbf{\dfrac{1}{p^{-8}m^2}}$

22. $\dfrac{xxx^3y^5y^{-2}}{x^{-3}yy^{-6}} = \mathbf{\dfrac{1}{x^{-8}y^{-8}}}$

23. $\dfrac{x^{-2}p^0}{y^4}\left(\dfrac{x^2}{p^4} - x^4p^6\right) = \dfrac{x^{-2}x^2}{y^4p^4} - \dfrac{x^{-2}x^4p^6}{y^4}$

$$= \mathbf{y^{-4}p^{-4} - x^2p^6y^{-4}}$$

24. $\dfrac{x^2}{y^2} - 3x^2y^{-2} + 4x^{-3}x^5y^{-2} - \dfrac{8y^{-2}}{x^{-2}}$

$$= x^2y^{-2} - 3x^2y^{-2} + 4x^2y^{-2} - 8x^2y^{-2} = \mathbf{-6x^2y^{-2}}$$

25. $xa^2y - 2a^2xy + 4ya^2x - \dfrac{6ax}{ay} = \mathbf{3a^2xy - 6xy^{-1}}$

26. $-a - |a - x| = -(-2) - |-2 - (-3)|$
$= 2 - |1| = \mathbf{1}$

27. $xy^0 - (x - y) = (-3)(5)^0 - (-3 - 5)$
$= -3 - (-8) = \mathbf{5}$

28. $p^{-3}n^2 - n(p) = (-2)^{-3}(-2)^2 - (-2)(-2)$
$= -\dfrac{1}{2} - 4 = \mathbf{-\dfrac{9}{2}}$

29. $-\dfrac{1}{(-4)^{-2}} - \sqrt[3]{-27} = -(-4)^2 - (-3) = \mathbf{-13}$

30. $\dfrac{2[(-4 - 6^0)(5 - 2)]}{6 - [-(-2)]} = \dfrac{2(-5)(3)}{6 - 2} = \dfrac{-30}{4}$

$$= \mathbf{-\dfrac{15}{2}}$$

PROBLEM SET 47

1. $8N = 3N - 10$
$5N = -10$
$N = \mathbf{-2}$

2. $P = 3, L = 13, T = 16$

$$\dfrac{3}{16} = \dfrac{P}{6816}$$

$$P = \dfrac{3 \cdot 6816}{16}$$

$$P = \mathbf{1278}$$

3. $WD(0.46) = 0.01058$
$WD = \mathbf{0.023}$

4. $2\dfrac{1}{5}x + 5 = -15$

$$\dfrac{11}{5}x = -20$$

$$x = \mathbf{-\dfrac{100}{11}}$$

5. $-4x - 3(x - 3) = x + 2$
$-7x + 9 = x + 2$
$7 = 8x$
$$\mathbf{\dfrac{7}{8}} = x$$

6. $-4x + (-2x + 5) = -2x$

$\qquad\qquad 5 = 4x$

$\qquad\qquad \dfrac{\mathbf{5}}{\mathbf{4}} = x$

7. $0.2p + 2.2 + 2.2p = 4.36$

$\quad 20p + 220 + 220p = 436$

$\qquad\qquad\qquad 240p = 216$

$\qquad\qquad\qquad\quad p = \mathbf{0.9}$

8. $5x + 4 = 3y$

$\quad \dfrac{3y}{3} = \dfrac{5x}{3} + \dfrac{4}{3}$

$\quad\; y = \dfrac{\mathbf{5}}{\mathbf{3}}x + \dfrac{\mathbf{4}}{\mathbf{3}}$

9. $2y - 5 = x$

$\quad \dfrac{2y}{2} = \dfrac{x}{2} + \dfrac{5}{2}$

$\quad\; y = \dfrac{\mathbf{1}}{\mathbf{2}}x + \dfrac{\mathbf{5}}{\mathbf{2}}$

10. $50 \,\cancel{\text{mi}}^2 \times \dfrac{5280 \,\cancel{\text{ft}}}{1 \,\cancel{\text{mi}}} \times \dfrac{5280 \,\cancel{\text{ft}}}{1 \,\cancel{\text{mi}}} \times \dfrac{12 \,\cancel{\text{in.}}}{1 \,\cancel{\text{ft}}} \times \dfrac{12 \,\cancel{\text{in.}}}{1 \,\cancel{\text{ft}}}$

$\quad \times \dfrac{2.54 \,\cancel{\text{cm}}}{1 \,\cancel{\text{in.}}} \times \dfrac{2.54 \,\cancel{\text{cm}}}{1 \,\cancel{\text{in.}}} \times \dfrac{1 \text{ m}}{100 \,\cancel{\text{cm}}} \times \dfrac{1 \text{ m}}{100 \,\cancel{\text{cm}}}$

$\quad = \dfrac{\mathbf{50(5280)(5280)(12)(12)(2.54)(2.54)}}{\mathbf{(100)(100)}} \,\text{m}^2$

11. $3x - 4 + x - 6 = 10$

$\qquad\qquad\quad 4x = 20$

$\qquad\qquad\quad\; x = 5$

$\quad 4 - 2x = 4 - 2(5) = \mathbf{-6}$

12. $5x - 9 + x - 3 = 6$

$\qquad\qquad\quad 6x = 18$

$\qquad\qquad\quad x = 3$

$\quad 9 - 3x = 9 - 3(3) = \mathbf{0}$

13. $x \geq \mathbf{-4}$

14. S.A. $= 2A_{\text{End}} + (C \times \text{length})$

$\quad = [2\pi(10)^2 + (20\pi)(15)](100)(100) \text{ cm}^2$

$\quad \approx \mathbf{15{,}700{,}000 \text{ cm}^2}$

15. $V = A_{\text{Base}} \times \text{height}$

$\quad = (A_{\text{Semicircle 14}} + A_{\text{Semicircle 10}}) \times \text{height}$

$\quad = \left(\dfrac{1}{2}(14)^2 \pi + \dfrac{1}{2}(10)^2 \pi\right)(10) \text{ in.}^3$

$\quad \approx [464.72](10) \text{ in.}^3$

$\quad \approx \mathbf{4647.2 \text{ one-inch sugar cubes}}$

$\quad$ S.A. $= 2A_{\text{End}} + (P \times \text{height})$

$\quad = [2(464.72) + (24\pi + 8)(10)] \text{ in.}^2$

$\quad \approx \mathbf{1763.04 \text{ in.}^2}$

16. $\dfrac{1}{2} + \dfrac{3}{4} + \dfrac{6}{7} = \dfrac{14}{28} + \dfrac{21}{28} + \dfrac{24}{28} = \dfrac{\mathbf{59}}{\mathbf{28}}$

17. $\dfrac{x}{y} + \dfrac{b}{4y} + c = \dfrac{4x}{4y} + \dfrac{b}{4y} + \dfrac{4cy}{4y}$

$\quad = \dfrac{\mathbf{4x + b + 4cy}}{\mathbf{4y}}$

18. $\dfrac{4}{a} + \dfrac{c}{4a} + 5 = \dfrac{16}{4a} + \dfrac{c}{4a} + \dfrac{20a}{4a}$

$\quad = \dfrac{\mathbf{16 + c + 20a}}{\mathbf{4a}}$

19. $\dfrac{ad}{4d^3} + \dfrac{8}{d} + \dfrac{mx}{d^4} = \dfrac{ad^2}{4d^4} + \dfrac{32d^3}{4d^4} + \dfrac{4mx}{4d^4}$

$\quad = \dfrac{\mathbf{ad^2 + 32\,d^3 + 4mx}}{\mathbf{4\,d^4}}$

20. $40: 2 \cdot 2 \cdot 2 \cdot 5;$

$\quad 35: 5 \cdot 7;$

$\quad 18: 2 \cdot 3 \cdot 3$

$\quad 2 \cdot 2 \cdot 2 \cdot 3 \cdot 3 \cdot 5 \cdot 7 = \mathbf{2520}$

21. $x^3y^2m^5 - 3x^2ym^6 = \mathbf{x^2ym^5(xy - 3m)}$

22. $\left(\dfrac{a^2}{x^{-1}} - 4a^6x^4\right)\dfrac{a^{-2}}{x} = \dfrac{a^2a^{-2}}{x^{-1}x} - \dfrac{4a^6x^4a^{-2}}{x}$

$\quad = \mathbf{1 - 4a^4x^3}$

23. $\dfrac{4ax - axy}{ax} = \dfrac{ax(4 - y)}{ax} = \mathbf{4 - y}$

24. $\dfrac{x^4y^2}{x^{-2}y^{-3}} = \mathbf{x^6y^5}$

25. $\dfrac{x^2xyy^{-4}}{x^4y^{-5}} = \mathbf{x^{-1}y^2}$

26. $\dfrac{a^2x^3}{y} - \dfrac{2x^3a^2}{y} + \dfrac{4xx^2a^2}{y} - 3a^2x^3$

$\quad = a^2x^3y^{-1} - 2a^2x^3y^{-1} + 4a^2x^3y^{-1} - 3a^2x^3$

$\quad = \mathbf{3a^2x^3y^{-1} - 3a^2x^3}$

27. $a^{-2}(2a - a^{-3}) = (-3)^{-2}(2(-3) - (-3)^{-3})$

$\quad = \dfrac{1}{9}\left(-6 + \dfrac{1}{27}\right) = \mathbf{-\dfrac{161}{243}}$

28. $x - y(x^0 - y) = -2 - 3((-2)^0 - 3)$

$\quad = -2 - 3(-2) = \mathbf{4}$

29. $\dfrac{1}{-3^{-3}} + \sqrt[5]{32} = -27 + 2 = \mathbf{-25}$

30. $\dfrac{-2[(-4 - 2) - (5^0 - 3)]}{-2 - |2|}$

$= \dfrac{-2(-6 + 2)}{-4} = \mathbf{-2}$

PROBLEM SET 48

1. $(4N + 5)3 = -N - 24$
$12N + 15 = -N - 24$
$13N = -39$
$N = \mathbf{-3}$

2. $M = 7, C = 2, T = 9$
$\dfrac{7}{9} = \dfrac{M}{324}$
$M = \dfrac{7 \cdot 324}{9}$
$M = \mathbf{252}$

3. $4\dfrac{1}{5}(WN) = 28$

$\left(\dfrac{\cancel{5}}{\cancel{21}}\right)\left(\dfrac{\cancel{21}}{\cancel{5}}\right)WN = \cancel{28}^{4}\left(\dfrac{5}{21}\right)_{3}$

$\qquad WN = \dfrac{\mathbf{20}}{\mathbf{3}}$

4. $3\dfrac{1}{3}x + 7 = -2$

$\qquad \dfrac{10}{3}x = -9$

$\qquad x = -9 \cdot \dfrac{3}{10} = -\dfrac{\mathbf{27}}{\mathbf{10}}$

5. $5p - 4p - (p - 2) = 3(p + 4)$
$2 = 3p + 12$
$-10 = 3p$
$-\dfrac{\mathbf{10}}{\mathbf{3}} = p$

6. $(-2)^3(-k - |-3|) - (-2) - 2k = k - 3^2$
$6k + 26 = k - 9$
$5k = -35$
$k = \mathbf{-7}$

7. $2x + 4y = 6$
$\qquad \dfrac{4y}{4} = -\dfrac{2x}{4} + \dfrac{6}{4}$
$\qquad y = -\dfrac{\mathbf{1}}{\mathbf{2}}x + \dfrac{\mathbf{3}}{\mathbf{2}}$

8. $3y - 4 = 2x$
$\qquad \dfrac{3y}{3} = \dfrac{2x}{3} + \dfrac{4}{3}$
$\qquad y = \dfrac{\mathbf{2}}{\mathbf{3}}x + \dfrac{\mathbf{4}}{\mathbf{3}}$

9. $8: 2 \cdot 2 \cdot 2;$
$36: 2 \cdot 2 \cdot 3 \cdot 3;$
$75: 3 \cdot 5 \cdot 5$
$2 \cdot 2 \cdot 2 \cdot 3 \cdot 3 \cdot 5 \cdot 5 = \mathbf{1800}$

10. $x: x;$
$c^2x^2: c \cdot c \cdot x \cdot x;$
$cdx: c \cdot d \cdot x$
$c \cdot c \cdot x \cdot x \cdot d = \mathbf{c^2x^2d}$

11. $\dfrac{1}{3} + \dfrac{2}{5} + \dfrac{3}{10} = \dfrac{10}{30} + \dfrac{12}{30} + \dfrac{9}{30} = \dfrac{\mathbf{31}}{\mathbf{30}}$

12. $\dfrac{3}{7} + \dfrac{8}{9} - \dfrac{1}{3} = \dfrac{27}{63} + \dfrac{56}{63} - \dfrac{21}{63} = \dfrac{\mathbf{62}}{\mathbf{63}}$

13. $\dfrac{a}{x} + \dfrac{b}{c^2x^2} + d = \dfrac{ac^2x}{c^2x^2} + \dfrac{b}{c^2x^2} + \dfrac{dc^2x^2}{c^2x^2}$

$= \dfrac{\mathbf{ac^2x + b + c^2dx^2}}{\mathbf{c^2x^2}}$

14. $\dfrac{4}{x^2} + \dfrac{6}{2x^3} - \dfrac{3}{4x^4} = \dfrac{16x^2}{4x^4} + \dfrac{12x}{4x^4} - \dfrac{3}{4x^4}$

$= \dfrac{\mathbf{16x^2 + 12x - 3}}{\mathbf{4x^4}}$

15. $\dfrac{4}{x^2} + \dfrac{c}{4x^3} + m = \dfrac{16x}{4x^3} + \dfrac{c}{4x^3} + \dfrac{4mx^3}{4x^3}$

$= \dfrac{\mathbf{16x + c + 4mx^3}}{\mathbf{4x^3}}$

16. $\dfrac{a}{b} + \dfrac{c}{4b^2} + \dfrac{a^2}{8b^3} = \dfrac{8b^2a}{8b^3} + \dfrac{2bc}{8b^3} + \dfrac{a^2}{8b^3}$

$= \dfrac{\mathbf{8ab^2 + 2bc + a^2}}{\mathbf{8b^3}}$

17. $\dfrac{m}{a^5} + \dfrac{k}{2a^4} - \dfrac{3}{4a^3} = \dfrac{4m}{4a^5} + \dfrac{2ka}{4a^5} - \dfrac{3a^2}{4a^5}$

$= \dfrac{\mathbf{4m + 2ak - 3a^2}}{\mathbf{4a^5}}$

18. $\dfrac{1}{2a^3} + \dfrac{3}{4ab^2} + \dfrac{c}{8a^2b^2}$

$= \dfrac{4b^2}{8a^3b^2} + \dfrac{6a^2}{8a^3b^2} + \dfrac{ac}{8a^3b^2}$

$= \dfrac{\mathbf{4b^2 + 6a^2 + ac}}{\mathbf{8a^3b^2}}$

19. Convert 1000 square inches to square miles:

$$1000 \text{ in.}^2 \times \frac{1 \text{ ft}}{12 \text{ in.}} \times \frac{1 \text{ ft}}{12 \text{ in.}} \times \frac{1 \text{ mi}}{5280 \text{ ft}} \times \frac{1 \text{ mi}}{5280 \text{ ft}}$$

$$= \frac{1000}{(12)(12)(5280)(5280)} \text{ mi}^2$$

20. $A = A_{\text{Triangle}} + A_{\text{Semicircle}}$

$$= \left(\frac{1}{2}(10)(6) + \frac{1}{2}(6)^2 \pi\right)(12)(12) \text{ in.}^2$$

$$\approx \textbf{12,458.88 one-inch square tiles}$$

21. $8m^3x^2y^4p - 4m^2xpm = \textbf{4}m^3xp(2xy^4 - 1)$

22. $\dfrac{x^{-2}}{y^{-3}}\left(\dfrac{x^2}{y^3} - \dfrac{ax^3}{y^{-4}}\right) = \dfrac{x^{-2}x^2}{y^{-3}y^3} - \dfrac{x^{-2}ax^3}{y^{-3}y^{-4}}$

$$= \textbf{1} - \textbf{axy}^7$$

23. $\dfrac{4x^4 - 4}{4} = \dfrac{4(x^4 - 1)}{4} = \textbf{x}^4 - \textbf{1}$

24. $\dfrac{mm^2p^3y^{-3}}{m^{-3}m^{-2}p^{-3}y^4} = \textbf{m}^8\textbf{p}^6\textbf{y}^{-7}$

25. $\dfrac{xx^{-3}y^5x^0}{x^2y^{-5}xy^2} = \textbf{x}^{-5}\textbf{y}^8$

26. $\dfrac{m}{y} - \dfrac{3m^2y}{my^2} - \dfrac{5m^{-3}m^4}{y^{-3}y^4} + \dfrac{2ym}{ym^2}$

$$= my^{-1} - 3my^{-1} - 5my^{-1} + 2m^{-1}$$

$$= \textbf{-7my}^{-1} + \textbf{2m}^{-1}$$

27. $-x - |xa|(x^0 - a)$

$$= -(-2) - |(-2)(-3)|((-2)^0 - (-3))$$

$$= 2 - 6(4) = \textbf{-22}$$

28. $-x^2 - y^2(xy) = -(-2)^2 - 3^2(-2)(3) = -4 + 54$

$$= \textbf{50}$$

29. $(-3)^{-2} = \dfrac{1}{(-3)^2} = \dfrac{\textbf{1}}{\textbf{9}}$

30. $-4[(-3 - 2^0) - (5 - 2) + |3|]$

$$= -4[-4 - 3 + 3] = \textbf{16}$$

Problem Set 49

1. $3N + 25 = -N + 5$

$$4N = -20$$

$$N = \textbf{-5}$$

2. $L = 14, M = 13, T = 27$

$$\dfrac{14}{27} = \dfrac{L}{1080}$$

$$L = \dfrac{14 \cdot 1080}{27}$$

$$L = \textbf{560}$$

3. $WF\left(2\dfrac{1}{8}\right) = \dfrac{1}{4}$

$$WF\left(\dfrac{17}{8}\right)\left(\dfrac{8}{17}\right) = \dfrac{1}{4}\left(\dfrac{8}{17}\right)$$

$$WF = \dfrac{\textbf{2}}{\textbf{17}}$$

4. $(14 + 11) + M = 48$

$$M = \textbf{23}$$

5. $16 \text{ ft}^3 \times \dfrac{12 \text{ in.}}{1 \text{ ft}} \times \dfrac{12 \text{ in.}}{1 \text{ ft}} \times \dfrac{12 \text{ in.}}{1 \text{ ft}}$

$$\times \dfrac{2.54 \text{ cm}}{1 \text{ in.}} \times \dfrac{2.54 \text{ cm}}{1 \text{ in.}} \times \dfrac{2.54 \text{ cm}}{1 \text{ in.}}$$

$$= \textbf{16(12)(12)(12)(2.54)(2.54)(2.54) cm}^3$$

6. $V = A_{\text{Base}} \times \text{height}$

$$= [A_{\text{Small Triangle}} + A_{\text{Large Triangle}}] \times \text{height}$$

$$= \left[\dfrac{1}{2}(4)(3) + \dfrac{1}{2}(8)(6)\right](100)(12)(12)$$

$$= [30](100)(144)$$

$$= \textbf{432,000 one-inch sugar cubes}$$

$\text{S.A.} = 2A_{\text{Base}} + (P \times \text{height})$

$$= [2(30)(12)(12) + 30(100)(12)] \text{ in.}^2$$

$$= \textbf{44,640 in.}^2$$

7. $\dfrac{WP}{100}(8300) = 996$

$$WP = \textbf{12 percent}$$

of 8300

996 is 12%

7304 is 88%

Before, 100%   After

8. $\dfrac{80}{100}(WN) = 1120$

$$WN = \textbf{1400}$$

of 1400

280 is 20%

1120 is 80%

Before, 100%   After

9. $4x - 5(x + 2) = -(2x - 4)$

$$-x - 10 = -2x + 4$$

$$x = \textbf{14}$$

10. $0.02 + 0.02x - 0.4 - 0.4x = 3.116$

$$20 + 20x - 400 - 400x = 3116$$

$$-380x = 3496$$

$$x = \textbf{-9.2}$$

11. $3x - 4y = 7$

$$\frac{4y}{4} = \frac{3x}{4} - \frac{7}{4}$$

$$y = \frac{3}{4}x - \frac{7}{4}$$

12. $-2y + 5 + 3x = 0$

$$\frac{2y}{2} = \frac{3x}{2} + \frac{5}{2}$$

$$y = \frac{3}{2}x + \frac{5}{2}$$

13. $21: 3 \cdot 7$;
    $24: 2 \cdot 2 \cdot 2 \cdot 3$;
    $60: 2 \cdot 2 \cdot 3 \cdot 5$
    $2 \cdot 2 \cdot 2 \cdot 3 \cdot 5 \cdot 7 = \mathbf{840}$

14. $4x^2: 2 \cdot 2 \cdot x \cdot x$;
    $yx^2: y \cdot x \cdot x$;
    $8m^3x^2: 2 \cdot 2 \cdot 2 \cdot m \cdot m \cdot m \cdot x \cdot x$
    $2 \cdot 2 \cdot 2 \cdot x \cdot x \cdot y \cdot m \cdot m \cdot m = \mathbf{8x^2ym^3}$

15. $\frac{3}{4} + \frac{2}{5} - \frac{3}{20} = \frac{15}{20} + \frac{8}{20} - \frac{3}{20} = \frac{20}{20} = \mathbf{1}$

16. $\frac{a}{x} + \frac{b}{c} + d = \frac{ac}{xc} + \frac{bx}{xc} + \frac{dcx}{xc}$

$$= \frac{ac + bx + cdx}{xc}$$

17. $\frac{m}{xc} + \frac{d^2}{xkc^3} - \frac{3p}{xk^2c^3}$

$$= \frac{mk^2c^2}{xk^2c^3} + \frac{d^2k}{xk^2c^3} - \frac{3p}{xk^2c^3}$$

$$= \frac{mk^2c^2 + d^2k - 3p}{xk^2c^3}$$

18. $\frac{4}{a^2b^2} - \frac{c}{ad} - \frac{m}{a^3b}$

$$= \frac{4ad}{a^3b^2d} - \frac{a^2cb^2}{a^3b^2d} - \frac{mbd}{a^3b^2d}$$

$$= \frac{4ad - a^2cb^2 - mbd}{a^3b^2d}$$

19. $x \nleq 2$
    $x > 2$

20. $2 \leq x < 5$

21. $18x^5y^2m - 9x^3ym^5 = \mathbf{9x^3ym(2x^2y - m^4)}$

22. $\frac{x^{-1}}{y}\left(\frac{y}{x} - \frac{3xy^{-5}}{p^6}\right) = \frac{x^{-1}y}{yx} - \frac{x^{-1}3xy^{-5}}{yp^6}$

$$= \mathbf{x^{-2} - 3y^{-6}p^{-6}}$$

23. $\frac{4x^2 - 4x}{4x} = \frac{4x(x - 1)}{4x} = \mathbf{x - 1}$

24. $\frac{kp^2k^{-1}p^{-3}p^{-4}}{k^2pp^2k^{-5}} = \frac{p^{-5}}{k^{-3}p^3} = \mathbf{k^3p^{-8}}$

25. $\frac{m^2xym^3x^{-5}}{yy^{-4}m^{-3}x^2} = \frac{m^5yx^{-4}}{y^{-3}m^{-3}x^2} = \mathbf{x^{-6}y^4m^8}$

26. $m^2x^2 - \frac{3m^{-2}x^{-2}}{m^4x^{-4}} + \frac{2m^2}{xm} - \frac{5x^{-1}}{m^{-1}}$

$$= m^2x^2 - 3m^{-6}x^2 + 2mx^{-1} - 5mx^{-1}$$

$$= \mathbf{m^2x^2 - 3m^{-6}x^2 - 3mx^{-1}}$$

27. $-p^{-2} - (p^2 - x) = -(-3)^{-2} - ((-3)^2 - 5)$

$$= -\frac{1}{9} - (4) = \mathbf{-\frac{37}{9}}$$

28. $-p^2 - p^0x^2 = -(-3)^2 - (-3)^0(2)^2 = -9 - 4$
    $= \mathbf{-13}$

29. $\frac{1}{-(-3)^{-2}} - \sqrt[3]{-64} = -(-3)^2 - \sqrt[3]{(-4)^3}$

$$= -9 + 4 = \mathbf{-5}$$

30. $-5[(-2 + 3)(-2 - 4^0) - |-5|] = -5[-3 - 5]$
    $= \mathbf{40}$

Problem Set 50

1. $4(2N - 5) = -N - 92$
    $8N - 20 = -N - 92$
    $9N = -72$
    $N = \mathbf{-8}$

2. $P = 7, M = 11, T = 18$

$$\frac{7}{18} = \frac{P}{756}$$

$$P = \frac{7 \cdot 756}{18}$$

$$P = \mathbf{294}$$

3. $WF\left(\frac{1}{3}\right) = \frac{2}{27}$

$$WF = \mathbf{\frac{2}{9}}$$

4. $\frac{8}{100}(WN) = 72$

$\qquad WN = \mathbf{900}$

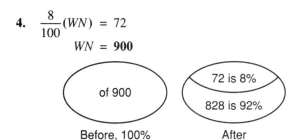

Before, 100%: of 900

After: 72 is 8% / 828 is 92%

5. $\frac{WP}{100}(860) = 43$

$\qquad WP = \mathbf{5\ percent}$

Before, 100%: of 860

After: 43 is 5% / 817 is 95%

6. $\frac{16}{100}(4200) = WN$

$\qquad \mathbf{672} = WN$

Before, 100%: of 4200

After: 672 is 16% / 3528 is 84%

7. $\frac{43}{100}(WN) = 2150$

$\qquad WN = \mathbf{5000}$

Before, 100%: of 5000

After: 2150 is 43% / 2850 is 57%

8. $\frac{WP}{100}(5400) = 108$

$\qquad WP = \mathbf{2\ percent}$

Before, 100%: of 5400

After: 108 is 2% / 5292 is 98%

9. $3x - 5(-2x - 8) + 4 = 2 - (x - 4)$

$\qquad 13x + 44 = 6 - x$

$\qquad 14x = -38$

$\qquad x = -\dfrac{19}{7}$

10. $-(-3)^3 - |-2| - 2^2 - (-k - 3)$

$\qquad = -4^2 - (3k - 4)$

$\qquad 24 + k = -3k - 12$

$\qquad 4k = -36$

$\qquad k = \mathbf{-9}$

11. $3x - 4y + 7 = 0$

$\qquad \dfrac{4y}{4} = \dfrac{3x}{4} + \dfrac{7}{4}$

$\qquad y = \dfrac{\mathbf{3}}{\mathbf{4}}x + \dfrac{\mathbf{7}}{\mathbf{4}}$

12. $250{:}\ 2 \cdot 5 \cdot 5 \cdot 5;$

$\qquad 75{:}\ 3 \cdot 5 \cdot 5;$

$\qquad 20{:}\ 2 \cdot 2 \cdot 5$

$\qquad 2 \cdot 2 \cdot 3 \cdot 5 \cdot 5 \cdot 5 = \mathbf{1500}$

13. $\dfrac{1}{7} + \dfrac{5}{21} + \dfrac{3}{5} = \dfrac{15}{105} + \dfrac{25}{105} + \dfrac{63}{105} = \dfrac{\mathbf{103}}{\mathbf{105}}$

14. $\dfrac{m}{x} + \dfrac{b}{xy} + \dfrac{ac}{x^2 ym}$

$\qquad = \dfrac{m^2 xy}{x^2 ym} + \dfrac{bxm}{x^2 ym} + \dfrac{ac}{x^2 ym}$

$\qquad = \dfrac{\mathbf{m^2 xy + bxm + ac}}{\mathbf{x^2 ym}}$

15. $\dfrac{3}{cd} + \dfrac{5}{4c^2 d} + \dfrac{7}{8cd^2}$

$\qquad = \dfrac{24cd}{8c^2 d^2} + \dfrac{10d}{8c^2 d^2} + \dfrac{7c}{8c^2 d^2}$

$\qquad = \dfrac{\mathbf{24cd + 10d + 7c}}{\mathbf{8c^2 d^2}}$

16. $\dfrac{p}{xa} + \dfrac{5}{xam} + x = \dfrac{pm}{xam} + \dfrac{5}{xam} + \dfrac{x^2 am}{xam}$

$\qquad = \dfrac{\mathbf{pm + 5 + x^2 am}}{\mathbf{xam}}$

17. $65{,}000\ \text{ft}^2 \times \dfrac{1\ \text{mi}}{5280\ \text{ft}} \times \dfrac{1\ \text{mi}}{5280\ \text{ft}}$

$\qquad = \dfrac{\mathbf{65{,}000}}{\mathbf{(5280)(5280)}}\ \mathbf{mi^2}$

18. $\left(\dfrac{200}{100} + \dfrac{100}{100} + \dfrac{80}{100} + \dfrac{100}{100}\right) \text{m}$

$\qquad + \left(\dfrac{280}{100} + \dfrac{200}{100}\right) \text{m} = \mathbf{9.6\ m}$

19. $x + 1 = 4$

$\qquad x = 3$

$\qquad y - 2 = 3$

$\qquad y = 5$

$\qquad x^2 - y^2 = (3)^2 - (5)^2 = \mathbf{-16}$

20. $(-x^3 - 2x - 3x^2 + 5) - 2(x^3 - x + 2x^2 - 3)$

$\qquad = -x^3 - 3x^2 - 2x + 5 - 2x^3 - 4x^2 + 2x + 6$

$\qquad = \mathbf{-3x^3 - 7x^2 + 11}$

21. $-4 < x \le 1$

$\qquad$ -5 -4 -3 -2 -1 0 1 2

22. $x^2ym - 4x^2ym^3 + 2x^4y^3m^6$

$= x^2ym(1 - 4m^2 + 2x^2y^2m^5)$

23. $\dfrac{4x^2 - 4x^4}{4x^2} = \dfrac{4x^2(1 - x^2)}{4x^2} = 1 - x^2$

24. $\dfrac{x^2y^{-2}m^{-5}y^0}{xxy^2y^{-5}x^{-3}} = \dfrac{x^2y^{-2}m^{-5}}{x^{-1}y^{-3}} = x^3ym^{-5}$

25. $\left(\dfrac{x^2}{yp^{-4}} - \dfrac{3x^2y}{p^{-4}}\right)\dfrac{x^{-2}}{y^4p} = \dfrac{x^2x^{-2}}{yp^{-4}y^4p} - \dfrac{3x^2yx^{-2}}{p^{-4}y^4p}$

$= y^{-5}p^3 - 3y^{-3}p^3$

26. $x^2y^{-2}p + \dfrac{3xxp}{y^2} - \dfrac{4x}{y^{-2}} + 6xy^2$

$= x^2y^{-2}p + 3x^2y^{-2}p - 4xy^2 + 6xy^2$

$= 4x^2y^{-2}p + 2xy^2$

27. $-xy(x - y) = -(-3)(5)(-3 - 5) = 15(-8)$

$= -120$

28. $-p^2 - p^{-3}(xp^0) = -(-2)^2 - (-2)^{-3}((-4)(-2)^0)$

$= -4 + \dfrac{1}{8}(-4) = -\dfrac{9}{2}$

29. $-3^{-3} = -\dfrac{1}{3^3} = -\dfrac{1}{27}$

30. $-2[(-4 - 3^0)(5 - 2) - (-6)] - \sqrt[3]{-125}$

$= -2[(-5)(3) + 6] + 5 = 23$

PROBLEM SET 51

1. $5N + 20 = -N - 28$

$6N = -48$

$N = -8$

2. $F = 3,\ P = 17,\ T = 20$

$\dfrac{17}{20} = \dfrac{P}{1620}$

$P = \dfrac{17 \cdot 1620}{20}$

$P = 1377$

3. $WF\left(7\dfrac{1}{8}\right) = 3\dfrac{2}{7}$

$WF\left(\dfrac{57}{8}\right)\left(\dfrac{8}{57}\right) = \dfrac{23}{7}\left(\dfrac{8}{57}\right)$

$WF = \dfrac{184}{399}$

4. $\dfrac{17}{100}(WN) = 952$

$WN = \mathbf{5600}$

of 5600 — Before, 100%

952 is 17%
4648 is 83% — After

5. $\dfrac{WP}{100}(300) = 60$

$WP = \mathbf{20\ percent}$

of 300 — Before, 100%

60 is 20%
240 is 80% — After

6. $\dfrac{38}{100}(700) = WN$

$\mathbf{266} = WN$

of 700 — Before, 100%

266 is 38%
434 is 62% — After

7. $-4x - x - 3(x - 2) = 4 - (x - 2)$

$-8x + 6 = -x + 6$

$x = \mathbf{0}$

8. $1.591 + 0.003k - 0.002 + 0.002k$

$= -(0.003 - k)$

$1591 + 3k - 2 + 2k = -3 + 1000k$

$1592 = 995k$

$\mathbf{1.6} = k$

9. $(4x^2 - 2x + 7x^5) - 2(x - 4 + 2x^2 - 3x^4)$

$= 7x^5 + 4x^2 - 2x + 6x^4 - 4x^2 - 2x + 8$

$= \mathbf{7x^5 + 6x^4 - 4x + 8}$

10. $(5x^2 + 12x + 7)(x + 1)$

$= 5x^3 + 12x^2 + 7x + 5x^2 + 12x + 7$

$= \mathbf{5x^3 + 17x^2 + 19x + 7}$

11. $28{,}000\ \text{in.}^2 \times \dfrac{2.54\ \text{cm}}{1\ \text{in.}} \times \dfrac{2.54\ \text{cm}}{1\ \text{in.}} \times \dfrac{1\ \text{m}}{100\ \text{cm}}$

$\times \dfrac{1\ \text{m}}{100\ \text{cm}} \times \dfrac{1\ \text{km}}{1000\ \text{m}} \times \dfrac{1\ \text{km}}{1000\ \text{m}}$

$= \dfrac{\mathbf{28{,}000(2.54)(2.54)}}{\mathbf{(100)(100)(1000)(1000)}}\ \mathbf{km^2}$

12. $-2 < x \le 4$

13. $(155{,}000 + 180{,}000 + 365{,}000) + B = 840{,}000$

$B = \mathbf{140{,}000}$

14. $A = A_{\text{Square}} + 3A_{\text{Semicircle}}$

$\quad = (2)(2) \text{ in.}^2 + 3\left[\dfrac{\pi(1)^2}{2}\right] \text{ in.}^2$

$\quad \approx \mathbf{8.71 \text{ one-inch square floor tiles}}$

15. $V = A_{\text{Base}} \times \text{height}$

$\quad = [A_{\text{Rect 1}} + A_{\text{Rect 2}} + A_{\text{Triangle}}] \times \text{height}$

$\quad = \left[(20)(13) + (18)(5) + \dfrac{(10)(18)}{2}\right](12) \text{ in.}^3$

$\quad = [440](12) \text{ in.}^3$

$\quad = \mathbf{5280 \text{ in.}^3}$

$\quad \text{S.A.} = 2A_{\text{Base}} + (P \times \text{height})$

$\quad\quad = [2(440) + (130.6)(12)] \text{ in.}^2$

$\quad\quad = \mathbf{2447.2 \text{ in.}^2}$

16. $15\colon 3 \cdot 5;$
$175\colon 5 \cdot 5 \cdot 7;$
$225\colon 3 \cdot 3 \cdot 5 \cdot 5$
$3 \cdot 3 \cdot 5 \cdot 5 \cdot 7 = \mathbf{1575}$

17. $\dfrac{1}{2a} + \dfrac{k}{4a^2} + \dfrac{x}{8m^2 a}$

$\quad = \dfrac{4am^2}{8a^2 m^2} + \dfrac{2km^2}{8a^2 m^2} + \dfrac{ax}{8a^2 m^2}$

$\quad = \dfrac{\mathbf{4am^2 + 2km^2 + ax}}{\mathbf{8a^2 m^2}}$

18. $\dfrac{m}{x^2 y} + \dfrac{4}{yx^2} - \dfrac{3y}{x^4} = \dfrac{mx^2}{x^4 y} + \dfrac{4x^2}{x^4 y} - \dfrac{3y^2}{x^4 y}$

$\quad = \dfrac{\mathbf{mx^2 + 4x^2 - 3y^2}}{\mathbf{x^4 y}}$

19. $\dfrac{1}{c} + \dfrac{x}{mc^2} + d = \dfrac{mc}{mc^2} + \dfrac{x}{mc^2} + \dfrac{dmc^2}{mc^2}$

$\quad = \dfrac{\mathbf{mc + x + dmc^2}}{\mathbf{mc^2}}$

20. $\dfrac{x}{ya} + \dfrac{b}{xa^2} - k = \dfrac{x^2 a}{a^2 xy} + \dfrac{by}{a^2 xy} - \dfrac{ka^2 xy}{a^2 xy}$

$\quad = \dfrac{\mathbf{x^2 a + by - ka^2 xy}}{\mathbf{a^2 xy}}$

21. $x \nleq 5$
$x > 5$

22. $xy - 4x^2 y^2 m - 3x^2 y = \mathbf{xy(1 - 4xym - 3x)}$

23. $\dfrac{3x^4 - 3x^2}{3x^2} = \dfrac{3x^2(x^2 - 1)}{3x^2} = \mathbf{x^2 - 1}$

24. $\dfrac{x^{-4} yy^{-3} x^0 x^2}{x^{-3} y^3 y^2 x^{-4}} = \dfrac{x^{-2} y^{-2}}{x^{-7} y^5} = \mathbf{x^5 y^{-7}}$

25. $\dfrac{x}{y^{-1}}\left(\dfrac{x}{y} - \dfrac{3x^2}{xy}\right) = \dfrac{xx}{y^{-1} y} - \dfrac{x3x^2}{y^{-1} xy}$

$\quad = x^2 - 3x^2 = \mathbf{-2x^2}$

26. $\dfrac{x^2 y}{p^{-3}} - \dfrac{4x^2 p^3}{y^{-1}} - \dfrac{2xp}{y^{-1} p^2} - \dfrac{5y}{p^{-3} x^{-2}}$

$\quad = x^2 yp^3 - 4x^2 yp^3 - 2xyp^{-1} - 5x^2 yp^3$

$\quad = \mathbf{-8x^2 yp^3 - 2xyp^{-1}}$

27. $-x - x^{-2} - xy^{-2} = -(-2) - (-2)^{-2} - (-2)(3)^{-2}$

$\quad = 2 - \dfrac{1}{4} + \dfrac{2}{9} = \dfrac{\mathbf{71}}{\mathbf{36}}$

28. $-x(x - y^0)|y| = -(-1)(-1 - (-4)^0)|-4|$

$\quad = -2(4) = \mathbf{-8}$

29. $\dfrac{1}{-4^{-2}} - \sqrt[5]{-243} = -4^2 - \sqrt[5]{(-3)^5} = -16 + 3$

$\quad = \mathbf{-13}$

30. $-3[(-2^0 + 5) - (-3 - 7) - |-2|]$

$\quad = -3[4 + 10 - 2] = \mathbf{-36}$

PROBLEM SET 52

1. $2N + 5 = -N - 13$
$\quad\quad 3N = -18$
$\quad\quad N = \mathbf{-6}$

2. $Q = 7, E = 2, T = 9$

$\quad \dfrac{7}{9} = \dfrac{Q}{3780}$

$\quad Q = \dfrac{7 \cdot 3780}{9}$

$\quad Q = \mathbf{2940}$

3. $WD(1.07) = 2.1721$
$\quad\quad WD = \mathbf{2.03}$

4. $-x - 11 = -9$
$\quad\quad -2 = x$
$\quad a + 1 = 1$
$\quad\quad a = 0$
$\quad x^2 - 2a = (-2)^2 - 2(0) = \mathbf{4}$

5. $A = A_{\text{Rectangle}} + A_{\text{Square}} + A_{\text{Triangle}}$

$\quad = \left[(4)(30) + (4)(4) + \left(\dfrac{1}{2}\right)(6)(22)\right] \text{ cm}^2$

$\quad = \mathbf{202 \text{ cm}^2}$

6. $\dfrac{WP}{100}(50) = 700$

$WP = \textbf{1400 percent}$

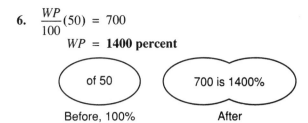

7. $5 + 3\dfrac{1}{2}x = 2\dfrac{1}{4}$

$\dfrac{7}{2}x = \dfrac{9}{4} - \dfrac{20}{4}$

$x = -\dfrac{11}{4} \cdot \dfrac{2}{7}$

$x = -\dfrac{\mathbf{11}}{\mathbf{14}}$

8. $3x - 5(x - 4) = 2x + 7$

$-2x + 20 = 2x + 7$

$13 = 4x$

$\dfrac{\mathbf{13}}{\mathbf{4}} = x$

9. $-2[(-k - 3)(-2) - 3] = (-3 - 3k)(-2)^3 - 3^2$

$-4k - 6 = 15 + 24k$

$-21 = 28k$

$-\dfrac{\mathbf{3}}{\mathbf{4}} = k$

10. $4(x^2 - 3x + 5) - 2(x^3 + 2x^2 - 4)$
$\quad - (2x^4 - 3x^3 + x^2 + 3)$

$= 4x^2 - 12x + 20 - 2x^3 - 4x^2 + 8$
$\quad - 2x^4 + 3x^3 - x^2 - 3$

$= \mathbf{-2x^4 + x^3 - x^2 - 12x + 25}$

11.
$$\begin{array}{r} 2x + 4 \\ 5x - 3 \\ \hline 10x^2 + 20x \\ - 6x - 12 \\ \hline \mathbf{10x^2 + 14x - 12} \end{array}$$

12. $(x + 3)^2$
$$\begin{array}{r} x + 3 \\ x + 3 \\ \hline x^2 + 3x \\ + 3x + 9 \\ \hline \mathbf{x^2 + 6x + 9} \end{array}$$

13. $(x + 3)(3x - 4)$
$$\begin{array}{r} x + 3 \\ 3x - 4 \\ \hline 3x^2 + 9x \\ - 4x - 12 \\ \hline \mathbf{3x^2 + 5x - 12} \end{array}$$

14. $(2x + 7)(2x - 7)$
$$\begin{array}{r} 2x + 7 \\ 2x - 7 \\ \hline 4x^2 + 14x \\ - 14x - 49 \\ \hline \mathbf{4x^2 - 49} \end{array}$$

15. $24:\ 2 \cdot 2 \cdot 2 \cdot 3;$
$60:\ 2 \cdot 2 \cdot 3 \cdot 5;$
$450:\ 2 \cdot 3 \cdot 3 \cdot 5 \cdot 5$
$2 \cdot 2 \cdot 2 \cdot 3 \cdot 3 \cdot 5 \cdot 5 = \mathbf{1800}$

16. $\dfrac{a}{x} + \dfrac{b}{cx^2} + d = \dfrac{acx}{cx^2} + \dfrac{b}{cx^2} + \dfrac{dcx^2}{cx^2}$

$= \dfrac{\mathbf{acx + b + dcx^2}}{\mathbf{cx^2}}$

17. $\dfrac{m}{p^2 k} - \dfrac{4a}{3pk} + \dfrac{6}{5pk^2}$

$= \dfrac{15mk}{15p^2 k^2} - \dfrac{20apk}{15p^2 k^2} + \dfrac{18p}{15p^2 k^2}$

$= \dfrac{\mathbf{15mk - 20apk + 18p}}{\mathbf{15p^2 k^2}}$

18. $a + \dfrac{bc}{m} - \dfrac{4mc}{x^2} = \dfrac{amx^2}{mx^2} + \dfrac{bcx^2}{mx^2} - \dfrac{4m^2 c}{mx^2}$

$= \dfrac{\mathbf{amx^2 + bcx^2 - 4m^2 c}}{\mathbf{mx^2}}$

19. $\dfrac{x}{mc} + \dfrac{b}{c} - \dfrac{4}{2kc^2}$

$= \dfrac{2kcx}{2kmc^2} + \dfrac{2bkcm}{2kmc^2} - \dfrac{4m}{2kmc^2}$

$= \dfrac{\mathbf{2kcx + 2bkcm - 4m}}{\mathbf{2kmc^2}}$

20. $\mathbf{4 \le x < 9}$

21. $4x^2 ym - 6xym + 2x^2 y^2 m^2$
$= \mathbf{2xym(2x - 3 + xym)}$

22. $\dfrac{5x - 5}{5} = \dfrac{5(x - 1)}{5} = \mathbf{x - 1}$

23. $\dfrac{x^3 y^{-4} p^0 y^4 p^2}{x^4 x x^{-7} y^2 p^4} = \dfrac{x^3 p^2}{x^{-2} y^2 p^4} = \mathbf{x^5 y^{-2} p^{-2}}$

24. $\left(\dfrac{ax^{-5}}{y^{-2}} + \dfrac{4x^3}{ay^2}\right)\dfrac{x^5}{ay^2} = \dfrac{ax^{-5} x^5}{y^{-2} ay^2} + \dfrac{4x^3 x^5}{ay^2 ay^2}$

$= \mathbf{1 + 4x^8 a^{-2} y^{-4}}$

25. $\dfrac{m^2 x}{y^{-1}} - \dfrac{3m^2 y}{x^{-1}} + 5mmyx - \dfrac{4x^2 ym^2}{x}$

$= m^2 xy - 3m^2 xy + 5m^2 xy - 4m^2 xy = \mathbf{-m^2 xy}$

26. $a^{-2}(a - a^3) = (-3)^{-2}(-3 - (-3)^3) = \frac{1}{9}(24)$

$= \dfrac{8}{3}$

27. $(p - a)(a - 2pa) = (5 - (-2))(-2 - 2(5)(-2))$
$= 7(18) = \mathbf{126}$

28. $-3^{-4} = -\dfrac{1}{3^4} = -\dfrac{1}{81}$

29. $\dfrac{1}{-2^{-4}} - \sqrt[3]{125} = -16 - 5 = \mathbf{-21}$

30. $4 - [5(6 - 5^0) - (-5 - 2) - |-7|]$
$= 4 - [25 + 7 - 7] = \mathbf{-21}$

PROBLEM SET 53

1. $-4N - 3 = N + 27$
$-30 = 5N$
$\mathbf{-6} = N$

2. $P = 7, \ Q = 4, \ T = 11$

$\dfrac{7}{11} = \dfrac{P}{14,740}$

$P = \dfrac{7 \cdot 14,740}{11}$

$P = \mathbf{9380}$

3. $WF\left(2\dfrac{1}{8}\right) = \dfrac{1}{4}$

$WF\left(\dfrac{17}{8}\right)\left(\dfrac{8}{17}\right) = \dfrac{1}{4}\left(\dfrac{8}{17}\right)^{2}$

$WF = \dfrac{2}{17}$

4. $\dfrac{130}{100}(WN) = 78$

$WN = \mathbf{60}$

of 60   78 is 130%

Before, 100%   After

5. $\dfrac{15}{100}(WN) = 10.5$

$WN = \mathbf{70}$

of 70   10.5 is 15%
59.5 is 85%

Before, 100%   After

6. $\dfrac{WP}{100}(450) = 288$

$WP = \mathbf{64 \ percent}$

of 450   162 is 36%
288 is 64%

Before, 100%   After

7. $3\dfrac{2}{5}x - 3 = 4\dfrac{1}{8}$

$\dfrac{17}{5}x = \dfrac{33}{8} + \dfrac{24}{8}$

$x = \dfrac{57}{8} \cdot \dfrac{5}{17}$

$x = \dfrac{\mathbf{285}}{\mathbf{136}}$

8. $0.4m - 2 - 0.2m = 1.4 + m$
$4m - 20 - 2m = 14 + 10m$
$-8m = 34$
$m = \mathbf{-4.25}$

9.
$3x - 2$
$x + 4$
$\overline{3x^2 - 2x}$
$ + 12x - 8$
$\overline{3x^2 + 10x - 8}$

10.
$5x - 3$
$5x - 3$
$\overline{25x^2 - 15x}$
$ - 15x + 9$
$\overline{25x^2 - 30x + 9}$

11.
$2x - 5$
$3x - 2$
$\overline{6x^2 - 15x}$
$ - 4x + 10$
$\overline{6x^2 - 19x + 10}$

12.
$5x - 7$
$6x - 1$
$\overline{30x^2 - 42x}$
$ - 5x + 7$
$\overline{30x^2 - 47x + 7}$

13. $V = A_{Base} \times height$

$= \left[(11)(22) + (39)(4) + \dfrac{(39)(12)}{2}\right](2) \text{ yd}^3$

$= [632](2) \text{ yd}^3$

$= \mathbf{1264 \text{ yd}^3}$

S.A. $= 2A_{Base} + (P \times height)$

$= [2(632) + (157.8)(2)] \text{ yd}^2$

$= \mathbf{1579.6 \text{ yd}^2}$

14. $400 \cancel{ft^2} \times \dfrac{12 \cancel{in.}}{1 \cancel{ft}} \times \dfrac{12 \cancel{in.}}{1 \cancel{ft}} \times \dfrac{2.54 \cancel{cm}}{1 \cancel{in.}} \times \dfrac{2.54 \cancel{cm}}{1 \cancel{in.}}$

$\times \dfrac{1 \cancel{m}}{100 \cancel{cm}} \times \dfrac{1 \cancel{m}}{100 \cancel{cm}} \times \dfrac{1 \text{ km}}{1000 \cancel{m}} \times \dfrac{1 \text{ km}}{1000 \cancel{m}}$

$= \dfrac{\mathbf{400(12)(12)(2.54)(2.54)}}{\mathbf{(100)(100)(1000)(1000)}} \text{ km}^2$

15. $(-3, 4)$

16. $(-1, -3)$

17. $4 + \dfrac{2}{x^2} - \dfrac{5}{a^2 x} = \dfrac{4a^2 x^2}{a^2 x^2} + \dfrac{2a^2}{a^2 x^2} - \dfrac{5x}{a^2 x^2}$

$= \dfrac{\mathbf{4a^2 x^2 + 2a^2 - 5x}}{\mathbf{a^2 x^2}}$

18. $\dfrac{p}{a^2 m} - \dfrac{4}{a} - k = \dfrac{p}{a^2 m} - \dfrac{4am}{a^2 m} - \dfrac{ka^2 m}{a^2 m}$

$= \dfrac{\mathbf{p - 4am - ka^2 m}}{\mathbf{a^2 m}}$

19. $\dfrac{3ax}{m} + \dfrac{4x}{am^2} + \dfrac{2}{mx}$

$= \dfrac{3a^2 x^2 m}{axm^2} + \dfrac{4x^2}{axm^2} + \dfrac{2am}{axm^2}$

$= \dfrac{\mathbf{3a^2 x^2 m + 4x^2 + 2am}}{\mathbf{axm^2}}$

20. $\dfrac{2a}{x} - \dfrac{5}{p^2 x} - 3m = \dfrac{2ap^2}{p^2 x} - \dfrac{5}{p^2 x} - \dfrac{3mp^2 x}{p^2 x}$

$= \dfrac{\mathbf{2ap^2 - 5 - 3mp^2 x}}{\mathbf{p^2 x}}$

21. $x \nleq 4$

$x > 4$

22. $\dfrac{3ax - 3a}{3a^2} = \dfrac{3a(x - 1)}{3a^2} = \dfrac{\mathbf{x - 1}}{\mathbf{a}}$

23. $\dfrac{myy^{-3}m^{-4}y^{-2}}{x^0 y^2 y^{-4} y^2 m^{-7}} = \dfrac{m^{-3} y^{-4}}{m^{-7}} = \mathbf{m^4 y^{-4}}$

24. $\dfrac{3x^{-4}}{y^4}\left(\dfrac{2x^{-4}}{y^4} - \dfrac{3x^2}{y^2 a}\right)$

$= \dfrac{3x^{-4} 2x^{-4}}{y^4 y^4} - \dfrac{3x^{-4} 3x^2}{y^4 y^2 a} = \dfrac{\mathbf{6x^{-8}}}{\mathbf{y^8}} - \dfrac{\mathbf{9x^{-2}}}{\mathbf{y^6 a}}$

25. $\dfrac{3x^2 y^{-2}}{m^5} - \dfrac{3x^2 y^2}{m^5} - \dfrac{4xx^3 m^{-5}}{x^2 y^2} + \dfrac{6m^{-5}}{x^{-2} y^{-2}}$

$= 3x^2 y^{-2} m^{-5} - 3x^2 y^2 m^{-5} - 4x^2 y^{-2} m^{-5}$

$+ 6x^2 y^2 m^{-5}$

$= \mathbf{-x^2 y^{-2} m^{-5} + 3x^2 y^2 m^{-5}}$

26. $-xa(a - xa^0) = -7(-3)(-3 - 7(-3)^0)$

$= 21(-3 - 7) = \mathbf{-210}$

27. $(xa - a)(-a^{-4}x) = (7(-3) - (-3))(-(-3)^{-4}(7))$

$= (-\cancel{18}^{2})\left(-\dfrac{7}{\cancel{81}_{9}}\right) = \dfrac{\mathbf{14}}{\mathbf{9}}$

28. $-(-2)^{-2} = -\dfrac{1}{(-2)^2} = \mathbf{-\dfrac{1}{4}}$

29. $\dfrac{1}{(-2)^{-3}} - \sqrt[5]{243} = (-2)^3 - \sqrt[5]{(3)^5} = \mathbf{-11}$

30. $4[(6 - 2^0) - (-3 + 5)2] = 4[5 - 4] = \mathbf{4}$

Problem Set 54

1. $(5N - 10)3 = -N - 22$

$15N - 30 = -N - 22$

$16N = 8$

$N = \dfrac{\mathbf{1}}{\mathbf{2}}$

2. $W = 2, U = 21, T = 23$

$\dfrac{2}{23} = \dfrac{W}{805}$

$W = \dfrac{2 \cdot 805}{23}$

$W = \mathbf{70}$

3. $WF\left(3\dfrac{1}{5}\right) = 2\dfrac{3}{4}$

$WF\left(\dfrac{\cancel{16}}{\cancel{5}}\right)\left(\dfrac{\cancel{5}}{\cancel{16}}\right) = \dfrac{11}{4}\left(\dfrac{5}{16}\right)$

$WF = \dfrac{55}{64}$

4. $\dfrac{375}{100}(1300) = WN$

$4875 = WN$

of 1300   4875 is 375%

Before, 100%   After

5. $\dfrac{65}{100}(WN) = 260$

$WN = 400$

of 400   140 is 35% / 260 is 65%

Before, 100%   After

6. $\dfrac{WP}{100}(18) = 27$

$WP = 150$ **percent**

of 18   27 is 150%

Before, 100%   After

7. $-1\dfrac{2}{9} + 2\dfrac{1}{5}p = -\dfrac{1}{3}$

$\dfrac{11}{5}p = -\dfrac{3}{9} + \dfrac{11}{9}$

$p = \dfrac{8}{9} \cdot \dfrac{5}{11}$

$p = \dfrac{40}{99}$

8. $3x - [-(-2)]x + (-3)(x + 2) = 5x + (-7)$

$-2x - 6 = 5x - 7$

$1 = 7x$

$\dfrac{1}{7} = x$

9. $(5x - 4)(2x + 3)$

$5x - 4$

$2x + 3$

$\overline{10x^2 - 8x}$

$ + 15x - 12$

$\overline{10x^2 + 7x - 12}$

10. $(-5x - 2)(-x + 4)$

$-5x - 2$

$-x + 4$

$\overline{5x^2 + 2x}$

$ - 20x - 8$

$\overline{5x^2 - 18x - 8}$

11. $(7x - 5)^2$

$7x - 5$

$7x - 5$

$\overline{49x^2 - 35x}$

$ - 35x + 25$

$\overline{49x^2 - 70x + 25}$

12. $V = A_{End} \times length$

$= \dfrac{1}{2}(12)(9)(12)(3)(3)(3) \text{ ft}^3$

$= 17{,}496 \text{ ft}^3$

S.A. $= 2A_{End} + A_{Bottom} + A_{Back} + A_{Top}$

$= [2(54) + 12(12) + 9(12) + 15(12)](3)(3) \text{ ft}^2$

$= [540](9) \text{ ft}^2$

$= 4860 \text{ ft}^2$

13. $x - 3^2 = -9$

$x = 0$

$x^4 = 0$

14. $(5 + 7 + 12 + 14 + 22) + S = 120$

$S = 60$

15. $y = -2x + 4$

x	0	3	4
y	4	-2	-4

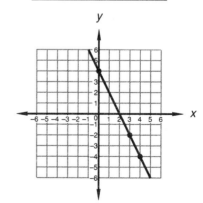

16. $y = x - 3$

x	0	-3	6
y	-3	-6	3

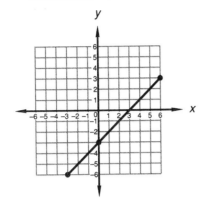

17. $4 + \dfrac{x}{y^2} - \dfrac{2a}{xy^3} = \dfrac{4xy^3}{xy^3} + \dfrac{x^2y}{xy^3} - \dfrac{2a}{xy^3}$

$= \dfrac{4xy^3 + x^2y - 2a}{xy^3}$

18. $\dfrac{a}{x^2c} - \dfrac{3a}{x^3c^2} - \dfrac{4}{xc} + \dfrac{3a+2}{x^3c}$

$= \dfrac{axc}{x^3c^2} - \dfrac{3a}{x^3c^2} - \dfrac{4x^2c}{x^3c^2} + \dfrac{3ac+2c}{x^3c^2}$

$= \dfrac{axc - 3a - 4x^2c + 3ac + 2c}{x^3c^2}$

19. $\dfrac{b}{m^2p} - \dfrac{1}{c^2m^3} + 4$

$= \dfrac{bmc^2}{m^3pc^2} - \dfrac{p}{m^3pc^2} + \dfrac{4m^3pc^2}{m^3pc^2}$

$= \dfrac{bmc^2 - p + 4m^3pc^2}{m^3pc^2}$

20. $x + \dfrac{4}{2x^2p^5} + \dfrac{xy}{4xp}$

$= \dfrac{4x^3p^5}{4x^2p^5} + \dfrac{8}{4x^2p^5} + \dfrac{x^2yp^4}{4x^2p^5}$

$= \dfrac{4x^3p^5 + 8 + x^2yp^4}{4x^2p^5}$

21. $-2 < x \le 4$

22. $\dfrac{4xy^2 - xy^2}{xy} = \dfrac{xy(4y - y)}{xy} = 3y$

23. $\dfrac{m^2p^4x^{-2}x^2x^0p^6}{m^2p^{-4}x^0p^0x^2} = \dfrac{m^2p^{10}}{m^2p^{-4}x^2} = p^{14}x^{-2}$

24. $\dfrac{x^3y^0x^{-1}p^2y^{-2}}{ppx^{-4}x^6y^{-2}} = \dfrac{x^2p^2y^{-2}}{p^2x^2y^{-2}} = 1$

25. $\dfrac{2x^{-4}}{y^2}\left(\dfrac{x^2}{2y^{-2}} - \dfrac{6x^4}{y^7p}\right)$

$= \dfrac{2x^{-4}x^2}{y^22y^{-2}} - \dfrac{2x^{-4}6x^4}{y^2y^7p} = x^{-2} - 12y^{-9}p^{-1}$

26. $\dfrac{x}{y} - \dfrac{3x^2x^{-1}y^2}{y^3} + \dfrac{2x^2}{xy^2} - \dfrac{4xxy^{-1}}{xy}$

$= xy^{-1} - 3xy^{-1} + 2xy^{-2} - 4xy^{-2}$

$= -2xy^{-1} - 2xy^{-2}$

27. $p - x(p^{-2} - x^0) = -2 - 5((-2)^{-2} - 5^0)$

$= -2 - 5\left(-\dfrac{3}{4}\right) = \dfrac{7}{4}$

28. $x - ax(x - ax)$

$= -4 - (-1)(-4)(-4 - (-1)(-4)) = -4 - 4(-8)$

$= 28$

29. $\dfrac{1}{-3^{-2}} - [3 - (-3)^3] = -9 - [3 + 27] = -39$

30. $-3[-2(-2^0 - 5) - (3 - 2) - |3|]$

$= -3[12 - 1 - 3] = -24$

PROBLEM SET 55

1. $-5N + 6 = -3N - 2$

$\qquad 8 = 2N$

$\qquad 4 = N$

2. $E = 2, U = 7, T = 9$

$\dfrac{2}{9} = \dfrac{E}{3717}$

$E = \dfrac{2 \cdot 3717}{9}$

$E = 826$

3. $WF\left(\dfrac{1}{5}\right) = 2\dfrac{7}{8}$

$WF\left(\dfrac{\cancel{1}}{\cancel{5}}\right)\left(\dfrac{\cancel{5}}{\cancel{1}}\right) = \dfrac{23}{8}\left(\dfrac{5}{1}\right)$

$WF = \dfrac{115}{8}$

4. $\frac{460}{100}(700) = WN$

$3220 = WN$

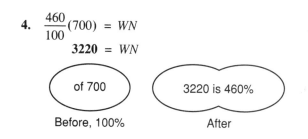

Before, 100% | After

5. $\frac{93}{100}(WN) = 651,000$

$WN = \mathbf{700,000}$

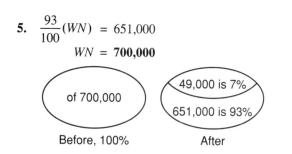

Before, 100% | After

6. $\frac{WP}{100}(2000) = 10$

$WP = \mathbf{0.5\ percent}$

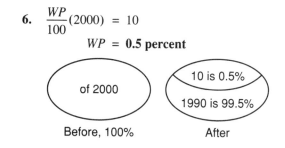

Before, 100% | After

7. $3\frac{1}{6}k + \frac{3}{4} = 2\frac{1}{5}$

$\frac{19}{6}k = \frac{11}{5} - \frac{3}{4}$

$\frac{19}{6}k = \frac{44}{20} - \frac{15}{20}$

$k = \frac{29}{20} \cdot \frac{6}{19}$

$k = \mathbf{\frac{87}{190}}$

8. $-(-x) - 3(-2x) + 3(-2 + x) = -(x - 5)$

$10x - 6 = -x + 5$

$11x = 11$

$x = \mathbf{1}$

9. $(3x + 5)(2x + 7) = 6x^2 + 10x + 21x + 35$

$= \mathbf{6x^2 + 31x + 35}$

10. $(4x - 3)^2 = (4x - 3)(4x - 3)$

$= 16x^2 - 12x - 12x + 9 = \mathbf{16x^2 - 24x + 9}$

11. 1575: $3 \cdot 3 \cdot 5 \cdot 5 \cdot 7$;

25: $5 \cdot 5$;

14: $2 \cdot 7$

$2 \cdot 3 \cdot 3 \cdot 5 \cdot 5 \cdot 7 = \mathbf{3150}$

12. $y = \frac{1}{3}x - 3$

x	0	6	-6
y	-3	-1	-5

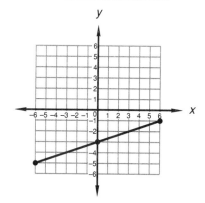

13. $y = -3$ (horizontal line)

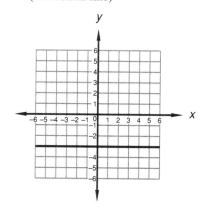

14. $V = A_{Base} \times \text{height}$

$= \left[(24)(2) + (8)(5) + \frac{(19)(6)}{2}\right](2)\ \text{yd}^3$

$= [145](2)\ \text{yd}^3$

$= \mathbf{290\ yd^3}$

S.A. $= 2A_{Base} + (P \times \text{height})$

$= 2(145)\ \text{yd}^2 + (74.9)(2)\ \text{yd}^2$

$= \mathbf{439.8\ yd^2}$

15. $(17 + 27 + 56) + P = 200$

$P = \mathbf{100}$

16. $24,000\ \text{km} \times \frac{1000\ \text{m}}{1\ \text{km}} \times \frac{100\ \text{cm}}{1\ \text{m}} \times \frac{1\ \text{in.}}{2.54\ \text{cm}}$

$\times \frac{1\ \text{ft}}{12\ \text{in.}} \times \frac{1\ \text{mi}}{5280\ \text{ft}} = \frac{\mathbf{24,000(1000)(100)}}{\mathbf{(2.54)(12)(5280)}}\ \text{mi}$

17. $x + \frac{2x}{m^2} - \frac{3}{m^2 x^3}$

$= \frac{m^2 x^4}{m^2 x^3} + \frac{2x^4}{m^2 x^3} - \frac{3}{m^2 x^3}$

$= \frac{m^2 x^4 + 2x^4 - 3}{m^2 x^3}$

18. $\dfrac{x}{k^2p} - \dfrac{3x}{k^2p} + 7 = -\dfrac{2x}{k^2p} + \dfrac{7k^2p}{k^2p}$

$= \dfrac{7k^2p - 2x}{k^2p}$

19. $-3x + \dfrac{2}{xp^2} - \dfrac{5x}{x^3p}$

$= \dfrac{-3x^3p^2}{x^2p^2} + \dfrac{2x}{x^2p^2} - \dfrac{5p}{x^2p^2}$

$= \dfrac{-3x^3p^2 + 2x - 5p}{x^2p^2}$

20. $\dfrac{k}{4m^2} + \dfrac{k^2}{8} - 3 = \dfrac{2k}{8m^2} + \dfrac{k^2m^2}{8m^2} - \dfrac{24m^2}{8m^2}$

$= \dfrac{2k + k^2m^2 - 24m^2}{8m^2}$

21. $-3 \nleq x$

$-3 > x$

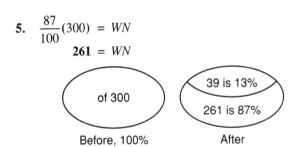

$\qquad -5 \quad -4 \quad -3 \quad -2 \quad -1$

22. $4k^2pz - 6k^3p^2z^5 - 2k^2p^2z^2 - 4kp$

$= 2kp(2kz - 3k^2pz^5 - kpz^2 - 2)$

23. $\dfrac{6xay - 24xay^2}{6xay} = \dfrac{6xay(1 - 4y)}{6xay} = 1 - 4y$

24. $\dfrac{k^2m^{-2}kp^{-2}k^5p^0}{p^5kp^{-5}k^{-4}m^4} = \dfrac{k^8m^{-2}p^{-2}}{k^{-3}m^4} = k^{11}m^{-6}p^{-2}$

25. $\left(\dfrac{x^2m^2}{3} - \dfrac{5x^5p^0}{m^{-4}} \right) \dfrac{3x^{-2}y^0}{m^2}$

$= \dfrac{x^2m^2 \, 3x^{-2}y^0}{3m^2} - \dfrac{5x^5 \, 3x^{-2}}{m^{-4}m^2} = 1 - 15x^3m^2$

26. $a^2k^2y^{-1} - \dfrac{4k^2}{a^{-2}y} + \dfrac{2k^2a}{a^{-1}y} - \dfrac{6k^{-4}}{k^2y}$

$= a^2k^2y^{-1} - 4a^2k^2y^{-1} + 2a^2k^2y^{-1} - 6k^{-6}y^{-1}$

$= -k^2a^2y^{-1} - 6k^{-6}y^{-1}$

27. $a^3(a - a^{-2}) = (-2)^3(-2 - (-2)^{-2})$

$= -8\left(-2 - \dfrac{1}{4}\right) = 18$

28. $p - pm(m - pm) = 4 - 4(-2)(-2 - 4(-2))$

$= 4 + 8(-2 + 8) = 52$

29. $27(-3)^{-3} - 5^2 - \sqrt[3]{-125} = -\dfrac{27}{27} - 25 - (-5)$

$= -21$

30. $-2(-1) - 3[(2 - 4^0) - 2(-3 - 5)] + |2|$

$= 2 - 3[1 + 16] + 2 = -47$

PROBLEM SET 56

1. $3N + 13 = -2N - 12$

$5N = -25$

$N = -5$

2. $Pr = 2, \ Pl = 23, \ T = 25$

$\dfrac{2}{25} = \dfrac{Pr}{3500}$

$Pr = \dfrac{2 \cdot 3500}{25} = 280$

3. $2.14(WN) = 0.00642$

$WN = 0.003$

4. $\dfrac{347}{100}(WN) = 2429$

$WN = 700$

```
  ⎛          ⎞     ⎛              ⎞
  ⎜  of 700   ⎟     ⎜ 2429 is 347% ⎟
  ⎝          ⎠     ⎝              ⎠
   Before, 100%          After
```

5. $\dfrac{87}{100}(300) = WN$

$261 = WN$

```
  ⎛          ⎞     ⎛   39 is 13%   ⎞
  ⎜  of 300   ⎟     ⎜──────────────⎟
  ⎝          ⎠     ⎝  261 is 87%   ⎠
   Before, 100%          After
```

6. $\dfrac{WP}{100}(460) = 1150$

$WP = 250 \text{ percent}$

```
  ⎛          ⎞     ⎛              ⎞
  ⎜  of 460   ⎟     ⎜ 1150 is 250% ⎟
  ⎝          ⎠     ⎝              ⎠
   Before, 100%          After
```

7. $3\dfrac{1}{8}p + 2\dfrac{1}{4} = \dfrac{1}{6}$

$\dfrac{25}{8}p = \dfrac{1}{6} - \dfrac{9}{4}$

$\dfrac{25}{8}p = \dfrac{2}{12} - \dfrac{27}{12}$

$p = -\dfrac{25}{12} \cdot \dfrac{8}{25}$

$p = -\dfrac{2}{3}$

8. $-[-|-3|(-2 - m) - 4] = -2[(-3 - m) - 2m]$
$$-2 - 3m = 6 + 6m$$
$$-8 = 9m$$
$$-\frac{8}{9} = m$$

9. $(4x - 2)(3x + 5) = 12x^2 - 6x + 20x - 10$
$$= \mathbf{12x^2 + 14x - 10}$$

10. $(5x - 1)^2 = (5x - 1)(5x - 1)$
$$= 25x^2 - 5x - 5x + 1 = \mathbf{25x^2 - 10x + 1}$$

11. $(5x - 7)(7x - 5) = 35x^2 - 49x - 25x + 35$
$$= \mathbf{35x^2 - 74x + 35}$$

12. $y = -3$ (horizontal line)

x	-1	0	1
y	-3	-3	-3

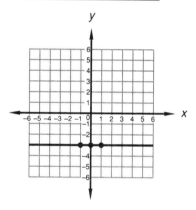

13. $x = 4$ (vertical line)

x	4	4	4
y	2	0	-2

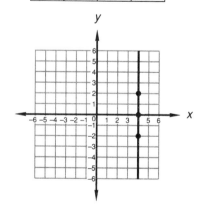

14. $y = -2x + 1$

x	0	2	-2
y	1	-3	5

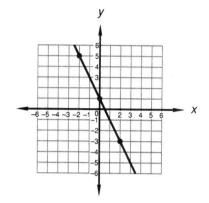

15. $y = 3x - 4$

x	0	1	2
y	-4	-1	2

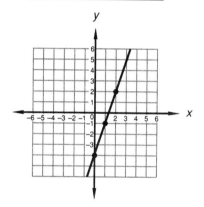

16. $\dfrac{3}{2x^2y} - \dfrac{ab}{4x^3y} - c$

$$= \frac{6x}{4x^3y} - \frac{ab}{4x^3y} - \frac{4cx^3y}{4x^3y}$$

$$= \frac{\mathbf{6x - ab - 4cx^3y}}{\mathbf{4x^3y}}$$

17. $\dfrac{a}{b + c} - x\left(\dfrac{4}{b^2}\right)$

$$= \frac{ab^2}{b^2(b + c)} - \frac{4x(b + c)}{b^2(b + c)}$$

$$= \frac{\mathbf{ab^2 - 4xb - 4xc}}{\mathbf{b^2(b + c)}}$$

18. $V = A_{Base} \times$ height

$= \left[(31)(15) + (5)(12) + \dfrac{(27)(10)}{2} \right] (2) \text{ m}^3$

$= [660](2) \text{ m}^3$

$= \textbf{1320 m}^3$

S.A. $= 2A_{Base} + (P \times$ height$)$

$= 2(660) \text{ m}^2 + (143.8)(2) \text{ m}^2$

$= \textbf{1607.6 m}^2$

19. $60{,}000 \ \cancel{mi} \times \dfrac{5280 \ \cancel{ft}}{1 \ \cancel{mi}} \times \dfrac{12 \ \cancel{in.}}{1 \ \cancel{ft}} \times \dfrac{2.54 \ \cancel{cm}}{1 \ \cancel{in.}}$

$\times \dfrac{1 \ \cancel{m}}{100 \ \cancel{cm}} \times \dfrac{1 \text{ km}}{1000 \ \cancel{m}}$

$= \dfrac{\textbf{60,000(5280)(12)(2.54)}}{\textbf{100(1000)}} \text{ \textbf{km}}$

20. $\dfrac{(3 \times 135) + (97 \times 163)}{3 + 97} = \dfrac{405 + 15811}{100}$

$= \textbf{162.16 pounds}$

21. $\mathbf{4 \le x < 7}$

22. $9k^2bm^4 - 3kb^4m^2 + 12kb^3m^3$

$= \textbf{3kbm}^2\textbf{(3km}^2 - \textbf{b}^3 + \textbf{4b}^2\textbf{m)}$

23. $\dfrac{3ap^2m - 6ap^2m^2}{3ap^2m} = \dfrac{3ap^2m(1 - 2m)}{3ap^2m}$

$= \textbf{1} - \textbf{2m}$

24. $\dfrac{m^{-2}mmm^{-3}xx^{-4}}{xm^3x^{-3}m^{-3}x^4} = \dfrac{m^{-3}x^{-3}}{x^2} = \textbf{m}^{-3}\textbf{x}^{-5}$

25. $\dfrac{x^2y^0p}{m^{-2}} \left(\dfrac{p^{-3}m^2}{k} - \dfrac{p^0pm^2}{x^2} \right)$

$= \dfrac{x^2pp^{-3}m^2}{m^{-2}k} - \dfrac{x^2ppm^2}{m^{-2}x^2} = \dfrac{\textbf{x}^2\textbf{m}^4}{\textbf{p}^2\textbf{k}} - \textbf{p}^2\textbf{m}^4$

26. $mx - \dfrac{3}{m^{-1}x^{-1}} + \dfrac{4mx}{m^2x^2} + \dfrac{5m^2x^{-1}}{mx^{-2}}$

$= mx - 3mx + 4m^{-1}x^{-1} + 5mx$

$= \textbf{3mx} + \textbf{4m}^{-1}\textbf{x}^{-1}$

27. $k^2 - kp - p(-k) = (-3)^2 - (-3)(5) - (5)(-(-3))$

$= 9 + 15 - 15 = \textbf{9}$

28. $x - x(x^{-2} - x^0) = -3 - (-3)((-3)^{-2} - (-3)^0)$

$= -3 + 3\left(\dfrac{1}{9} - 1 \right) = -\dfrac{\textbf{17}}{\textbf{3}}$

29. $\dfrac{1}{(-2)^{-3}} + \sqrt[3]{27} = -8 + 3 = \textbf{-5}$

30. $-\{ [(-2) - 3^0] - [(2 - 3)(-2) + 3] \}$

$= -\{ -3 - [5] \} = \textbf{8}$

PROBLEM SET 57

1. $(N - 5)(-3) = -9N + 2$

$-3N + 15 = -9N + 2$

$13 = -6N$

$-\dfrac{\textbf{13}}{\textbf{6}} = N$

2. $P = 13, N = 5, T = 18$

$\dfrac{13}{18} = \dfrac{P}{756}$

$P = \dfrac{13 \cdot 756}{18}$

$P = \textbf{546}$

3. $WF\left(3\dfrac{7}{8} \right) = \dfrac{1}{4}$

$WF\left(\dfrac{\cancel{31}}{\cancel{8}} \right)\left(\dfrac{\cancel{8}}{\cancel{31}} \right) = \dfrac{1}{\cancel{4}}\left(\dfrac{\cancel{8}}{31} \right)^{2}$

$WF = \dfrac{\textbf{2}}{\textbf{31}}$

4. $\dfrac{320}{100}(WN) = 192$

$WN = \textbf{60}$

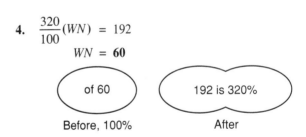

Before, 100%   After

5. $\dfrac{WP}{100}(98) = 3.92$

$WP = \textbf{4 percent}$

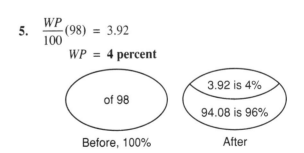

Before, 100%   After

6. $\dfrac{230}{100}(72) = WN$

$\textbf{165.6} = WN$

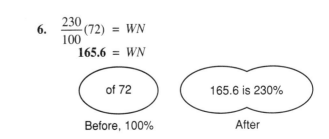

Before, 100%   After

7. $\dfrac{1}{4} + 2\dfrac{1}{5}k + 3\dfrac{2}{9} = 0$

$$\dfrac{11}{5}k = -\dfrac{29}{9} - \dfrac{1}{4}$$

$$\dfrac{11}{5}k = -\dfrac{116}{36} - \dfrac{9}{36}$$

$$k = -\dfrac{125}{36} \cdot \dfrac{5}{11}$$

$$k = -\dfrac{\mathbf{625}}{\mathbf{396}}$$

8. $-[-(-k)] - (-2)(-2 + k) = -k - (4k + 3)$

$$k - 4 = -5k - 3$$

$$6k = 1$$

$$k = \dfrac{\mathbf{1}}{\mathbf{6}}$$

9. $(2x - 4)(x - 3) = 2x^2 - 4x - 6x + 12$

$$= \mathbf{2x^2 - 10x + 12}$$

10. $(3x + 5)^2 = (3x + 5)(3x + 5)$

$$= 9x^2 + 15x + 15x + 25 = \mathbf{9x^2 + 30x + 25}$$

11. $x = -1\dfrac{1}{2}$ (vertical line)

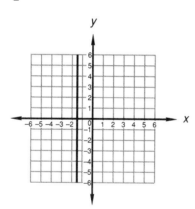

12. $y = 2x + 2$

x	0	2	-4
y	2	6	-6

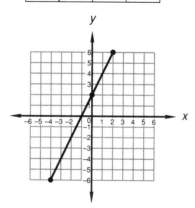

13. $y = -\dfrac{1}{3}x - 2$

x	0	6	-6
y	-2	-4	0

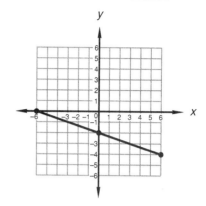

14. $\dfrac{x + y}{x^2 y} + \dfrac{y}{x^4} = \dfrac{x^2(x + y)}{x^4 y} + \dfrac{y^2}{x^4 y}$

$$= \dfrac{\mathbf{x^3 + x^2 y + y^2}}{\mathbf{x^4 y}}$$

15. $\dfrac{4}{x - y} - \dfrac{3}{y} = \dfrac{4y}{y(x - y)} - \dfrac{3(x - y)}{y(x - y)}$

$$= \dfrac{4y - 3x + 3y}{y(x - y)} = \dfrac{\mathbf{7y - 3x}}{\mathbf{y(x - y)}}$$

16. $\dfrac{9 + 2b}{x} - 3 + \dfrac{6}{x^2 y}$

$$= \dfrac{(9 + 2b)xy}{x^2 y} - \dfrac{3x^2 y}{x^2 y} + \dfrac{6}{x^2 y}$$

$$= \dfrac{\mathbf{9xy + 2bxy - 3x^2 y + 6}}{\mathbf{x^2 y}}$$

17. $4 \not< x$

$$4 > x$$

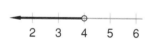

18. $12x^4 y p^3 - 4x^3 y^2 pz - 8x^2 p^2 y^2$

$$= \mathbf{4x^2 yp(3x^2 p^2 - xyz - 2yp)}$$

19. $2000 \text{ mi}^2 \times \dfrac{5280 \text{ ft}}{1 \text{ mi}} \times \dfrac{5280 \text{ ft}}{1 \text{ mi}} \times \dfrac{12 \text{ in.}}{1 \text{ ft}} \times \dfrac{12 \text{ in.}}{1 \text{ ft}}$

$$= \mathbf{2000(5280)(5280)(12)(12) \text{ in.}^2}$$

20. $A = A_{\text{Rectangle 1}} + A_{\text{Rectangle 2}}$

$$= (1)(2) \text{ m}^2 + (2)(1) \text{ m}^2 = \mathbf{4 \text{ m}^2}$$

21. $\dfrac{mx - 5mx}{mx} = \dfrac{mx(1 - 5)}{mx} = \mathbf{-4}$

22. $(2x^2y^{-2}z)^{-2}(xy)^4 = \dfrac{x^{-4}y^4z^{-2}}{4}\left(\dfrac{x^4y^4}{1}\right) = \dfrac{y^8}{4z^2}$

23. $(5x^{-3}y^2)^2(x^0y)^5xy = 25x^{-6}y^4y^5xy = \mathbf{25x^{-5}y^{10}}$

24. $(xy)x(x^{-4}y)^2(x)^3 = xyxx^{-8}y^2x^3 = \mathbf{x^{-3}y^3}$

25. $\dfrac{3x^{-2}}{y^{-4}}\left(\dfrac{ax^2}{3y^4} - \dfrac{3x^5}{y^{-2}}\right) = \dfrac{3x^{-2}ax^2}{y^{-4}3y^4} - \dfrac{3x^{-2}3x^5}{y^{-4}y^{-2}}$
$= \mathbf{a - 9x^3y^6}$

26. $2xy - 3yx + x^2y - y^2x + 4y^2xy^{-1} - \dfrac{2x^4x^{-2}}{y^{-1}}$
$= 2xy - 3xy + x^2y - xy^2 + 4xy - 2x^2y$
$= \mathbf{3xy - x^2y - y^2x}$

27. $xy - y^2(x - y) = (-2)(3) - (3)^2(-2 - 3)$
$= -6 - 9(-5) = \mathbf{39}$

28. $x^{-3} - x^2(-x) = (-2)^{-3} - (-2)^2(-(-2))$
$= -\dfrac{1}{8} - 8 = -\dfrac{65}{8}$

29. $\dfrac{1}{-2^{-3}} - 2 - \sqrt[4]{16} = -8 - 2 - 2 = \mathbf{-12}$

30. $-2\{(2 - 4) - (3 - 6^0)(-2) - 2[(-3)(-2 - 1)]\}$
$= -2\{-2 + 4 - 2[9]\} = \mathbf{32}$

PROBLEM SET 58

1. $\dfrac{47}{100}(WN) = 188$
$WN = \mathbf{400}$

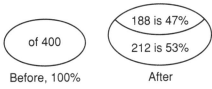

Before, 100%   After

(ovals: "of 400"; "188 is 47%"; "212 is 53%")

2. $\dfrac{WP}{100}(68) = 95.2$
$WP = \mathbf{140\ percent}$

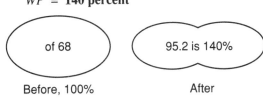

Before, 100%   After

(ovals: "of 68"; "95.2 is 140%")

3. $\dfrac{310}{100}(80) = WN$
$\mathbf{248} = WN$

(ovals: "of 80 Before, 100%"; "248 is 310% After")

4. $-2[(-3 - 2) - 2(-2 + m)] = -3m - 4^2 - |-2|$
$2 + 4m = -3m - 18$
$7m = -20$
$m = -\dfrac{20}{7}$

5. (a) $2x + y = 7$
(b) $x = -3y + 11$
Substitute (b) into (a) and get:
(a') $2(-3y + 11) + y = 7$
$-5y + 22 = 7$
$-5y = -15$
$y = 3$

(b) $x = -3(3) + 11 = 2$
(2, 3)

6. (a) $2x + 3y = -14$
(b) $y = 2x - 7$
Substitute (b) into (a) and get:
(a') $2x + 3(2x - 7) = -14$
$8x - 21 = -14$
$8x = 7$
$x = \dfrac{7}{8}$

(b) $y = 2\left(\dfrac{7}{8}\right) - 7 = -\dfrac{21}{4}$
$\left(\dfrac{7}{8}, -\dfrac{21}{4}\right)$

7. $1000\ \text{m}^2 \times \dfrac{100\ \text{cm}}{1\ \text{m}} \times \dfrac{100\ \text{cm}}{1\ \text{m}} \times \dfrac{1\ \text{in.}}{2.54\ \text{cm}}$
$\times \dfrac{1\ \text{in.}}{2.54\ \text{cm}} \times \dfrac{1\ \text{ft}}{12\ \text{in.}} \times \dfrac{1\ \text{ft}}{12\ \text{in.}}$
$= \dfrac{\mathbf{1000(100)(100)}}{\mathbf{(2.54)(2.54)(12)(12)}}\ \text{ft}^2$

8. $\dfrac{(2 \times 90) + (8 \times 95)}{2 + 8} = \dfrac{180 + 760}{10} = \mathbf{94}$

9. V = A$_{Base}$ × height

$$= \left[3(6) + 11(3) + 17(5) + \frac{7(8)}{2}\right](24) \text{ in.}^3$$

$$= [164](24) \text{ in.}^3$$

$$= \textbf{3936 in.}^3$$

S.A. = 2A$_{Base}$ + (P × height)

$$= 2(164) \text{ in.}^2 + (89.6)(2)(12) \text{ in.}^2$$

$$= \textbf{2478.4 in.}^2$$

10. 175: 5 · 5 · 7;
147: 3 · 7 · 7;
45: 3 · 3 · 5
3 · 3 · 5 · 5 · 7 · 7 = **11,025**

11. $(3 - x)^2 = (3 - x)(3 - x) = 9 - 3x - 3x + x^2$
$= 9 - 6x + x^2 = \boldsymbol{x^2 - 6x + 9}$

12. $y = -3\frac{1}{2}$ (horizontal line)

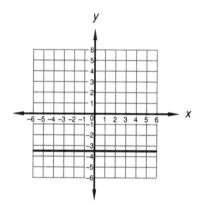

13. $y = 2x - 5$

x	0	5	3
y	−5	5	1

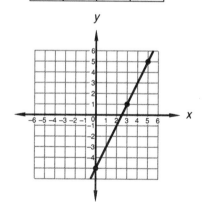

14. $y = -\frac{1}{2}x + 4$

x	0	6	−4
y	4	1	6

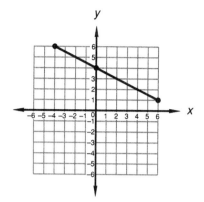

15. $\dfrac{-x}{a^2 b} + \dfrac{a - b}{b} = \dfrac{-x}{a^2 b} + \dfrac{a^2(a - b)}{a^2 b}$

$$= \dfrac{-x + a^3 - a^2 b}{a^2 b}$$

16. $\dfrac{a + b}{a} - \dfrac{3}{ax} = \dfrac{x(a + b)}{ax} - \dfrac{3}{ax}$

$$= \dfrac{ax + bx - 3}{ax}$$

17. $4 - \dfrac{7}{a} + \dfrac{a + b}{a^2} = \dfrac{4a^2}{a^2} - \dfrac{7a}{a^2} + \dfrac{a + b}{a^2}$

$$= \dfrac{4a^2 - 6a + b}{a^2}$$

18. $25x^2 y^5 p^2 - 15x^5 y^4 p^4 + 10x^4 y^4 p^4 z$
$= \boldsymbol{5x^2 y^4 p^2(5y - 3x^3 p^2 + 2x^2 p^2 z)}$

19. $\dfrac{5pq - 5p^2 q^2}{5pq} = \dfrac{5pq(1 - pq)}{5pq} = \boldsymbol{1 - pq}$

20. $x(x^2)(x^3)^{-3} x^{-2} y^2 = xx^{-9} y^2 = \boldsymbol{x^{-8} y^2}$

21. $(x^2 y^0)(x^3 y^2)xy = \boldsymbol{x^6 y^3}$

22. $xx(x^2)^{-2}(x^2)(x^{-3} y^0)^5 = x^2 x^{-4} x^2 x^{-15} = \boldsymbol{x^{-15}}$

23. $\left(\dfrac{3x^{-2} y^5}{p^{-3}}\right)^{-2}\left(\dfrac{2x^{-2}}{y}\right)^2 = \dfrac{x^4 y^{-10}}{9p^6}\left(\dfrac{4}{x^4 y^2}\right)$

$$= \boldsymbol{\dfrac{4}{9}p^{-6} y^{-12}}$$

24. $\dfrac{x(x^2 y^0)^{-2} xy^{-2}}{(xy^{-3})^2 xy^{-3}} = \dfrac{xx^{-4} y^0 xy^{-2}}{x^2 y^{-6} xy^{-3}} = \dfrac{x^{-2} y^{-2}}{x^3 y^{-9}}$

$$= \boldsymbol{x^{-5} y^7}$$

25. $\left(\dfrac{x^2}{2y^{-1}} - \dfrac{4x^{-2}}{y}\right)\dfrac{2x^{-2}}{y}$

$= \dfrac{x^2\,2x^{-2}}{2y^{-1}y} - \dfrac{4x^{-2}\,2x^{-2}}{yy} = \mathbf{1 - 8x^{-4}y^{-2}}$

26. $x^2(p^5)^2y - \dfrac{3x^2p^{10}}{y^{-1}} + \dfrac{4x^3py}{x^2p^{-2}} - 2xp^{10}y$

$= x^2p^{10}y - 3x^2p^{10}y + 4xp^3y - 2xp^{10}y$

$= \mathbf{-2x^2p^{10}y + 4xp^3y - 2xp^{10}y}$

27. $x^2 - xy^{-2} - (-y)^{-2} = 3^2 - 3(-3)^{-2} - (-(-3))^{-2}$

$= 9 - \dfrac{3}{9} - \dfrac{1}{9} = \mathbf{\dfrac{77}{9}}$

28. $p^2x - xp^0(x - p) = 3^2(-3) - (-3)(3)^0(-3 - 3)$

$= -27 + 3(-6) = \mathbf{-45}$

29. $\dfrac{1}{-2^{-3}} + 8 + \sqrt{64} = -8 + 8 + 8 = \mathbf{8}$

30. $-3\{(-4 - 2) - (-2 - 1^0)$
$\qquad - [(-2) - (-2 - 1)]\}$
$= -3\{-6 + 3 - 1\} = \mathbf{12}$

PROBLEM SET 59

1. $2N + 7 = -N - 2$
$\qquad 3N = -9$
$\qquad N = \mathbf{-3}$

2. $P = 5,\ R = 2,\ T = 7$

$\dfrac{5}{7} = \dfrac{P}{98}$

$P = \dfrac{5 \cdot 98}{7}$

$P = \mathbf{70}$

3. $WF\left(\dfrac{1}{4}\right) = 3\dfrac{7}{8}$

$WF\left(\dfrac{\cancel{1}}{\cancel{4}}\right)\left(\dfrac{\cancel{4}}{\cancel{1}}\right) = \dfrac{31}{\cancel{8}_2}\left(\dfrac{\cancel{4}}{1}\right)$

$WF = \mathbf{\dfrac{31}{2}}$

4. $\dfrac{72}{100}(WN) = 216$

$WN = \mathbf{300}$

of 300

Before, 100%

84 is 28%

216 is 72%

After

5. $\dfrac{135}{100}(WN) = 405$

$WN = \mathbf{300}$

of 300

Before, 100%

405 is 135%

After

6. $\dfrac{350}{100}(48) = WN$

$\mathbf{168} = WN$

of 48

Before, 100%

168 is 350%

After

7. $2\dfrac{1}{4} + 3\dfrac{1}{5}k + \dfrac{1}{8} = 0$

$\dfrac{16}{5}k = -\dfrac{1}{8} - \dfrac{18}{8}$

$k = -\dfrac{19}{8} \cdot \dfrac{5}{16} = \mathbf{-\dfrac{95}{128}}$

8. $-[-(-p)] - (-4)(-2 - p) = -(4 - 2p)$
$\qquad -5p - 8 = -4 + 2p$
$\qquad -4 = 7p$
$\qquad -\dfrac{4}{7} = p$

9. (a) $3x + 2y = 7$
(b) $x = 7 - 3y$
Substitute (b) into (a) and get:
(a$'$) $3(7 - 3y) + 2y = 7$
$\qquad\qquad -7y = -14$
$\qquad\qquad y = 2$

(b) $x = 7 - 3(2) = 1$
$\mathbf{(1, 2)}$

10. (a) $x + 2y = -6$
(b) $y = 3x + 4$
Substitute (b) into (a) and get:
(a$'$) $x + 2(3x + 4) = -6$
$\qquad\qquad 7x = -14$
$\qquad\qquad x = -2$
(b) $y = 3(-2) + 4 = -2$
$\mathbf{(-2, -2)}$

11. (a) $x + y = 6$
(b) $x = 9 - 2y$
Substitute (b) into (a) and get:
(a$'$) $(9 - 2y) + y = 6$
$\qquad\qquad 3 = y$
(b) $x = 9 - 2(3) = 3$
$\mathbf{(3, 3)}$

12. $(3x - 4)(2 - x) = 6x - 8 - 3x^2 + 4x$
$\qquad = \mathbf{-3x^2 + 10x - 8}$

13. $(x + 1)(x^2 + 2x + 2)$
$= x^3 + 2x^2 + 2x + x^2 + 2x + 2$
$= x^3 + 3x^2 + 4x + 2$

14. $y = -3$ (horizontal line)

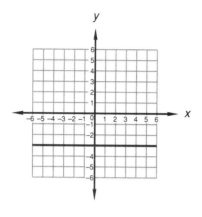

15. $y = -3x - 2$

x	0	1	-2
y	-2	-5	4

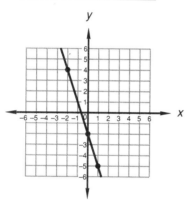

16. $y = \dfrac{1}{2}x - 2$

x	0	6	-6
y	-2	1	-5

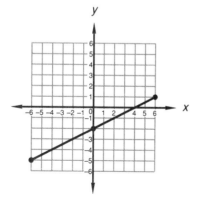

17. $\dfrac{\frac{m}{n}}{z} = \dfrac{\frac{m}{n}}{z} \cdot \dfrac{\frac{1}{z}}{\frac{1}{z}} = \dfrac{m}{nz}$

18. $\dfrac{m + 1}{\frac{n}{d}} = \dfrac{\frac{m + 1}{1}}{\frac{n}{d}} \cdot \dfrac{\frac{d}{n}}{\frac{d}{n}} = \dfrac{d(m + 1)}{n}$

19. $\dfrac{\frac{am}{n}}{\frac{x}{dc}} = \dfrac{\frac{am}{n}}{\frac{x}{dc}} \cdot \dfrac{\frac{dc}{x}}{\frac{dc}{x}} = \dfrac{amdc}{nx}$

20. $A = A_{\text{Triangle}} + A_{\text{Semicircle}}$
$= \left(\dfrac{1}{2}(5)(8) + \dfrac{1}{2}\pi(4)^2 \right)(100)(100) \text{ cm}^2$
$\approx \mathbf{451{,}200 \text{ cm}^2}$

21. $\dfrac{4}{x + y} - \dfrac{3}{y^2} = \dfrac{4y^2}{y^2(x + y)} - \dfrac{3(x + y)}{y^2(x + y)}$
$= \dfrac{4y^2 - 3x - 3y}{xy^2 + y^3}$

22. $\dfrac{a}{x^2 y} + 4a - \dfrac{m}{x + y} = \dfrac{a(x + y)}{x^2 y(x + y)}$
$+ \dfrac{4ax^2 y(x + y)}{x^2 y(x + y)} - \dfrac{mx^2 y}{x^2 y(x + y)}$
$= \dfrac{ax + ay + 4ax^3 y + 4ax^2 y^2 - mx^2 y}{x^2 y(x + y)}$

23. $\dfrac{x + y}{a^2} + \dfrac{y^2}{a} = \dfrac{x + y}{a^2} + \dfrac{ay^2}{a^2}$
$= \dfrac{x + y + ay^2}{a^2}$

24. $\dfrac{(x^2)^{-3}(yx)^2 x^0}{x^2 y^{-2}(xy^{-2})^3} = \dfrac{x^{-6} y^2 x^2}{x^2 y^{-2} x^3 y^{-6}} = x^{-9} y^{10}$

25. $\left(\dfrac{x^{-2}}{y^4} \right)^2 \left(\dfrac{x}{y} \right) = \dfrac{x^{-4} x}{y^8 y} = x^{-3} y^{-9}$

26. $\dfrac{p^9 (3x)^2 y}{x^0 (x^{-1} y^{-2})^3} = \dfrac{p^9 9x^2 y}{x^{-3} y^{-6}} = 9p^9 x^5 y^7$

27. $\dfrac{4x^2 - 4}{4} = \dfrac{4(x^2 - 1)}{4} = x^2 - 1$

28. $\dfrac{x^{-4}y}{p^2}\left(\dfrac{y^{-1}}{x^4} + \dfrac{2x^{-4}p^{-2}}{y^{-1}}\right)$

$= \dfrac{x^{-4}yy^{-1}}{p^2x^4} + \dfrac{x^{-4}y2x^{-4}p^{-2}}{p^2y^{-1}}$

$= x^{-8}p^{-2} + 2x^{-8}p^{-4}y^2$

29. $\dfrac{xy}{z} - \dfrac{3x^2y^2}{xyz} + \dfrac{2x^3x^{-2}yz^{-2}}{z^{-1}} + \dfrac{5xy}{zy^{-2}}$

$= xyz^{-1} - 3xyz^{-1} + 2xyz^{-1} + 5xy^3z^{-1} = \mathbf{5xy^3z^{-1}}$

30. $-\{3(-3 \cdot 2^0)[-(3 - 2)(-2)] - |-4|\} + \sqrt[3]{64}$

$= -\{-9[2] - 4\} + 4 = \mathbf{26}$

PROBLEM SET 60

1. $\dfrac{190}{100}N = 76$

$N = \mathbf{40}$

of 40   76 is 190%

Before, 100%   After

2. $\dfrac{WP}{100}(180) = 36$

$WP = \mathbf{20\ percent}$

of 180   36 is 20%

144 is 80%

Before, 100%   After

3. $\dfrac{90}{100}(0.4) = WN$

$\mathbf{0.36} = WN$

of 0.4   0.04 is 10%

0.36 is 90%

Before, 100%   After

4. $\dfrac{160}{100}(170) = WN$

$\mathbf{272} = WN$

of 170   272 is 160%

Before, 100%   After

5. Overall average $= \dfrac{(5 \times 200) + (20 \times 400)}{5 + 20}$

$= \dfrac{1000 + 8000}{25}$

$= \mathbf{360}$

6. $V = A_{Base} \times \text{height}$

$= \left[(20)(12) + \dfrac{1}{2}(28)(13)\right]\text{m}^2 \times \dfrac{10}{100}\ \text{m}$

$= \dfrac{(422)(10)}{100}\ \text{m}^3 = \mathbf{42.2\ m^3}$

S.A. $= 2(A_{Base}) + (\text{perimeter})(\text{height})$

$= 2(422)\ \text{m}^2 + (109.9)\left(\dfrac{10}{100}\right)\text{m}^2$

$= (844 + 10.99)\ \text{m}^2 = \mathbf{854.99\ m^2}$

7. (a) $2x - 2y = 18$

(b) $x = 6 - 2y$

Substitute (b) into (a) and get:

(a') $2(6 - 2y) - 2y = 18$

$\qquad 12 - 4y - 2y = 18$

$\qquad\qquad\qquad -6y = 6$

$\qquad\qquad\qquad\quad y = -1$

(b) $x = 6 - 2(-1) = 6 + 2 = 8$

$\mathbf{(8, -1)}$

8. (a) $3x - y = 4$

(b) $y = 6 - 2x$

Substitute (b) into (a) and get:

(a') $3x - (6 - 2x) = 4$

$\qquad 3x - 6 + 2x = 4$

$\qquad\qquad\qquad 5x = 10$

$\qquad\qquad\qquad\ x = 2$

(b) $y = 6 - 2(2) = 6 - 4 = 2$

$\mathbf{(2, 2)}$

9. (a) $5x - 3y = 6$

(b) $y = 2x + 3$

Substitute (b) into (a) and get:

(a') $5x - 3(2x + 3) = 6$

$\qquad 5x - 6x - 9 = 6$

$\qquad\qquad\qquad -x = 15$

$\qquad\qquad\qquad\ x = -15$

(b) $y = 2(-15) + 3 = -30 + 3 = -27$

$\mathbf{(-15, -27)}$

10. $(x + 12)^2 = (x + 12)(x + 12)$

$= x^2 + 12x + 12x + 144 = \mathbf{x^2 + 24x + 144}$

11. $(2x - 3)(2x^2 - 3x + 4)$

$= 4x^3 - 6x^2 + 8x - 6x^2 + 9x - 12$

$= \mathbf{4x^3 - 12x^2 + 17x - 12}$

12. $A = \{0, 1, 3, 5, 7\}$
$B = \{2, 4, 6, 8\}$
$C = \{0, 1, 2, 3, 4, 5\}$

(a) $0 \in B$ — False, because 0 is not a member of B.
(b) $0 \in C$ — True, because 0 is a member of C.
(c) $2 \notin B$ — False, because 2 is a member of B.
(d) $2 \notin A$ — True, because 2 is not a member of A.

13. $3y + 2x = 3$
$3y = -2x + 3$
$y = -\dfrac{2}{3}x + 1$

x	0	3	-3
y	1	-1	3

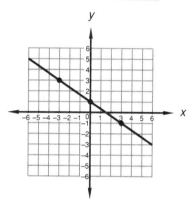

14. $\dfrac{\frac{1}{a}}{x} = \dfrac{1}{a} \cdot \dfrac{\frac{1}{x}}{\frac{1}{x}} = \dfrac{1}{a} \cdot \dfrac{1}{x} = \dfrac{1}{ax}$

15. $\dfrac{\frac{b}{c}}{\frac{1}{a+b}} = \dfrac{b}{c} \cdot \dfrac{a+b}{1} = \dfrac{ab+b^2}{c}$

16. $\dfrac{\frac{x}{c}}{x+y} = \dfrac{x}{c} \cdot \dfrac{1}{x+y} = \dfrac{x}{xc+yc}$

17. $\dfrac{\frac{m}{a}}{mc^2} = \dfrac{m}{1} \cdot \dfrac{mc^2}{a} = \dfrac{m^2c^2}{a}$

18. $\dfrac{4}{2x^2} - \dfrac{3}{4x^2y} + \dfrac{2a}{8x^3p}$

$= \dfrac{4(4xyp)}{8x^3yp} - \dfrac{3(2xp)}{8x^3yp} + \dfrac{2a(y)}{8x^3yp}$

$= \dfrac{16xyp - 6xp + 2ay}{8x^3yp}$

19. $\dfrac{m}{b(b+c)} + \dfrac{k}{b} = \dfrac{m + k(b+c)}{b(b+c)}$

$= \dfrac{m + kb + kc}{b^2 + bc}$

20. $\dfrac{3p}{xm^2} - \dfrac{a}{2m^3} + \dfrac{4k}{m^4a}$

$= \dfrac{3p(2m^2a)}{2m^4ax} - \dfrac{a(xma)}{2m^4ax} + \dfrac{4k(2x)}{2m^4ax}$

$= \dfrac{6apm^2 - a^2xm + 8kx}{2m^4ax}$

21. $4k^2ax - 8ka^2x^2 + 12k^3a^4x^2$
$= 4kax(k - 2ax + 3k^2a^3x)$

22. $\dfrac{x^2y - x^2yz}{xyz} = \dfrac{xy(x - xz)}{xyz} = \dfrac{x - xz}{z}$

23. $(4x^0y^2m)^{-2}(2y^{-4}m^0x)^4 = (16^{-1}y^{-4}m^{-2})(16y^{-16}x^4)$
$= x^4y^{-20}m^{-2}$

24. $\dfrac{(k^3p^0)^{-2}k^2p^5}{p^{-5}p^0k^{-1}} = k^{-6}k^2p^5p^5k = k^{-3}p^{10}$

25. $\left(\dfrac{x^2y^{-2}}{p^4k^0}\right)^{-2}\left(\dfrac{y^{-2}}{x}\right) = x^{-4}y^4p^8y^{-2}x^{-1} = x^{-5}y^2p^8$

26. $\dfrac{x^{-2}}{4m^2}\left(\dfrac{4x^2}{m^{-2}} - \dfrac{8m^{-2}k}{x^{-2}}\right)$

$= \dfrac{x^{-2}4x^2}{4m^2m^{-2}} - \dfrac{x^{-2}8m^{-2}k}{4m^2x^{-2}} = 1 - 2m^{-4}k$

27. $3x^2y^2m - \dfrac{m}{x^{-2}y^{-2}} + \dfrac{4x^2y^2}{m^{-1}} - \dfrac{3x^4y^4}{xy}$
$= 3x^2y^2m - x^2y^2m + 4x^2y^2m - 3x^3y^3$
$= 6x^2y^2m - 3x^3y^3$

28. $a^{-3} - a(x - a) = (-2)^{-3} - (-2)(4 - (-2))$
$= -\dfrac{1}{8} + 12 = \dfrac{95}{8}$

29. $-3(-2 - x) - 3^2 - |-2| = -(-2x - 3)$
$6 + 3x - 9 - 2 = 2x + 3$
$3x - 5 = 2x + 3$
$x = 8$

30. $-2\{-[(3^0 - 5) - (2 - 4)] - |-3| + 2\} + \sqrt[3]{27}$
$= -2\{-[-4 + 2] - 3 + 2\} + 3 = -2\{1\} + 3$
$= 1$

PROBLEM SET 61

1. $\frac{230}{100}N = 920$

$N = \mathbf{400}$

2. $\frac{WP}{100}(240) = 60$

$WP = \mathbf{25\%}$

3. $\frac{70}{100}WN = 4900$

$WN = \mathbf{7000}$

4. $\left(\frac{120}{100}\right)(240) = WN$

$\mathbf{288} = WN$

5. Overall Average $= \dfrac{(7 \times 21) + (3 \times 11)}{7 + 3}$

$= \dfrac{180}{10} = \mathbf{18}$

6. $V_{Cylinder} = A_{Base} \times \text{height}$

$= [\pi(10)^2] \text{ cm}^2 \times 20 \text{ cm}$

$= (100\pi)(20) \text{ cm}^3 \approx \mathbf{6280 \text{ cm}^3}$

$V_{Sphere} = \dfrac{2}{3}V_{Cylinder}$

$= \dfrac{2}{3}(100\pi)(20) \text{ cm}^3$

$\approx \mathbf{4186.67 \text{ cm}^3}$

7. (a) $2x + 3y = 7$

(b) $x = y - 1$

Substitute (b) into (a) and get:

(a′) $2(y - 1) + 3y = 7$

$2y - 2 + 3y = 7$

$5y = 9$

$y = \dfrac{9}{5}$

(b) $x = \left(\dfrac{9}{5}\right) - 1 = \dfrac{4}{5}$

$\left(\dfrac{4}{5}, \dfrac{9}{5}\right)$

8. (a) $3x - y = 3$

(b) $y = 2x - 1$

Substitute (b) into (a) and get:

(a′) $3x - (2x - 1) = 3$

$3x - 2x + 1 = 3$

$x = 2$

(b) $y = 2(2) - 1 = 3$

$\mathbf{(2, 3)}$

9. (a) $4x + y = 9$

(b) $x = 3y - 1$

Substitute (b) into (a) and get:

(a′) $4(3y - 1) + y = 9$

$12y - 4 + y = 9$

$13y = 13$

$y = 1$

(b) $x = 3(1) - 1 = 2$

$\mathbf{(2, 1)}$

10. $(x + 5)^2 = (x + 5)(x + 5)$

$= x^2 + 5x + 5x + 25 = \mathbf{x^2 + 10x + 25}$

11. $(2x - 3)(3x^2 - 2x + 2)$

$= 6x^3 - 4x^2 + 4x - 9x^2 + 6x - 6$

$= \mathbf{6x^3 - 13x^2 + 10x - 6}$

12. $A = \{0, 5, 10, 12, 13\}$

$B = \{5, 10, 12\}$

$C = \{10, 12\}$

(a) $0 \in C$ False, because 0 is not a member of C.

(b) $0 \in A$ True, because 0 is a member of A.

(c) $6 \notin B$ True, because 6 is not a member of B.

13. $4y + 8x = 12$

$4y = -8x + 12$

$y = -2x + 3$

x	0	3	-1
y	3	-3	5

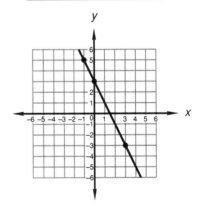

14. $\dfrac{\frac{1}{x}}{a} = \dfrac{1}{x} \cdot \dfrac{1}{a} = \dfrac{1}{xa}$

15. $\dfrac{\frac{1}{x+y}}{\frac{a}{b}} = \dfrac{1}{x+y} \cdot \dfrac{b}{a} = \dfrac{b}{ax + ay}$

16. $\dfrac{x+y}{\frac{1}{c}} = (x + y)(c) = \mathbf{cx + cy}$

17. $\dfrac{x}{\frac{a}{b}} = \dfrac{x}{1} \cdot \dfrac{b}{a} = \dfrac{xb}{a}$

18. $\dfrac{2}{3x^4} - \dfrac{1}{3x^2 y} + \dfrac{a}{2x^3 p}$

$= \dfrac{2(2py)}{6x^4 yp} - \dfrac{2x^2 p}{6x^4 yp} + \dfrac{a(3xy)}{6x^4 yp}$

$= \dfrac{4py - 2x^2 p + 3axy}{6x^4 yp}$

19. $\dfrac{m}{k(k + c)} + \dfrac{m}{k} = \dfrac{m + mk + mc}{k(k + c)}$

20. $\dfrac{3x}{2xp^2} - \dfrac{m}{p^3} + \dfrac{4z}{p^4 a^2}$

$= \dfrac{3(p^2 a^2)}{2p^4 a^2} - \dfrac{m(2pa^2)}{2p^4 a^2} + \dfrac{4z(2)}{2p^4 a^2}$

$= \dfrac{3p^2 a^2 - 2mpa^2 + 8z}{2p^4 a^2}$

21. $2p^2 bc - 8b^2 c^2 + 12p^3 b^4 c^2$
$= 2bc(p^2 - 4bc + 6p^3 b^3 c)$

22. $\dfrac{4x^2 + 4}{4} = \dfrac{4(x^2 + 1)}{4} = x^2 + 1$

23. $(2m^2 y^0)^{-2}(2m^2 yx)^4 = 4^{-1}m^{-4}16m^8 y^4 x^4$
$= 4m^4 y^4 x^4$

24. $\dfrac{(x^3 m^0)^{-2} x^2 m^5}{m^{-5} m^0 x^{-1}} = x^{-6} x^2 m^5 m^5 x = x^{-3} m^{10}$

25. $\left(\dfrac{m^2 x^{-2}}{p^4 k^0}\right)^{-2}\left(\dfrac{x^{-2}}{m}\right) = \dfrac{m^{-4} x^4 x^{-2}}{p^{-8} m}$
$= m^{-4} x^4 x^{-2} p^8 m^{-1} = m^{-5} p^8 x^2$

26. $\dfrac{p^{-3}}{4m^2}\left(\dfrac{2p^2}{m^{-2}} - \dfrac{8m^{-2}}{a^2 b^3 p}\right)$

$= \dfrac{p^{-3} 2p^2}{4m^2 m^{-2}} - \dfrac{p^{-3} 8m^{-2}}{4m^2 a^2 b^3 p}$

$= \dfrac{p^{-1}}{2} - 2m^{-4} p^{-4} a^{-2} b^{-3}$

27. $\dfrac{4x^3 m^4}{y} + 3xx^2 y^{-1} m^4 + \dfrac{2x^4 m^4}{x^2 y}$

$= \dfrac{4x^3 m^4}{y} + \dfrac{3x^3 m^4}{y} + \dfrac{2x^2 m^4}{y}$

$= \dfrac{7x^3 m^4 + 2x^2 m^4}{y} = \dfrac{x^2 m^4(7x + 2)}{y}$

28. $a^2 - x(a^{-3} - x) = (-2)^2 - 2((-2)^{-3} - 2)$
$= 4 - 2\left(-\dfrac{1}{8} - \dfrac{16}{8}\right) = 4 + \dfrac{17}{4} = \dfrac{33}{4}$

29. $-2(-3 - x) - 3^2 + 1 - 4 = -(3x + 2)$
$6 + 2x - 9 - 3 = -3x - 2$
$2x - 6 = -3x - 2$
$5x = 4$
$x = \dfrac{4}{5}$

30. $-x\{-[(2^0 - 3) - (1 - 4)]\} + 3|-2| + \sqrt[3]{-27}$
$= -x\{-[-2 + 3]\} + 6 - 3 = -x(-1) + 3$
$= x + 3$

PROBLEM SET 62

1. $(6N + 7)4 = 30(-N) + 10$
$24N + 28 = -30N + 10$
$54N = -18$
$N = -\dfrac{1}{3}$

2. $\dfrac{(5 \times 6.5) + (15 \times 4.5)}{5 + 15} = \dfrac{100}{20} = 5$

3. $V_{Prism} = A_{Base} \times \text{height}$

$= \left[(16)(13) + \dfrac{1}{2}(17)(11)\right] m^2 \times 10 \text{ m}$

$= (301.5)(10) \text{ m}^3 = 3015 \text{ m}^3$

$V_{Pyramid} = \dfrac{1}{3} V_{Prism}$

$= \dfrac{1}{3}\left[\left((16)(13) + \dfrac{1}{2}(17)(11)\right)(11)\right] m^3$

$= \dfrac{1}{3}(301.5)(11) \text{ m}^3 = 1105.5 \text{ m}^3$

4. $420 \text{ km} \times \dfrac{1000 \text{ m}}{1 \text{ km}} \times \dfrac{100 \text{ cm}}{1 \text{ m}} \times \dfrac{1 \text{ in.}}{2.54 \text{ cm}}$

$\times \dfrac{1 \text{ ft}}{12 \text{ in.}} = \dfrac{420(1000)(100)}{(2.54)(12)} \text{ ft}$

5. $\left(5\dfrac{1}{8}\right)WN = \dfrac{3}{16}$

$\dfrac{41}{8} WN = \dfrac{3}{16}$

$WN = \dfrac{3}{16}\left(\dfrac{8}{41}\right)$

$WN = \dfrac{3}{82}$

6. $WD(0.004) = 0.00008$
$WD = 0.02$

7. $3\frac{2}{5}p + 1\frac{1}{2} = -2\frac{3}{8}$

$$\frac{17}{5}p = -\frac{19}{8} - \frac{3}{2}$$

$$\frac{17}{5}p = -\frac{19}{8} - \frac{12}{8}$$

$$p = -\frac{31}{8} \cdot \frac{5}{17} = -\frac{155}{136}$$

8. $-(-k) - (-2)(2k - 5) + 7 = -(2k + 4)$

$$k + 4k - 10 + 7 = -2k - 4$$

$$5k - 3 = -2k - 4$$

$$7k = -1$$

$$k = -\frac{1}{7}$$

9. $2 < x \le 4$

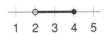

10. $K = \{0, 1, 2, 5, 7\}$

11. $A = \{1, 2, 3\}$ and $B = \{2, 3, 4, 0\}$

(a) $7 \in B$ False, because 7 is not a member of B.
(b) $3 \notin A$ False, because 3 is a member of A.
(c) $0 \in B$ True, because 0 is a member of B.

12. (a) $x = -19 - 6y$
(b) $2x + 3y = -11$
Substitute (a) into (b) and get:
(b′) $2(-19 - 6y) + 3y = -11$
$$-38 - 12y + 3y = -11$$
$$-9y = 27$$
$$y = -3$$

(a) $x = -19 - 6(-3) = -1$
(−1, −3)

13. (a) $2x - 3y = 5$
(b) $x = -2y - 8$
Substitute (b) into (a) and get:
(a′) $2(-2y - 8) - 3y = 5$
$$-4y - 16 - 3y = 5$$
$$-7y = 21$$
$$y = -3$$

(b) $x = -2(-3) - 8 = -2$
(−2, −3)

14. (a) $y = 4x + 9$
(b) $3x + y = -12$
Substitute (a) into (b) and get:
(b′) $3x + (4x + 9) = -12$
$$7x = -21$$
$$x = -3$$

(a) $y = 4(-3) + 9 = -3$
(−3, −3)

15. $(5 + 3x)(8 - 2x) = 40 + 24x - 10x - 6x^2$
$$= \mathbf{-6x^2 + 14x + 40}$$

16. $(4x + 2)^2 = (4x + 2)(4x + 2)$
$$= 16x^2 + 8x + 8x + 4 = \mathbf{16x^2 + 16x + 4}$$

17. $y = -3$ (horizontal line)

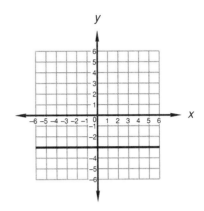

18. $3y + x = -9$
$$3y = -x - 9$$
$$y = -\frac{1}{3}x - 3$$

x	0	3	-3
y	-3	-4	-2

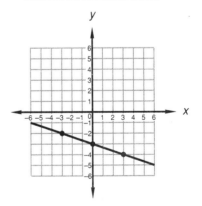

19. $\dfrac{x}{\dfrac{1}{a + b}} = x(a + b) = \mathbf{ax + bx}$

20. $\dfrac{\dfrac{1}{a + b}}{x} = \dfrac{1}{a + b} \cdot \dfrac{1}{x} = \dfrac{1}{\mathbf{ax + bx}}$

21. $\dfrac{\dfrac{a}{b}}{\dfrac{1}{x}} = \dfrac{a}{b} \cdot x = \dfrac{\mathbf{ax}}{\mathbf{b}}$

22. $\dfrac{\dfrac{a + b}{x}}{\dfrac{1}{x}} = \dfrac{a + b}{x} \cdot x = \boldsymbol{a + b}$

23. $\dfrac{x}{y} + \dfrac{1}{y + 1} = \dfrac{x(y + 1)}{y(y + 1)} + \dfrac{y}{y(y + 1)}$

$= \dfrac{xy + x + y}{y^2 + y}$

24. $1 + \dfrac{x}{y} = \dfrac{y + x}{y}$

25. $y - \dfrac{1}{y} = \dfrac{y^2 - 1}{y}$

26. $10x^2y^5z - 5x^5y^2z^5 - 10x^4y^4z^4$
$= \boldsymbol{5x^2y^2z(2y^3 - x^3z^4 - 2x^2y^2z^3)}$

27. $\dfrac{(x^2y^0m)(m^{-2}y)}{m^2(my^{-2})} = \dfrac{x^2mm^{-2}y}{m^2my^{-2}} = x^2m^{-1}ym^{-3}y^2$
$= \boldsymbol{x^2y^3m^{-4}}$

28. $\dfrac{(x^0y^2)^{-2}y^5x}{x^2x^{-5}yy^{-3}} = \dfrac{y^{-4}y^5x}{x^{-3}y^{-2}} = yxx^3y^2 = \boldsymbol{x^4y^3}$

29. $\left(\dfrac{xy^{-2}}{m^2}\right)^{-3} \dfrac{(y^{-2})^0}{(2x^2)^{-3}} = \dfrac{x^{-3}y^6}{m^{-6}8^{-1}x^{-6}}$
$= x^{-3}y^6m^68x^6 = \boldsymbol{8m^6x^3y^6}$

30. $-2\{[(3 - 5) - (2^0 - 6) - 2]$
$- [(4 - 3) - 2(-3)]\} + \sqrt[3]{-8}$
$= -2\{[-2 + 5 - 2] - [1 + 6]\} - 2$
$= -2\{[1] - [7]\} - 2 = \boldsymbol{10}$

PROBLEM SET 63

1.

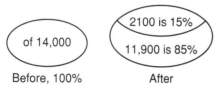

Before, 100%   After

$\dfrac{15}{100}WN = 2100$

$WN = \boldsymbol{14{,}000}$

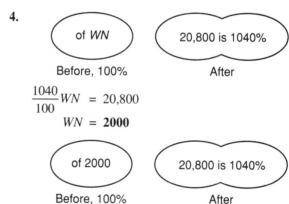

Before, 100%   After

2.

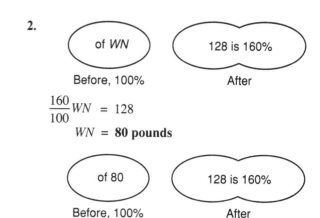

$\dfrac{160}{100}WN = 128$

$WN = \boldsymbol{80 \text{ pounds}}$

of 80 — Before, 100%   128 is 160% — After

3.

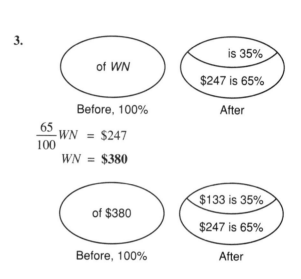

$\dfrac{65}{100}WN = \$247$

$WN = \boldsymbol{\$380}$

of \$380 — Before, 100%   \$133 is 35%, \$247 is 65% — After

4.

of WN — Before, 100%   20,800 is 1040% — After

$\dfrac{1040}{100}WN = 20{,}800$

$WN = \boldsymbol{2000}$

of 2000 — Before, 100%   20,800 is 1040% — After

5. $\dfrac{7}{9} = \dfrac{x}{1098}$
$x = \boldsymbol{854}$

6. $A = \{1, 5, 7, 0\}$
$B = \{0, 1, 5\}$

   (a) $1 \notin A$ False, because 1 is a member of A.
   (b) $7 \notin B$ True, because 7 is not a member of B.
   (c) $0 \in A$ True, because 0 is a member of A.

7. $\dfrac{(60)(1000) + (240)(800)}{60 + 240} = \dfrac{252{,}000}{300}$
$= \boldsymbol{840 \text{ gallons}}$

8. Convert 300,000 square centimeters to square miles:

$$300{,}000 \ \cancel{cm^2} \times \frac{1 \ \cancel{in.}}{2.54 \ \cancel{cm}} \times \frac{1 \ \cancel{in.}}{2.54 \ \cancel{cm}} \times \frac{1 \ \cancel{ft}}{12 \ \cancel{in.}}$$

$$\times \frac{1 \ \cancel{ft}}{12 \ \cancel{in.}} \times \frac{1 \ mi}{5280 \ \cancel{ft}} \times \frac{1 \ mi}{5280 \ \cancel{ft}}$$

$$= \frac{300{,}000}{(2.54)(2.54)(12)(12)(5280)(5280)} \ mi^2$$

9. $V_{Prism} = A_{Base} \times height$

$$= \left[(40)(7) + \frac{1}{2}(24)(12) \right] m^2 \times 10 \ m$$

$$= (424)(10)(100)(100)(100) \ cm^3$$

$$= \mathbf{4{,}240{,}000{,}000 \ cm^3}$$

$$V_{Pyramid} = \frac{1}{3} V_{Prism}$$

$$= \frac{1}{3}(424)(10)(100)(100)(100) \ cm^3$$

$$= \mathbf{1{,}413{,}333{,}333.3 \ cm^3}$$

10. (a) $3x - 5y = 36$
(b) $x + 3y = -16$
$$x = -3y - 16$$
Substitute (b) into (a) and get:
(a′) $3(-3y - 16) - 5y = 36$
$$-9y - 48 - 5y = 36$$
$$-14y = 84$$
$$y = -6$$

(b) $x = -3(-6) - 16 = 2$
$(\mathbf{2, -6})$

11. $(2x - 4)(x - 4) = 2x^2 - 4x - 8x + 16$
$$= \mathbf{2x^2 - 12x + 16}$$

12. $(4 - 2x)(x^2 + 3x + 2)$
$$= 4x^2 + 12x + 8 - 2x^3 - 6x^2 - 4x$$
$$= \mathbf{-2x^3 - 2x^2 + 8x + 8}$$

13. $y = -2$ (horizontal line)

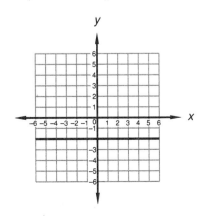

14. $y = -2x$

x	0	−1	1
y	0	2	−2

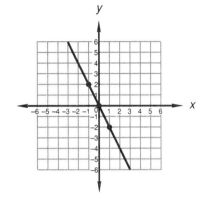

15. $y + 2x + 2 = 0$
$$y = -2x - 2$$

x	0	−1	1
y	−2	0	−4

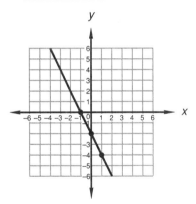

16. $\dfrac{\dfrac{a}{b}}{a + b} = a \cdot \dfrac{a + b}{b} = \dfrac{a^2 + ab}{b}$

17. $\dfrac{\dfrac{a}{c}}{d + c} = \dfrac{a}{c} \cdot \dfrac{1}{d + c} = \dfrac{a}{cd + c^2}$

18. $V_{Sphere} = \dfrac{2}{3} V_{Cylinder}$

$$= \frac{2}{3} \left[A_{Base} \times height \right]$$

$$= \frac{2}{3} \left[\pi(8)^2 \times 16 \right] m^3$$

$$= \frac{2}{3}(64\pi)(16) \ m^3 \approx \mathbf{2143.57 \ m^3}$$

19. $\dfrac{x}{x + y} + y = \dfrac{x + xy + y^2}{x + y}$

20. $\dfrac{a}{x^2c} + c^3 = \dfrac{a + c^4x^2}{x^2c}$

21. $\dfrac{m}{c^2} - \dfrac{1}{c} + \dfrac{b}{c + b}$

$= \dfrac{m(c + b)}{c^2(c + b)} - \dfrac{c(c + b)}{c^2(c + b)} + \dfrac{b(c^2)}{c^2(c + b)}$

$= \dfrac{mc + mb - c^2 - bc + bc^2}{c^3 + c^2b}$

22. $3x^3yp^6 - 3x^2y^2p^2 + 9x^2yp^5$
$= 3x^2yp^2(xp^4 - y + 3p^3)$

23. $\dfrac{x^2ym + 3x^2ymz}{x^2ym} = \dfrac{x^2ym(1 + 3z)}{x^2ym} = 1 + 3z$

24. $\dfrac{(x^{-2})^0(x^2y^{-2})^{-2}}{p^0x^{-4}(y^2)^{-2}} = x^{-4}y^4x^4y^4 = y^8$

25. $\left(\dfrac{x^2p^2}{4y^{-2}}\right)^{-2}\dfrac{(y^{-2})^2}{2y^0p^5} = x^{-4}p^{-4}16y^{-4}y^{-4}2^{-1}p^{-5}$
$= 8x^{-4}y^{-8}p^{-9}$

26. $\dfrac{(m^2xy)mxy}{(m^2x^2y)^{-2}(xy)} = \dfrac{m^3xy}{m^{-4}x^{-4}y^{-2}} = m^3xym^4x^4y^2$
$= m^7x^5y^3$

27. $\dfrac{-x^{-2}}{y^2}\left(-x^2y^2 + \dfrac{3x^4}{xy^2}\right)$
$= \dfrac{x^{-2}x^2y^2}{y^2} - \dfrac{x^{-2}3x^4}{xy^2y^2} = 1 - 3xy^{-4}$

28. $xym - \dfrac{3x^2y^2m}{xy} + \dfrac{4x^{-2}y^2}{x^{-3}m^{-1}y} - \dfrac{3xy}{m^{-1}}$
$= xym - 3xym + 4xym - 3xym = -xym$

29. $x - xy(y^0 - x^{-3}) = (-2) - (-2)(3)(3^0 - (-2)^{-3})$
$= -2 + 6\left(1 + \dfrac{1}{8}\right) = -2 + \dfrac{27}{4} = \dfrac{19}{4}$

30. $-2(-3 - |-2|)x - 2 - 3x = -2 - \dfrac{1}{(-2)^{-3}}$
$10x - 2 - 3x = -2 + 8$
$7x = 8$
$x = \dfrac{8}{7}$

1. $Pa = 2;\; Pl = 13;\; T = 15$
$\dfrac{13}{15} = \dfrac{Pl}{315}$
$Pl = \mathbf{273}$

2.

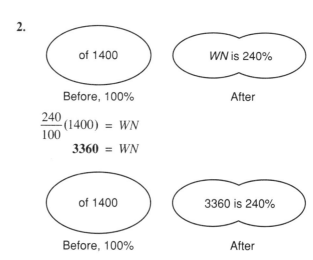

$\dfrac{240}{100}(1400) = WN$
$\mathbf{3360} = WN$

3.

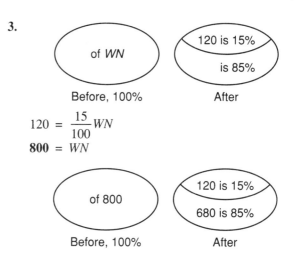

$120 = \dfrac{15}{100}WN$
$\mathbf{800} = WN$

4. $\left(7\dfrac{2}{5}\right)WN = 1\dfrac{7}{10}$
$\left(\dfrac{5}{37}\right)\dfrac{37}{5}WN = \dfrac{17}{10}\left(\dfrac{5}{37}\right)$
$WN = \dfrac{17}{74}$

5. $WF\left(14\dfrac{1}{4}\right) = \dfrac{3}{8}$
$WF\left(\dfrac{57}{4}\right) = \dfrac{3}{8}$
$WF = \dfrac{3}{8} \cdot \dfrac{4}{57}$
$WF = \dfrac{1}{38}$

6. $7\frac{2}{5}x + 5\frac{1}{3} = \frac{1}{15}$

$\quad\quad \frac{37}{5}x = \frac{1}{15} - \frac{80}{15}$

$\quad\quad\quad x = -\frac{79}{15} \cdot \frac{5}{37} = -\frac{79}{111}$

7. $-[-(-2p)] - 3(-3p + 15) = -(-4)(p - 12)$

$\quad -2p + 9p - 45 = 4p - 48$

$\quad\quad\quad 7p - 45 = 4p - 48$

$\quad\quad\quad\quad 3p = -3$

$\quad\quad\quad\quad p = -1$

8. $x \not\geq -2$

$\quad x < -2$

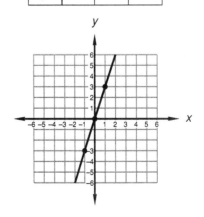

$\quad\quad -4 \quad -3 \quad -2 \quad -1 \quad\;\; 0$

9. $a^{-3}(a^{-2} - 2a) = (-2)^{-3}((-2)^{-2} - 2(-2))$

$\quad = -\frac{1}{8}\left(\frac{1}{4} + 4\right) = -\frac{1}{8}\left(\frac{17}{4}\right) = -\frac{17}{32}$

10. $3\sqrt{2} \in$ **Reals, irrationals**

11. $V_{Prism} = A_{Base} \times$ height

$\quad\quad = \left[(20)(20) + \frac{1}{2}(15)(20)\right] \text{ft}^2 \times 2(3) \text{ ft}$

$\quad\quad = (550)(2)(3) \text{ ft}^3 = \mathbf{3300 \text{ ft}^3}$

$\quad V_{Pyramid} = \frac{1}{3}V_{Prism}$

$\quad\quad\quad = \frac{1}{3}(550)(2)(3) \text{ ft}^3 = \mathbf{1100 \text{ ft}^3}$

12. (a) $4x + y = -5$

$\quad\quad\quad y = -4x - 5$

$\quad$ (b) $2x - y = -1$

$\quad$ Substitute (a) into (b) and get:

$\quad$ (b') $2x - (-4x - 5) = -1$

$\quad\quad\quad 2x + 4x + 5 = -1$

$\quad\quad\quad\quad 6x = -6$

$\quad\quad\quad\quad x = -1$

$\quad$ (a) $y = -4(-1) - 5 = -1$

$\quad$ **(–1, –1)**

13. (a) $x - 3y = -7$

$\quad\quad\quad x = 3y - 7$

$\quad$ (b) $3x + y = -1$

$\quad$ Substitute (a) into (b) and get:

$\quad$ (b') $3(3y - 7) + y = -1$

$\quad\quad\quad 9y - 21 + y = -1$

$\quad\quad\quad\quad 10y = 20$

$\quad\quad\quad\quad y = 2$

$\quad$ (a) $x = 3(2) - 7 = -1$

$\quad$ **(–1, 2)**

14. (a) $4x - y = -7$

$\quad\quad\quad -y = -4x - 7$

$\quad\quad\quad y = 4x + 7$

$\quad$ (b) $2x + 2y = 4$

$\quad$ Substitute (a) into (b) and get:

$\quad$ (b') $2x + 2(4x + 7) = 4$

$\quad\quad\quad 2x + 8x + 14 = 4$

$\quad\quad\quad\quad 10x = -10$

$\quad\quad\quad\quad x = -1$

$\quad$ (a) $y = 4(-1) + 7 = 3$

$\quad$ **(–1, 3)**

15. $(4x - 3)(x + 2) = 4x^2 - 3x + 8x - 6$

$\quad\quad = \mathbf{4x^2 + 5x - 6}$

16. $(4x + 3)^2 = (4x + 3)(4x + 3)$

$\quad\quad = 16x^2 + 12x + 12x + 9 = \mathbf{16x^2 + 24x + 9}$

17. $y = -3x$

x	0	1	-1
y	0	-3	3

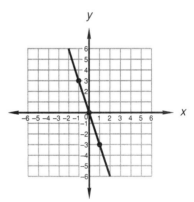

18. $y = 3x$

x	0	-1	1
y	0	-3	3

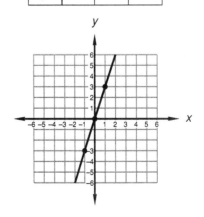

19. $4 + 3x - y = 0$

$\qquad 4 + 3x = y$

x	0	-1	-2
y	4	1	-2

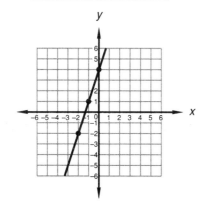

20. $\dfrac{\dfrac{a}{b}}{c + x} = \dfrac{a}{b} \cdot \dfrac{1}{c + x} = \dfrac{a}{bc + bx}$

21. $\dfrac{a}{\dfrac{b}{c + x}} = a \cdot \dfrac{c + x}{b} = \dfrac{ac + ax}{b}$

22. $\dfrac{1}{\dfrac{1}{a + b}} = a + b$

23. $\dfrac{4}{xyc} - \dfrac{5m}{xy(c + 1)} - \dfrac{3k}{xy^2}$

$\qquad = \dfrac{4y(c + 1) - 5mcy - 3kc(c + 1)}{xy^2 c(c + 1)}$

24. $k + \dfrac{1}{k} = \dfrac{k^2 + 1}{k}$

25. $my + \dfrac{p}{y} = \dfrac{my^2 + p}{y}$

26. $20x^2 m^5 k^6 - 10xm^4 k^4 + 30x^5 m^4 k^6$

$\qquad = \mathbf{10xm^4 k^4 (2xmk^2 - 1 + 3x^4 k^2)}$

27. $\dfrac{(x^2 y^0)^2 y^0 k^2}{(2x^2 k^5)^{-4} y} = \dfrac{x^4 k^2}{16^{-1} x^{-8} k^{-20} y}$

$\qquad = x^4 k^2 16 x^8 k^{20} y^{-1} = \mathbf{16x^{12} k^{22} y^{-1}}$

28. $\dfrac{a^0 x^2 x^0}{m^2 y^0 m^{-2}} = \boldsymbol{x^2}$

29. $\left(\dfrac{p^2 x}{y}\right)^2 \left(\dfrac{x^{-2} y}{p^2}\right)^3 = p^4 x^2 y^{-2} x^{-6} y^3 p^{-6} = \boldsymbol{x^{-4} y p^{-2}}$

30. $-2\{[(-2 - 2) - 3^0(-2 - 1)]$

$\qquad - [-2(-3 + 5) - 2]\} - |-2| + \sqrt[3]{-8}$

$= -2\{-4 + 3 - (-4 - 2)\} - 2 - 2$

$= -2\{5\} - 4 = \boldsymbol{-14}$

PROBLEM SET 65

1.

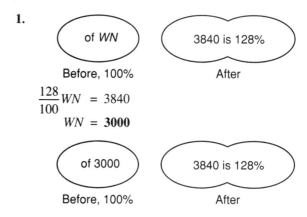

$\dfrac{128}{100} WN = 3840$

$\qquad WN = \mathbf{3000}$

2.

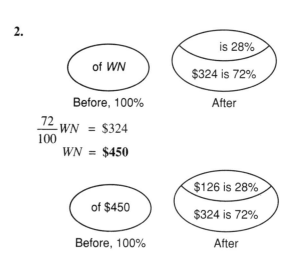

$\dfrac{72}{100} WN = \$324$

$\qquad WN = \mathbf{\$450}$

3.

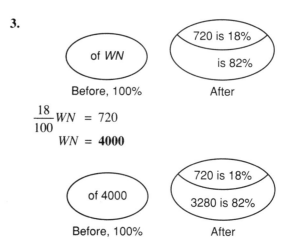

$\dfrac{18}{100} WN = 720$

$\qquad WN = \mathbf{4000}$

4. $5\frac{1}{2} \in$ **Reals, rationals**

5. $-2 \in$ **Integers, rationals, and reals**

6. $\sqrt{x} - 6 = \sqrt{36} - 6 = 6 - 6 = \mathbf{0}$

7. $\sqrt{8}$ between $2 \times 2 = 4$ and $3 \times 3 = 9$,
closer to 3.
Try 2.5 $2.5 \times 2.5 = 6.25$
Try 2.8 $2.8 \times 2.8 = 7.84$
Try 2.85 $2.85 \times 2.85 = 8.1225$
Try 2.82 $2.82 \times 2.82 = 7.9524$
$\sqrt{8} \approx \mathbf{2.8}$

8. (a) $3x - 2y = -1$
(b) $y = x - 1$
Substitute (b) into (a) and get:
(a') $3x - 2(x - 1) = -1$
$\quad\quad 3x - 2x + 2 = -1$
$\quad\quad\quad\quad\quad\quad x = -3$

(b) $y = (-3) - 1 = -4$
$(-3, -4)$

9. (a) $5x - 3y = 1$
(b) $7x - y = -5$
$\quad\quad\quad y = 7x + 5$
Substitute (b) into (a) and get:
(a') $5x - 3(7x + 5) = 1$
$\quad\quad 5x - 21x - 15 = 1$
$\quad\quad\quad\quad -16x = 16$
$\quad\quad\quad\quad\quad\quad x = -1$

(b) $y = 7(-1) + 5 = -2$
$(-1, -2)$

10. (a) $5x + 2y = -21$
(b) $-2x + y = 3$
$\quad\quad\quad\quad y = 2x + 3$
Substitute (b) into (a) and get:
(a') $5x + 2(2x + 3) = -21$
$\quad\quad 5x + 4x + 6 = -21$
$\quad\quad\quad\quad\quad 9x = -27$
$\quad\quad\quad\quad\quad\quad x = -3$

(b) $y = 2(-3) + 3 = -3$
$(-3, -3)$

11. $(2x - 5)(2x + 5) = 4x^2 - 10x + 10x - 25$
$= \mathbf{4x^2 - 25}$

12. $(3x - 2)^2 = (3x - 2)(3x - 2)$
$= 9x^2 - 6x - 6x + 4 = \mathbf{9x^2 - 12x + 4}$

13. $y = -3$ (horizontal line)

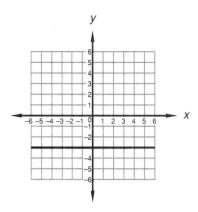

14. $y = -3x$

x	0	1	-1
y	0	-3	3

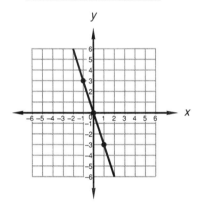

15. $3y + 9x + 9 = 0$
$\quad\quad 3y = -9x - 9$
$\quad\quad\quad y = -3x - 3$

x	0	1	-1
y	-3	-6	0

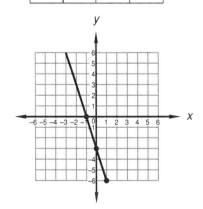

16. $\dfrac{\frac{m}{x + y}}{\frac{a}{x + y}} = \dfrac{m}{x + y} \cdot \dfrac{x + y}{a} = \dfrac{m}{a}$

17. $\dfrac{\dfrac{m}{x + y}}{\dfrac{m}{x}} = \dfrac{m}{x + y} \cdot \dfrac{x}{m} = \dfrac{x}{x + y}$

18. $\dfrac{\dfrac{m}{1}}{m} = m \cdot m = \boldsymbol{m^2}$

19. $\dfrac{a}{x^2 y} + \dfrac{m + c}{x + y}$

$= \dfrac{a(x + y)}{x^2 y(x + y)} + \dfrac{(m + c)x^2 y}{x^2 y(x + y)}$

$= \dfrac{ax + ay + mx^2 y + cx^2 y}{x^3 y + x^2 y^2}$

20. $1 + \dfrac{y}{x} = \dfrac{x + y}{x}$

21. $y + \dfrac{y}{x} = \dfrac{xy + y}{x}$

22. $9x^3 y m^5 + 6m^2 y^4 p^4 - 3y^3 m^3$
$= \boldsymbol{3ym^2(3x^3 m^3 + 2y^3 p^4 - y^2 m)}$

23. $\dfrac{4kp + 4kpx}{4kp} = \dfrac{4kp(1 + x)}{4kp} = \boldsymbol{1 + x}$

24. $mx(x^0 y)m^2 x^2(y^2) = \boldsymbol{m^3 x^3 y^3}$

25. $\dfrac{a^{-2} p^2 a(a^0)^2}{(a^{-3})^2 (p^{-2})^{-2}} = a^{-1} p^2 a^6 p^{-4} = \boldsymbol{a^5 p^{-2}}$

26. $\dfrac{(mx)(mx^0)}{3^{-2} xyyx^{-3} m} = 9m^2 xy^{-2} x^2 m^{-1} = \boldsymbol{9my^{-2} x^3}$

27. $\dfrac{-x^{-3}}{y}\left(\dfrac{x^3}{y^{-1}} - \dfrac{3x^{-3}}{y^2}\right) = \dfrac{-x^{-3} x^3}{yy^{-1}} + \dfrac{x^{-3} 3x^{-3}}{yy^2}$
$= \boldsymbol{-1 + 3x^{-6} y^{-3}}$

28. $-2^0 x^2 y^2 x^{-2} + \dfrac{3y^2}{x^2} - \dfrac{4x^{-2}}{y^{-2}} + 5y^2$
$= -y^2 + 3y^2 x^{-2} - 4x^{-2} y^2 + 5y^2 = \boldsymbol{4y^2 - x^{-2} y^2}$

29. $-x^0 - x(x^0 - y) = -(-3)^0 - (-3)((-3)^0 - (-2))$
$= -1 + 3(1 + 2) = \boldsymbol{8}$

30. $-k(-2 - 3) - (-2)(-k - 5)$
$= -2 - (-2k + 4) + \sqrt[3]{-27}$
$5k - 2k - 10 = -2 + 2k - 4 - 3$
$3k - 10 = 2k - 9$
$k = \boldsymbol{1}$

PROBLEM SET 66

1. $-3(-N) - 7 = N + 1$
$3N - 7 = N + 1$
$2N = 8$
$N = \boldsymbol{4}$

2.

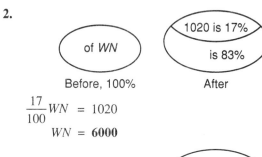

Before, 100%   After

$\dfrac{17}{100}WN = 1020$
$WN = \boldsymbol{6000}$

Before, 100%   After

3.

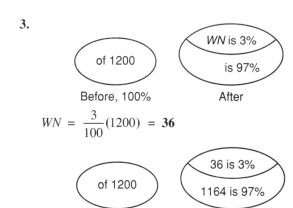

Before, 100%   After

$WN = \dfrac{3}{100}(1200) = \boldsymbol{36}$

Before, 100%   After

4. $(1.05)WN = 4.221$
$WN = \boldsymbol{4.02}$

5. $WF\left(3\dfrac{1}{8}\right) = \dfrac{7}{4}$
$WF\left(\dfrac{25}{8}\right) = \dfrac{7}{4}$
$WF = \boldsymbol{\dfrac{14}{25}}$

6. $-3\dfrac{1}{2} + 1\dfrac{2}{5}p - 4\dfrac{2}{3} = 0$
$\dfrac{7}{5}p = \dfrac{14}{3} + \dfrac{7}{2}$
$\dfrac{7}{5}p = \dfrac{28}{6} + \dfrac{21}{6}$
$p = \dfrac{49}{6} \cdot \dfrac{5}{7}$
$p = \boldsymbol{\dfrac{35}{6}}$

7. $0.3k - 0.2 + 0.2k - 0.05 = -2(k - 3)$
$30k - 20 + 20k - 5 = -200k + 600$
$250k = 625$
$k = \textbf{2.5}$

8. $4 < x \le 7$

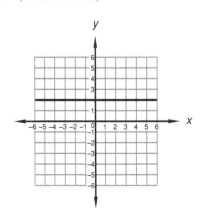

$\begin{array}{cccccc} 3 & 4 & 5 & 6 & 7 & 8 \end{array}$

9. $\dfrac{\sqrt{3}}{2} \in$ **Irrationals and reals**

10. $4 \in$ **Naturals, wholes, integers, rationals, and reals**

11. (a) $5x - 4y = -6$
(b) $x - 2y = -6$
$x = 2y - 6$
Substitute (b) into (a) and get:
(a') $5(2y - 6) - 4y = -6$
$10y - 30 - 4y = -6$
$6y = 24$
$y = 4$

(b) $x = 2(4) - 6 = 2$
(2, 4)

12. (a) $x - 2y = 7$
$x = 2y + 7$
(b) $2x - 3y = -4$
Substitute (a) into (b) and get:
(b') $2(2y + 7) - 3y = -4$
$4y + 14 - 3y = -4$
$y = -18$

(a) $x = 2(-18) + 7 = -29$
(−29, −18)

13. (a) $4x + y = 14$
$y = -4x + 14$
(b) $2x - 2y = 22$
Substitute (a) into (b) and get:
(b') $2x - 2(-4x + 14) = 22$
$2x + 8x - 28 = 22$
$10x = 50$
$x = 5$

(a) $y = -4(5) + 14 = -6$
(5, −6)

14. $x + 4 = 20$
$x = 16$

$\sqrt{x} + \dfrac{1}{4^{-2}} = \sqrt{16} + 4^2 = 4 + 16 = \textbf{20}$

15. $V_{\text{Prism}} = A_{\text{Base}} \times \text{height}$

$= \left[(10)(36) + \dfrac{1}{2}(36)(10) \right] \text{ft}^2 \times (2)(3)\,\text{ft}$

$= (540)(2)(3) \text{ ft}^3$

$= \textbf{3240 ft}^3$

$V_{\text{Pyramid}} = \dfrac{1}{3} V_{\text{Prism}}$

$= \dfrac{1}{3}(540)(2)(3) \text{ ft}^3$

$= \textbf{1080 ft}^3$

16. $8 \text{ yd}^3 \cdot \dfrac{3 \text{ ft}}{1 \text{ yd}} \cdot \dfrac{3 \text{ ft}}{1 \text{ yd}} \cdot \dfrac{3 \text{ ft}}{1 \text{ yd}} \cdot \dfrac{12 \text{ in.}}{1 \text{ ft}} \cdot \dfrac{12 \text{ in.}}{1 \text{ ft}}$

$\cdot \dfrac{12 \text{ in.}}{1 \text{ ft}} \cdot \dfrac{2.54 \text{ cm}}{1 \text{ in.}} \cdot \dfrac{2.54 \text{ cm}}{1 \text{ in.}} \cdot \dfrac{2.54 \text{ cm}}{1 \text{ in.}}$

$\cdot \dfrac{1 \text{ m}}{100 \text{ cm}} \cdot \dfrac{1 \text{ m}}{100 \text{ cm}} \cdot \dfrac{1 \text{ m}}{100 \text{ cm}}$

$= \dfrac{8(3)(3)(3)(12)(12)(12)(2.54)(2.54)(2.54)}{(100)(100)(100)} \text{ m}^3$

17. $\dfrac{(70 \times 90) + (30 \times 100)}{70 + 30} = \dfrac{9300}{100}$
$= \textbf{93 pounds}$

18. $V_{\text{Cylinder}} = A_{\text{Base}} \times \text{height}$

$= \left[\pi(20)^2 \right] \text{m}^2 \times 40 \text{ m}$

$= (400\pi)(40) \text{ m}^3$

$\approx \textbf{50,240 m}^3$

$V_{\text{Sphere}} = \dfrac{2}{3} V_{\text{Cylinder}}$

$= \dfrac{2}{3}(400\pi)(40) \text{ m}^3$

$\approx \textbf{33,493.33 m}^3$

19. $y = 2$ (horizontal line)

20. $y = 2x$

x	0	1	−1
y	0	2	−2

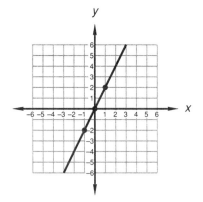

21. $y - 2x = 2$
$\quad y = 2x + 2$

x	0	1	−1
y	2	4	0

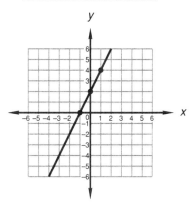

22. $\dfrac{\dfrac{a}{1}}{a + b} = a(a + b) = \boldsymbol{a^2 + ab}$

23. $\dfrac{\dfrac{x}{x + y}}{x} = x\left(\dfrac{x}{x + y}\right) = \dfrac{\boldsymbol{x^2}}{\boldsymbol{x + y}}$

24. $\dfrac{1}{x} + \dfrac{3}{x + y} = \dfrac{(x + y)}{x(x + y)} + \dfrac{3(x)}{x(x + y)}$
$\quad = \dfrac{x + y + 3x}{x^2 + xy} = \dfrac{\boldsymbol{4x + y}}{\boldsymbol{x^2 + xy}}$

25. $x + \dfrac{1}{y} = \dfrac{\boldsymbol{xy + 1}}{\boldsymbol{y}}$

26. $1 + \dfrac{1}{y} = \dfrac{\boldsymbol{y + 1}}{\boldsymbol{y}}$

27. $15m^2x^5k^4 - 5m^6x^6k^6 + 20m^4xk^5$
$\quad = \boldsymbol{5m^2xk^4(3x^4 - m^4x^5k^2 + 4m^2k)}$

28. $\dfrac{3x^2m^5(2x^4m^2)}{3x^2m^5m^{-4}} = \dfrac{6x^6m^7}{3x^2m} = \boldsymbol{2x^4m^6}$

29. $\dfrac{4(p^{-2})^0(p^5)}{4^{-1}p^6x^{-5}} = 16p^5p^{-6}x^5 = \boldsymbol{16p^{-1}x^5}$

30. $\left(\dfrac{3x^{-2}}{y^{-3}}\right)^{-2}\left(\dfrac{x^4}{y^6}\right)^2 = 9^{-1}x^4y^{-6}x^8y^{-12} = \dfrac{\boldsymbol{x^{12}}}{\boldsymbol{9y^{18}}}$

31. $-2^0 - 2^2(2^0) - (2^0)^{-3} - \sqrt[3]{-27}$
$\quad = -1 - 4 - 1 + 3 = \boldsymbol{-3}$

PROBLEM SET 67

1. $WN = \dfrac{380}{100}(30{,}000)$
$WN = \boldsymbol{114{,}000}$

2. $3600 = \dfrac{60}{100}WN$
$\boldsymbol{6000} = WN$

3. $\dfrac{40}{100}(WN) = 184$
$\qquad WN = \boldsymbol{460}$

4. $\sqrt{72} = \sqrt{6}\sqrt{6}\sqrt{2} = \boldsymbol{6\sqrt{2}}$

5. $3\sqrt{75} = 3\sqrt{5}\sqrt{5}\sqrt{3} = \boldsymbol{15\sqrt{3}}$

6. $4\sqrt{324} = 4\sqrt{4}\sqrt{81} = \boldsymbol{72}$

7. $(4x - 3)(12x + 2) = 48x^2 - 36x + 8x - 6$
$\quad = \boldsymbol{48x^2 - 28x - 6}$

8. $y = -2$ (horizontal line)

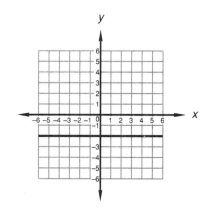

9. $y = -2x - 5$

x	0	-1	-2
y	-5	-3	-1

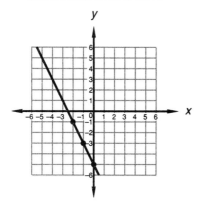

10. $y = -2x + 5$

x	0	1	4
y	5	3	-3

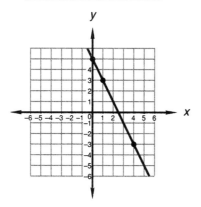

11. $x \ngtr 4$; $D = \{\text{Integers}\}$
   $x \le 4$

12. S.A. $= 2(A_{\text{Front}}) + 2(A_{\text{Top}}) + 2(A_{\text{Side}})$
   $= [2(3)(4) + 2(3)(4) + 2(3)(3)] \text{ ft}^2$
   $= 66 \text{ ft}^2 = 66(12)(12) \text{ in.}^2 = \mathbf{9504 \text{ in.}^2}$

13. (a) $3x - 2y = 15$
   (b) $5x + y = 12$
   $\quad\quad y = -5x + 12$
   Substitute (b) into (a) and get:
   (a′) $3x - 2(-5x + 12) = 15$
   $\quad\quad 3x + 10x - 24 = 15$
   $\quad\quad\quad\quad\quad\quad 13x = 39$
   $\quad\quad\quad\quad\quad\quad\quad x = 3$

   (b) $y = -5(3) + 12 = -3$
   (3, −3)

14. (a) $y + 2x = 12$
   (b) $x + 2y = 12$
   $\quad\quad x = -2y + 12$
   Substitute (b) into (a) and get:
   (a′) $y + 2(-2y + 12) = 12$
   $\quad\quad y - 4y + 24 = 12$
   $\quad\quad\quad\quad -3y = -12$
   $\quad\quad\quad\quad\quad y = 4$

   (b) $x = -2(4) + 12 = 4$
   (4, 4)

15. $\sqrt{27}$ is between $5 \times 5 = 25$ and $6 \times 6 = 36$,
   closer to 5
   Try 5.2 $\quad\quad 5.2 \times 5.2 = 27.04$
   Try 5.1 $\quad\quad 5.1 \times 5.1 = 26.01$
   Try 5.15 $\quad 5.15 \times 5.15 = 26.5225$
   Try 5.18 $\quad 5.18 \times 5.18 = 26.8324$
   Try 5.19 $\quad 5.19 \times 5.19 = 26.9361$
   $\sqrt{27} \approx \mathbf{5.2}$

16. $\dfrac{\dfrac{x}{y}}{\dfrac{1}{y}} = \dfrac{x}{y} \cdot y = x$

17. $\dfrac{\dfrac{x}{x}}{y} = x \cdot \dfrac{y}{x} = y$

18. $\dfrac{1}{\dfrac{1}{y}} = y$

19. $\dfrac{4}{a^2 x} + \dfrac{7}{x(x + a)}$

   $= \dfrac{4(x + a)}{a^2 x(x + a)} + \dfrac{7(a^2)}{a^2 x(x + a)}$

   $= \dfrac{\mathbf{4x + 4a + 7a^2}}{\mathbf{a^2 x^2 + a^3 x}}$

20. $2 + \dfrac{3}{y} = \dfrac{\mathbf{2y + 3}}{\mathbf{y}}$

21. $1 + \dfrac{x}{y} = \dfrac{\mathbf{y + x}}{\mathbf{y}}$

22. $40x^4 ym^7 z - 20x^5 y^5 m^2 z + 20xy^2 m$
   $= \mathbf{20xym(2x^3 m^6 z - x^4 y^4 mz + y)}$

23. $\dfrac{4x + 4x^2}{4x} = \dfrac{4x(1 + x)}{4x} = \mathbf{1 + x}$

24. $\dfrac{kp^{-2} k(p^0)^2}{kp(k)(p^{-2})^2} = \dfrac{k^2 p^{-2}}{k^2 p^{-3}} = \mathbf{p}$

25. $\left(\dfrac{3m^2}{y^{-4}}\right)^2\left(\dfrac{m}{y}\right) = 9m^4y^8my^{-1} = \mathbf{9m^5y^7}$

26. $\dfrac{2p^2x^{-4}(x)(x^2)}{y^{-4}(p^2)^{-2}x} = \dfrac{2p^2x^{-1}}{y^{-4}p^{-4}x} = 2p^6x^{-2}y^4$

27. $-|-3^0| - 3^0(-2)(-3)(-2-3) = -1 - 6(-5)$
$= \mathbf{29}$

28. $-\dfrac{3x^2y^{-2}}{x^{-2}y^{-2}} - 2x^4yy^{-1} + 4x^3xyy^{-1} - \dfrac{2x^2}{x^{-2}}$
$= -3x^4 - 2x^4 + 4x^4 - 2x^4 = \mathbf{-3x^4}$

29. $-\dfrac{x^{-2}}{y^4}\left(x^2y^4 - \dfrac{3x^{-2}}{y^4}\right)$
$= -\dfrac{x^{-2}x^2y^4}{y^4} + \dfrac{x^{-2}3x^{-2}}{y^4y^4} = \mathbf{-1 + 3x^{-4}y^{-8}}$

30. $x - (x^2)^0(x-y) - |x-y|$
$= (-2) - ((-2)^2)^0((-2)-(-3)) - |(-2)-(-3)|$
$= -2 - (1) - 1 = \mathbf{-4}$

PROBLEM SET 68

1. $\dfrac{2}{9} = \dfrac{P}{9180}$
$P = \mathbf{2040}$

2. $\dfrac{80}{100}WN = 2{,}300{,}000$
$WN = \mathbf{2{,}875{,}000}$

3. $\dfrac{117}{100}WN = 5850$
$WN = \mathbf{5000}$

4. $2\dfrac{1}{8}WN = \dfrac{1}{16}$
$\dfrac{17}{8}WN = \dfrac{1}{16}$
$WN = \mathbf{\dfrac{1}{34}}$

5. $WF\,2\dfrac{1}{7} = \dfrac{3}{14}$
$WF\dfrac{15}{7} = \dfrac{3}{14}$
$WF = \mathbf{\dfrac{1}{10}}$

6. $3\dfrac{1}{5}x + \dfrac{2}{3} = 5\dfrac{1}{2}$
$\dfrac{16}{5}x = \dfrac{11}{2} - \dfrac{2}{3}$
$\dfrac{16}{5}x = \dfrac{33}{6} - \dfrac{4}{6}$
$x = \dfrac{29}{6} \cdot \dfrac{5}{16} = \mathbf{\dfrac{145}{96}}$

7. $-|-2| - 2^2 - (-3-k) = -2(k - |-3|)$
$-2 - 4 + 3 + k = -2k + 6$
$-3 + k = -2k + 6$
$k = \mathbf{3}$

8. $x \geq -3;\ D = \{\text{Integers}\}$ or
$x > -4;\ D = \{\text{Integers}\}$

9. $V_{\text{Prism}} = A_{\text{Base}} \times \text{height}$
$= \left[(13)(29) + \dfrac{(17)(8)}{2}\right](1)(3)(12)\ \text{in.}^3$
$= (445)(3)(12)\ \text{in.}^3 = \mathbf{16{,}020\ in.^3}$

S.A. $= 2(A_{\text{Base}}) + (\text{perimeter})(\text{height})$
$= 2(445)\ \text{in.}^2 + (93.8)(3)(12)\ \text{in.}^2$
$= [890 + 93.8(3)(12)]\ \text{in.}^2$
$= \mathbf{4266.8\ in.^2}$

$V_{\text{Pyramid}} = \dfrac{1}{3}V_{\text{Prism}}$
$= \dfrac{1}{3}(445)(3)(12)\ \text{in.}^3$
$= \mathbf{5340\ in.^3}$

10. (a) $3x - y = 1$
(b) $x + 2y = 5$
$\qquad x = -2y + 5$
Substitute (b) into (a) and get:
(a′) $3(-2y + 5) - y = 1$
$\qquad -6y + 15 - y = 1$
$\qquad\qquad -7y = -14$
$\qquad\qquad\quad y = 2$

(b) $x = -2(2) + 5 = 1$
(1, 2)

11. (a) $3x + y = -12$
$\qquad y = -3x - 12$
(b) $2x - 3y = 3$
Substitute (a) into (b) and get:
(b′) $2x - 3(-3x - 12) = 3$
$\qquad 2x + 9x + 36 = 3$
$\qquad\qquad 11x = -33$
$\qquad\qquad\quad x = -3$

(a) $y = -3(-3) - 12 = -3$
(−3, −3)

12. (a) $5x - 4y = 12$

(b) $9x + y = 38$

$y = -9x + 38$

Substitute (b) into (a) and get:

(a′) $5x - 4(-9x + 38) = 12$

$5x + 36x - 152 = 12$

$41x = 164$

$x = 4$

(b) $y = -9(4) + 38 = 2$

(4, 2)

13. $4\sqrt{50} = 4\sqrt{25}\sqrt{2} = \mathbf{20\sqrt{2}}$

14. $6\sqrt{45} = 6\sqrt{9}\sqrt{5} = \mathbf{18\sqrt{5}}$

15. $2\sqrt{12} = 2\sqrt{4}\sqrt{3} = \mathbf{4\sqrt{3}}$

16. $5\sqrt[5]{-32} = 5\sqrt[5]{(-2)^5} = \mathbf{-10}$

17. $(2x - 5)^2 = (2x - 5)(2x - 5)$

$= 4x^2 - 10x - 10x + 25 = \mathbf{4x^2 - 20x + 25}$

18. $y = -4$ (horizontal line)

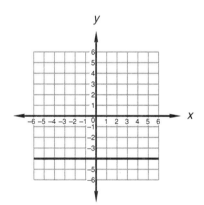

19. $y = 3x - 2$

x	0	1	−1
y	−2	1	−5

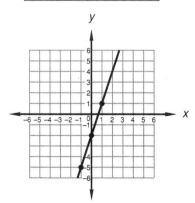

20. $2y + 3x = 4$

$2y = -3x + 4$

$y = -\dfrac{3}{2}x + 2$

x	0	2	−2
y	2	−1	5

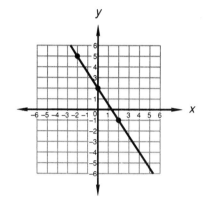

21. $\dfrac{x}{\dfrac{1}{xy + b}} = x(xy + b) = \mathbf{x^2y + bx}$

22. $\dfrac{\dfrac{x}{a}}{\dfrac{1}{b}} = \dfrac{x}{a} \cdot b = \dfrac{\mathbf{bx}}{\mathbf{a}}$

23. $-3^0 - 3^2 - 3(2^0 - 1) + \sqrt[3]{27}$

$= -1 - 9 - 3(0) + 3 = \mathbf{-7}$

24. $\dfrac{1}{x^2} + \dfrac{m}{x^3y} + \dfrac{c}{y} = \dfrac{xy}{x^3y} + \dfrac{m}{x^3y} + \dfrac{c(x^3)}{x^3y}$

$= \dfrac{\mathbf{xy + m + cx^3}}{\mathbf{x^3y}}$

25. $y + \dfrac{1}{x} = \dfrac{\mathbf{xy + 1}}{\mathbf{x}}$

26. $1 + \dfrac{1}{xy} = \dfrac{\mathbf{xy + 1}}{\mathbf{xy}}$

27. $30a^2b^3c^4 - 15ab^4c^5 + 45ab^4c^4$

$= \mathbf{15ab^3c^4(2a - bc + 3b)}$

28. $\dfrac{xx(x^{-2})^2y(y)}{x^{-2}x^0xx^{-3}} = xx^{-4}y^2x^2x^3 = \mathbf{x^2y^2}$

29. $\dfrac{4(2x^2y^4p^{-2})}{4x(y^2)^{-2}p^0} = 2x^2y^4p^{-2}x^{-1}y^4 = \mathbf{2xp^{-2}y^8}$

30. $\dfrac{(x^{-2})^{-2}(2y^2)^2(y)}{x^{-2}x^{-5}x^0xx^{-2}} = x^4 4y^4yx^2x^5x = \mathbf{4x^{12}y^5}$

PROBLEM SET 69

1. $\dfrac{18}{100}WN = 45$

   $WN = \mathbf{250}$

2. $\dfrac{1(75) + 2(80) + 3(88) + 4(93)}{1 + 2 + 3 + 4} = \dfrac{871}{10}$

   $= \mathbf{87.1}$

3. $\dfrac{230}{100}WN = 1610$

   $WN = \mathbf{700}$

4. $5\sqrt{80} = 5\sqrt{16}\sqrt{5} = \mathbf{20\sqrt{5}}$

5. $3\sqrt{120} = 3\sqrt{4}\sqrt{30} = \mathbf{6\sqrt{30}}$

6. $7\sqrt{5} - \sqrt{5} + 5\sqrt{3} - 3\sqrt{3} = \mathbf{6\sqrt{5} + 2\sqrt{3}}$

7. $V_{\text{Cylinder}} = A_{\text{Base}} \times \text{height}$

   $= \left[10(30) + \dfrac{30(10)}{2} + \dfrac{\pi(10)^2}{2} \right](2)(12) \text{ in.}^3$

   $= (450 + 50\pi)(2)(12) \text{ in.}^3$

   $\approx (607)(24) \text{ in.}^3$

   $\approx \mathbf{14{,}568 \text{ in.}^3}$

   $\text{S.A.} = 2(A_{\text{Base}}) + (\text{perimeter})(\text{height})$

   $= 2(607) + \left[71.6 + \dfrac{2\pi(10)}{2} \right](2)(12) \text{ in.}^2$

   $\approx [1214 + (71.6 + 10\pi)(2)(12)] \text{ in.}^2$

   $\approx \mathbf{3686 \text{ in.}^2}$

   $V_{\text{Cone}} = \dfrac{1}{3}V_{\text{Cylinder}}$

   $= \dfrac{1}{3}(607)(2)(12) \text{ in.}^3$

   $= \mathbf{4856 \text{ in.}^3}$

8. $(3p - 4)(2p + 5) = 6p^2 - 8p + 15p - 20$

   $= \mathbf{6p^2 + 7p - 20}$

9. $x = -\dfrac{1}{2}$ (vertical line)

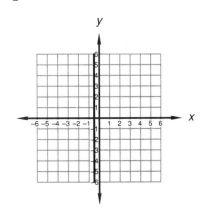

10. $y = -\dfrac{1}{2}x$

x	0	-2	2
y	0	1	-1

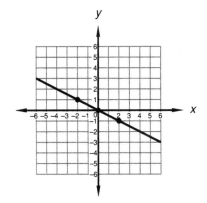

11. $2y = x - 8$

   $y = \dfrac{1}{2}x - 4$

x	0	2	-2
y	-4	-3	-5

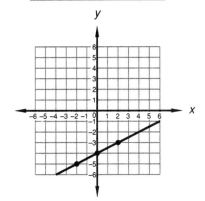

12. $x + 3 > -7; \ D = \{\text{Positive integers}\}$

   $x > -10$

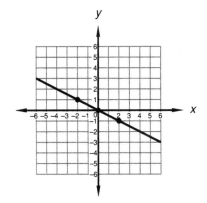

13. (a) $x + y = 10$

   (b) $-x + y = 0$

   $y = x$

   Substitute (b) into (a) and get:

   (a′) $x + (x) = 10$

   $2x = 10$

   $x = 5$

   (b) $y = 5$

   $\mathbf{(5, 5)}$

14. (a) $3x - 3y = 3$
(b) $x - 5y = -3$
$\quad\quad x = 5y - 3$
Substitute (b) into (a) and get:
(a') $3(5y - 3) - 3y = 3$
$\quad\quad 15y - 9 - 3y = 3$
$\quad\quad\quad\quad\quad 12y = 12$
$\quad\quad\quad\quad\quad\quad y = 1$

(b) $x = 5(1) - 3 = 2$
(2, 1)

15. (a) $3x - y = 8$
(b) $x - 3y = -8$
$\quad\quad x = 3y - 8$
Substitute (b) into (a) and get:
(a') $3(3y - 8) - y = 8$
$\quad\quad 9y - 24 - y = 8$
$\quad\quad\quad\quad\quad 8y = 32$
$\quad\quad\quad\quad\quad\quad y = 4$

(b) $x = 3(4) - 8 = 4$
(4, 4)

16. $\dfrac{\dfrac{a}{x}}{\dfrac{1}{a^2}} = \dfrac{a}{x} \cdot a^2 = \dfrac{a^3}{x}$

17. $\dfrac{\dfrac{a}{a+b}}{a} = \dfrac{a}{a+b} \cdot \dfrac{1}{a} = \dfrac{1}{a+b}$

18. $\dfrac{\dfrac{x}{y}}{\dfrac{1}{y}} = \dfrac{x}{y} \cdot y = x$

19. $\dfrac{a}{x+y} + \dfrac{5}{x^2} = \dfrac{ax^2 + 5x + 5y}{x^3 + x^2y}$

20. $1 + \dfrac{a}{b} = \dfrac{b+a}{b}$

21. $x + \dfrac{1}{x} = \dfrac{x^2 + 1}{x}$

22. $4x^2y^2z - 8x^2y^2z^5 = \mathbf{4x^2y^2z(1 - 2z^4)}$

23. $-3x^{-2}y^2\left(\dfrac{y^{-2}}{x^{-2}} + 4x^2y\right)$
$= -3x^{-2}y^2y^{-2}x^2 + (-3)x^{-2}y^24x^2y = \mathbf{-3 - 12y^3}$

24. $\dfrac{4kx - 4kx^2}{4kx} = \dfrac{4kx(1-x)}{4kx} = \mathbf{1 - x}$

25. $\dfrac{m^0(p^{-2})^2x^2y^4}{(y^{-2})^2yy^0x^{-2}} = p^{-4}x^2y^4y^4y^{-1}x^2 = \mathbf{p^{-4}x^4y^7}$

26. $\left(\dfrac{2x^{-2}y}{p}\right)^2\left(\dfrac{p^2x}{2}\right)^{-2} = 4x^{-4}y^2p^{-2}p^{-4}x^{-2}4$
$= \mathbf{16p^{-6}x^{-6}y^2}$

27. $\dfrac{x^2x^{-2}x^0y^2}{y^2(x^{-4})^2} = y^2y^{-2}x^8 = \mathbf{x^8}$

28. $\dfrac{3a^2x}{m} + \dfrac{5xm^{-1}}{a^{-2}} - \dfrac{4aax^{-1}}{x^{-2}m}$
$= 3a^2xm^{-1} + 5a^2xm^{-1} - 4a^2xm^{-1} = \mathbf{4a^2xm^{-1}}$

29. $-x^{-4} - x^2(x - m) = -(-2)^{-4} - (-2)^2((-2) - 3)$
$= -\dfrac{1}{16} - 4(-5) = -\dfrac{1}{16} + 20 = \mathbf{\dfrac{319}{16}}$

30. $-3^0 - 3(-2 - 2^0)(-8^0 - 5) + \sqrt[4]{16}$
$= -1 - 3(-3)(-6) + 2 = \mathbf{-53}$

PROBLEM SET 70

1. $(-N)3 - 7 = 3 + 2N$
$\quad -3N - 7 = 3 + 2N$
$\quad\quad -5N = 10$
$\quad\quad\quad N = \mathbf{-2}$

2. $\dfrac{80}{100}WN = 60$
$\quad\quad WN = \mathbf{75}$

3. $\dfrac{37}{100}(300) = WN$
$\quad\quad \mathbf{111} = WN$

4. $4\dfrac{2}{7}WN = 20\dfrac{1}{2}$
$\quad \dfrac{30}{7}WN = \dfrac{41}{2}$
$\quad\quad WN = \mathbf{\dfrac{287}{60}}$

5. $WD(20.2) = 1.01$
$\quad\quad WD = \mathbf{0.05}$

6. $2\frac{1}{8}x - \frac{1}{5} = (5^2)(2^{-3})$

$\quad\quad \frac{17}{8}x = \frac{25}{8} + \frac{1}{5}$

$\quad\quad \frac{17}{8}x = \frac{125}{40} + \frac{8}{40}$

$\quad\quad\quad x = \frac{133}{40} \cdot \frac{8}{17}$

$\quad\quad\quad x = \mathbf{\frac{133}{85}}$

7. $0.003k + 0.188 - 0.001k = 0.2k - 0.01$

$\quad\quad 3k + 188 - k = 200k - 10$

$\quad\quad\quad\quad 198 = 198k$

$\quad\quad\quad\quad\quad 1 = k$

8. $x - 3 \not< -5; \; D = \{\text{Positive integers}\}$
$\quad x - 3 \geq -5$
$\quad\quad x \geq -2$

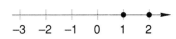

9. (a) $5x - y = 18$
$\quad\quad\quad y = 5x - 18$
(b) $4x - 3y = 10$
Substitute (a) into (b) and get:
(b') $4x - 3(5x - 18) = 10$
$\quad\quad 4x - 15x + 54 = 10$
$\quad\quad\quad\quad -11x = -44$
$\quad\quad\quad\quad\quad x = 4$

(a) $y = 5(4) - 18 = 2$
(4, 2)

10. (a) $x + 2y = 0$
$\quad\quad\quad x = -2y$
(b) $3x + y = -10$
Substitute (a) into (b) and get:
(b') $3(-2y) + y = -10$
$\quad\quad -6y + y = -10$
$\quad\quad\quad -5y = -10$
$\quad\quad\quad\quad y = 2$

(a) $x = -2(2) = -4$
(−4, 2)

11. (a) $5x + 4y = -28$
(b) $x - y = -2$
$\quad\quad\quad x = y - 2$
Substitute (b) into (a) and get:
(a') $5(y - 2) + 4y = -28$
$\quad\quad 5y - 10 + 4y = -28$
$\quad\quad\quad\quad 9y = -18$
$\quad\quad\quad\quad y = -2$

(b) $x = (-2) - 2 = -4$
(−4, −2)

12. $V_{\text{Prism}} = A_{\text{Base}} \times \text{height}$

$\quad = \left[50(5) + \frac{36(25)}{2} + 20(14)\right](1)(100) \text{ cm}^3$

$\quad = (980)(100) \text{ cm}^3$

$\quad = \mathbf{98,000 \text{ cm}^3}$

S.A. $= 2(A_{\text{Base}}) + (\text{perimeter})(\text{height})$

$\quad = 2(980) \text{ cm}^2 + (182.8)(100) \text{ cm}^2$

$\quad = [1960 + (182.8)(100)] \text{ cm}^2$

$\quad = \mathbf{20,240 \text{ cm}^2}$

$V_{\text{Pyramid}} = \frac{1}{3}V_{\text{Prism}}$

$\quad\quad = \frac{1}{3}(980)(100) \text{ cm}^3$

$\quad\quad = \mathbf{32,666.67 \text{ cm}^3}$

13. $x + \sqrt{36} = 12$
$\quad\quad\quad x = 12 - \sqrt{36}$
$\quad\quad\quad x = 6$

$x^2 - 6 = (6)^2 - 6 = \mathbf{30}$

14. $5\sqrt{20} - 6\sqrt{32}$
$\quad = 5\sqrt{2 \cdot 2 \cdot 5} - 6\sqrt{2 \cdot 2 \cdot 2 \cdot 2 \cdot 2}$
$\quad = 5\sqrt{2}\sqrt{2}\sqrt{5} - 6\sqrt{2}\sqrt{2}\sqrt{2}\sqrt{2}\sqrt{2}$
$\quad = \mathbf{10\sqrt{5} - 24\sqrt{2}}$

15. $2\sqrt{45} - 3\sqrt{20} = 2\sqrt{3 \cdot 3 \cdot 5} - 3\sqrt{2 \cdot 2 \cdot 5}$
$\quad = 2\sqrt{3}\sqrt{3}\sqrt{5} - 3\sqrt{2}\sqrt{2}\sqrt{5} = 6\sqrt{5} - 6\sqrt{5} = \mathbf{0}$

16. $(4x + 5)^2 = (4x + 5)(4x + 5)$
$\quad = 16x^2 + 20x + 20x + 25 = \mathbf{16x^2 + 40x + 25}$

17. $y = 2x + 2$

x	0	1	−1
y	2	4	0

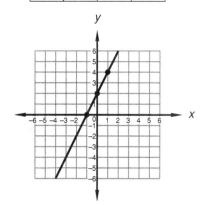

18. $y = 2x - 2$

x	0	1	-1
y	-2	0	-4

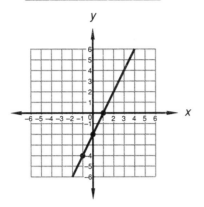

19. $3\sqrt{2} \in$ **Irrationals and reals**

20. $\dfrac{a}{\frac{1}{x}} = \dfrac{a}{1} \cdot \dfrac{x}{1} = \boldsymbol{ax}$

21. $\dfrac{\frac{a}{b}}{\frac{1}{c}} = \dfrac{a}{b} \cdot \dfrac{c}{1} = \dfrac{\boldsymbol{ac}}{\boldsymbol{b}}$

22. $\dfrac{\frac{a}{b}}{c} = \dfrac{a}{b} \cdot \dfrac{1}{c} = \dfrac{\boldsymbol{a}}{\boldsymbol{bc}}$

23. $\dfrac{a}{x^2 y} + \dfrac{b}{x + y}$

$= \dfrac{a(x + y)}{x^2 y(x + y)} + \dfrac{bx^2 y}{x^2 y(x + y)}$

$= \dfrac{\boldsymbol{ax + ay + bx^2 y}}{\boldsymbol{x^3 y + x^2 y^2}}$

24. $k + \dfrac{1}{y^2} = \dfrac{\boldsymbol{ky^2 + 1}}{\boldsymbol{y^2}}$

25. $m + \dfrac{1}{m^2} = \dfrac{\boldsymbol{m^3 + 1}}{\boldsymbol{m^2}}$

26. $12x^2 y^3 p^4 - 4x^3 y^2 p^6 + 16x^4 y^4 p^4$
$= \boldsymbol{4x^2 y^2 p^4(3y - xp^2 + 4x^2 y^2)}$

27. $(3x^2 y^5 m^2)^2 (x^2 y)^{-2} = 9x^4 y^{10} m^4 x^{-4} y^{-2} = \boldsymbol{9m^4 y^8}$

28. $\dfrac{(2xy)^3 (xy)^{-2}}{x^2 y^0 y^{-4}} = 8x^3 y^3 x^{-2} y^{-2} x^{-2} y^4 = \boldsymbol{8x^{-1} y^5}$

29. $\dfrac{(4x^{-2})^2 (x^2 y^0)^{-3}}{x^2 y y^{-2} y^4} = 16x^{-4} x^{-6} x^{-2} y^{-1} y^2 y^{-4}$
$= \boldsymbol{16x^{-12} y^{-3}}$

30. $\left[(-3 - 4^0) - (-3 - 2)\right] - \sqrt{25} = [-4 + 5] - 5$
$= \boldsymbol{-4}$

PROBLEM SET 71

1. $\dfrac{135}{100} WN = 297$ lbs
$WN = \boldsymbol{220 \text{ pounds}}$

2. $WN = \dfrac{87}{100}(3000)$
$WN = \boldsymbol{2610}$

3. $\dfrac{78}{100} WN = 3900$ tons
$WN = \boldsymbol{5000 \text{ tons}}$

4. $6\sqrt{45} + \sqrt{180}$
$= 6\sqrt{3 \cdot 3 \cdot 5} + \sqrt{3 \cdot 3 \cdot 2 \cdot 2 \cdot 5}$
$= 6\sqrt{3}\sqrt{3}\sqrt{5} + \sqrt{3}\sqrt{3}\sqrt{2}\sqrt{2}\sqrt{5} = 18\sqrt{5} + 6\sqrt{5}$
$= \boldsymbol{24\sqrt{5}}$

5. $2\sqrt{8} - 3\sqrt{32}$
$= 2\sqrt{2 \cdot 2 \cdot 2} - 3\sqrt{2 \cdot 2 \cdot 2 \cdot 2 \cdot 2}$
$= 2\sqrt{2}\sqrt{2}\sqrt{2} - 3\sqrt{2}\sqrt{2}\sqrt{2}\sqrt{2}\sqrt{2}$
$= 4\sqrt{2} - 12\sqrt{2} = \boldsymbol{-8\sqrt{2}}$

6. $2\sqrt{12} - 3\sqrt{18} = 2\sqrt{2 \cdot 2 \cdot 3} - 3\sqrt{3 \cdot 3 \cdot 2}$
$= 2\sqrt{2}\sqrt{2}\sqrt{3} - 3\sqrt{3}\sqrt{3}\sqrt{2} = \boldsymbol{4\sqrt{3} - 9\sqrt{2}}$

7. $y = -\dfrac{1}{2}x + 3$

x	0	2	-2
y	3	2	4

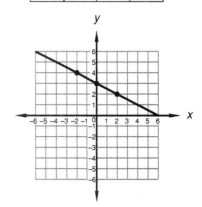

8. $x = -2\frac{1}{2}$ (vertical line)

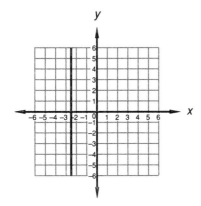

9. (a) $4x + y = 25$
  (b) $x - 3y = -10$
  $\quad\quad x = 3y - 10$
  Substitute (b) into (a) and get:
  (a') $4(3y - 10) + y = 25$
  $\quad\quad 12y - 40 + y = 25$
  $\quad\quad\quad\quad\quad 13y = 65$
  $\quad\quad\quad\quad\quad\quad y = 5$
  (b) $x = 3(5) - 10 = 5$
  (5, 5)

10. $x - 3 \not> 1$; $D = \{\text{Reals}\}$
  $x - 3 \leq 1$
  $\quad\quad x \leq 4$

11. $V_{\text{Cyl.}} = A_{\text{Base}} \times \text{height}$

$$= \left[6(8) + \frac{6(8)}{2} + \frac{\pi(4)^2}{2} \right](5)(12) \text{ in.}^3$$

$$+ \left[\frac{\pi(6)^2}{2} - \frac{\pi(3)^2}{2} \right](5)(12) \text{ in.}^3$$

$$= \left(72 + \frac{43}{2}\pi \right)(5)(12) \text{ in.}^3$$

$$\approx \textbf{8370.6 in.}^3$$

$$V_{\text{Cone}} = \frac{1}{3} V_{\text{Cylinder}}$$

$$= \frac{1}{3}\left(72 + \frac{43}{2}\pi \right)(5)(12) \text{ in.}^3$$

$$\approx \textbf{2790.2 in.}^3$$

12. Convert 200 cubic meters to cubic inches:

$$200 \text{ m}^3 \times \frac{100 \text{ cm}}{1 \text{ m}} \times \frac{100 \text{ cm}}{1 \text{ m}} \times \frac{100 \text{ cm}}{1 \text{ m}}$$

$$\times \frac{1 \text{ in.}}{2.54 \text{ cm}} \times \frac{1 \text{ in.}}{2.54 \text{ cm}} \times \frac{1 \text{ in.}}{2.54 \text{ cm}}$$

$$= \frac{\textbf{200(100)(100)(100)}}{\textbf{(2.54)(2.54)(2.54)}} \text{ in.}^3$$

13. $\dfrac{1(88) + 2(93)}{1 + 2} = \dfrac{274}{3} = 91\dfrac{1}{3}$

14. (a) $2x - 4y = -4$
  (b) $3x + 2y = 18$

$\quad\quad$(a) $2x - 4y = -4$
  2(b) $6x + 4y = 36$
  $\quad\quad\overline{\quad 8x \quad\quad\quad = 32}$
  $\quad\quad\quad\quad\quad\quad x = 4$

$\quad\quad$(a) $2(4) - 4y = -4$
  $\quad\quad\quad\quad -4y = -12$
  $\quad\quad\quad\quad\quad\quad y = 3$
  (4, 3)

15. (a) $3x - y = 7$
  (b) $2x + 2y = 10$

$\quad\quad$2(a) $6x - 2y = 14$
  $\quad\quad$(b) $2x + 2y = 10$
  $\quad\quad\overline{\quad 8x \quad\quad\quad = 24}$
  $\quad\quad\quad\quad\quad\quad x = 3$

$\quad\quad$(b) $2(3) + 2y = 10$
  $\quad\quad\quad\quad\quad\quad 2y = 4$
  $\quad\quad\quad\quad\quad\quad\quad y = 2$
  (3, 2)

16. $\dfrac{a}{\dfrac{1}{x^2 a}} = a \cdot x^2 a = \boldsymbol{x^2 a^2}$

17. $\dfrac{a}{\dfrac{a^2}{a + b}} = a \cdot \dfrac{a + b}{a^2} = \dfrac{\boldsymbol{a + b}}{\boldsymbol{a}}$

18. $\dfrac{m}{x^2 a} + \dfrac{3}{a(a + x)} = \dfrac{m(a + x) + 3x^2}{ax^2(a + x)}$

$$= \dfrac{\boldsymbol{ma + mx + 3x^2}}{\boldsymbol{a^2 x^2 + ax^3}}$$

19. $4x + \dfrac{1}{y} = \dfrac{\boldsymbol{4xy + 1}}{\boldsymbol{y}}$

20. $1 + \dfrac{x}{y} = \dfrac{\boldsymbol{y + x}}{\boldsymbol{y}}$

21. $\dfrac{12mx + 12mxy}{12mx} = \dfrac{12mx(1 + y)}{12mx} = \boldsymbol{1 + y}$

22. $\dfrac{x^2(y^{-2})^2 xx^4(p^0)^2}{(x^{-3}y^{-2})^2 y} = x^2y^{-4}xx^4x^6y^4y^{-1} = \boldsymbol{x^{13}y^{-1}}$

23. $(4x^2y^3p^4)^3 = \boldsymbol{64x^6y^9p^{12}}$

24. $\left(\dfrac{y^{-5}}{x^2} - \dfrac{3y^5x^{-2}}{p}\right)\dfrac{x^{-2}}{y^5}$

$= \dfrac{y^{-5}x^{-2}}{x^2y^5} - \dfrac{3y^5x^{-2}x^{-2}}{py^5}$

$= y^{-5}x^{-2}x^{-2}y^{-5} - 3y^5x^{-2}p^{-1}x^{-2}y^{-5}$

$= \boldsymbol{x^{-4}y^{-10} - 3x^{-4}p^{-1}}$

25. $-x^0 - x^2 - a(x - a) - |x^{-3}|$

$= -(-2)^0 - 4 - (4)((-2) - 4) - |(-2)^{-3}|$

$= -1 - 4 - 4(-6) - \dfrac{1}{8} = 19 - \dfrac{1}{8} = \boldsymbol{\dfrac{151}{8}}$

26. $-2\{[(-2 - 3) - (-2^0 - 2) - 2] - 2\}$

$= -2\{[-5 + 3 - 2] - 2\}$

$= -2\{-4 - 2\} = \boldsymbol{12}$

27. $\dfrac{x^3 - a}{a^3 + 8} = \dfrac{(1)^3 - (-2)}{(-2)^3 + 8} = \dfrac{1 + 2}{-8 + 8}$

$= \boldsymbol{undefined}$

28. $x^2 - a^2 = (2)^2 - (10)^2 = 4 - 100 = \boldsymbol{-96}$

29. $x^2 + 2xy + y^2 = (5)^2 + 2(5)(-4) + (-4)^2$

$= 25 - 40 + 16 = \boldsymbol{1}$

PROBLEM SET 72

1. $N(7) + 42 = 87 + 2(-N)$

$7N + 42 = 87 - 2N$

$9N = 45$

$N = \boldsymbol{5}$

2. $\dfrac{230}{100}WN = 345$

$WN = \boldsymbol{150}$

3. $\dfrac{37}{100}WN = 1110$

$WN = \boldsymbol{3000}$

4. $24\dfrac{1}{2}(WN) = 120$

$\dfrac{49}{2}WN = 120$

$WN = \boldsymbol{\dfrac{240}{49}}$

5. $WF(105) = 5\dfrac{1}{3}$

$WF(105) = \dfrac{16}{3}$

$WF = \boldsymbol{\dfrac{16}{315}}$

6. $20\dfrac{1}{4}x + 5\dfrac{1}{2} = 7\dfrac{1}{16}$

$\dfrac{81}{4}x = \dfrac{113}{16} - \dfrac{11}{2}$

$\dfrac{81}{4}x = \dfrac{113}{16} - \dfrac{88}{16}$

$x = \dfrac{25}{16} \cdot \dfrac{4}{81}$

$x = \boldsymbol{\dfrac{25}{324}}$

7. $-(-3)^3 - 2^2 = -2(-3k - 4)$

$27 - 4 = 6k + 8$

$15 = 6k$

$\dfrac{5}{2} = k$

8. $x - 3 \not< -2;\ D = \{\text{Positive integers}\}$

$x - 3 \geq -2$

$x \geq 1$

9. $\{\text{Integers}\} \subset \{\text{Reals}\}$
True

10. (a) $x + 2y = 15$

$x = -2y + 15$

(b) $3x - y = 10$

Substitute (a) into (b) and get:

(b′) $3(-2y + 15) - y = 10$

$-6y + 45 - y = 10$

$-7y = -35$

$y = 5$

(a) $x = -2(5) + 15 = 5$
(5, 5)

11. (a) $4x - 3y = 14$

(b) $x + 3y = -4$

$x = -3y - 4$

Substitute (b) into (a) and get:

(a′) $4(-3y - 4) - 3y = 14$

$-12y - 16 - 3y = 14$

$-15y = 30$

$y = -2$

(b) $x = -3(-2) - 4 = 2$
(2, −2)

12. $x = 3\frac{1}{2}$ (vertical line)

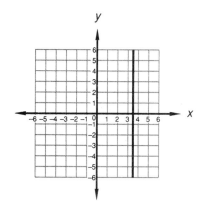

13. $y = -2x + 4$

x	0	2	−1
y	4	0	6

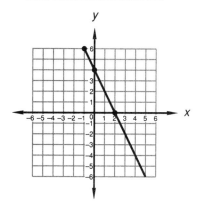

14. (a) $5x - 2y = 10$
(b) $7x - 3y = 13$

$$\begin{array}{ll} 3(a) & 15x - 6y = 30 \\ (-2)(b) & \underline{-14x + 6y = -26} \\ & x = 4 \end{array}$$

(a) $5(4) - 2y = 10$
$ -2y = -10$
$ y = 5$

(4, 5)

15. (a) $5x + 3y = 1$
(b) $7x + 3y = 5$

$$\begin{array}{ll} (-1)(a) & -5x - 3y = -1 \\ (b) & \underline{7x + 3y = 5} \\ & 2x = 4 \\ & x = 2 \end{array}$$

(a) $5(2) + 3y = 1$
$ 3y = -9$
$ y = -3$

(2, −3)

16. (a) $14x - 2y = 12$
(b) $x + 2y = 3$

(a) $14x - 2y = 12$
(b) $\underline{x + 2y = 3}$
$ 15x = 15$
$ x = 1$

(b) $(1) + 2y = 3$
$ 2y = 2$
$ y = 1$

(1, 1)

17. $\dfrac{\dfrac{a}{b}}{\dfrac{x}{y}} = \dfrac{a}{b} \cdot \dfrac{y}{x} = \boldsymbol{\dfrac{ay}{bx}}$

18. $\dfrac{3 - \dfrac{a}{b}}{\dfrac{1}{b} + b} = \dfrac{\dfrac{3b - a}{b}}{\dfrac{1 + b^2}{b}} = \dfrac{3b - a}{b} \cdot \dfrac{b}{1 + b^2}$

$ = \boldsymbol{\dfrac{3b - a}{1 + b^2}}$

19. $V_{\text{Cylinder}} = A_{\text{Base}} \times \text{height}$

$= \left[\dfrac{\pi(12)^2}{2} + 17(12) + \dfrac{11(12)}{2} \right]\left(\dfrac{4}{100} \right) \text{m}^3$

$= (72\pi + 270)\left(\dfrac{4}{100} \right) \text{m}^3$

$\approx \textbf{19.84 m}^3$

S.A. $= 2(A_{\text{Base}}) + (\text{perimeter})(\text{height})$

$= 2(72\pi + 270) + \left[\dfrac{2\pi(12)}{2} + 73.3 \right]\left(\dfrac{4}{100} \right) \text{m}^2$

$= \left[144\pi + 540 + \dfrac{(12\pi + 73.3)(4)}{100} \right] \text{m}^2$

$\approx \textbf{996.60 m}^2$

$V_{\text{Cone}} = \dfrac{1}{3} V_{\text{Cylinder}}$

$= \dfrac{1}{3}(72\pi + 270)\left(\dfrac{4}{100} \right) \text{m}^3$

$\approx \textbf{6.61 m}^3$

20. $(\sqrt{x})^{-5} - 19 = (\sqrt{4})^{-5} - 19 = \dfrac{1}{32} - 19$

$= -\boldsymbol{\dfrac{607}{32}}$

21. Convert 12,000 cubic meters to cubic yards:

$$12,000\ m^3 \cdot \frac{100\ cm}{1\ m} \cdot \frac{100\ cm}{1\ m} \cdot \frac{100\ cm}{1\ m}$$

$$\cdot \frac{1\ in.}{2.54\ cm} \cdot \frac{1\ in.}{2.54\ cm} \cdot \frac{1\ in.}{2.54\ cm} \cdot \frac{1\ ft}{12\ in.}$$

$$\cdot \frac{1\ ft}{12\ in.} \cdot \frac{1\ ft}{12\ in.} \cdot \frac{1\ yd}{3\ ft} \cdot \frac{1\ yd}{3\ ft} \cdot \frac{1\ yd}{3\ ft}$$

$$= \frac{12,000(100)(100)(100)}{(2.54)(2.54)(2.54)(12)(12)(12)(3)(3)(3)}\ yd^3$$

22. $\dfrac{(4)(3)\ +\ (8)(27)}{3\ +\ 27} = \dfrac{228}{30} = \textbf{7.6 jousts}$

23. $4\sqrt{8} - 3\sqrt{12} = 4\sqrt{2 \cdot 2 \cdot 2} - 3\sqrt{2 \cdot 2 \cdot 3}$
$= 4\sqrt{2}\sqrt{2}\sqrt{2} - 3\sqrt{2}\sqrt{2}\sqrt{3} = \mathbf{8\sqrt{2} - 6\sqrt{3}}$

24. $2\sqrt{75} - 4\sqrt{243}$

$= 2\sqrt{5 \cdot 5 \cdot 3} - 4\sqrt{3 \cdot 3 \cdot 3 \cdot 3 \cdot 3}$

$= 2\sqrt{5}\sqrt{5}\sqrt{3} - 4\sqrt{3}\sqrt{3}\sqrt{3}\sqrt{3}\sqrt{3} = 10\sqrt{3} - 36\sqrt{3}$

$= \mathbf{-26\sqrt{3}}$

25. $-x^2y + 3yx^2 - \dfrac{4y^3x}{y^2x^{-1}} - \dfrac{7x^{-2}}{x^{-4}y^{-1}}$

$= -x^2y + 3x^2y - 4x^2y - 7x^2y = \mathbf{-9x^2y}$

26. $(4x^{-2}y^2m)^{-2}y = \dfrac{x^4y^{-4}m^{-2}y}{16} = \dfrac{\boldsymbol{x^4}}{\boldsymbol{16m^2y^3}}$

27. $\dfrac{(x^{-2}y^2p)^2(x^2yp)^{-4}}{(xyp^2)^2}$

$= x^{-4}y^4p^2x^{-8}y^{-4}p^{-4}x^{-2}y^{-2}p^{-4} = \mathbf{x^{-14}p^{-6}y^{-2}}$

28. $\left(\dfrac{x^{-1}}{y^{-1}}\right)^{-2}\left(\dfrac{y^2}{x^2}\right)^{-4} = x^2y^{-2}y^{-8}x^8 = \mathbf{x^{10}y^{-10}}$

29. $\dfrac{x^{-2}y^{-2}(p^0)^2}{(x^2y^{-2}p^3)^{-2}} = x^{-2}y^{-2}x^4y^{-4}p^6 = \mathbf{x^2y^{-6}p^6}$

30. $-3^2 - \dfrac{1}{(-3)^{-3}} + (-3)^0 = -9 + 27 + 1 = \mathbf{19}$

PROBLEM SET 73

1. Convert 600 cubic yards to cubic meters:

$$600\ yd^3 \times \frac{3\ ft}{1\ yd} \times \frac{3\ ft}{1\ yd} \times \frac{3\ ft}{1\ yd} \times \frac{12\ in.}{1\ ft}$$

$$\times \frac{12\ in.}{1\ ft} \times \frac{12\ in.}{1\ ft} \times \frac{2.54\ cm}{1\ in.} \times \frac{2.54\ cm}{1\ in.}$$

$$\times \frac{2.54\ cm}{1\ in.} \times \frac{1\ m}{100\ cm} \times \frac{1\ m}{100\ cm} \times \frac{1\ m}{100\ cm}$$

$$= \frac{600(3)(3)(3)(12)(12)(12)(2.54)(2.54)(2.54)}{(100)(100)(100)}\ m^3$$

2. $V_{Solid} = A_{Base} \times \text{height}$

$= \left[\dfrac{\pi(6)^2}{2} + \dfrac{\pi(6)^2}{2} + (24)(12)\right] ft^2 \times 1\ ft$

$= (36\pi + 288)\ ft^3 \approx \mathbf{401.04\ ft^3}$

S.A. $= 2(A_{Base}) + (\text{perimeter})(\text{height})$

$= 2(36\pi + 288)\ ft^2 + \left[2\left(\dfrac{2\pi(6)}{2}\right) + 48\right](1)\ ft^2$

$= (84\pi + 624)\ ft^2 \approx \mathbf{887.76\ ft^2}$

$V_{Cone} = \dfrac{1}{3}V_{Solid}$

$= \dfrac{1}{3}(36\pi + 288)\ ft^3$

$\approx \mathbf{133.68\ ft^3}$

3. $(x^2 - 5)(x^{-3} - x) = [(-3)^2 - 5][(-3)^{-3} - (-3)]$

$= (4)\left(-\dfrac{1}{27} + 3\right) = 4\left(\dfrac{80}{27}\right) = \dfrac{\mathbf{320}}{\mathbf{27}}$

4. $x^2 + 6x - 16$

$(-2)(8) = -16\quad$ and $\quad(-8)(2) = -16$
$-2 + 8 = 6\qquad\qquad -8 + 2 = -6$

$x^2 + 6x - 16 = \mathbf{(x - 2)(x + 8)}$

5. $x^2 - 6x + 9$

$(-3)(-3) = 9\quad$ and $\quad(3)(3) = 9$
$-3 + (-3) = -6\qquad\quad 3 + (3) = 6$

$x^2 - 6x + 9 = \mathbf{(x - 3)(x - 3)}$

6. $x^2 - 6x - 27$

$(-9)(3) = -27\quad$ and $\quad(9)(-3) = -27$
$-9 + 3 = -6\qquad\qquad 9 + (-3) = 6$

$x^2 - 6x - 27 = \mathbf{(x - 9)(x + 3)}$

7. $p^2 - p - 20$

$(-4)(5) = -20$ and $(4)(-5) = -20$
$-4 + (5) = 1$ $\qquad$ $4 + (-5) = -1$

$p^2 - p - 20 = (p + 4)(p - 5)$

8. $x^2 - 2x - 15$

$(3)(-5) = -15$ and $(-3)(5) = -15$
$3 + (-5) = -2$ $\qquad$ $(-3) + 5 = 2$

$x^2 - 2x - 15 = (x + 3)(x - 5)$

9. $p^2 - 4p - 21$

$(3)(-7) = -21$ and $(-3)(7) = -21$
$3 + (-7) = -4$ $\qquad$ $(-3) + 7 = 4$

$p^2 - 4p - 21 = (p + 3)(p - 7)$

10. $p^2 + p - 20$

$(-4)(5) = -20$ and $(4)(-5) = -20$
$-4 + 5 = 1$ $\qquad$ $4 + (-5) = -1$

$p^2 + p - 20 = (p - 4)(p + 5)$

11. $k^2 - 3k - 40$

$(-8)(5) = -40$ and $(8)(-5) = -40$
$-8 + 5 = -3$ $\qquad$ $8 + (-5) = 3$

$k^2 - 3k - 40 = (k - 8)(k + 5)$

12. $m^2 + 9m + 20$

$(4)(5) = 20$ and $(-4)(-5) = 20$
$4 + 5 = 9$ $\qquad$ $-4 + (-5) = -9$

$m^2 + 9m + 20 = (m + 4)(m + 5)$

13. $x^2 + 33 + 14x = x^2 + 14x + 33$

$(3)(11) = 33$ and $(-3)(-11) = 33$
$3 + 11 = 14$ $\qquad$ $-3 + (-11) = -14$

$x^2 + 14x + 33 = (x + 3)(x + 11)$

14. $-13p + p^2 + 36 = p^2 - 13p + 36$

$(-9)(-4) = 36$ and $(9)(4) = 36$
$-9 + (-4) = -13$ $\qquad$ $9 + 4 = 13$

$p^2 - 13p + 36 = (p - 9)(p - 4)$

15. $-30 + m^2 - m = m^2 - m - 30$

$(5)(-6) = -30$ and $(-5)(6) = -30$
$5 + (-6) = -1$ $\qquad$ $-5 + 6 = 1$

$m^2 - m - 30 = (m + 5)(m - 6)$

16. $11n + n^2 + 18 = n^2 + 11n + 18$

$(2)(9) = 18$ and $(-2)(-9) = 18$
$2 + 9 = 11$ $\qquad$ $-2 + (-9) = -11$

$n^2 + 11n + 18 = (n + 2)(n + 9)$

17. $x^2 + 27 + 12x = x^2 + 12x + 27$

$(9)(3) = 27$ and $(-9)(-3) = 27$
$9 + 3 = 12$ $\qquad$ $-9 + (-3) = -12$

$x^2 + 12x + 27 = (x + 3)(x + 9)$

18. $x^2 + 90 - 19x = x^2 - 19x + 90$

$(-9)(-10) = 90$ and $(9)(10) = 90$
$-9 + (-10) = -19$ $\qquad$ $9 + 10 = 19$

$x^2 - 19x + 90 = (x - 9)(x - 10)$

19. $x^2 + x - 132$

$(-12)(11) = -132$ and $(12)(-11) = -132$
$-12 + 11 = -1$ $\qquad$ $12 + (-11) = 1$

$x^2 + x - 132 = (x + 12)(x - 11)$

20. $a^2 + 90 - 47a = a^2 - 47a + 90$

$(2)(45) = 90$ and $(-2)(-45) = 90$
$2 + 45 = 47$ $\qquad$ $-2 + (-45) = -47$

$a^2 - 47a + 90 = (a - 2)(a - 45)$

21. $10m + m^2 + 16 = m^2 + 10m + 16$

$(2)(8) = 16$ and $(-2)(-8) = 16$
$2 + 8 = 10$ $\qquad$ $-2 + (-8) = -10$

$m^2 + 10m + 16 = (m + 2)(m + 8)$

22. (a) $3x + y = 9$
(b) $x - 4y = -10$
$\quad x = 4y - 10$
Substitute (b) into (a) and get:
(a') $3(4y - 10) + y = 9$
$\quad 12y - 30 + y = 9$
$\quad\quad\quad 13y = 39$
$\quad\quad\quad\quad y = 3$

(b) $x = 4(3) - 10 = 2$
(2, 3)

23. (a) $2x + 5y = 7$
(b) $x + 3y = 4$
$\quad x = -3y + 4$
Substitute (b) into (a) and get:
(a') $2(-3y + 4) + 5y = 7$
$\quad -6y + 8 + 5y = 7$
$\quad\quad\quad\quad -y = -1$
$\quad\quad\quad\quad\quad y = 1$

(b) $x = -3(1) + 4 = 1$
(1, 1)

24. (a) $3x + 4y = -7$
(b) $3x - 3y = 21$

$\quad\quad$(a)$\quad 3x + 4y = -7$
(-1)(b)$\quad \underline{-3x + 3y = -21}$
$\quad\quad\quad\quad\quad 7y = -28$
$\quad\quad\quad\quad\quad\quad y = -4$

(b) $3x - 3(-4) = 21$
$\quad\quad 3x + 12 = 21$
$\quad\quad\quad\quad 3x = 9$
$\quad\quad\quad\quad\quad x = 3$
(3, -4)

25. (a) $2x - 2y = -2$
(b) $4x - 5y = -9$

(-2)(a)$\quad -4x + 4y = \quad 4$
$\quad$(b)$\quad \underline{4x - 5y = -9}$
$\quad\quad\quad\quad -\ y = -5$
$\quad\quad\quad\quad\quad\ y = 5$

(a) $2x - 2(5) = -2$
$\quad\quad 2x - 10 = -2$
$\quad\quad\quad\quad 2x = 8$
$\quad\quad\quad\quad\ x = 4$
(4, 5)

26. $7\sqrt{20} - 5\sqrt{32}$

$= 7\sqrt{2 \cdot 2 \cdot 5} - 5\sqrt{2 \cdot 2 \cdot 2 \cdot 2 \cdot 2}$
$= 7\sqrt{2}\sqrt{2}\sqrt{5} - 5\sqrt{2}\sqrt{2}\sqrt{2}\sqrt{2}\sqrt{2}$
$= \mathbf{14\sqrt{5} - 20\sqrt{2}}$

27. $2\sqrt{18} - 5\sqrt{8} + 4\sqrt{50}$

$= 2\sqrt{2 \cdot 3 \cdot 3} - 5\sqrt{2 \cdot 2 \cdot 2} + 4\sqrt{2 \cdot 5 \cdot 5}$
$= 2\sqrt{2}\sqrt{3}\sqrt{3} - 5\sqrt{2}\sqrt{2}\sqrt{2} + 4\sqrt{2}\sqrt{5}\sqrt{5}$
$= 6\sqrt{2} - 10\sqrt{2} + 20\sqrt{2} = \mathbf{16\sqrt{2}}$

28. $\dfrac{1 + \dfrac{1}{y}}{\dfrac{1}{y}} = \dfrac{\dfrac{y + 1}{y}}{\dfrac{1}{y}} = \dfrac{y + 1}{y} \cdot \dfrac{y}{1} = y + 1$

29. $\dfrac{\dfrac{a}{b} - 4}{\dfrac{x}{b} - b} = \dfrac{\dfrac{a - 4b}{b}}{\dfrac{x - b^2}{b}} \cdot \dfrac{\dfrac{b}{x - b^2}}{\dfrac{b}{x - b^2}}$

$= \dfrac{a - 4b}{b} \cdot \dfrac{b}{x - b^2} = \dfrac{\mathbf{a - 4b}}{\mathbf{x - b^2}}$

30. $\dfrac{\dfrac{a}{x} - a}{x + \dfrac{y}{x}} = \dfrac{\dfrac{a - ax}{x}}{\dfrac{x^2 + y}{x}} \cdot \dfrac{\dfrac{x}{x^2 + y}}{\dfrac{x}{x^2 + y}}$

$= \dfrac{a - ax}{x} \cdot \dfrac{x}{x^2 + y} = \dfrac{\mathbf{a - ax}}{\mathbf{x^2 + y}}$

PROBLEM SET 74

1. $x^2 - 3x - 10$

$\quad (-5)(2) = -10 \quad$ and $\quad (5)(-2) = -10$
$\quad -5 + 2 = -3 \quad\quad\quad 5 + (-2) = 3$

$\quad x^2 - 3x - 10 = (x - 5)(x + 2)$

2. $x^2 + 12 + 7x = x^2 + 7x + 12$

$\quad (4)(3) = 12 \quad$ and $\quad (-4)(-3) = 12$
$\quad 4 + 3 = 7 \quad\quad\quad -4 + (-3) = -7$

$\quad x^2 + 7x + 12 = (x + 4)(x + 3)$

3. $-30 - x + x^2 = x^2 - x - 30$

$\quad (6)(-5) = -30 \quad$ and $\quad (-6)(5) = -30$
$\quad 6 + (-5) = 1 \quad\quad\quad -6 + 5 = -1$

$\quad x^2 - x - 30 = (x - 6)(x + 5)$

4. $x^2 + 10 + 7x = x^2 + 7x + 10$

$\quad (5)(2) = 10 \quad$ and $\quad (-5)(-2) = 10$
$\quad 5 + 2 = 7 \quad\quad\quad -5 + (-2) = -7$

$\quad x^2 + 7x + 10 = (x + 2)(x + 5)$

5. $x^2 + 12 + 8x = x^2 + 8x + 12$

$(6)(2) = 12$ and $(-6)(-2) = 12$
$6 + 2 = 8$ $\qquad -6 + (-2) = -8$

$x^2 + 8x + 12 = \mathbf{(x + 6)(x + 2)}$

6. $4 - 4x + x^2 = x^2 - 4x + 4$

$(2)(2) = 4$ and $(-2)(-2) = 4$
$2 + 2 = 4$ $\qquad -2 + (-2) = -4$

$x^2 - 4x + 4 = \mathbf{(x - 2)(x - 2)}$

7. $x^2 + 14 + 9x = x^2 + 9x + 14$

$(7)(2) = 14$ and $(-7)(-2) = 14$
$7 + 2 = 9$ $\qquad -7 + (-2) = -9$

$x^2 + 9x + 14 = \mathbf{(x + 2)(x + 7)}$

8. $x^2 - 14 - 5x = x^2 - 5x - 14$

$(7)(-2) = -14$ and $(-7)(2) = -14$
$7 + (-2) = 5$ $\qquad -7 + 2 = -5$

$x^2 - 5x - 14 = \mathbf{(x - 7)(x + 2)}$

9. $-3x - 18 + x^2 = x^2 - 3x - 18$

$(6)(-3) = -18$ and $(-6)(3) = -18$
$6 + (-3) = 3$ $\qquad -6 + 3 = -3$

$x^2 - 3x - 18 = \mathbf{(x - 6)(x + 3)}$

10. $6x + 8 + x^2 = x^2 + 6x + 8$

$(-4)(-2) = 8$ and $(4)(2) = 8$
$-4 + (-2) = -6$ $\qquad 4 + 2 = 6$

$x^2 + 6x + 8 = \mathbf{(x + 4)(x + 2)}$

11. $-8 + 2x + x^2 = x^2 + 2x - 8$

$(-4)(2) = -8$ and $(4)(-2) = -8$
$-4 + 2 = -2$ $\qquad 4 + (-2) = 2$

$x^2 + 2x - 8 = \mathbf{(x + 4)(x - 2)}$

12. $-8 - 2x + x^2 = x^2 - 2x - 8$

$(-4)(2) = -8$ and $(4)(-2) = -8$
$-4 + 2 = -2$ $\qquad 4 + (-2) = 2$

$x^2 - 2x - 8 = \mathbf{(x - 4)(x + 2)}$

13. $2x^2 + 10x + 12 = 2(x^2 + 5x + 6)$

$(2)(3) = 6$ and $(-2)(-3) = 6$
$2 + 3 = 5$ $\qquad -2 + (-3) = -5$

$2(x^2 + 5x + 6) = \mathbf{2(x + 2)(x + 3)}$

14. $5x^2 + 30x + 40 = 5(x^2 + 6x + 8)$

$(4)(2) = 8$ and $(-4)(-2) = 8$
$4 + 2 = 6$ $\qquad -4 + (-2) = -6$

$5(x^2 + 6x + 8) = \mathbf{5(x + 4)(x + 2)}$

15. $x^3 - x^2 - 20x = x(x^2 - x - 20)$

$(4)(-5) = -20$ and $(-4)(5) = -20$
$4 + (-5) = -1$ $\qquad -4 + 5 = 1$

$x(x^2 - x - 20) = \mathbf{x(x + 4)(x - 5)}$

16. $ax^2 + 6ax + 9a = a(x^2 + 6x + 9)$

$(3)(3) = 9$ and $(-3)(-3) = 9$
$3 + 3 = 6$ $\qquad -3 + (-3) = -6$

$a(x^2 + 6x + 9) = \mathbf{a(x + 3)(x + 3)}$

17. $abx^2 - 6ab + abx = ab(x^2 + x - 6)$

$(3)(-2) = -6$ and $(-3)(2) = -6$
$3 + (-2) = 1$ $\qquad -3 + (2) = -1$

$ab(x^2 + x - 6) = \mathbf{ab(x + 3)(x - 2)}$

18. $x^3 + 20x + 9x^2 = x(x^2 + 9x + 20)$

$(-4)(-5) = 20$ and $(4)(5) = 20$
$-4 + (-5) = -9$ $\qquad 4 + 5 = 9$

$x(x^2 + 9x + 20) = \mathbf{x(x + 4)(x + 5)}$

19. $-b^3 + 5b^2 + 24b = (-b)(b^2 - 5b - 24)$

$(-3)(8) = -24$ and $(3)(-8) = -24$
$-3 + 8 = 5$ $\qquad 3 + (-8) = -5$

$(-b)(b^2 - 5b - 24) = \mathbf{(-b)(b + 3)(b - 8)}$

20. $-3m^2 - 30m - 48 = (-3)(m^2 + 10m + 16)$

$(8)(2) = 16$ and $(-8)(-2) = 16$
$8 + 2 = 10$ $\qquad -8 + (-2) = -10$

$(-3)(m^2 + 10m + 16) = \mathbf{(-3)(m + 8)(m + 2)}$

21. $-2p^2 + 110 + 12p = (-2)(p^2 - 6p - 55)$

$(11)(-5) = -55$ and $(-11)(5) = -55$
$11 + (-5) = 6$ $\quad\quad -11 + 5 = -6$

$(-2)(p^2 - 6p - 55) = (-2)(p - 11)(p + 5)$

22. $10{,}000 \ \cancel{km^2} \times \dfrac{1000 \ \cancel{m}}{1 \ \cancel{km}} \times \dfrac{1000 \ \cancel{m}}{1 \ \cancel{km}} \times \dfrac{100 \ \cancel{cm}}{1 \ \cancel{m}}$

$\times \dfrac{100 \ \cancel{cm}}{1 \ \cancel{m}} \times \dfrac{1 \ \cancel{in.}}{2.54 \ \cancel{cm}} \times \dfrac{1 \ \cancel{in.}}{2.54 \ \cancel{cm}} \times \dfrac{1 \ \cancel{ft}}{12 \ \cancel{in.}}$

$\times \dfrac{1 \ \cancel{ft}}{12 \ \cancel{in.}} \times \dfrac{1 \ mi}{5280 \ \cancel{ft}} \times \dfrac{1 \ mi}{5280 \ \cancel{ft}}$

$= \dfrac{10{,}000(1000)(1000)(100)(100)}{(2.54)(2.54)(12)(12)(5280)(5280)} \ mi^2$

23. $\text{Per} = \dfrac{2(5)\pi}{2} \ ft + \dfrac{2(5)\pi}{2} \ ft + 10 \ ft + 10 \ ft$
$= 5\pi \ ft + 5\pi \ ft + 20 \ ft$
$= (10\pi + 20) \ ft \approx \mathbf{51.4 \ ft}$

24. $x^2 - 2x^{-2} - 4 = (-3)^2 - 2(-3)^{-2} - 4$
$= 9 - \dfrac{2}{9} - 4 = 5 - \dfrac{2}{9} = \dfrac{\mathbf{43}}{\mathbf{9}}$

25. $\dfrac{18x}{3^2 - 9} = \dfrac{18x}{9 - 9} = \dfrac{18x}{0} = \mathbf{undefined}$

26. $\dfrac{\dfrac{1}{x}}{\dfrac{1}{x} - 1} = \dfrac{\dfrac{1}{x}}{\dfrac{1 - x}{x}} \cdot \dfrac{\dfrac{x}{1 - x}}{\dfrac{x}{1 - x}}$

$= \dfrac{1}{x} \cdot \dfrac{x}{1 - x} = \dfrac{\mathbf{1}}{\mathbf{1 - x}}$

27. $5\sqrt{8} - 14\sqrt{50} = 5\sqrt{2 \cdot 2 \cdot 2} - 14\sqrt{5 \cdot 5 \cdot 2}$
$= 5\sqrt{2}\sqrt{2}\sqrt{2} - 14\sqrt{5}\sqrt{5}\sqrt{2} = 10\sqrt{2} - 70\sqrt{2}$
$= \mathbf{-60\sqrt{2}}$

28. $\dfrac{\dfrac{a}{x} + x}{\dfrac{1}{x} - 1} = \dfrac{\dfrac{a + x^2}{x}}{\dfrac{1 - x}{x}} \cdot \dfrac{\dfrac{x}{1 - x}}{\dfrac{x}{1 - x}}$

$= \dfrac{a + x^2}{x} \cdot \dfrac{x}{1 - x} = \dfrac{\mathbf{a + x^2}}{\mathbf{1 - x}}$

29. $\dfrac{\dfrac{1}{a}}{a + \dfrac{1}{a}} = \dfrac{\dfrac{1}{a}}{\dfrac{a^2 + 1}{a}} \cdot \dfrac{\dfrac{a}{a^2 + 1}}{\dfrac{a}{a^2 + 1}}$

$= \dfrac{1}{a} \cdot \dfrac{a}{a^2 + 1} = \dfrac{\mathbf{1}}{\mathbf{a^2 + 1}}$

30. $\dfrac{1 + \dfrac{4}{x}}{7} = \dfrac{\dfrac{x + 4}{x}}{\dfrac{7}{1}} \cdot \dfrac{\dfrac{1}{7}}{\dfrac{1}{7}} = \dfrac{x + 4}{x} \cdot \dfrac{1}{7}$

$= \dfrac{\mathbf{x + 4}}{\mathbf{7x}}$

PROBLEM SET 75

1. $m^2 + 10m + 16$
$(8)(2) = 16; \ 8 + 2 = 10$
$\mathbf{(m + 8)(m + 2)}$

2. $-48 - 8n + n^2 = n^2 - 8n - 48$
$(-12)(4) = -48; \ -12 + 4 = -8$
$\mathbf{(n - 12)(n + 4)}$

3. $y^2 + 56 - 15y = y^2 - 15y + 56$
$(-7)(-8) = 56; \ -7 + (-8) = -15$
$\mathbf{(y - 7)(y - 8)}$

4. $p^2 - 55 - 6p = p^2 - 6p - 55$
$(-11)(5) = -55; \ -11 + 5 = -6$
$\mathbf{(p - 11)(p + 5)}$

5. $12t + 35 + t^2 = t^2 + 12t + 35$
$(5)(7) = 35; \ 5 + 7 = 12$
$\mathbf{(t + 5)(t + 7)}$

6. $y^2 + 50 + 51y = y^2 + 51y + 50$
$(50)(1) = 50; \ 50 + 1 = 51$
$\mathbf{(y + 1)(y + 50)}$

7. $77 - 18r + r^2 = r^2 - 18r + 77$
$(-7)(-11) = 77; \ -7 + (-11) = -18$
$\mathbf{(r - 7)(r - 11)}$

8. $m^2 + 21m + 90$
$(6)(15) = 90; \ 6 + 15 = 21$
$\mathbf{(m + 6)(m + 15)}$

9. $55 + v^2 + 16v = v^2 + 16v + 55$
$(5)(11) = 55; \ 5 + 11 = 16$
$\mathbf{(v + 5)(v + 11)}$

10. $-63 - 2h + h^2 = h^2 - 2h - 63$
$(-9)(7) = -63; \ -9 + 7 = -2$
$\mathbf{(h - 9)(h + 7)}$

11. $-30 - 13x + x^2 = x^2 - 13x - 30$
$(-15)(2) = -30;\ -15 + 2 = -13$
$(x - 15)(x + 2)$

12. $w^2 + 22 - 13w = w^2 - 13w + 22$
$(-11)(-2) = 22;\ -11 + (-2) = -13$
$(w - 11)(w - 2)$

13. $-x^2 - 12 + 7x = (-1)(x^2 - 7x + 12)$
$(-4)(-3) = 12;\ -4 + (-3) = -7$
$-(x - 4)(x - 3)$

14. $-s^2 - 15 - 8s = (-1)(s^2 + 8s + 15)$
$(5)(3) = 15;\ 5 + 3 = 8$
$-(s + 5)(s + 3)$

15. $-a^2 + 40 - 3a = (-1)(a^2 + 3a - 40)$
$(8)(-5) = -40;\ 8 + (-5) = 3$
$-(a - 5)(a + 8)$

16. $2x^3 + 30x + 16x^2 = 2x(x^2 + 8x + 15)$
$(5)(3) = 15;\ 5 + 3 = 8$
$2x(x + 5)(x + 3)$

17. $4a^2 - 160 + 12a = 4(a^2 + 3a - 40)$
$(-5)(8) = -40;\ -5 + 8 = 3$
$4(a - 5)(a + 8)$

18. $abx^2 - 24ab - 5abx = ab(x^2 - 5x - 24)$
$(-8)(3) = -24;\ -8 + 3 = -5$
$ab(x - 8)(x + 3)$

19. $(x - 1)x^2 + 7x(x - 1) + 10(x - 1)$
$= (x - 1)(x^2 + 7x + 10)$
$(5)(2) = 10;\ 5 + 2 = 7$
$(x - 1)(x + 5)(x + 2)$

20. $-5 < x \le 2;\ D = \{\text{Reals}\}$

21. $A_{\text{Shaded}} = A_{\text{Triangle}} - A_{\text{Circle}}$

$= \left[\dfrac{1}{2}(36)(20)\right] \text{m}^2 - [\pi(6)^2]\,\text{m}^2$

$= (360 - 36\pi)(100)(100)\ \text{cm}^2$

$\approx \textbf{2,469,600 cm}^2$

22. (a) $x + y = 10$
$x = 10 - y$
(b) $x + 2y = 15$
Substitute (a) into (b) and get:
(b') $(10 - y) + 2y = 15$
$10 + y = 15$
$y = 5$

(a) $x = 10 - (5) = 5$
$(5, 5)$

23. (a) $10N_D + 25N_Q = 495$
(b) $N_Q = N_D + 10$
Substitute (b) into (a) and get:
(a') $10N_D + 25(N_D + 10) = 495$
$10N_D + 25N_D + 250 = 495$
$35N_D = 245$
$N_D = 7$

(b) $N_Q = (7) + 10 = 17$

24. (a) $5x - 2y = 9$
(b) $3x - y = 6$

$(-1)(a)\ -5x + 2y = -9$
$\underline{\ 2(b)\ \ \ \ 6x - 2y = 12\ }$
$x\ \ \ \ \ \ \ = 3$

(b) $3(3) - y = 6$
$-y = -3$
$y = 3$
$(3, 3)$

25. (a) $2x - 2y = 2$
(b) $3x + y = 7$

$(a)\ \ \ \ 2x - 2y = 2$
$\underline{2(b)\ \ 6x + 2y = 14\ }$
$8x\ \ \ \ \ \ \ = 16$
$x = 2$

(b) $3(2) + y = 7$
$y = 1$
$(2, 1)$

26. $3\sqrt{98} - 4\sqrt{50} = 3\sqrt{2 \cdot 7 \cdot 7} - 4\sqrt{5 \cdot 5 \cdot 2}$
$= 3\sqrt{2}\sqrt{7}\sqrt{7} - 4\sqrt{5}\sqrt{5}\sqrt{2} = 21\sqrt{2} - 20\sqrt{2} = \sqrt{2}$

27. $2\sqrt{45} - 2\sqrt{180}$
$= 2\sqrt{3 \cdot 3 \cdot 5} - 2\sqrt{3 \cdot 3 \cdot 2 \cdot 2 \cdot 5}$
$= 2\sqrt{3}\sqrt{3}\sqrt{5} - 2\sqrt{3}\sqrt{3}\sqrt{2}\sqrt{2}\sqrt{5}$
$= 6\sqrt{5} - 12\sqrt{5} = \mathbf{-6\sqrt{5}}$

28. $\dfrac{a + \dfrac{b}{a}}{\dfrac{1}{a} - 4} = \dfrac{\dfrac{a^2 + b}{a}}{\dfrac{1 - 4a}{a}} \cdot \dfrac{\dfrac{a}{1 - 4a}}{\dfrac{a}{1 - 4a}}$

$= \dfrac{a^2 + b}{a} \cdot \dfrac{a}{1 - 4a} = \dfrac{a^2 + b}{1 - 4a}$

29. $\dfrac{\dfrac{m}{p} + p}{\dfrac{1}{p} - x} = \dfrac{\dfrac{m + p^2}{p}}{\dfrac{1 - xp}{p}} \cdot \dfrac{\dfrac{p}{1 - px}}{\dfrac{p}{1 - px}}$

$= \dfrac{m + p^2}{p} \cdot \dfrac{p}{1 - px} = \dfrac{\boldsymbol{m + p^2}}{\boldsymbol{1 - px}}$

30. $-0.003k - 0.03k - 0.3k - 666 = 0$

$-3k - 30k - 300k - 666000 = 0$

$-333k = 666000$

$k = \boldsymbol{-2000}$

PROBLEM SET 76

1. $\dfrac{250}{100} \times E = 900$

$E = 900 \cdot \dfrac{100}{250}$

$E = \boldsymbol{360}$

2. $\dfrac{5}{18} = \dfrac{S}{360}$

$\boldsymbol{100} = S$

3. $\dfrac{(4)(2000) + (96)(100)}{4 + 96} = \boldsymbol{176 \text{ pounds}}$

4. $-6 \le x \le 3$

5. $25{,}000 \,\cancel{\text{mi}^2} \times \dfrac{5280 \,\cancel{\text{ft}}}{1 \,\cancel{\text{mi}}} \times \dfrac{5280 \,\cancel{\text{ft}}}{1 \,\cancel{\text{mi}}} \times \dfrac{12 \,\cancel{\text{in.}}}{1 \,\cancel{\text{ft}}}$

$\times \dfrac{12 \,\cancel{\text{in.}}}{1 \,\cancel{\text{ft}}} \times \dfrac{2.54 \,\cancel{\text{cm}}}{1 \,\cancel{\text{in.}}} \times \dfrac{2.54 \,\cancel{\text{cm}}}{1 \,\cancel{\text{in.}}} \times \dfrac{1 \,\cancel{\text{m}}}{100 \,\cancel{\text{cm}}}$

$\times \dfrac{1 \,\cancel{\text{m}}}{100 \,\cancel{\text{cm}}} \times \dfrac{1 \text{ km}}{1000 \,\cancel{\text{m}}} \times \dfrac{1 \text{ km}}{1000 \,\cancel{\text{m}}}$

$= \dfrac{\boldsymbol{25{,}000(5280)(5280)(12)(12)(2.54)(2.54)}}{\boldsymbol{(100)(100)(1000)(1000)}} \,\textbf{km}^2$

6. S.A. $= 2(A_{\text{End}}) + (\text{Circumference})(\text{length})$

$= 2[\pi(15)^2] \text{ m}^2 + [2\pi(15)](100) \text{ m}^2$

$= (3450\pi)(100)(100) \text{ cm}^2$

$\approx \boldsymbol{108{,}330{,}000 \text{ cm}^2}$

$V_{\text{Cylinder}} = A_{\text{End}} \times \text{length}$

$= [\pi(15)^2] \text{ m}^2 \times 100 \text{ m}$

$= (225\pi)(100)(100)(100)(100) \text{ cm}^3$

$\approx \boldsymbol{70{,}650{,}000{,}000 \text{ cm}^3}$

$V_{\text{Sphere}} = \dfrac{2}{3} V_{\text{Cylinder}}$

$= \dfrac{2}{3}\left[\pi(15)^2 \text{ m}^2 \times 30 \text{ m}\right]$

$= \dfrac{13{,}500\pi}{3}(100)(100)(100) \text{ cm}^3$

$\approx \boldsymbol{14{,}130{,}000{,}000 \text{ cm}^3}$

7. $4p^2x^2 - k^2 = (2px)^2 - (k)^2$

$= \boldsymbol{(2px - k)(2px + k)}$

8. $-4m^2 + 25p^2x^2 = 25p^2x^2 - 4m^2$

$= (5px)^2 - (2m)^2 = \boldsymbol{(5px - 2m)(5px + 2m)}$

9. $-9x^2 + 4y^2 = 4y^2 - 9x^2 = (2y)^2 - (3x)^2$

$= \boldsymbol{(2y - 3x)(2y + 3x)}$

10. $9k^2a^2 - 49 = (3ka)^2 - (7)^2$

$= \boldsymbol{(3ka - 7)(3ka + 7)}$

11. $p^2 - 4k^2 = (p)^2 - (2k)^2 = \boldsymbol{(p - 2k)(p + 2k)}$

12. $36a^2x^2 - k^2 = (6ax)^2 - (k)^2$

$= \boldsymbol{(6ax - k)(6ax + k)}$

13. $x^2 - x - 20$

$(-5)(4) = -20; \; -5 + 4 = -1$

$\boldsymbol{(x - 5)(x + 4)}$

14. $4x^2 - 4x - 80 = 4(x^2 - x - 20)$

$(-5)(4) = -20; \; -5 + 4 = -1$

$\boldsymbol{4(x - 5)(x + 4)}$

15. $2b^2 - 48 - 10b = 2(b^2 - 5b - 24)$

$(-8)(3) = -24; \; -8 + 3 = -5$

$\boldsymbol{2(b - 8)(b + 3)}$

16. $-90 - 39x + 3x^2 = 3(x^2 - 13x - 30)$

$(-15)(2) = -30; \; -15 + 2 = -13$

$\boldsymbol{3(x - 15)(x + 2)}$

17. $(a + b)x^2 + 7(a + b)x + 10(a + b)$

$= (a + b)(x^2 + 7x + 10)$

$(5)(2) = 10; \; 5 + 2 = 7$

$\boldsymbol{(a + b)(x + 5)(x + 2)}$

18. $pm^2 + 9pm + 20p = p(m^2 + 9m + 20)$

$(4)(5) = 20; \; 4 + 5 = 9$

$\boldsymbol{p(m + 4)(m + 5)}$

19. $5k^2 + 30 + 25k = 5(k^2 + 5k + 6)$

$(2)(3) = 6; \; 2 + 3 = 5$

$\boldsymbol{5(k + 2)(k + 3)}$

20. $-x^2 - 8x - 7 = -(x^2 + 8x + 7)$

$(7)(1) = 7; \; 7 + 1 = 8$

$\boldsymbol{-(x + 7)(x + 1)}$

21. $5m^2 + 5 - 10m = 5(m^2 - 2m + 1)$

$(-1)(-1) = 1; \; -1 + (-1) = -2$

$\boldsymbol{5(m - 1)(m - 1)}$

22. (a) $x + 2y = 12$

(b) $3x + y = 16$

$$y = 16 - 3x$$

Substitute (b) into (a) and get:

(a′) $x + 2(16 - 3x) = 12$

$$x + 32 - 6x = 12$$
$$-5x = -20$$
$$x = 4$$

(b) $y = 16 - 3(4) = 4$

(4, 4)

23. (a) $2x - y = 9$

(b) $3x + y = 6$

$$y = 6 - 3x$$

Substitute (b) into (a) and get:

(a′) $2x - (6 - 3x) = 9$

$$2x - 6 + 3x = 9$$
$$5x = 15$$
$$x = 3$$

(b) $y = 6 - 3(3) = -3$

(3, −3)

24. (a) $5x - 2y = 3$

(b) $2x - 3y = -1$

$$
\begin{array}{r}
3(a) \quad 15x - 6y = 9 \\
(-2)(b) \quad -4x + 6y = 2 \\
\hline
11x \quad\quad\ = 11 \\
x = 1
\end{array}
$$

(a) $5(1) - 2y = 3$

$$-2y = -2$$
$$y = 1$$

(1, 1)

25. (a) $N_P + N_N = 175$

(b) $N_P + 5N_N = 475$

$$
\begin{array}{r}
(-1)(a) \quad -N_P - \ N_N = -175 \\
(b) \quad N_P + 5N_N = \ 475 \\
\hline
4N_N = \ 300 \\
N_N = 75
\end{array}
$$

(a) $N_P + (75) = 175$

$$N_P = \mathbf{100}$$

26. $3\sqrt{125} + 2\sqrt{45} = 3\sqrt{5 \cdot 5 \cdot 5} + 2\sqrt{3 \cdot 3 \cdot 5}$

$= 3\sqrt{5}\sqrt{5}\sqrt{5} + 2\sqrt{3}\sqrt{3}\sqrt{5} = 15\sqrt{5} + 6\sqrt{5}$

$= \mathbf{21\sqrt{5}}$

27. $5\sqrt{12} - 2\sqrt{27} = 5\sqrt{2 \cdot 2 \cdot 3} - 2\sqrt{3 \cdot 3 \cdot 3}$

$= 5\sqrt{2}\sqrt{2}\sqrt{3} - 2\sqrt{3}\sqrt{3}\sqrt{3} = 10\sqrt{3} - 6\sqrt{3}$

$= \mathbf{4\sqrt{3}}$

28. $\dfrac{\dfrac{1}{x} + 1}{\dfrac{y}{x} + x} = \dfrac{\dfrac{1 + x}{x}}{\dfrac{y + x^2}{x}} \cdot \dfrac{\dfrac{x}{y + x^2}}{\dfrac{x}{y + x^2}}$

$= \dfrac{1 + x}{x} \cdot \dfrac{x}{y + x^2} = \dfrac{\mathbf{1 + x}}{\mathbf{y + x^2}}$

29. $\dfrac{x}{x(x + y)} + \dfrac{1}{x} = \dfrac{x + (x + y)}{x(x + y)}$

$= \dfrac{\mathbf{2x + y}}{\mathbf{x^2 + xy}}$

30. $-[2(-3 - k)] = -4(-3) - |-3|k$

$$-[-6 - 2k] = 12 - 3k$$
$$6 + 2k = 12 - 3k$$
$$5k = 6$$
$$k = \dfrac{\mathbf{6}}{\mathbf{5}}$$

PROBLEM SET 77

1. $\dfrac{3}{14} = \dfrac{W}{5600}$

$\mathbf{1200} = W$

2. $\dfrac{P}{100} \times \text{of} = \text{is}$

$\dfrac{120}{100} \cdot 74{,}000 = C$

$\mathbf{\$88{,}800} = C$

3. $\dfrac{P}{100} \times \text{of} = \text{is}$

$\dfrac{70}{100} \times F = 4900$

$F = \mathbf{\$7000}$

4. $\dfrac{9}{10} = \dfrac{B}{130}$

$\mathbf{117} = B$

5. $x - 3 \not> 4; \ D = \{\text{Reals}\}$

$x - 3 \le 4$

$x \le 7$

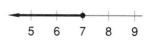

6. $(4 + x)(x^2 + 2x + 3)$

$= 4x^2 + 8x + 12 + x^3 + 2x^2 + 3x$

$= \mathbf{x^3 + 6x^2 + 11x + 12}$

7. $\dfrac{1}{xc^2} + \dfrac{b}{x(c + x)} + \dfrac{5}{x^2c^2}$

$= \dfrac{x(c + x) + b(xc^2) + 5(c + x)}{x^2c^2(c + x)}$

$= \dfrac{xc + x^2 + bxc^2 + 5c + 5x}{x^2c^2(c + x)}$

8. $\dfrac{x + \dfrac{a}{b}}{1 - \dfrac{1}{b}} = \dfrac{\dfrac{xb + a}{b}}{\dfrac{b - 1}{b}} \cdot \dfrac{\dfrac{b}{b - 1}}{\dfrac{b}{b - 1}}$

$= \dfrac{xb + a}{b} \cdot \dfrac{b}{b - 1} = \dfrac{\mathbf{xb + a}}{\mathbf{b - 1}}$

9. $0.4x - 4 - 0.4 = -0.2(4 - x)$

$4x - 40 - 4 = -2(4 - x)$

$4x - 44 = -8 + 2x$

$2x = 36$

$x = \mathbf{18}$

10. $\dfrac{x + 9}{2} = 18$

$x + 9 = 36$

$x = 27$

$\left(\dfrac{x}{3}\right)^2 = \left(\dfrac{27}{3}\right)^2 = (9)^2 = \mathbf{81}$

11. S.A. $= 2A_{\text{End}} + A_{\text{Bottom}} + 2A_{\text{Side 1}}$

$= \left[2\left(\dfrac{(6)(4)}{2}\right) + (6)(20) + 2[(20)(5)]\right] \text{m}^2$

$= (344)(100)(100) \text{ cm}^2$

$= \mathbf{3,440,000 \text{ cm}^2}$

$V_{\text{Prism}} = A_{\text{End}} \times \text{Length}$

$= \left[\dfrac{1}{2}(6)(4)\right] \text{m}^2 \times 20 \text{ m}$

$= (240)(100)(100)(100) \text{ cm}^3$

$= \mathbf{240,000,000 \text{ cm}^3}$

$V_{\text{Pyramid}} = \dfrac{1}{3}V_{\text{Prism}}$

$= \dfrac{1}{3}(240)(100)(100)(100) \text{ cm}^3$

$= \mathbf{80,000,000 \text{ cm}^3}$

12. $\dfrac{(6)(7.80) + (4)(11.2)}{6 + 4} = \dfrac{91.6}{10} = \mathbf{9.16 \text{ points}}$

13. $0.000478 = \mathbf{4.78 \times 10^{-4}}$

14. $y = -2x - 3\dfrac{1}{2}$

x	0	1	-1
y	$-3\dfrac{1}{2}$	$-5\dfrac{1}{2}$	$-1\dfrac{1}{2}$

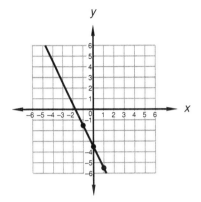

15. (a) $7x + y = -18$

$y = -7x - 18$

(b) $4x - 2y = 0$

Substitute (a) into (b) and get:

(b') $4x - 2(-7x - 18) = 0$

$4x + 14x + 36 = 0$

$18x = -36$

$x = -2$

(a) $y = -7(-2) - 18 = -4$

$\mathbf{(-2, -4)}$

16. (a) $N_D + N_Q = 40$

(b) $10N_D + 25N_Q = 475$

$(-10)(a)\quad -10N_D - 10N_Q = -400$

$(b)\quad \underline{10N_D + 25N_Q = 475}$

$15N_Q = 75$

$N_Q = \mathbf{5}$

(a) $N_D + (5) = 40$

$N_D = \mathbf{35}$

17. $\dfrac{2x^2}{y^2}\left(\dfrac{-x^2}{2y^{-2}} + \dfrac{x^2a^4}{a^{-2}4^{-2}}\right)$

$= \dfrac{-2x^2x^2}{2y^2y^{-2}} + \dfrac{2x^2x^2a^4}{y^2a^{-2}4^{-2}} = \mathbf{-x^4 + 32x^4a^6y^{-2}}$

18. $\dfrac{x^{-3}xy^2(y)^{-2}x^{-4}}{(x^0yy^{-2})^2(x^2y^{-3})^{-2}} = \dfrac{x^{-6}}{y^4x^{-4}} = \mathbf{x^{-2}y^{-4}}$

19. $4\sqrt{60} - 7\sqrt{135}$

$= 4\sqrt{2 \cdot 2 \cdot 3 \cdot 5} - 7\sqrt{3 \cdot 3 \cdot 3 \cdot 5}$

$= 4\sqrt{2}\sqrt{2}\sqrt{3}\sqrt{5} - 7\sqrt{3}\sqrt{3}\sqrt{3}\sqrt{5} = 8\sqrt{15} - 21\sqrt{15}$

$= \mathbf{-13\sqrt{15}}$

20. $4\sqrt{80} + 8\sqrt{45}$

$= 4\sqrt{2 \cdot 2 \cdot 2 \cdot 2 \cdot 5} + 8\sqrt{3 \cdot 3 \cdot 5}$

$= 4\sqrt{2}\sqrt{2}\sqrt{2}\sqrt{2}\sqrt{5} + 8\sqrt{3}\sqrt{3}\sqrt{5}$

$= 16\sqrt{5} + 24\sqrt{5} = \mathbf{40\sqrt{5}}$

21. $x^2 + 9x + 20 = \mathbf{(x + 4)(x + 5)}$

22. $x^2 + 15 + 8x = x^2 + 8x + 15$

$= \mathbf{(x + 5)(x + 3)}$

23. $x^2 + 11x + 28 = \mathbf{(x + 7)(x + 4)}$

24. $x^3 + 10x^2 + 24x = x(x^2 + 10x + 24)$

$= \mathbf{x(x + 4)(x + 6)}$

25. $ax^2 - 2ax - 15a = a(x^2 - 2x - 15)$

$= \mathbf{a(x - 5)(x + 3)}$

26. $5x^2 - 140 + 15x = 5(x^2 + 3x - 28)$

$= \mathbf{5(x - 4)(x + 7)}$

27. $5x^2 - 5y^2 = 5(x^2 - y^2) = \mathbf{5(x + y)(x - y)}$

28. $45x^2 - 20m^2 = 5(9x^2 - 4m^2)$

$= \mathbf{5(3x + 2m)(3x - 2m)}$

29. $4a^2 - 9b^2 = \mathbf{(2a + 3b)(2a - 3b)}$

30. $49a^2p^2 - k^2 = \mathbf{(7ap + k)(7ap - k)}$

Problem Set 78

1. $\dfrac{P}{100} \times \text{of} = \text{is}$

$\dfrac{3}{100} \times C = 120$

$C = 120 \cdot \dfrac{100}{3}$

$C = \mathbf{4000}$

2. $\dfrac{P}{100} \times \text{of} = \text{is}$

$\dfrac{34}{100} \cdot 4800 = S$

$\mathbf{1632} = S$

3. $\dfrac{WP}{100} \cdot 1400 = 784$

$WP = \mathbf{56\% \text{ patched}}$

$100\% - \% \text{ patched} = \% \text{ not patched}$

$100\% - 56\% = \mathbf{44\% \text{ not patched}}$

4. $WF(210) = 5\dfrac{1}{4}$

$WF = \dfrac{21}{4}\left(\dfrac{1}{210}\right)$

$WF = \mathbf{\dfrac{1}{40}}$

5. $-3 \in$ **Integers, rationals, reals**

6. $x = 2\dfrac{1}{2}$ (vertical line)

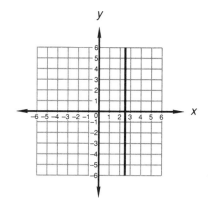

7. $\dfrac{4}{x^2c} + \dfrac{5}{xc} + \dfrac{6}{x(c + x)}$

$= \dfrac{4(c + x) + 5x(c + x) + 6xc}{x^2c(c + x)}$

$= \dfrac{4c + 4x + 5xc + 5x^2 + 6xc}{x^2c^2 + x^3c}$

$= \dfrac{\mathbf{5x^2 + 4x + 11xc + 4c}}{\mathbf{x^2c^2 + x^3c}}$

8. $\dfrac{x^{-2}y^0(x^{-2})^{-2}y^2}{(y^2x^{-4})^2(y^3x^2)} = \dfrac{x^2y^2}{y^7x^{-6}} = \mathbf{x^8y^{-5}}$

9. $\dfrac{1}{-3^{-3}} = -3^3 = \mathbf{-27}$

10. $\dfrac{5}{-3^{-2}} - \sqrt[5]{-32} = -5(3)^2 - (-2) = \mathbf{-43}$

11. $\dfrac{4ax^2}{x} - \dfrac{3a^{-4}x}{a^{-5}} - \dfrac{2x}{a^{-1}} + \dfrac{6a^2a^{-1}}{x}$

$= 4ax - 3ax - 2ax + 6ax^{-1}$

$= \mathbf{-ax + 6ax^{-1}}$

12. $0.00123 \times 10^{-5} = 1.23 \times 10^{-3} \times 10^{-5}$

$= \mathbf{1.23 \times 10^{-8}}$

13. $0.00123 \times 10^8 = 1.23 \times 10^{-3} \times 10^8$
$= \mathbf{1.23 \times 10^5}$

14. {Negative integers}

ADDITION: Closed. The sum of any two negative integers is a negative integer.

SUBTRACTION: Not closed. $-5 - (-7) = +2$

MULTIPLICATION: Not closed. $(-1)(-3) = +3$

DIVISION: Not closed. $\dfrac{-6}{-3} = +2$

Thus, the set of negative integers is closed for **addition**.

15. $\{-1, 0, 1, 2\}$

ADDITION: Not closed. $1 + 2 = 3$

SUBTRACTION: Not closed. $-1 - 2 = -3$

MULTIPLICATION: Not closed. $(2)(-1) = -2$

DIVISION: Not closed. $\dfrac{1}{0}$ is not defined.

Thus the set $\{-1, 0, 1, 2\}$ is closed for **none** of the operations.

16. $y = -\dfrac{1}{3}x - 3$

x	0	3	-3
y	-3	-4	-2

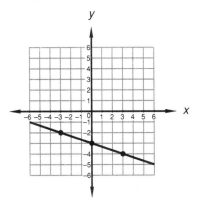

17. (a) $y + 3x = -2$
$\quad\quad y = -3x - 2$
(b) $2x - 4y = 22$
Substitute (a) into (b) and get:
(b′) $2x - 4(-3x - 2) = 22$
$\quad\quad 2x + 12x + 8 = 22$
$\quad\quad\quad\quad\quad 14x = 14$
$\quad\quad\quad\quad\quad\quad x = 1$

(a) $y = -3(1) - 2 = -5$
(1, −5)

18. (a) $4x - 5y = -13$
(b) $2x + 3y = 5$

$\begin{array}{r} (-1)(a) \quad -4x + 5y = 1 \\ 2(b) \quad \underline{4x + 6y = 10} \\ 11y = 11 \\ y = 1 \end{array}$

(a) $4x - 5(1) = -1$
$\quad\quad\quad 4x = 4$
$\quad\quad\quad\ x = 1$
(1, 1)

19. $\dfrac{4x^2}{y^2}\left(\dfrac{x^{-2}}{4y^2} - \dfrac{a^{-2}x^{-1}}{y^{-1}}\right)$

$= \dfrac{4x^2 x^{-2}}{y^2 4y^2} - \dfrac{4x^2 a^{-2} x^{-1}}{y^2 y^{-1}} = \mathbf{y^{-4} - 4xa^{-2}y^{-1}}$

20. $15\sqrt{8} - 30\sqrt{18} + 4\sqrt{50}$
$= 15\sqrt{2 \cdot 2 \cdot 2} - 30\sqrt{3 \cdot 3 \cdot 2} + 4\sqrt{5 \cdot 5 \cdot 2}$
$= 15\sqrt{2}\sqrt{2}\sqrt{2} - 30\sqrt{3}\sqrt{3}\sqrt{2} + 4\sqrt{5}\sqrt{5}\sqrt{2}$
$= 30\sqrt{2} - 90\sqrt{2} + 20\sqrt{2} = \mathbf{-40\sqrt{2}}$

21. $x^2 + 3x - 10 = \mathbf{(x + 5)(x - 2)}$

22. $4x + x^2 - 21 = x^2 + 4x - 21$
$= \mathbf{(x + 7)(x - 3)}$

23. $18 + 9x + x^2 = x^2 + 9x + 18$
$= \mathbf{(x + 3)(x + 6)}$

24. $5x^2 - 15x - 50 = 5(x^2 - 3x - 10)$
$= \mathbf{5(x - 5)(x + 2)}$

25. $x^3 - 3x^2 + 2x = x(x^2 - 3x + 2)$
$= \mathbf{x(x - 1)(x - 2)}$

26. $18x - x^3 + 3x^2 = -x(x^2 - 3x - 18)$
$= \mathbf{-x(x - 6)(x + 3)}$

27. $b^3x^2 - 4b^3 = b^3(x^2 - 4) = \mathbf{b^3(x + 2)(x - 2)}$

28. $16x^2 - a^2 = \mathbf{(4x + a)(4x - a)}$

29. $-m^2 + 9p^2 = 9p^2 - m^2 = (3p + m)(3p - m)$

30. S.A. $= 2(A_{End}) + (Circumference)(Length)$

$= 2[\pi(10)^2] \, m^2 + [2\pi(10)](100) \, m^2$

$= 2200\pi \, m^2$

$= (2200\pi)(100)(100) \, cm^2$

$\approx$ **69,080,000 cm²**

$V_{Cylinder} = A_{End} \times Length$

$= [\pi(10)^2] \, m^2 \times 100 \, m$

$= (10,000\pi)(100)(100)(100) \, cm^3$

$\approx$ **31,400,000,000 cm³**

$V_{Cone} = \dfrac{1}{3}V_{Cylinder}$

$= \dfrac{1}{3}(10,000\pi)(100)(100)(100) \, cm^3$

$\approx$ **10,466,666,666.67 cm³**

$V_{Sphere} = \dfrac{2}{3}V_{Cylinder}$

$= \dfrac{2}{3}\Big[A_{End} \times \text{height}\Big]$

$= \dfrac{2}{3}\Big[\pi(10)^2 \, m^2 \times 20 \, m\Big]$

$= \dfrac{2}{3}(2000\pi) \, m^3$

$= \dfrac{2}{3}(2000\pi)(100)(100)(100) \, cm^3$

$\approx$ **4,186,666,666.67 cm³**

PROBLEM SET 79

1. {Negative integers}

ADDITION: Closed. The sum of any two negative integers is a negative integer.

SUBTRACTION: Not closed. $-4 - (-8) = +4$

MULTIPLICATION: Not closed. $(-4)(-2) = +8$

DIVISION: Not closed. $\dfrac{-4}{-2} = +2$

Thus the set of negative integers is closed for **addition**.

2. {Whole numbers}

ADDITION: Closed. The sum of any two whole numbers is a whole number.

SUBTRACTION: Not closed. $5 - 9 = -4$

MULTIPLICATION: Closed. The product of any two whole numbers is a whole number.

DIVISION: Not closed. $\dfrac{3}{4}$

Thus the set of whole numbers is closed for **addition** and **multiplication**.

3. $N \quad N + 1 \quad N + 2 \quad N + 3$

$2(N + N + 2) = 3(N + 1) + 11$

$2(2N + 2) = 3N + 14$

$N = 10$

The desired integers are **10, 11, 12,** and **13**.

Check: $2(10 + 12) = 3(11) + 11$

$2(22) = 33 + 11$

$44 = 44$ check

4. $\dfrac{x + 7}{2} = 5$

$x + 7 = 10$

$x = 3$

$\left(\dfrac{27}{x}\right)^2 = \left(\dfrac{27}{3}\right)^2 = (9)^2 = $ **81**

5. $31\dfrac{1}{5}x - 2\dfrac{3}{5} = 14$

$\dfrac{156}{5}x = \dfrac{13}{5} + \dfrac{70}{5}$

$x = \dfrac{83}{5} \cdot \dfrac{5}{156}$

$x = \dfrac{83}{156}$

6. $-x + 4 - (-2)(-x - 5) = -(-2x + |4|)$

$-x + 4 - 2x - 10 = 2x - 4$

$-3x - 6 = 2x - 4$

$-5x = 2$

$x = -\dfrac{2}{5}$

7. {Rationals} $\subset$ {Integers}

False {Integers} $\subset$ {Rationals}

8. $y = -\dfrac{1}{3}x + 2$

x	0	3	-3
y	2	1	3

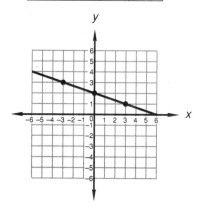

9. $\dfrac{1}{(-3)^{-2}} + 3^0 + 2^0 - \sqrt[3]{-8}$

$= (-3)^2 + 1 + 1 - (-2) = 9 + 1 + 1 + 2$

$= \mathbf{13}$

10. $430{,}000 \times 10^{-2} = 4.30 \times 10^5 \times 10^{-2}$

$= \mathbf{4.30 \times 10^3}$

11. $4300 \times 10^7 = 4.30 \times 10^3 \times 10^7 = \mathbf{4.30 \times 10^{10}}$

12. $\dfrac{P}{100} \times \text{of} = \text{is}$

$\dfrac{78}{100} \cdot 18{,}400 = S$

$\mathbf{14{,}352} = S$

13. $\dfrac{a}{x^2} + \dfrac{2}{ax^2} + \dfrac{b}{cx^3} = \dfrac{a^2cx + 2cx + ab}{acx^3}$

14. $\dfrac{a}{x} + \dfrac{b}{x+6} = \dfrac{a(x+6) + bx}{x(x+6)}$

$= \dfrac{ax + 6a + bx}{x^2 + 6x}$

15. $\dfrac{aa(a^{-3})^0 a^{-2}}{a^4(x^2)^{-2}} = \dfrac{a^2 a^{-2}}{a^4 x^{-4}} = a^{-4}x^4$

16. $\dfrac{a^2x^5}{y} - 3aax^6x^{-1}y^{-1} + \dfrac{4a^2y^{-1}}{x^{-5}} - \dfrac{3aax^3y^{-2}}{y}$

$= a^2x^5y^{-1} - 3a^2x^5y^{-1} + 4a^2x^5y^{-1} - 3a^2x^3y^{-3}$

$= \mathbf{2a^2x^5y^{-1} - 3a^2x^3y^{-3}}$

17. (a) $N_N = N_Q + 15$

(b) $5N_N + 25N_Q = 525$

Substitute (a) into (b) and get:

(b′) $5(N_Q + 15) + 25N_Q = 525$

$5N_Q + 75 + 25N_Q = 525$

$30N_Q = 450$

$N_Q = \mathbf{15}$

(b) $N_N = (15) + 15 = \mathbf{30}$

18. (a) $2x + 2y = 14$

(b) $3x - 2y = -4$

$\begin{array}{r} \text{(a)}\quad 2x + 2y = 14 \\ \text{(b)}\quad 3x - 2y = -4 \\ \hline 5x \qquad\quad = 10 \\ x = 2 \end{array}$

(a) $2(2) + 2y = 14$

$2y = 10$

$y = 5$

$\mathbf{(2, 5)}$

19. $\dfrac{3x^2y^{-2}}{ax^{-1}}\left(\dfrac{x^3}{y^2} - \dfrac{2x^{-2}a}{y^2}\right)$

$= \dfrac{3x^2y^{-2}x^3}{ax^{-1}y^2} - \dfrac{3x^2y^{-2}2x^{-2}a}{ax^{-1}y^2}$

$= \mathbf{3x^6y^{-4}a^{-1} - 6xy^{-4}}$

20. $3\sqrt{20} - 2\sqrt{80} + 2\sqrt{125}$

$= 3\sqrt{2 \cdot 2 \cdot 5} - 2\sqrt{2 \cdot 2 \cdot 2 \cdot 2 \cdot 5}$

$\quad + 2\sqrt{5 \cdot 5 \cdot 5}$

$= 3\sqrt{2}\sqrt{2}\sqrt{5} - 2\sqrt{2}\sqrt{2}\sqrt{2}\sqrt{2}\sqrt{5} + 2\sqrt{5}\sqrt{5}\sqrt{5}$

$= 6\sqrt{5} - 8\sqrt{5} + 10\sqrt{5} = \mathbf{8\sqrt{5}}$

21. $x^2 - 5x - 14 = \mathbf{(x - 7)(x + 2)}$

22. $-x^3 + 4x^2 + 12x = -x(x^2 - 4x - 12)$

$= \mathbf{-x(x - 6)(x + 2)}$

23. $ax^2 + 7xa + 10a = a(x^2 + 7x + 10)$

$= \mathbf{a(x + 5)(x + 2)}$

24. $24x + 2x^2 + 70 = 2(x^2 + 12x + 35)$

$= \mathbf{2(x + 7)(x + 5)}$

25. $24 + 27x + 3x^2 = 3(x^2 + 9x + 8)$

$= \mathbf{3(x + 8)(x + 1)}$

26. $-px + px^2 - 2p = p(x^2 - x - 2)$

$= \mathbf{p(x - 2)(x + 1)}$

27. $-9x^2 + m^2 = m^2 - 9x^2 = \mathbf{(m - 3x)(m + 3x)}$

28. $4x^2 - 9m^2 = \mathbf{(2x + 3m)(2x - 3m)}$

29. $125m^2 - 5x^2 = 5(25m^2 - x^2)$

$= \mathbf{5(5m - x)(5m + x)}$

30. $-72k^2 + 2x^2 = 2(x^2 - 36k^2)$

$= \mathbf{2(x - 6k)(x + 6k)}$

PROBLEM SET 80

1. $N \qquad N + 2 \qquad N + 4 \qquad N + 6$

$(N + 2) + (N + 4) = (N + 6) + 19$

$2N + 6 = N + 25$

$N = 19$

The desired integers are **19, 21, 23,** and **25.**

2. $6.4T = 46.08$

$T = \mathbf{7.2}$

3. $\{4, 3, 2\}$
  ADDITION: Not closed. $4 + 3 = 7$
  SUBTRACTION: Not closed. $4 - 3 = 1$
  MULTIPLICATION: Not closed. $(3)(2) = 6$

  DIVISION: Not closed. $\dfrac{2}{4} = 0.5$

  Thus the set $\{4, 3, 2\}$ is closed for **none** of the operations.

4. Average $= \dfrac{495}{3} = \mathbf{165}$

5. $V_{\text{Cylinder}} = A_{\text{Base}} \times \text{height}$

$$= \left[\frac{(7)(8)}{2} + (8)(8) - \frac{\pi(4)^2}{2}\right](6) \text{ ft}^3$$

$$= (92 - 8\pi)(6)(12)(12)(12) \text{ in.}^3$$

$$\approx 693,411.84 \text{ in.}^3$$

$$\approx \mathbf{693,411.84 \text{ one-inch sugar cubes}}$$

S.A. $= 2(A_{\text{Base}}) + (\text{Perimeter})(\text{height})$

$$= 2(92 - 8\pi) + (33.6 + 4\pi)(6) \text{ ft}^2$$

$$= (184 - 16\pi) \text{ ft}^2 + (201.6 + 24\pi) \text{ ft}^2$$

$$= (385.6 + 8\pi)(12)(12) \text{ in.}^2$$

$$\approx \mathbf{59,143.68 \text{ in.}^2}$$

$V_{\text{Cone}} = \dfrac{1}{3} V_{\text{Cylinder}}$

$$= \frac{1}{3}(92 - 8\pi)(6)(12)(12)(12) \text{ in.}^3$$

$$\approx \mathbf{231,137.28 \text{ in.}^3}$$

6. $4 \le x < 10; \ D = \{\text{Integers}\}$

$$\begin{array}{cccccccc} & \bullet & \bullet & \bullet & \bullet & \bullet & \bullet & \\ \hline 3 & 4 & 5 & 6 & 7 & 8 & 9 & 10 \end{array}$$

7. $\dfrac{1}{xc^2} + \dfrac{a}{xc} + \dfrac{m}{c(x + c)}$

$$= \frac{(x + c) + ac(x + c) + mxc}{xc^2(x + c)}$$

$$= \frac{x + c + acx + ac^2 + mxc}{xc^2(x + c)}$$

8. $\dfrac{x + \dfrac{1}{y}}{\dfrac{x^2}{y} - 5} = \dfrac{\dfrac{xy + 1}{y}}{\dfrac{x^2 - 5y}{y}} \cdot \dfrac{\dfrac{x^2 - 5y}{y}}{\dfrac{y}{x^2 - 5y}}$

$$= \frac{xy + 1}{y} \cdot \frac{y}{x^2 - 5y} = \frac{xy + 1}{x^2 - 5y}$$

9. $-2|-2| - 2^2 - 3(-2 - x) = -2(x - 3 - 2)$
$$-2(2) - 4 + 6 + 3x = -2x + 10$$
$$-2 + 3x = -2x + 10$$
$$5x = 12$$
$$x = \frac{12}{5}$$

10. $7000 \times 10^{-15} = 7 \times 10^3 \times 10^{-15} = \mathbf{7 \times 10^{-12}}$

11. $0.000007 \times 10^{-15} = 7 \times 10^{-6} \times 10^{-15}$
$$= \mathbf{7 \times 10^{-21}}$$

12. $\{\text{Positive real numbers}\}$
  ADDITION: Closed. The sum of any two positive real numbers is a positive real number.
  SUBTRACTION: Not closed. $(7) - (9) = -2$
  MULTIPLICATION: Closed. The product of any two positive real numbers is a positive real number.
  DIVISION: Closed. The quotient of any two positive real numbers is a positive real number.

  The set of positive real numbers is closed for **addition, multiplication, and division.**

13. $y = 2x - 2$

x	0	1	-1
y	-2	0	-4

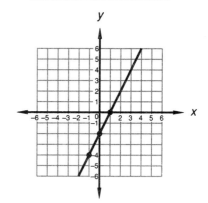

14. $y = -4$ (horizontal line)

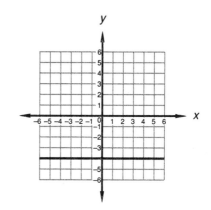

15. (a) $x + 3y = 16$
  (b) $2x - y = 4$
  $y = 2x - 4$
Substitute (b) into (a) and get:
(a′) $x + 3(2x - 4) = 16$
  $x + 6x - 12 = 16$
  $7x = 28$
  $x = 4$

(b) $y = 2(4) - 4 = 4$
(4, 4)

16. (a) $N_N + N_D = 500$
  (b) $5N_N + 10N_D = 3000$

  (-5)(a) $-5N_N - 5N_D = -2500$
  (b) $\underline{5N_N + 10N_D = 3000}$
  $5N_D = 500$
  $N_D = \mathbf{100}$

(a) $N_N + (100) = 500$
  $N_N = \mathbf{400}$

17. $\dfrac{3a^2 x}{y^2}\left(\dfrac{y^{-2}a^{-2}}{x^{-1}} - \dfrac{4ax}{y}\right)$

$= \dfrac{3a^2 x y^{-2} a^{-2}}{y^2 x^{-1}} - \dfrac{3a^2 x \, 4ax}{y^2 y}$

$= 3x^2 y^{-4} - 12a^3 x^2 y^{-3}$

18. $\dfrac{(2x^0 x^{-3})^{-2}(y^{-5})^{-2} x}{(x^2 y)(xy^2)} = \dfrac{x^6 y^{10} x}{4x^2 \, yxy^2} = \dfrac{x^7 y^{10}}{4x^3 y^3}$

$= \dfrac{x^4 y^7}{4}$

19. $2\sqrt{60} - 2\sqrt{135}$
$= 2\sqrt{2 \cdot 2 \cdot 3 \cdot 5} - 2\sqrt{3 \cdot 3 \cdot 3 \cdot 5}$
$= 2\sqrt{2}\sqrt{2}\sqrt{3}\sqrt{5} - 2\sqrt{3}\sqrt{3}\sqrt{3}\sqrt{5} = 4\sqrt{15} - 6\sqrt{15}$
$= \mathbf{-2\sqrt{15}}$

20. $2\sqrt{75} - 6\sqrt{27} = 2\sqrt{5 \cdot 5 \cdot 3} - 6\sqrt{3 \cdot 3 \cdot 3}$
$= 2\sqrt{5}\sqrt{5}\sqrt{3} - 6\sqrt{3}\sqrt{3}\sqrt{3} = 10\sqrt{3} - 18\sqrt{3}$
$= \mathbf{-8\sqrt{3}}$

21. $x^2 - 6x + 9 = (x - 3)(x - 3)$

22. $2x^2 - 8x + 8 = 2(x^2 - 4x + 4)$
$= 2(x - 2)(x - 2)$

23. $2x^2 + 8x + 8 = 2(x^2 + 4x + 4)$
$= 2(x + 2)(x + 2)$

24. $2x^2 + 20x + 50 = 2(x^2 + 10x + 25)$
$= 2(x + 5)(x + 5)$

25. $3x^2 - 30x + 75 = 3(x^2 - 10x + 25)$
$= 3(x - 5)(x - 5)$

26. $ax^2 - 12ax + 36a = a(x^2 - 12x + 36)$
$= a(x - 6)(x - 6)$

27. $4x^2 - 49 = (2x + 7)(2x - 7)$

28. $k^2 - 9x^2 y^2 = (k - 3xy)(k + 3xy)$

29. $3p^2 - 12k^2 = 3(p^2 - 4k^2) = 3(p + 2k)(p - 2k)$

30. $-4m^2 + k^2 = k^2 - 4m^2 = (k + 2m)(k - 2m)$

PROBLEM SET 81

1. $N \quad N + 1 \quad N + 2$
  $3(N + N + 1) + 49 = N + 2$
  $6N + 3 + 49 = N + 2$
  $5N = -50$
  $N = -10$
The desired integers are **−10, −9,** and **−8.**

2. $N \quad N + 2 \quad N + 4 \quad N + 6$
  $4(N + N + 4) = 4(N + 6) + 4$
  $8N + 16 = 4N + 24 + 4$
  $4N = 12$
  $N = 3$
The desired integers are **3, 5, 7,** and **9.**

3. $\dfrac{228}{100} \cdot CN = 9120$
  $CN = \mathbf{4000}$

4. $\dfrac{7}{10} \cdot F = 4200$
  $F = \mathbf{6000}$

5. $WF(36) = 9$
  $WF = \dfrac{1}{4}$

6. $-2\sqrt{3} \in$ **Irrationals and reals**

7. $\dfrac{a}{x^2 y} + \dfrac{b}{x^2 y^2} + \dfrac{c}{x^2 y^3} = \dfrac{ay^2 + by + c}{x^2 y^3}$

8. $\dfrac{x^0 x^2 y^{-2}(x^0)^{-2}}{(x^2)^{-3}(y^{-2})^3 y^0} = x^2 y^{-2} x^6 y^6 = \mathbf{x^8 y^4}$

9. $-3^{-3} = \dfrac{-1}{3^3} = -\dfrac{1}{27}$

10. $3^0 - (2^0 - 3)(-3 - 2) - \sqrt[3]{-8}$
$= 1 - (-2)(-5) + 2 = 1 - 10 + 2 = \mathbf{-7}$

11. $\dfrac{m^2xy}{x} - \dfrac{4m^3y}{m} + \dfrac{my}{m^{-1}} - \dfrac{3x^0y}{m^{-2}}$

$= m^2y - 4m^2y + m^2y - 3m^2y = \mathbf{-5m^2y}$

12. $0.0003 \times 10^{-15} = 3 \times 10^{-4} \times 10^{-15}$

$= \mathbf{3 \times 10^{-19}}$

13. $4000 \times 10^{-40} = 4 \times 10^3 \times 10^{-40}$

$= \mathbf{4 \times 10^{-37}}$

14. $y = -3x + 4$

x	0	1	3
y	4	1	-5

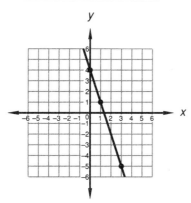

15. (a) $N_Q = N_D + 300$

(b) $10N_D + 25N_Q = 8200$

Substitute (a) into (b) and get:

(b′) $10N_D + 25(N_D + 300) = 8200$

$10N_D + 25N_D + 7500 = 8200$

$35N_D = 700$

$N_D = \mathbf{20}$

(a) $N_Q = (20) + 300 = \mathbf{320}$

16. (a) $4x - 3y = -3$

(b) $2x + 4y = -18$

$\begin{array}{r} \text{(a)} \quad 4x - 3y = -3 \\ (-2)\text{(b)} \quad -4x - 8y = 36 \\ \hline -11y = 33 \\ y = -3 \end{array}$

(b) $2x + 4(-3) = -18$

$2x - 12 = -18$

$2x = -6$

$x = -3$

$\mathbf{(-3, -3)}$

17. $\left(\dfrac{ax^2}{y^2} - \dfrac{3x}{xy^2}\right)\dfrac{2x^{-3}}{y^2} = \dfrac{2x^{-3}ax^2}{y^2y^2} - \dfrac{2x^{-3}3x}{y^2xy^2}$

$= \mathbf{2x^{-1}ay^{-4} - 6x^{-3}y^{-4}}$

18. $3\sqrt{28} - 5\sqrt{56} + 2\sqrt{63}$

$= 3\sqrt{2 \cdot 2 \cdot 7} - 5\sqrt{2 \cdot 2 \cdot 2 \cdot 7}$

$\quad + 2\sqrt{3 \cdot 3 \cdot 7}$

$= 3\sqrt{2}\sqrt{2}\sqrt{7} - 5\sqrt{2}\sqrt{2}\sqrt{2}\sqrt{7} + 2\sqrt{3}\sqrt{3}\sqrt{7}$

$= 6\sqrt{7} - 10\sqrt{14} + 6\sqrt{7}$

$= \mathbf{12\sqrt{7} - 10\sqrt{14}}$

19. $\dfrac{80.2 + 91.6 + 123 + 204.7 + N}{5} = 790.6$

$499.5 + N = \mathbf{3953}$

20. Area $= A_{\text{Triangle}} + A_{\text{Semicircle}}$

$= \left[\dfrac{1}{2}(10)(6) + \dfrac{1}{2}\pi(6)^2\right] \text{ft}^2$

$= (30 + 18\pi)(12)(12) \text{ in.}^2$

$\approx \mathbf{12{,}458.88 \text{ one-inch-square tiles}}$

21. $\dfrac{x - 12}{2} = 10$

$x - 12 = 20$

$x = 32$

$\left(\sqrt[3]{\dfrac{x}{4}}\right)^{-2}(x^{-1}x) = \left(\sqrt[3]{\dfrac{32}{4}}\right)^{-2}\left[(32)^{-1}(32)\right]$

$= \left(\sqrt[3]{8}\right)^{-2}(1) = 2^{-2} = \mathbf{\dfrac{1}{4}}$

22. $\dfrac{y}{7} + \dfrac{y + 1}{4} = 6$

$\dfrac{y}{7}(28) + \dfrac{(y + 1)}{4}(28) = 6(28)$

$4y + 7y + 7 = 168$

$11y = 161$

$y = \mathbf{\dfrac{161}{11}}$

23. $x^2 - 9x + 20 = \mathbf{(x - 4)(x - 5)}$

24. $2ax^2 - 20ax + 42a = 2a(x^2 - 10x + 21)$

$= \mathbf{2a(x - 7)(x - 3)}$

25. $13mx + 42m + mx^2 = m(x^2 + 13x + 42)$

$= \mathbf{m(x + 7)(x + 6)}$

26. $16x^2 - 9a^2 = \mathbf{(4x - 3a)(4x + 3a)}$

27. $25m^2 - 4 = \mathbf{(5m - 2)(5m + 2)}$

28. $-36k^2 + 9m^2y^2 = 9(m^2y^2 - 4k^2)$

$= \mathbf{9(my - 2k)(my + 2k)}$

29. {Real numbers}

ADDITION: Closed. The sum of any two real numbers is a real number.

SUBTRACTION: Closed. The difference between any two real numbers is a real number.

MULTIPLICATION: Closed. The product of any two real numbers is a real number.

DIVISION: Closed. The quotient of any two real numbers is a real number.

Thus the set of real numbers is closed for **addition, subtraction, multiplication,** and **division,** if we exclude division by zero.

PROBLEM SET 82

1. $N \quad N+2 \quad N+4 \quad N+6$

$4(N+N+6) - 8 = 12(N+4)$

$8N + 24 - 8 = 12N + 48$

$-4N = 32$

$N = -8$

The desired integers are **−8, −6, −4,** and **−2.**

2. $2\frac{3}{10} \times GN = 4\frac{3}{5}$

$\frac{23}{10} \times GN = \frac{23}{5}$

$GN = \mathbf{2}$

3. $WN = \frac{116}{100} \cdot 125$

$WN = \mathbf{145 \ pounds}$

4. $\frac{67}{100} \cdot F = 268$

$F = \mathbf{400 \ acres}$

5. $\frac{1}{8} \cdot W = 400$

$W = \mathbf{3200}$

6. $2 \in$ **naturals, wholes, integers, rationals,** and **reals**

7. $3\frac{1}{8}x - 4\frac{2}{5} = 7\frac{1}{2}$

$\frac{25}{8}x = \frac{22}{5} + \frac{15}{2}$

$\frac{25}{8}x = \frac{44}{10} + \frac{75}{10}$

$x = \frac{119}{10} \cdot \frac{8}{25} = \mathbf{\frac{476}{125}}$

8. $-[-2(x-4) - |-3|] = -2x - 8$

$-[-2x + 8 - 3] = -2x - 8$

$2x - 5 = -2x - 8$

$4x = -3$

$x = -\frac{3}{4}$

9. $0.000135 \times 10^{-17} = 1.35 \times 10^{-4} \times 10^{-17}$

$= \mathbf{1.35 \times 10^{-21}}$

10. $135,000 \times 10^{-17} = 1.35 \times 10^{5} \times 10^{-17}$

$= \mathbf{1.35 \times 10^{-12}}$

11. $\frac{a}{xy} + \frac{4}{x(x+y)} = \frac{a(x+y) + 4y}{xy(x+y)}$

$= \frac{ax + ay + 4y}{xy(x+y)}$

12. $\frac{a^0(2x)^{-2}}{a^2(4a^0)^2} = 4^{-1}x^{-2}a^{-2}4^{-2} = \frac{1}{64x^2a^2}$

13. $3x^2y - \frac{4x^{-2}y^{-2}}{x^{-4}y^{-3}} + \frac{5xx}{y^{-1}} - \frac{3x^2y^2}{y^{-2}}$

$= 3x^2y - 4x^2y + 5x^2y - 3x^2y^4 = \mathbf{4x^2y - 3x^2y^4}$

14. (a) $x + 3y = 16$

$x = -3y + 16$

(b) $2x - 3y = -4$

Substitute (a) into (b) and get:

(b′) $2(-3y + 16) - 3y = -4$

$-6y + 32 - 3y = -4$

$-9y = -36$

$y = 4$

(a) $x = -3(4) + 16 = 4$

(4, 4)

15. (a) $N_N + N_D = 22$

(b) $5N_N + 10N_D = 135$

$(-5)(a) \quad -5N_N - 5N_D = -110$

$(b) \quad \underline{5N_N + 10N_D = 135}$

$5N_D = 25$

$N_D = \mathbf{5}$

(a) $N_N + (5) = 22$

$N_N = \mathbf{17}$

16. $\frac{x^{-2}y^{-2}}{m^2}\left(x^2y^2m^2 - \frac{3x^4y^{-4}}{m^{-2}}\right)$

$= \frac{x^{-2}y^{-2}x^2y^2m^2}{m^2} - \frac{x^{-2}y^{-2}3x^4y^{-4}}{m^2m^{-2}}$

$= \mathbf{1 - 3x^2y^{-6}}$

17. $5\sqrt{45} - 3\sqrt{180} + 2\sqrt{20} = 5\sqrt{3 \cdot 3 \cdot 5}$
$\qquad - 3\sqrt{3 \cdot 3 \cdot 2 \cdot 2 \cdot 5} + 2\sqrt{2 \cdot 2 \cdot 5}$
$\qquad = 5\sqrt{3}\sqrt{3}\sqrt{5} - 3\sqrt{3}\sqrt{3}\sqrt{2}\sqrt{2}\sqrt{5} + 2\sqrt{2}\sqrt{2}\sqrt{5}$
$\qquad = 15\sqrt{5} - 18\sqrt{5} + 4\sqrt{5} = \boldsymbol{\sqrt{5}}$

18.
$$\frac{x}{4} - \frac{x + 2}{3} = 12$$
$$\frac{x}{4}(12) - \frac{(x + 2)}{3}(12) = 12(12)$$
$$3x - 4x - 8 = 144$$
$$-x = 152$$
$$x = \boldsymbol{-152}$$

19.
$$\frac{2y}{4} - \frac{y}{7} = \frac{y - 3}{2}$$
$$\frac{2y}{4}(28) - \frac{y}{7}(28) = \frac{(y - 3)}{2}(28)$$
$$14y - 4y = 14y - 42$$
$$-4y = -42$$
$$y = \boldsymbol{\frac{21}{2}}$$

20.
$$\frac{p}{6} - \frac{2p}{5} = \frac{4p - 5}{15}$$
$$\frac{p}{6}(30) - \frac{2p}{5}(30) = \frac{(4p - 5)}{15}(30)$$
$$5p - 12p = 8p - 10$$
$$-15p = -10$$
$$p = \boldsymbol{\frac{2}{3}}$$

21. (a) $R_P = 25$
(b) $T_P = 9$
(c) $T_A = 5$
(d) $R_A T_A + R_P T_P = 500$
Substitute (a), (b), and (c) into (d) and get:
(d′) $R_A(5) + (25)(9) = 500$
$$5R_A + 225 = 500$$
$$5R_A = 275$$
$$R_A = \boldsymbol{55}$$

22. $\dfrac{x + 20}{5} = -21$
$$x = -125$$
$$\frac{\sqrt[3]{x}}{5} = \frac{\sqrt[3]{-125}}{5} = \frac{-5}{5} = \boldsymbol{-1}$$

23. Convert 23,000 cubic meters to cubic feet:

$23,000 \ \cancel{m^3} \times \dfrac{100 \ \cancel{cm}}{1 \ \cancel{m}} \times \dfrac{100 \ \cancel{cm}}{1 \ \cancel{m}} \times \dfrac{100 \ \cancel{cm}}{1 \ \cancel{m}}$

$\times \dfrac{1 \ \cancel{in.}}{2.54 \ \cancel{cm}} \times \dfrac{1 \ \cancel{in.}}{2.54 \ \cancel{cm}} \times \dfrac{1 \ \cancel{in.}}{2.54 \ \cancel{cm}} \times \dfrac{1 \ ft}{12 \ \cancel{in.}}$

$\times \dfrac{1 \ ft}{12 \ \cancel{in.}} \times \dfrac{1 \ ft}{12 \ \cancel{in.}}$

$= \dfrac{\boldsymbol{23{,}000(100)(100)(100)}}{\boldsymbol{(2.54)(2.54)(2.54)(12)(12)(12)}} \ \boldsymbol{ft^3}$

24. S.A. $= A_{Base} + 4(A_{Side})$
$$= \left[(4)(4) + 4\left(\frac{1}{2}\right)(4)(6) \right] in.^2$$
$$= \boldsymbol{64 \ in.^2}$$

25. $p^2 - 55 - 6p = p^2 - 6p - 55$
$\qquad = \boldsymbol{(p - 11)(p + 5)}$

26. $-30 - 13x + x^2 = x^2 - 13x - 30$
$\qquad = \boldsymbol{(x - 15)(x + 2)}$

27. $2m^2 - 24m + 70 = 2(m^2 - 12m + 35)$
$\qquad = \boldsymbol{2(m - 7)(m - 5)}$

28. $-x^3 + 14x^2 - 40x = -x(x^2 - 14x + 40)$
$\qquad = \boldsymbol{-x(x - 4)(x - 10)}$

29. $4m^2 - 49x^2p^2 = \boldsymbol{(2m - 7xp)(2m + 7xp)}$

30. {Real numbers}

ADDITION:	Closed. The sum of any two real numbers is a real number.
SUBTRACTION:	Closed. The difference between any two real numbers is a real number.
MULTIPLICATION:	Closed. The product of any two real numbers is a real number.
DIVISION:	Not closed. $\dfrac{2}{0}$ is undefined

Thus the set of real numbers is closed for **addition, subtraction,** and **multiplication**.

PROBLEM SET 83

1. $N \qquad N + 2 \qquad N + 4$
$3[N + (N + 2) + (N + 4)] - 20 = 8(N + 4)$
$\qquad\qquad 3(3N + 6) - 20 = 8N + 32$
$\qquad\qquad 9N + 18 - 20 = 8N + 32$
$\qquad\qquad\qquad\qquad\qquad N = 34$
The desired integers are **34, 36,** and **38.**

2. $N \qquad N + 2 \qquad N + 4 \qquad N + 6$
$6(N + N + 4) - 3 = 5(-1)(N + 6)$
$\qquad 6(2N + 4) - 3 = -5N - 30$
$\qquad 12N + 24 - 3 = -5N - 30$
$\qquad\qquad\qquad 17N = -51$
$\qquad\qquad\qquad\quad N = -3$
The desired integers are **−3, −1, 1,** and **3.**

3. $\frac{230}{100} \cdot H = 460$

$H = 460 \cdot \frac{100}{230}$

$H = \mathbf{200}$

4. $\frac{86}{100} \cdot C = 43$

$C = 43 \cdot \frac{100}{86}$

$C = \mathbf{50\ farthings}$

5. $\frac{5}{13} \cdot E = 4125$

$E = 4125 \cdot \frac{13}{5}$

$E = \mathbf{10,725\ pounds}$

6. $x \nleq 4;\ D = \{\text{Positive integers}\}$
$x > 4$

7. $\frac{3}{a} + \frac{4}{a^2} + \frac{7}{a^2(a+x)}$

$= \frac{3a(a+x) + 4(a+x) + 7}{a^2(a+x)}$

$= \frac{3a^2 + 3ax + 4a + 4x + 7}{a^2(a+x)}$

8. $-0.013 - 0.013x + 0.026 = 0.039$
$-13 - 13x + 26 = 39$
$-13x = 26$
$x = \mathbf{-2}$

9. $\dfrac{4 + \dfrac{1}{y^2}}{\dfrac{x}{y} + \dfrac{m}{y^2}} = \dfrac{\dfrac{4y^2 + 1}{y^2}}{\dfrac{xy + m}{y^2}} \cdot \dfrac{\dfrac{y^2}{xy + m}}{\dfrac{y^2}{xy + m}}$

$= \frac{4y^2 + 1}{y^2} \cdot \frac{y^2}{xy + m} = \mathbf{\frac{4y^2 + 1}{xy + m}}$

10. $\frac{x - 9}{3} = 21$

$x - 9 = 63$

$x = 72$

$\sqrt[4]{x + 9} + \left(\frac{\sqrt{x}}{2}\right)^{-2}$

$= \sqrt[4]{72 + 9} + \left(\frac{\sqrt{72}}{2}\right)^{-2}$

$= \sqrt[4]{81} + \frac{4}{72} = 3 + \frac{1}{18} = \mathbf{\frac{55}{18}}$

11. $V_{\text{Cylinder}} = A_{\text{Base}} \times \text{height}$

$= \left[\frac{1}{2}(6)(8) + \frac{1}{2}(6)(8)\right](10\ \text{ft})$

$\quad + \left[\frac{1}{2}(3)^2 \pi + \frac{1}{2}(5)^2 \pi\right](10\ \text{ft})$

$= (48 + 17\pi)(10)(12)(12)(12)\ \text{in.}^3$

$\approx \mathbf{1{,}751{,}846.4\ in.^3}$

S.A. $= 2A_{\text{Base}} + (P \times \text{height})$
$= [2(48 + 17\pi) + (16 + 8\pi)(10)](12)(12)$
$\approx \mathbf{88{,}410.24\ in.^2}$

$V_{\text{Cone}} = \frac{1}{3}V_{\text{Cylinder}}$

$= \frac{1}{3}(48 + 17\pi)(10)(12)(12)(12)\ \text{in.}^3$

$\approx \mathbf{583{,}948.8\ in.^3}$

12. $\frac{15}{17} \cdot T = 3000$

$T = 3000 \cdot \frac{17}{15}$

$T = \mathbf{3400}$

13. $y = -4\frac{1}{2}$ (horizontal line)

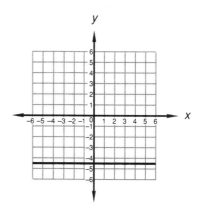

14. (a) $N_N = N_D + 12$
(b) $5N_N + 10N_D = 510$

Substitute (a) into (b) and get:
(b') $5(N_D + 12) + 10N_D = 510$
$5N_D + 60 + 10N_D = 510$
$15N_D = 450$
$N_D = \mathbf{30}$

(a) $N_N = (30) + 12 = \mathbf{42}$

15. (a) $7x - 4y = 29$
(b) $3x + 5y = -1$
5(a) $35x - 20y = 145$
4(b) $12x + 20y = -4$
$$\overline{ 47x = 141}$$
$x = 3$
(b) $3(3) + 5y = -1$
$5y = -10$
$y = -2$

(3, -2)

16. $\dfrac{x^{-2}}{y^2 a}\left(\dfrac{y^2 a^{-3}}{x^{-2}} + \dfrac{3x^{-4}}{y^{-2}a^{-4}}\right)$

$= \dfrac{x^{-2}y^2 a^{-3}}{y^2 a x^{-2}} + \dfrac{x^{-2}\,3x^{-4}}{y^2 a y^{-2} a^{-4}} = a^{-4} + 3x^{-6}a^3$

17. $\dfrac{[\,x^2(y^5)^{-2}\,]^{-3}}{(x^0 y^2)y^{-2}} = \dfrac{x^{-6}y^{30}}{y^2 y^{-2}} = x^{-6}y^{30}$

18. $3\sqrt{8} - 5\sqrt{18} + 6\sqrt{72} - 3\sqrt{50}$
$= 3\sqrt{2 \cdot 2 \cdot 2} - 5\sqrt{3 \cdot 3 \cdot 2}$
$\quad + 6\sqrt{3 \cdot 3 \cdot 2 \cdot 2 \cdot 2} - 3\sqrt{5 \cdot 5 \cdot 2}$
$= 3\sqrt{2}\sqrt{2}\sqrt{2} - 5\sqrt{3}\sqrt{3}\sqrt{2} + 6\sqrt{3}\sqrt{3}\sqrt{2}\sqrt{2}\sqrt{2}$
$\quad - 3\sqrt{5}\sqrt{5}\sqrt{2}$
$= 6\sqrt{2} - 15\sqrt{2} + 36\sqrt{2} - 15\sqrt{2} = \mathbf{12\sqrt{2}}$

19. $\dfrac{3x}{2} - \dfrac{5 - x}{3} = 7$

$\dfrac{3x}{2}(6) - \dfrac{(5 - x)}{3}(6) = 7(6)$
$9x - 10 + 2x = 42$
$11x = 52$
$x = \dfrac{\mathbf{52}}{\mathbf{11}}$

20. $\dfrac{2x - 3}{5} - \dfrac{2x}{10} = \dfrac{1}{2}$

$\dfrac{(2x - 3)}{5}(10) - \dfrac{2x}{10}(10) = \dfrac{1}{2}(10)$
$4x - 6 - 2x = 5$
$2x = 11$
$x = \dfrac{\mathbf{11}}{\mathbf{2}}$

21. (a) $R_F T_F = R_S T_S$
(b) $T_S = 6$
(c) $T_F = 5$
(d) $R_F - 16 = R_S$
Substitute (b) and (c) into (a) and get:
(a′) $5R_F = 6R_S$
Substitute (d) into (a′) and get:
(a″) $5R_F = 6(R_F - 16)$
$5R_F = 6R_F - 96$
$\mathbf{96 = R_F}$

(d) $R_S = (96) - 16 = \mathbf{80}$

22. (a) $R_M T_M = R_R T_R$
(b) $R_M = 8$
(c) $R_R = 2$
(d) $T_R = 5 - T_M$
Substitute (b) and (c) into (a) and get:
(a′) $8T_M = 2T_R$
Substitute (d) into (a′) and get:
(a″) $8T_M = 2(5 - T_M)$
$8T_M = 10 - 2T_M$
$10T_M = 10$
$T_M = \mathbf{1}$

(d) $T_R = 5 - (1) = \mathbf{4}$

23. (a) $R_G T_G + R_B T_B = 100$
(b) $R_G = 4$
(c) $R_B = 10$
(d) $T_B = T_G + 3$
Substitute (b) and (c) into (a) and get:
(a′) $4T_G + 10T_B = 100$
Substitute (d) into (a′) and get:
(a″) $4T_G + 10(T_G + 3) = 100$
$4T_G + 10T_G + 30 = 100$
$14T_G = 70$
$T_G = \mathbf{5}$

(d) $T_B = (5) + 3 = \mathbf{8}$

24. $\dfrac{(0.08 \times 10^7)(900{,}000)}{(20{,}000)(0.000003)}$

$= \dfrac{(8 \times 10^5)(9 \times 10^5)}{(2 \times 10^4)(3 \times 10^{-6})}$

$= \dfrac{8 \cdot 9}{2 \cdot 3} \times \dfrac{10^5 \cdot 10^5}{10^4 \cdot 10^{-6}} = \dfrac{72}{6} \times \dfrac{10^{10}}{10^{-2}}$

$= 12 \times 10^{12} = \mathbf{1.2 \times 10^{13}}$

25. $\dfrac{(0.0006 \times 10^{-31})(8000 \times 10^9)}{(0.0000002)(400{,}000)}$

$= \dfrac{(6 \times 10^{-35})(8 \times 10^{12})}{(2 \times 10^{-7})(4 \times 10^5)}$

$= \dfrac{6 \cdot 8}{2 \cdot 4} \times \dfrac{10^{-35} \cdot 10^{12}}{10^{-7} \cdot 10^5} = \dfrac{48}{8} \times \dfrac{10^{-23}}{10^{-2}}$

$= \mathbf{6 \times 10^{-21}}$

26. $x^3 + 9x^2 + 8x = x(x^2 + 9x + 8)$
$= \mathbf{x(x + 8)(x + 1)}$

27. $-ax^2 + 48a - 13xa = -a(x^2 + 13x - 48)$
$= \mathbf{-a(x - 3)(x + 16)}$

28. $bcx^2 - a^2 cb = bc(x^2 - a^2) = \mathbf{bc(x - a)(x + a)}$

29. $-m^3 + k^2m = m(k^2 - m^2) = \boldsymbol{m(k + m)(k - m)}$

30. {Negative real numbers}

ADDITION: Closed. The sum of any two negative real numbers is a negative real number.

SUBTRACTION: Not closed. $(-4) - (-5) = 1$

MULTIPLICATION: Not closed. $-3 \times -4 = 12$

DIVISION: Not closed. $-6 \div -2 = 3$

Thus the set of negative real numbers is closed for the operation of **addition**.

PROBLEM SET 84

1. $N \qquad N + 2 \qquad N + 4$

$4(N + N + 4) = 7(N + 2) + 16$

$8N + 16 = 7N + 14 + 16$

$N = 14$

The desired integers are **14, 16**, and **18**.

2. $N \qquad N + 1 \qquad N + 2 \qquad N + 3$

$(N + (N + 2)) + 10 = 4(N + 3) + 6$

$2N + 12 = 4N + 12 + 6$

$-2N = 6$

$N = -3$

The desired integers are **−3, −2, −1,** and **0**.

3. $WN = \dfrac{7}{5}(300) = \boldsymbol{420 \text{ pounds}}$

4. $\dfrac{35}{100}(T) = 105$

$T = 300$

$L = T - R = (300) - 105 = \boldsymbol{195}$

5. $WF\left(7\dfrac{2}{5}\right) = 49\dfrac{1}{3}$

$\left(\dfrac{5}{37}\right)WF\left(\dfrac{37}{5}\right) = \dfrac{\overset{4}{148}}{3}\left(\dfrac{5}{37}\right)$

$WF = \dfrac{\boldsymbol{20}}{\boldsymbol{3}}$

6. $-\dfrac{\sqrt{3}}{2} \in$ **Irrationals and reals**

7. $\dfrac{\dfrac{x}{y} - 1}{\dfrac{x}{y} + m} = \dfrac{\dfrac{x - y}{y}}{\dfrac{x + my}{y}} \cdot \dfrac{y}{x + my}$

$= \dfrac{x - y}{y} \cdot \dfrac{y}{x + my} = \dfrac{\boldsymbol{x - y}}{\boldsymbol{x + my}}$

8. $\dfrac{x^2(2y^{-2})^{-3}}{(4x^2)^{-2}} = \dfrac{x^2(8^{-1})y^6}{(16^{-1})x^{-4}} = \dfrac{16x^6y^6}{8}$

$= \boldsymbol{2x^6y^6}$

9. $\dfrac{1}{-3^{-2}} + (-3^0)(-3 - 5) = -3^2 + (-1)(-8)$

$= -9 + 8 = \boldsymbol{-1}$

10. $\dfrac{ax^{-4}}{(x^{-2})^2} + \dfrac{3a^{-2}a^3}{a^0} - \dfrac{6a^5}{(a^{-2})^{-2}} + 3a$

$= a + 3a - 6a + 3a = \boldsymbol{a}$

11. $\dfrac{(0.003 \times 10^7)(700{,}000)}{(5000)(0.0021 \times 10^{-6})}$

$= \dfrac{(3 \times 10^4)(7 \times 10^5)}{(5 \times 10^3)(2.1 \times 10^{-9})}$

$= \dfrac{3 \cdot 7}{5 \cdot 2.1} \times \dfrac{10^4 \cdot 10^5}{10^3 \cdot 10^{-9}} = \dfrac{21}{10.5} \times \dfrac{10^9}{10^{-6}}$

$= \boldsymbol{2 \times 10^{15}}$

12. $\dfrac{(0.0007 \times 10^{-10})(4000 \times 10^5)}{(0.0004)(7000)}$

$= \dfrac{(7 \times 10^{-14})(4 \times 10^8)}{(4 \times 10^{-4})(7 \times 10^3)}$

$= \dfrac{7 \cdot 4}{4 \cdot 7} \times \dfrac{10^{-14} \cdot 10^8}{10^{-4} \cdot 10^3} = \dfrac{28}{28} \times \dfrac{10^{-6}}{10^{-1}}$

$= \boldsymbol{1 \times 10^{-5}}$

13. $\dfrac{1}{5}D = 140$

$D = \boldsymbol{700}$

14. $\dfrac{x - 22}{5} = (2)^3$

$x - 22 = 40$

$x = 62$

$\dfrac{\sqrt[3]{x + 2} + 11}{3} = \dfrac{\sqrt[3]{62 + 2} + 11}{3}$

$= \dfrac{\sqrt[3]{64} + 11}{3} = \dfrac{4 + 11}{3} = \dfrac{15}{3} = \boldsymbol{5}$

15. $V_{\text{Prism}} = A_{\text{Base}} \times \text{height}$

$= (3 \text{ m})(4 \text{ m}) \times 2 \text{ m}$

$= (12)(2)(100)(100)(100) \text{ cm}^3$

$= \boldsymbol{24{,}000{,}000 \text{ cm}^3}$

S.A. $= 2A_{\text{Base}} + (P \times \text{height})$

$= 2(12 \text{ m}^2) + (14 \text{ m})(2 \text{ m})$

$= 52(100)(100) \text{ cm}^2$

$= \boldsymbol{520{,}000 \text{ cm}^2}$

$V_{\text{Pyramid}} = \dfrac{1}{3}V_{\text{Prism}}$

$= \dfrac{1}{3}(24{,}000{,}000) \text{ cm}^3$

$= \boldsymbol{8{,}000{,}000 \text{ cm}^3}$

16. (a) $x + 5y = 17$
(b) $2x - 4y = -8$
$$2x = 4y - 8$$
$$x = 2y - 4$$
Substitute (b) into (a) and get:
(a′) $(2y - 4) + 5y = 17$
$$7y = 21$$
$$y = 3$$

(b) $x = 2(3) - 4 = 2$
(2, 3)

17. (a) $N_N + N_D = 30$
(b) $5N_N + 10N_D = 250$

(−5)(a) $-5N_N - 5N_D = -150$
(b) $\underline{ 5N_N + 10N_D = 250}$
$$5N_D = 100$$
$$N_D = \mathbf{20}$$

(a) $N_N + (20) = 30$
$$N_N = \mathbf{10}$$

18.
$$\frac{x}{3} + \frac{5x + 3}{2} = 5$$
$$\frac{x}{3}(6) + \frac{(5x + 3)}{2}(6) = 5(6)$$
$$2x + 15x + 9 = 30$$
$$17x = 21$$
$$x = \frac{21}{17}$$

19.
$$\frac{y + 3}{2} - \frac{4y}{3} = \frac{1}{6}$$
$$\frac{(y + 3)}{2}(6) - \frac{4y}{3}(6) = \frac{1}{6}(6)$$
$$3y + 9 - 8y = 1$$
$$-5y = -8$$
$$y = \frac{8}{5}$$

20. $\dfrac{x^{-2}}{a^2 y^{-2}}\left(\dfrac{x^4 a^5}{y^4} - \dfrac{3x^{-4}}{a^{-4} y^2}\right)$

$= \dfrac{x^{-2} x^4 a^5}{a^2 y^{-2} y^4} - \dfrac{x^{-2} 3x^{-4}}{a^2 y^{-2} a^{-4} y^2}$

$= x^2 a^3 y^{-2} - 3x^{-6} a^2$

21. $4\sqrt{28} - 3\sqrt{63} + \sqrt{175}$
$= 4\sqrt{2 \cdot 2 \cdot 7} - 3\sqrt{3 \cdot 3 \cdot 7} + \sqrt{5 \cdot 5 \cdot 7}$
$= 4\sqrt{2}\sqrt{2}\sqrt{7} - 3\sqrt{3}\sqrt{3}\sqrt{7} + \sqrt{5}\sqrt{5}\sqrt{7}$
$= 8\sqrt{7} - 9\sqrt{7} + 5\sqrt{7}$
$= \mathbf{4\sqrt{7}}$

22. (a) $R_G T_G + R_B T_B = 120$
(b) $R_G = 4$
(c) $R_B = 10$
(d) $T_G = T_B + 2$
Substitute (b) and (c) into (a) and get:
(a′) $4T_G + 10T_B = 120$
Substitute (d) into (a′) and get:
(a″) $4(T_B + 2) + 10T_B = 120$
$$4T_B + 8 + 10T_B = 120$$
$$14T_B = 112$$
$$T_B = \mathbf{8}$$

(d) $T_G = (8) + 2 = \mathbf{10}$

23. (a) $R_K T_K = R_N T_N$
(b) $R_K = 6$
(c) $R_N = 3$
(d) $T_K = T_N - 8$
Substitute (b) and (c) into (a) and get:
(a′) $6T_K = 3T_N$
Substitute (d) into (a′) and get:
(a″) $6(T_N - 8) = 3T_N$
$$6T_N - 48 = 3T_N$$
$$3T_N = 48$$
$$T_N = \mathbf{16}$$

(d) $T_K = (16) - 8 = \mathbf{8}$

24. (a) $y = x - 6$
(b) $y = -x$
The first step is to graph each of these lines.

$y = x - 6$

x	0	3	5
y	−6	−3	−1

$y = -x$

x	0	3	−3
y	0	−3	3

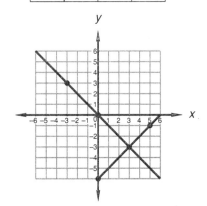

It appears that the lines cross at $x = 3$ and $y = -3$, so **(3, −3)** is the solution.

25. (a) $y = x + 1$
(b) $y = -x - 1$
The first step is to graph each of these lines.

$y = x + 1$

x	0	3	-3
y	1	4	-2

$y = -x - 1$

x	0	3	-3
y	-1	-4	2

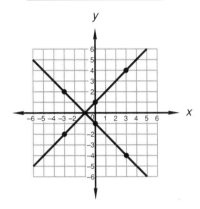

It appears that the lines cross at $x = -1$ and $y = 0$, so $(-1, 0)$ is the solution.

26. $ax^2 + 6a - 7ax = a(x^2 - 7x + 6)$
$= \boldsymbol{a(x - 6)(x - 1)}$

27. $-mx^2 - 8m - 6mx = -m(x^2 + 6x + 8)$
$= \boldsymbol{-m(x + 2)(x + 4)}$

28. $mx^2 - 9ma^2 = m(x^2 - 9a^2)$
$= \boldsymbol{m(x - 3a)(x + 3a)}$

29. $-k^2 + 4m^2x^2 = 4m^2x^2 - k^2$
$= \boldsymbol{(2mx + k)(2mx - k)}$

30. {Negative even integers}
ADDITION: Closed. The sum of any two negative even integers is a negative even integer.
SUBTRACTION: Not closed. $(-4) - (-6) = 2$
MULTIPLICATION: Not closed. $-2 \times -4 = 8$
DIVISION: Not closed. $-6 \div -2 = 3$
Thus the set of negative even integers is closed for the operation of **addition**.

PROBLEM SET 85

1. $N \quad N + 1 \quad N + 2$
$5(N + N + 1) = -(N + 2) + 7$
$10N + 5 = -N - 2 + 7$
$11N = 0$
$N = 0$
The desired integers are **0, 1,** and **2.**

2. $N \quad N + 2 \quad N + 4 \quad N + 6$
$3(N + N + 2) = 5(N + 4) + 18$
$6N + 6 = 5N + 20 + 18$
$N = 32$
The desired integers are **32, 34, 36,** and **38.**

3. $\left(\dfrac{\cancel{100}}{\cancel{86}}\right)\dfrac{\cancel{86}}{\cancel{100}}OP = 3440\left(\dfrac{100}{86}\right)$

$\qquad OP = \boldsymbol{\$4000}$

$\dfrac{14}{100}(4000) = PR$

$\qquad PR = \boldsymbol{\$560}$

4. $WN = \dfrac{370}{100}(1400) = \boldsymbol{5180}$

5. $(1.62)J = 7452$
$J = \boldsymbol{4600}$

6. $\dfrac{7\sqrt{2}}{3} \in$ **Irrationals and reals**

7. $-2(4 - 1)(-1 - 2^0) + |-3 + 5|$
$= -2(3)(-2) + |2| = 12 + 2 = \boldsymbol{14}$

8. $WF\left(2\dfrac{1}{4}\right) = 7\dfrac{3}{8}$

$\left(\dfrac{\cancel{4}}{\cancel{9}}\right)WF\left(\dfrac{\cancel{9}}{\cancel{4}}\right) = \dfrac{59}{\underset{2}{\cancel{8}}}\left(\dfrac{\cancel{4}}{9}\right)$

$\qquad WF = \boldsymbol{\dfrac{59}{18}}$

9. $2.2x - 0.1x + 0.02x = -2 - 0.332$
$2200x - 100x + 20x = -2000 - 332$
$2120x = -2332$
$x = \boldsymbol{-1.1}$

10. $\dfrac{x - 50}{10} = -30$
$x - 50 = -300$
$x = -250$

$\dfrac{\sqrt[5]{x + 7}}{3} = \dfrac{\sqrt[5]{-250 + 7}}{3} = \dfrac{\sqrt[5]{-243}}{3} = \dfrac{-3}{3}$
$= \boldsymbol{-1}$

11. vertical line: $x = \pm k$; $\boldsymbol{x = -3}$

12. The desired equation is $y = mx + b$.
By inspection, $b = +2$.
By inspection, the sign of m is $-$.

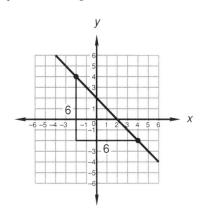

$|m| = \dfrac{6}{6} = 1$

So $b = 2$ and $m = -1$: $\boldsymbol{y = -x + 2}$

13. $A = \dfrac{\pi(3)^2}{2} + \dfrac{\pi(5)^2}{2} + \dfrac{\pi(4)^2}{2} + \dfrac{(8)(6)}{2}$

$= \dfrac{9}{2}\pi \text{ m}^2 + \dfrac{25}{2}\pi \text{ m}^2 + \dfrac{16}{2}\pi \text{ m}^2 + 24 \text{ m}^2$

$= (25\pi + 24) \text{ m}^2$

$= (25\pi + 24)(100)(100) \text{ cm}^2$

$\approx \boldsymbol{1{,}025{,}000 \text{ cm}^2}$

14. $\dfrac{(0.0056 \times 10^{-5})(100{,}000 \times 10^{-14})}{8000 \times 10^{15}}$

$= \dfrac{(5.6 \times 10^{-8})(1 \times 10^{-9})}{8 \times 10^{18}}$

$= \dfrac{5.6 \cdot 1}{8} \times \dfrac{10^{-8} \cdot 10^{-9}}{10^{18}} = \dfrac{5.6}{8} \times \dfrac{10^{-17}}{10^{18}}$

$= 0.7 \times 10^{-35} = \boldsymbol{7 \times 10^{-36}}$

15. $\dfrac{\dfrac{x^2}{y} + y}{a - \dfrac{x}{y}} = \dfrac{\dfrac{x^2 + y^2}{y}}{\dfrac{ay - x}{y}} \cdot \dfrac{\dfrac{ay - x}{y}}{\dfrac{ay - x}{y}}$

$= \dfrac{x^2 + y^2}{y} \cdot \dfrac{y}{ay - x} = \dfrac{\boldsymbol{x^2 + y^2}}{\boldsymbol{ay - x}}$

16. $\dfrac{4}{x + y} + \dfrac{6}{x} - \dfrac{4}{ax}$

$= \dfrac{4ax + 6a(x + y) - 4(x + y)}{ax(x + y)}$

$= \dfrac{4ax + 6ax + 6ay - 4x - 4y}{ax(x + y)}$

$= \dfrac{\boldsymbol{10ax + 6ay - 4x - 4y}}{\boldsymbol{ax(x + y)}}$

17. $\dfrac{x^{-2}a}{y^2}\left(\dfrac{a^4 y^{-2}}{x} - \dfrac{3x^2 a}{y^2}\right)$

$= \dfrac{x^{-2}aa^4 y^{-2}}{y^2 x} - \dfrac{x^{-2}a3x^2 a}{y^2 y^2}$

$= \boldsymbol{a^5 x^{-3} y^{-4} - 3a^2 y^{-4}}$

18. $a^2 xy - \dfrac{3a^2 x}{y^{-1}} + \dfrac{4x}{y^{-1}a^2} + \dfrac{5x^{-1}y}{a^2}$

$= a^2 xy - 3a^2 xy + 4a^{-2}xy + 5a^{-2}x^{-1}y$

$= \boldsymbol{-2a^2 xy + 4a^{-2}xy + 5a^{-2}x^{-1}y}$

19. (a) $y = x + 4$
(b) $y = -x + 2$
The first step is to graph each of these lines.

$y = x + 4$

x	0	-2	2
y	4	2	6

$y = -x + 2$

x	0	-2	2
y	2	4	0

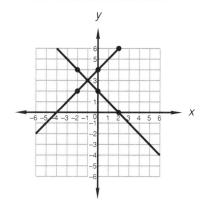

It appears that the lines cross at $x = -1$ and $y = 3$, so $\boldsymbol{(-1, 3)}$ is the solution.

20. (a) $5N_N + 10N_D = 450$
(b) $N_D = N_N + 30$

Substitute (b) into (a) and get:
(a′) $5N_N + 10(N_N + 30) = 450$
$\qquad 5N_N + 10N_N + 300 = 450$
$\qquad\qquad\qquad\quad 15N_N = 150$
$\qquad\qquad\qquad\qquad N_N = \boldsymbol{10}$

(b) $N_D = (10) + 30 = \boldsymbol{40}$

21. (a) $5x - 2y = 7$
(b) $4x + y = 3$

$$\begin{array}{rl} \text{(a)} & 5x - 2y = 7 \\ 2\text{(b)} & \underline{8x + 2y = 6} \\ & 13x \quad\quad = 13 \\ & \quad\quad x = 1 \end{array}$$

(b) $4(1) + y = 3$
$y = -1$

(1, –1)

22.
$$\frac{p}{4} - \frac{p+2}{6} = -4$$
$$\frac{p}{4}(12) - \frac{(p+2)}{6}(12) = -4(12)$$
$$3p - 2p - 4 = -48$$
$$p = \mathbf{-44}$$

23.
$$\frac{k+2}{5} - \frac{k}{10} = \frac{3}{20}$$
$$\frac{(k+2)}{5}(20) - \frac{k}{10}(20) = \frac{3}{20}(20)$$
$$4k + 8 - 2k = 3$$
$$k = \mathbf{-\frac{5}{2}}$$

24. $3\sqrt{72} - 14\sqrt{18} + 6\sqrt{8}$
$= 3\sqrt{3 \cdot 3 \cdot 2 \cdot 2 \cdot 2} - 14\sqrt{3 \cdot 3 \cdot 2}$
$\quad + 6\sqrt{2 \cdot 2 \cdot 2}$
$= 3\sqrt{3}\sqrt{3}\sqrt{2}\sqrt{2}\sqrt{2} - 14\sqrt{3}\sqrt{3}\sqrt{2} + 6\sqrt{2}\sqrt{2}\sqrt{2}$
$= 18\sqrt{2} - 42\sqrt{2} + 12\sqrt{2} = \mathbf{-12\sqrt{2}}$

25. (a) $R_T T_T = R_B T_B$
(b) $R_T = 80$
(c) $R_B = 20$
(d) $T_B = T_T + 18$
Substitute (b) and (c) into (a) and get:
(a′) $80T_T = 20T_B$
Substitute (d) into (a′) and get:
(a″) $80T_T = 20(T_T + 18)$
$80T_T = 20T_T + 360$
$60T_T = 360$
$T_T = \mathbf{6}$
(d) $T_B = (6) + 18 = \mathbf{24}$

26. (a) $R_L T_L = R_S T_S$
(b) $R_L = 120$
(c) $R_S = 280$
(d) $T_S = 20 - T_L$
Substitute (b) and (c) into (a) and get:
(a′) $120T_L = 280T_S$
Substitute (d) into (a′) and get:
(a″) $120T_L = 280(20 - T_L)$
$120T_L = 5600 - 280T_L$
$400T_L = 5600$
$T_L = \mathbf{14}$
(d) $T_S = 20 - (14) = \mathbf{6}$

27. $4x^2 + 40x + 100 = 4(x^2 + 10x + 25)$
$= \mathbf{4(x+5)(x+5)}$

28. $-x^3 - 30x - 11x^2 = -x(x^2 + 11x + 30)$
$= \mathbf{-x(x+6)(x+5)}$

29. $ax^2 - 35a + 2ax = a(x^2 + 2x - 35)$
$= \mathbf{a(x-5)(x+7)}$

30. {Positive odd integers}
ADDITION: Not closed. $3 + 5 = 8$
SUBTRACTION: Not closed. $3 - 5 = -2$
MULTIPLICATION: Closed. The product of any two positive odd integers is a positive odd integer.

DIVISION: Not closed. $\frac{7}{3}$ is not a positive integer.

Thus the set of positive odd integers is closed for **multiplication.**

PROBLEM SET 86

1. (a) $N_N + N_D = 51$
(b) $5N_N + 10N_D = 410$

$$\begin{array}{rl} (-5)\text{(a)} & -5N_N - 5N_D = -255 \\ \text{(b)} & \underline{5N_N + 10N_D = 410} \\ & \quad\quad 5N_D = 155 \\ & \quad\quad N_D = 31 \end{array}$$

(a) $N_N + (31) = 51$
$N_N = 20$
11 (more dimes than nickels)

2. $V_{Cylinder} = A_{Base} \times \text{height}$

$$= \left[(2)(3) - \frac{\pi(1)^2}{2} + \frac{(3)(2)}{2} \right](8) \text{ ft}^3$$
$$\approx [7.43](8)(12)(12)(12) \text{ in.}^3$$
$$\approx \mathbf{102{,}712.32 \text{ in.}^3}$$

S.A. $= 2A_{Base} + (\text{Perimeter})(h)$
$= 2[7.43] \text{ ft}^2 + (12.6 + \pi)(8) \text{ ft}^2$
$\approx 14.86 \text{ ft}^2 + 125.92 \text{ ft}^2$
$\approx [140.78](12)(12) \text{ in.}^2$
$\approx \mathbf{20{,}272.32 \text{ in.}^2}$

$V_{Cone} = \frac{1}{3}V_{Cylinder}$

$= \frac{1}{3}(102{,}712.32) \text{ in.}^3$

$\approx \mathbf{34{,}237.44 \text{ in.}^3}$

3. $\dfrac{(10)(\$650.50) + (20)(\$874.75)}{10 + 20} = \dfrac{\$24,000}{30}$

$= \mathbf{\$800}$

4. $\dfrac{17}{19} = \dfrac{S}{7600}$

$S = \dfrac{7600 \cdot 17}{19}$

$S = \mathbf{6800}$

5. $\dfrac{(0.0016 \times 10^{-7})(3000 \times 10^{5})}{1,200,000}$

$= \dfrac{(1.6 \times 10^{-10})(3 \times 10^{8})}{1.2 \times 10^{6}}$

$= \dfrac{1.6 \cdot 3}{1.2} \times \dfrac{10^{-10} \cdot 10^{8}}{10^{6}} = \dfrac{4.8}{1.2} \times \dfrac{10^{-2}}{10^{6}}$

$= \mathbf{4 \times 10^{-8}}$

6. $\dfrac{(0.003 \times 10^{-5})(700 \times 10^{14})}{21,000,000}$

$= \dfrac{(3 \times 10^{-8})(7 \times 10^{16})}{(2.1 \times 10^{7})}$

$= \dfrac{3 \cdot 7}{2.1} \times \dfrac{10^{-8} \cdot 10^{16}}{10^{7}} = 10 \times 10^{1}$

$= \mathbf{1 \times 10^{2}}$

7. A: Every point on this line is four units to the right of the y-axis, so $x = \mathbf{4}$.

B: The desired equation is $y = mx + b$.
By inspection, $b = 0$.
By inspection, the sign of m is +.

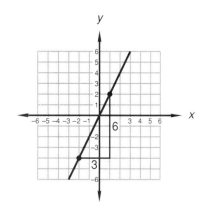

$|m| = \dfrac{6}{3} = 2$

So $b = 0$ and $m = 2$: $y = \mathbf{2x}$

8. {Counting numbers}

ADDITION:	Closed. The sum of any two counting numbers is a counting number.
SUBTRACTION:	Not closed. $5 - 8 = -3$
MULTIPLICATION:	Closed. The product of any two counting numbers is a counting number.
DIVISION:	Not closed. $\dfrac{1}{3}$ is not a counting number.

Thus the set of counting numbers is closed for **addition** and **multiplication**.

9. (a) $y = x + 2$
(b) $y = -x$
The first step is to graph each of these lines.

$y = x + 2$

x	0	2	-3
y	2	4	-1

$y = -x$

x	0	3	-3
y	0	-3	3

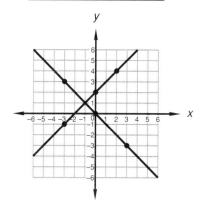

It appears that the lines cross at $x = -1$ and $y = 1$, so $(\mathbf{-1, 1})$ is the solution.

10. (a) $3x + 2y = 11$
(b) $2x - 3y = 16$

$\begin{array}{ll} 3\text{(a)} & 9x + 6y = 33 \\ 2\text{(b)} & \underline{4x - 6y = 32} \\ & 13x \quad\quad = 65 \\ & \quad x = 5 \end{array}$

(b) $2(5) - 3y = 16$
$-3y = 6$
$y = -2$

$\mathbf{(5, -2)}$

11. $4\sqrt{8} - 5\sqrt{32} + 6\sqrt{18}$
$= 4\sqrt{2 \cdot 2 \cdot 2} - 5\sqrt{2 \cdot 2 \cdot 2 \cdot 2 \cdot 2}$
$\quad + 6\sqrt{3 \cdot 3 \cdot 2}$
$= 4\sqrt{2}\sqrt{2}\sqrt{2} - 5\sqrt{2}\sqrt{2}\sqrt{2}\sqrt{2}\sqrt{2} + 6\sqrt{3}\sqrt{3}\sqrt{2}$
$= 8\sqrt{2} - 20\sqrt{2} + 18\sqrt{2} = \mathbf{6\sqrt{2}}$

12. $\left(3\frac{1}{4}\right)WN = 15\frac{1}{2}$

$\left(\frac{\cancel{4}}{\cancel{13}}\right)\frac{\cancel{13}}{\cancel{4}}WN = \frac{31}{\cancel{2}}\left(\frac{\cancel{4}}{13}\right)^{\!2}$

$\qquad WN = \mathbf{\dfrac{62}{13}}$

13. $-3 \le x < 2;\ D = \{\text{Positive integers}\}$

14. (a) $R_M T_M + R_S T_S = 170$
(b) $R_M = 20$
(c) $R_S = 30$
(d) $T_M = T_S + 1$
Substitute (b) and (c) into (a) and get:
(a′) $20T_M + 30T_S = 170$
Substitute (d) into (a′) and get:
(a″) $20(T_S + 1) + 30T_S = 170$
$\qquad 20T_S + 20 + 30T_S = 170$
$\qquad\qquad\qquad\qquad T_S = \mathbf{3}$
(d) $T_M = (3) + 1 = \mathbf{4}$

15. (a) $R_P T_P = R_M T_M$
(b) $R_P = 45$
(c) $R_M = 15$
(d) $T_P = T_M + 8$
Substitute (b) and (c) into (a) and get:
(a′) $45T_P = 15T_M$
Substitute (d) into (a′) and get:
(a″) $45(T_M + 8) = 15T_M$
$\qquad 45T_M + 360 = 15T_M$
$\qquad\qquad 30T_M = -360$
$\qquad\qquad\quad T_M = \mathbf{-12}$
(d) $T_P = (-12) + 8 = \mathbf{-4}$

16. (a) $R_G T_G + 10 = R_P T_P$
(b) $T_G = 4$
(c) $T_P = 2$
(d) $R_P = R_G + 45$
Substitute (b) and (c) into (a) and get:
(a′) $R_G(4) + 10 = R_P(2)$
Substitute (d) into (a′) and get:
(a″) $R_G(4) + 10 = (R_G + 45)2$
$\qquad 4R_G + 10 = 2R_G + 90$
$\qquad\qquad\quad R_G = \mathbf{40}$
(d) $R_P = (40) + 45 = \mathbf{85}$

17. $\dfrac{x}{3} - 2 = \dfrac{4 - x}{5}$

$\dfrac{x}{3}(15) - 2(15) = \dfrac{(4 - x)}{5}(15)$

$\qquad 5x - 30 = 12 - 3x$

$\qquad\qquad 8x = 42$

$\qquad\qquad x = \mathbf{\dfrac{21}{4}}$

18. $\dfrac{x}{4} - \dfrac{1}{2} = \dfrac{2 - x}{8}$

$\dfrac{x}{4}(8) - \dfrac{1}{2}(8) = \dfrac{(2 - x)}{8}(8)$

$\qquad 2x - 4 = 2 - x$

$\qquad\qquad 3x = 6$

$\qquad\qquad x = \mathbf{2}$

19. $-\dfrac{x + 2}{3} - \dfrac{2x + 8}{7} = 4$

$-\dfrac{(x + 2)}{3}(21) - \dfrac{(2x + 8)}{7}(21) = 4(21)$

$\qquad -7x - 14 - 6x - 24 = 84$

$\qquad\qquad\qquad -13x = 122$

$\qquad\qquad\qquad x = \mathbf{-\dfrac{122}{13}}$

20. $\dfrac{x}{4} - \dfrac{2x + 5}{2} = 7$

$\dfrac{x}{4}(4) - \dfrac{(2x + 5)}{2}(4) = 7(4)$

$\qquad x - 4x - 10 = 28$

$\qquad\qquad -3x = 38$

$\qquad\qquad x = \mathbf{-\dfrac{38}{3}}$

21. $\dfrac{1}{a^2} + \dfrac{2b}{a^3} - \dfrac{3b}{4a^3} = \dfrac{4a + 2b(4) - 3b}{4a^3}$

$= \mathbf{\dfrac{4a + 5b}{4a^3}}$

22. $\dfrac{4}{a + b} + \dfrac{6}{a^2} = \dfrac{4a^2 + 6(a + b)}{a^2(a + b)}$

$= \mathbf{\dfrac{4a^2 + 6a + 6b}{a^2(a + b)}}$

23. $x = -2:\ y + 3 = \sqrt{81} - 3$
$\qquad\qquad\quad y + 3 = 9 - 3$
$\qquad\qquad\qquad\quad y = 3$

$x(x^{-5} - y) - x^2 = (-2)((-2)^{-5} - 3) - (-2)^2$

$= -2\left(-\dfrac{1}{32} - 3\right) - 4 = \cancel{-2}\left(-\dfrac{97}{\underset{16}{\cancel{32}}}\right) - 4$

$= \dfrac{97}{16} - \dfrac{64}{16} = \mathbf{\dfrac{33}{16}}$

24. $\dfrac{x + \dfrac{x}{y}}{\dfrac{ax}{y} + 1} = \dfrac{\dfrac{xy + x}{y}}{\dfrac{ax + y}{y}} \cdot \dfrac{\dfrac{y}{ax + y}}{\dfrac{y}{ax + y}}$

$= \dfrac{xy + x}{y} \cdot \dfrac{y}{ax + y} = \dfrac{\boldsymbol{xy + x}}{\boldsymbol{ax + y}}$

25. $\dfrac{\dfrac{ab}{c} - \dfrac{1}{c^2}}{4 - \dfrac{a}{c^2}} = \dfrac{\dfrac{abc - 1}{c^2}}{\dfrac{4c^2 - a}{c^2}} \cdot \dfrac{\dfrac{c^2}{4c^2 - a}}{\dfrac{c^2}{4c^2 - a}}$

$= \dfrac{abc - 1}{c^2} \cdot \dfrac{c^2}{4c^2 - a} = \dfrac{\boldsymbol{abc - 1}}{\boldsymbol{4c^2 - a}}$

26. $-4^{-2} = -\dfrac{1}{4^2} = \boldsymbol{-\dfrac{1}{16}}$

27. $28x + 11x^2 + x^3 = x(x^2 + 11x + 28)$
$= \boldsymbol{x(x + 7)(x + 4)}$

28. $-xy^2 + 4a^2x = x(4a^2 - y^2) = \boldsymbol{x(2a + y)(2a - y)}$

29. $\dfrac{x^{-2}}{y^2}\left(x^2y^2 - \dfrac{3a^0x^2}{y^2} \right)$

$= \dfrac{x^{-2}x^2y^2}{y^2} - \dfrac{x^{-2}3a^0x^2}{y^2y^2} = \boldsymbol{1 - 3y^{-4}}$

30. $\dfrac{(x^2)^{-3}y^2p^0x^4}{[(x^2)^{-3}y]^{-2}x^{-4}} = \dfrac{x^{-6}y^2x^4}{x^{12}y^{-2}x^{-4}} = \boldsymbol{x^{-10}y^4}$

31. $\dfrac{x^2yyy^3}{(x^2y)^0} = \boldsymbol{x^2y^5}$

PROBLEM SET 87

1. (a) $N_P + N_N = 175$
(b) $N_P + 5N_N = 475$

$(-1)(a) \quad -N_P - N_N = -175$
$(b) \quad \underline{N_P + 5N_N = 475}$
$ 4N_N = 300$
$ N_N = \boldsymbol{75}$

(a) $N_P + (75) = 175$
$ N_P = \boldsymbol{100}$

2. (a) $N_N = N_D + 12$
(b) $5N_N + 10N_D = 510$
Substitute (a) into (b) and get:
(b') $5(N_D + 12) + 10N_D = 510$
$ 5N_D + 60 + 10N_D = 510$
$ 15N_D = 450$
$ N_D = \boldsymbol{30}$
(a) $N_N = (30) + 12 = \boldsymbol{42}$

3. $\dfrac{80}{100}T = 128$

$\left(\dfrac{100}{80}\right)\dfrac{80}{100}T = 128\left(\dfrac{100}{80}\right)$

$T = \boldsymbol{160}$

4. $N \qquad N + 2 \qquad N + 4$
$3(N + N + 2) = 14(-N - 4) - 58$
$ 6N + 6 = -14N - 56 - 58$
$ 20N = -120$
$ N = -6$
The desired integers are $\boldsymbol{-6, -4}$, and $\boldsymbol{-2}$.

5. $\dfrac{(0.00032 \times 10^{-5})(4000 \times 10^7)}{(160,000)(0.00002)}$

$= \dfrac{(3.2 \times 10^{-9})(4 \times 10^{10})}{(1.6 \times 10^5)(2 \times 10^{-5})}$

$= \dfrac{3.2 \cdot 4}{1.6 \cdot 2} \times \dfrac{10^{-9} \cdot 10^{10}}{10^5 \cdot 10^{-5}} = \dfrac{12.8}{3.2} \times \dfrac{10^1}{10^0}$

$= \boldsymbol{4 \times 10^1}$

6. Every point on this line is four units above the x-axis, so $\boldsymbol{y = 4}$

7. The desired equation is $y = mx + b$.
By inspection, $b = -2$.
By inspection, the sign of m is $-$.

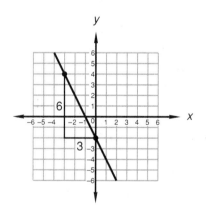

$|m| = \dfrac{6}{3} = 2$

So $b = -2$ and $m = -2$; $\boldsymbol{y = -2x - 2}$

8. $A = \left[(10)(16) - \dfrac{1}{2}(6)(8) \right] m^2$

$= (136)(100)(100) \text{ cm}^2$

$= \boldsymbol{1,360,000 \text{ one-cm-square tiles}}$

9. $x \not< -3$; $D = \{\text{Integers}\}$

10. $5\sqrt{2}(2\sqrt{3} + \sqrt{6}) = 5\sqrt{2} \cdot 2\sqrt{3} + 5\sqrt{2}\sqrt{6}$
$= 5 \cdot 2\sqrt{2}\sqrt{3} + 5\sqrt{2}\sqrt{2}\sqrt{3} = \boldsymbol{10\sqrt{6} + 10\sqrt{3}}$

11. $5\sqrt{8} - 4\sqrt{32}$
$= 5\sqrt{2 \cdot 2 \cdot 2} - 4\sqrt{2 \cdot 2 \cdot 2 \cdot 2 \cdot 2}$
$= 5\sqrt{2}\sqrt{2}\sqrt{2} - 4\sqrt{2}\sqrt{2}\sqrt{2}\sqrt{2}\sqrt{2} = 10\sqrt{2} - 16\sqrt{2}$
$= \mathbf{-6\sqrt{2}}$

12. (a) $y = -2x - 2$
(b) $y = -4$
The first step is to graph each of these equations.

$$y = -2x - 2$$

x	0	1	−1
y	−2	−4	0

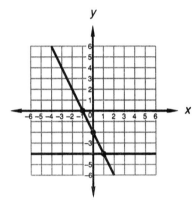

It appears that the lines cross at $x = 1$ and $y = -4$, so $\mathbf{(1, -4)}$ is the solution.

13. (a) $4x + 3y = -14$
(b) $3x + 2y = -10$

$(-2)(a)\quad -8x - 6y = 28$
$3(b)\quad9x + 6y = -30$
$\overline{\quad x = -2}$

(a) $4(-2) + 3y = -14$
$ 3y = -6$
$ y = -2$

$\mathbf{(-2, -2)}$

14. $WF\left(3\dfrac{1}{8}\right) = 1\dfrac{1}{8}$

$\left(\dfrac{\cancel{8}}{25}\right)WF\left(\dfrac{25}{\cancel{8}}\right) = \dfrac{9}{8}\left(\dfrac{\cancel{8}}{25}\right)$

$\phantom{\left(\dfrac{8}{25}\right)}WF = \dfrac{\mathbf{9}}{\mathbf{25}}$

15. $-4 \in$ **Integers, rationals,** and **reals**

16. $\dfrac{3 + x}{4} - \dfrac{x}{3} = 5$

$\dfrac{(3 + x)}{4}(12) - \dfrac{x}{3}(12) = 5(12)$

$9 + 3x - 4x = 60$

$-x = 51$

$x = \mathbf{-51}$

17. $\dfrac{1}{2} - \dfrac{2x}{5} = 7$

$\dfrac{1}{2}(10) - \dfrac{2x}{5}(10) = 7(10)$

$5 - 4x = 70$

$-4x = 65$

$x = -\dfrac{\mathbf{65}}{\mathbf{4}}$

18. (a) $R_M T_M = R_K T_K$
(b) $R_M = 30$
(c) $R_K = 10$
(d) $T_M = 16 - T_K$
Substitute (b) and (c) into (a) and get:
(a') $30T_M = 10T_K$
Substitute (d) into (a') and get:
(a'') $30(16 - T_K) = 10T_K$
$ 480 - 30T_K = 10T_K$
$ 480 = 40T_K$
$ \mathbf{12 = T_K}$

(d) $T_M = 16 - (12) = \mathbf{4}$

19. $\dfrac{1}{x^2} - \dfrac{3a}{x - a} + \dfrac{2}{x}$

$= \dfrac{x - a - 3ax^2 + 2x(x - a)}{x^2(x - a)}$

$= \dfrac{x - a - 3ax^2 + 2x^2 - 2ax}{x^2(x - a)}$

20. $-\dfrac{a}{x} + \dfrac{b}{x^2c} - \dfrac{d}{x^3c^2} = \dfrac{\mathbf{-ax^2c^2 + bxc - d}}{\mathbf{x^3c^2}}$

21. $\dfrac{a + \dfrac{1}{a}}{\dfrac{3}{a^2} - b} = \dfrac{\dfrac{a^2 + 1}{a}}{\dfrac{3 - a^2b}{a^2}} \cdot \dfrac{\dfrac{a^2}{3 - a^2b}}{\dfrac{a^2}{3 - a^2b}}$

$= \dfrac{a^2 + 1}{a} \cdot \dfrac{a^2}{3 - a^2b} = \dfrac{\mathbf{a^3 + a}}{\mathbf{3 - a^2b}}$

22. $\dfrac{\dfrac{abx}{c} - 4}{\dfrac{1}{c} + a} = \dfrac{\dfrac{abx - 4c}{c}}{\dfrac{1 + ac}{c}} \cdot \dfrac{\dfrac{c}{1 + ac}}{\dfrac{c}{1 + ac}}$

$= \dfrac{abx - 4c}{c} \cdot \dfrac{c}{1 + ac} = \dfrac{\mathbf{abx - 4c}}{\mathbf{1 + ac}}$

23. $-x^2(x^{-2} - y) - |x - y^{-4}|$
$= -(-3)^2((-3)^{-2} - (-2)) - |(-3) - (-2)^{-4}|$
$= -9\left(\dfrac{1}{9} + 2\right) - \left|-3 - \dfrac{1}{16}\right|$
$= -9\left(\dfrac{19}{9}\right) - \left|-\dfrac{49}{16}\right| = -19 - \dfrac{49}{16} = -\dfrac{\mathbf{353}}{\mathbf{16}}$

24. $-2^0[(3^0 - 5) - 2^2(2 - 3) + 5]$
$= -[-4 - 4(-1) + 5] = -[5] = \mathbf{-5}$

25. $-3[(-2 - 2) - 2^0 - (4 - 3)(-2)]$
$= -3[-4 - 1 - (1)(-2)] = -3[-3] = \mathbf{9}$

26. $-0.2 - 0.02 - 0.02x = 0.4(1 - x) - 0.012$
$-200 - 20 - 20x = 400(1 - x) - 12$
$-220 - 20x = 400 - 400x - 12$
$380x = 608$
$x = \mathbf{1.6}$

27. $\dfrac{3x^{-2}}{a^2y^5}\left(\dfrac{x^2a^2}{y^5} - \dfrac{x^{-3}y}{a}\right)$

$= \dfrac{3x^{-2}x^2a^2}{a^2y^5y^5} - \dfrac{3x^{-2}x^{-3}y}{a^2y^5a}$

$= \mathbf{3y^{-10} - 3x^{-5}y^{-4}a^{-3}}$

28. $\dfrac{(a^{-3})^0(a^2)^0(a^{-2})^{-2}}{a^4(x^{-5})^{-2}xx^2} = \dfrac{a^4}{a^4x^{10}x^3} = \mathbf{x^{-13}}$

29. $\dfrac{(x^2y)xy^{-2}}{x^2yy} = \dfrac{x^3y^{-1}}{x^2y^2} = \mathbf{xy^{-3}}$

30. {Rational numbers}

ADDITION: Closed. The sum of any two rational numbers is a rational number.

SUBTRACTION: Closed. The difference of any two rational numbers is a rational number.

MULTIPLICATION: Closed. The product of any two rational numbers is a rational number.

DIVISION: Not closed. $\dfrac{1}{0}$ is not defined.

Thus the set of rational numbers is closed for the operations of **addition, subtraction,** and **multiplication.**

PROBLEM SET 88

1. (a) $N_D + N_Q = 40$
(b) $10N_D + 25N_Q = 475$

$(-10)(a)$ $\underline{-10N_D - 10N_Q = -400}$
(b) $\quad 10N_D + 25N_Q = \quad 475$
$\overline{\qquad\qquad 15N_Q = \quad 75}$
$N_Q = \mathbf{5}$

(a) $N_D + (5) = 40$
$N_D = \mathbf{35}$

2. (a) $5N_N + 25N_Q = 525$
(b) $N_N = N_Q + 15$
Substitute (b) into (a) and get:
(a′) $5(N_Q + 15) + 25N_Q = 525$
$5N_Q + 75 + 25N_Q = 525$
$30N_Q = 450$
$N_Q = \mathbf{15}$

(b) $N_N = (15) + 15 = \mathbf{30}$

3. $\quad N \qquad N + 2 \qquad N + 4 \qquad N + 6$
$-3(N + N + 6) + 30 = 10(-N - 4)$
$-6N - 18 + 30 = -10N - 40$
$4N = -52$
$N = -13$
The desired integers are **−13, −11, −9,** and **−7.**

4. $\left(\dfrac{\cancel{100}}{\cancel{64}}\right)\dfrac{\cancel{64}}{\cancel{100}}T = 224\left(\dfrac{100}{64}\right)$
$T = \mathbf{350}$

5. $\dfrac{(0.0003 \times 10^{-8})(8000 \times 10^6)}{0.004 \times 10^5}$

$= \dfrac{(3 \times 10^{-12})(8 \times 10^9)}{4 \times 10^2}$

$= \dfrac{3 \cdot 8}{4} \times \dfrac{10^{-12} \cdot 10^9}{10^2} = \mathbf{6 \times 10^{-5}}$

6. The desired equation is $y = mx + b$.
By inspection, $b = 4$.
By inspection, the sign for m is −.

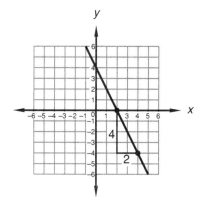

$|m| = \dfrac{4}{2} = 2$
Since $b = 4$ and $m = -2$: $\mathbf{y = -2x + 4}$

7. vertical line: $x = \pm k$; $x = \mathbf{-3}$

8. $4\sqrt{3} \cdot 6\sqrt{6} = 4 \cdot 6\sqrt{3}\sqrt{3 \cdot 2} = \mathbf{72\sqrt{2}}$

9. $3\sqrt{2}(7\sqrt{2} - \sqrt{6}) = 3 \cdot 7\sqrt{2}\sqrt{2} - 3\sqrt{2}\sqrt{2 \cdot 3}$
$= \mathbf{42 - 6\sqrt{3}}$

10. $5\sqrt{45} - \sqrt{180}$
$= 5\sqrt{3 \cdot 3 \cdot 5} - \sqrt{3 \cdot 3 \cdot 2 \cdot 2 \cdot 5}$
$= 15\sqrt{5} - 6\sqrt{5} = \mathbf{9\sqrt{5}}$

11. $\dfrac{\sqrt[3]{x - a}}{2} = \dfrac{\sqrt[3]{-100 - (-73)}}{2} = \dfrac{\sqrt[3]{-27}}{2}$
$= \mathbf{-\dfrac{3}{2}}$

12. $V_{\text{Cyl.}} = A_{\text{Base}} \times \text{height}$

$= \left[\dfrac{\pi(10)^2}{2} + \dfrac{\pi(10)^2}{2} + \dfrac{20(20)}{2} \right](5) \text{ ft}^3$

$= [100\pi + 200](5) \text{ ft}^3$

$= \mathbf{(100\pi + 200)(5)(12)(12)(12) \text{ in.}^3}$

S.A. $= 2A_{\text{Base}} + (P \times \text{height})$

$= \left[2(100\pi + 200) + (28.3 + 20\pi)(5) \right] \text{ ft}^2$

$\approx \mathbf{(1483.5)(12)(12) \text{ in.}^2}$

$V_{\text{Cone}} = \dfrac{1}{3} V_{\text{Cylinder}}$

$= \mathbf{\dfrac{1}{3}(100\pi + 200)(5)(12)(12)(12) \text{ in.}^3}$

13. $(-5x^3 + 14x^2 - x + 10) \div (x + 2)$

$$
\begin{array}{r}
-5x^2 + 24x - 49 \\
x + 2 \overline{) -5x^3 + 14x^2 - x + 10} \\
\underline{-5x^3 - 10x^2} \\
24x^2 - x \\
\underline{24x^2 + 48x} \\
-49x + 10 \\
\underline{-49x - 98} \\
108
\end{array}
$$

$\mathbf{-5x^2 + 24x - 49 + \dfrac{108}{x + 2}}$

14. $x^0 + (3x)^0 - 2 - x = -4(x + 2)$
$1 + 1 - 2 - x = -4x - 8$
$3x = -8$
$x = \mathbf{-\dfrac{8}{3}}$

15. $\dfrac{5}{x^2 + y} + \dfrac{3}{x^2} + \dfrac{2}{x}$

$= \dfrac{5x^2 + 3(x^2 + y) + 2x(x^2 + y)}{x^2(x^2 + y)}$

$= \dfrac{5x^2 + 3x^2 + 3y + 2x^3 + 2xy}{x^2(x^2 + y)}$

$= \mathbf{\dfrac{8x^2 + 3y + 2x^3 + 2xy}{x^2(x^2 + y)}}$

16. $\dfrac{\dfrac{x}{y^2} + \dfrac{4}{x}}{\dfrac{1}{y^2} + \dfrac{2}{xy}} = \dfrac{\dfrac{x^2 + 4y^2}{xy^2}}{\dfrac{x + 2y}{xy^2}} \cdot \dfrac{\dfrac{xy^2}{x + 2y}}{\dfrac{xy^2}{x + 2y}}$

$= \dfrac{x^2 + 4y^2}{xy^2} \cdot \dfrac{xy^2}{x + 2y} = \mathbf{\dfrac{x^2 + 4y^2}{x + 2y}}$

17. $\dfrac{a^{-2}}{x^4 y} \left(\dfrac{x^4 a^2}{y^{-1}} - \dfrac{3a^{-2}y}{x^4} \right)$

$= \dfrac{a^{-2}x^4 a^2}{x^4 yy^{-1}} - \dfrac{a^{-2}3a^{-2}y}{x^4 yx^4} = \mathbf{1 - 3a^{-4}x^{-8}}$

18. $\dfrac{4x^2 y}{xy} - \dfrac{3x^{-3}y^0}{x^{-4}} + \dfrac{2}{x^{-1}} - \dfrac{4x}{y}$

$= 4x - 3x + 2x - 4xy^{-1} = \mathbf{3x - 4xy^{-1}}$

19. (a) $y = 3x - 2$
(b) $y = -x + 2$
The first step is to graph each of these lines.

$y = 3x - 2$

x	0	2	-1
y	-2	4	-5

$y = -x + 2$

x	0	2	-2
y	2	0	4

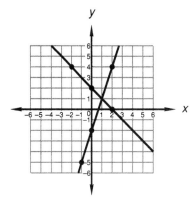

It appears that the lines cross at $x = 1$ and $y = 1$, so **(1, 1)** is the solution.

20. (a) $4x - 5y = -26$
(b) $x - y = -6$
$x = y - 6$
Substitute (b) into (a) and get:
(a′) $4(y - 6) - 5y = -26$
$4y - 24 - 5y = -26$
$2 = y$

(b) $x = (2) - 6 = -4$
(−4, 2)

21. (a) $4x - 5y = 45$
(b) $2x - 3y = 25$

$$
\begin{array}{rrr}
(a) & 4x - 5y = & 45 \\
(-2)(b) & -4x + 6y = & -50 \\
\hline
& y = & -5
\end{array}
$$

(b) $2x - 3(-5) = 25$
$2x = 10$
$x = 5$

(5, −5)

22.
$$\frac{x}{2} - \frac{3 + x}{4} = \frac{1}{6}$$
$$\frac{x}{2}(12) - \frac{(3 + x)}{4}(12) = \frac{1}{6}(12)$$
$$6x - 9 - 3x = 2$$
$$3x = 11$$
$$x = \frac{11}{3}$$

23.
$$\frac{3x}{2} - \frac{4x + 1}{5} = 4$$
$$\frac{3x}{2}(10) - \frac{(4x + 1)}{5}(10) = 4(10)$$
$$15x - 8x - 2 = 40$$
$$7x = 42$$
$$x = 6$$

24. (a) $R_M T_M + 6 = R_D T_D$
(b) $R_M = 3$
(c) $R_D = 12$
(d) $T_M = 4 + T_D$
Substitute (b) and (c) into (a) and get:
(a′) $3T_M + 6 = 12T_D$
Substitute (d) into (a′) and get:
(a″) $3(4 + T_D) + 6 = 12T_D$
$12 + 3T_D + 6 = 12T_D$
$18 = 9T_D$
$2 = T_D$

(d) $T_M = 4 + (2) = 6$

25. $\dfrac{xx^{-3}x^4(y^2)}{x^2(2x)^{-3}} = \dfrac{x^2y^2}{x^2 8^{-1}x^{-3}} = 8x^3y^2$

26. $ax^2 + 4ax + 4a = a(x^2 + 4x + 4)$
$= a(x + 2)(x + 2)$

27. $-10 - 3x + x^2 = x^2 - 3x - 10$
$= (x - 5)(x + 2)$

28. $-4ax^2 + 9a = a(9 - 4x^2) = a(3 - 2x)(3 + 2x)$

29. $20x + 12x^2 + x^3 = x(x^2 + 12x + 20)$
$= x(x + 10)(x + 2)$

30. {Negative rational numbers}
ADDITION: Closed. The sum of any two negative rational numbers is a rational number.
SUBTRACTION: Not closed. $(-3) - (-5) = 2$
MULTIPLICATION: Not closed. $(-4)(-1) = 4$
DIVISION: Not closed. $\dfrac{-4}{-2} = 2$

Thus the set of negative rational numbers is closed for the operation of **addition.**

PROBLEM SET 89

1. (a) $5N_N + 10N_D = 3000$
(b) $N_N + N_D = 500$

$$
\begin{array}{rrr}
(a) & 5N_N + 10N_D = & 3000 \\
(-5)(b) & -5N_N - 5N_D = & -2500 \\
\hline
& 5N_D = & 500 \\
& N_D = & \mathbf{100}
\end{array}
$$

(b) $N_N + (100) = 500$
$N_N = \mathbf{400}$

2. (a) $10N_D + 25N_Q = 8200$
(b) $N_Q = N_D + 300$
Substitute (b) into (a) and get:
(a′) $10N_D + 25(N_D + 300) = 8200$
$10N_D + 25N_D + 7500 = 8200$
$35N_D = 700$
$N_D = \mathbf{20}$

(b) $N_Q = (20) + 300 = \mathbf{320}$

3. $N \quad N + 1 \quad N + 2 \quad N + 3$
$3(N + N + 2) = -N - 1 + 84$
$6N + 6 = -N + 83$
$7N = 77$
$N = 11$
The desired integers are **11, 12, 13,** and **14.**

4. $WN = \dfrac{90}{100}(1930)$
$WN = \mathbf{1737}$

5. $\dfrac{(0.0072 \times 10^{-4})(100,000)}{6000 \times 10^{-24}}$
$= \dfrac{(7.2 \times 10^{-7})(1 \times 10^5)}{6 \times 10^{-21}}$
$= \dfrac{7.2 \cdot 1}{6} \times \dfrac{10^{-7} \cdot 10^5}{10^{-21}} = \mathbf{1.2 \times 10^{19}}$

6. horizontal line: $y = \pm k$; $y = 3$

7. The desired equation is $y = mx + b$.
By inspection, $b = -4$.
By inspection, the sign for m is $-$.

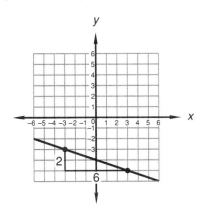

$$|m| = \frac{2}{6} = \frac{1}{3}$$

So $b = -4$ and $m = -\frac{1}{3}$: $\mathbf{y = -\frac{1}{3}x - 4}$

8. $3\sqrt{2}(4\sqrt{2} + 6\sqrt{6}) = 3 \cdot 4\sqrt{2}\sqrt{2} + 3 \cdot 6\sqrt{2}\sqrt{2 \cdot 3}$
$= \mathbf{24 + 36\sqrt{3}}$

9. $5\sqrt{3}(2\sqrt{3} - 6\sqrt{12})$
$= 5 \cdot 2\sqrt{3}\sqrt{3} - 5 \cdot 6\sqrt{3}\sqrt{3 \cdot 2 \cdot 2} = 30 - 180$
$= \mathbf{-150}$

10. $(x^3 - 2x^2 + 4x) \div (x - 2)$

$$
\begin{array}{r}
x^2 + \ 0 \ + 4 \\
x - 2 \overline{)\ x^3 - 2x^2 + 4x + 0} \\
\underline{x^3 - 2x^2} \\
0 + 4x + 0 \\
\underline{0 + 4x - 8} \\
8
\end{array}
$$

$$\mathbf{x^2 + 4 + \frac{8}{x - 2}}$$

11. $(2x^3 - 3x^2 + 2x - 4) \div (x + 3)$

$$
\begin{array}{r}
2x^2 - 9x \ + \ 29 \\
x + 3 \overline{)\ 2x^3 - 3x^2 + \ 2x \ - \ 4} \\
\underline{2x^3 + 6x^2} \\
-9x^2 + \ 2x \\
\underline{-9x^2 - 27x} \\
29x \ - \ 4 \\
\underline{29x + 87} \\
-91
\end{array}
$$

$$\mathbf{2x^2 - 9x + 29 - \frac{91}{x + 3}}$$

12. $(0.05)WN = 0.0009$
$WN = \mathbf{0.018}$

13. $\dfrac{x}{24a} + \dfrac{y}{70a^2} = \dfrac{\mathbf{35ax + 12y}}{\mathbf{840a^2}}$

14. $\dfrac{k}{42} - \dfrac{3x}{18} = \dfrac{k}{42} - \dfrac{x}{6} = \dfrac{\mathbf{k - 7x}}{\mathbf{42}}$

15. $\dfrac{\dfrac{x}{y} - 1}{\dfrac{a}{y} + b} = \dfrac{\dfrac{x - y}{y}}{\dfrac{a + by}{y}} \cdot \dfrac{\dfrac{y}{a + by}}{\dfrac{y}{a + by}}$

$= \dfrac{x - y}{y} \cdot \dfrac{y}{a + by} = \dfrac{\mathbf{x - y}}{\mathbf{a + by}}$

16. $\dfrac{x^3 y}{xy^{-1}} + 3xxy^2 - \dfrac{2x^4 x}{x^2 xy^{-2}} - \dfrac{5x^2}{xy}$
$= x^2y^2 + 3x^2y^2 - 2x^2y^2 - 5xy^{-1}$
$= \mathbf{2x^2y^2 - 5xy^{-1}}$

17. $(3x)^0(-2 - 3x) - x = -3(-2 - 3)$
$-2 - 3x - x = 15$
$-4x = 17$
$x = \mathbf{-\dfrac{17}{4}}$

18. (a) $y = -2$
(b) $y = 2x - 2$
The first step is to graph each of these lines.

$y = 2x - 2$

x	0	3	-2
y	-2	4	-6

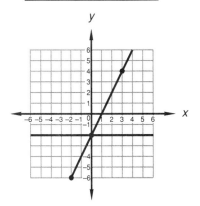

It appears that the lines cross at $x = 0$ and $y = -2$, so $\mathbf{(0, -2)}$ is the solution.

19. (a) $x + y = 2$
$x = 2 - y$
(b) $2x - 3y = -1$
Substitute (a) into (b) and get:
(b′) $2(2 - y) - 3y = -1$
$4 - 2y - 3y = -1$
$-5y = -5$
$y = 1$

(a) $x = 2 - (1) = 1$
$\mathbf{(1, 1)}$

20. (a) $3x - y = 8$
(b) $x + 2y = 12$

2(a) $6x - 2y = 16$
(b) $\underline{x + 2y = 12}$
$7x = 28$
$x = 4$

(b) $(4) + 2y = 12$
$2y = 8$
$y = 4$
(4, 4)

21. $\left(x^2y - \dfrac{3x^{-4}a}{y}\right)\dfrac{x^{-2}}{y}$

$= \dfrac{x^2yx^{-2}}{y} - \dfrac{3x^{-4}ax^{-2}}{yy} = \mathbf{1 - 3ax^{-6}y^{-2}}$

22. $\dfrac{4 + x}{2} - \dfrac{1}{3} = \dfrac{1}{6}$

$\dfrac{(4 + x)}{2}(6) - \dfrac{1}{3}(6) = \dfrac{1}{6}(6)$
$12 + 3x - 2 = 1$
$3x = -9$
$x = -3$

23. $-b \pm \sqrt{b^2} = -49 \pm \sqrt{(49)^2} = -49 \pm 49$
$= \mathbf{0, -98}$

24. (a) $R_TT_T + R_JT_J = 180$
(b) $R_J + R_T = 20$
$R_J = 20 - R_T$
(c) $T_T = 8$
(d) $T_J = 10$
Substitute (c) and (d) into (a) and get:
(a′) $8R_T + 10R_J = 180$
Substitute (b) into (a′) and get:
(a″) $8R_T + 10(20 - R_T) = 180$
$8R_T + 200 - 10R_T = 180$
$20 = 2R_T$
$\mathbf{10} = R_T$

(b) $R_J = 20 - (10) = \mathbf{10}$

25. $\dfrac{(x^2)^{-2}(y^0)^2\,yy^3}{(y^{-2})^3\,yy^4y^{-1}x} = \dfrac{x^{-4}y^4}{y^{-6}y^4x} = \mathbf{x^{-5}y^6}$

26. $max^2 + 9xma + 14ma = ma(x^2 + 9x + 14)$
$= \mathbf{ma(x + 7)(x + 2)}$

27. $-x^3 - 35x - 12x^2 = -x(x^2 + 12x + 35)$
$= \mathbf{-x(x + 7)(x + 5)}$

28. {Irrational numbers}
ADDITION: Not closed.
$(1 - \sqrt{2}) + \sqrt{2} = 1$
SUBTRACTION: Not closed. $\sqrt{2} - \sqrt{2} = 0$
MULTIPLICATION: Not closed. $\sqrt{3}\sqrt{3} = 3$
DIVISION: Not closed. $\dfrac{\sqrt{5}}{\sqrt{5}} = 1$
Thus the set of irrational numbers is closed for **none** of the operations.

29. S.A. $= 2(A_{End}) + $ (Circumference $\times$ length)
$= 2(\pi(8)^2)$ in.$^2 + (2\pi)(8)(40)$ in.^{2}
$\approx \mathbf{2411.52}$ **in.**^{2}

$V_{Sphere} = \dfrac{2}{3}V_{Cylinder}$

$= \dfrac{2}{3}[A_{Base} \times \text{height}]$

$= \dfrac{2}{3}(\pi(8)^2 \times 16)$ in.^{3}

$= \dfrac{2}{3}(64\pi)(16)$ in.^{3}

$\approx \mathbf{2143.57}$ **in.**^{3}

30. $(a + \sqrt{2}b)^2 = (a + \sqrt{2}b)(a + \sqrt{2}b)$
$= a^2 + ab\sqrt{2} + ab\sqrt{2} + 2b^2$
$= \mathbf{a^2 + 2ab\sqrt{2} + 2b^2}$

PROBLEM SET 90

1. (a) $N_Q = N_S - 143$
(b) $25N_Q + 100N_S = 15{,}300$
Substitute (a) into (b) and get:
(b′) $25(N_S - 143) + 100N_S = 15{,}300$
$25N_S - 3575 + 100N_S = 15{,}300$
$125N_S = 18{,}875$
$N_S = \mathbf{151}$

2. (a) $N_N + N_D = 60$
(b) $5N_N + 10N_D = 500$

(-10)(a) $-10N_N - 10N_D = -600$
(b) $\underline{5N_N + 10N_D = 500}$
$-5N_N = -100$
$N_N = \mathbf{20}$

3. $WN = \dfrac{40}{100}(570) = \mathbf{228}$

4. $N \qquad N + 1 \qquad N + 2$
$-4(N + N + 2) = 7(-N - 1) - 13$
$-8N - 8 = -7N - 7 - 13$
$12 = N$
The desired integers are **12, 13,** and **14.**

5. $\dfrac{(0.00035 \times 10^{-8})(2000 \times 10^{-3})}{(0.0007 \times 10^{6})(2{,}000{,}000)}$

$= \dfrac{(3.5 \times 10^{-12})(2 \times 10^{0})}{(7 \times 10^{2})(2 \times 10^{6})}$

$= \dfrac{3.5 \cdot 2}{7 \cdot 2} \times \dfrac{10^{-12}}{10^{2} \cdot 10^{6}} = \mathbf{5 \times 10^{-21}}$

6. The desired equation is $y = mx + b$.
By inspection, $b = 0$.
By inspection, the sign for m is –.

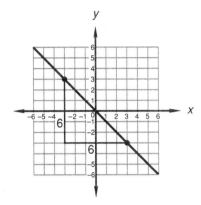

$|m| = \dfrac{6}{6} = 1$
So $b = 0$ and $m = -1$: $\mathbf{y = -x}$

7. The desired equation is $y = mx + b$.
By inspection, $b = 0$.
By inspection, the sign for m is +.

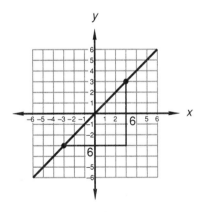

$|m| = \dfrac{6}{6} = 1$
So $b = 0$ and $m = 1$: $\mathbf{y = x}$

8. $5\sqrt{2}(3\sqrt{2} - 2\sqrt{12}) = 5 \cdot 3\sqrt{2}\sqrt{2} - 5 \cdot 2\sqrt{2}\sqrt{2 \cdot 6}$
$= \mathbf{30 - 20\sqrt{6}}$

9. $3\sqrt{5}(2\sqrt{5} - 6\sqrt{15}) = 3 \cdot 2\sqrt{5}\sqrt{5} - 3 \cdot 6\sqrt{5}\sqrt{5 \cdot 3}$
$= \mathbf{30 - 90\sqrt{3}}$

10. $-b \pm \sqrt{b^2 - 4a} = -4 \pm \sqrt{16 - 12}$
$= -4 \pm 2 = \mathbf{-6, -2}$

11. $(3x^3 - x - 7) \div (x - 5)$

$$
\begin{array}{r}
3x^2 + 15x + 74 \\
x - 5 \overline{)\, 3x^3 + 0x^2 - x - 7} \\
\underline{3x^3 - 15x^2} \\
15x^2 - x \\
\underline{15x^2 - 75x} \\
74x - 7 \\
\underline{74x - 370} \\
363
\end{array}
$$

$$3x^2 + 15x + 74 + \dfrac{363}{x - 5}$$

12. (a) $x = 2$
(b) $y = 2x - 4$
The first step is to graph each of these lines.

$y = 2x - 4$

x	0	2	-1
y	-4	0	-6

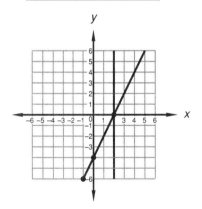

It appears that the lines cross at $x = 2$ and $y = 0$, so **(2, 0)** is the solution.

13. (a) $2x + y = 1$
$\qquad\quad y = 1 - 2x$
(b) $5x - 2y = 7$
Substitute (a) into (b) get:
(b′) $5x - 2(1 - 2x) = 7$
$\qquad\quad 5x - 2 + 4x = 7$
$\qquad\qquad\qquad\quad 9x = 9$
$\qquad\qquad\qquad\quad\; x = 1$

(a) $y = 1 - 2(1) = -1$
(1, −1)

14. (a) $7x + 2y = 3$
(b) $3x - 3y = 9$

3(a) $21x + 6y = 9$
2(b) $\underline{6x - 6y = 18}$
$27x = 27$
$x = 1$

(a) $7(1) + 2y = 3$
$2y = -4$
$y = -2$

(1, −2)

15. $3\sqrt{2}(4\sqrt{2} - \sqrt{12}) = 3 \cdot 4\sqrt{2}\sqrt{2} - 3\sqrt{2}\sqrt{2 \cdot 6}$
$= \mathbf{24 - 6\sqrt{6}}$

16. $2\sqrt{2}(5\sqrt{2} - 3\sqrt{20})$
$= 2 \cdot 5\sqrt{2}\sqrt{2} - 2 \cdot 3\sqrt{2}\sqrt{2 \cdot 10} = \mathbf{20 - 12\sqrt{10}}$

17. $2\sqrt{3}(\sqrt{3} - 2\sqrt{15}) = 2\sqrt{3}\sqrt{3} - 2 \cdot 2\sqrt{3}\sqrt{3 \cdot 5}$
$= \mathbf{6 - 12\sqrt{5}}$

18. $2\frac{1}{4}p - 3\frac{1}{8} = \frac{1}{5}$

$\frac{9}{4}p = \frac{1}{5} + \frac{25}{8}$

$\frac{9}{4}p = \frac{8}{40} + \frac{125}{40}$

$p = \frac{133}{40} \cdot \frac{4}{9} = \mathbf{\frac{133}{90}}$

19. $x \not< 3$; $D = \{$Positive integers$\}$
$x \geq 3$

20. $\frac{x}{4} - \frac{x - 2}{3} = \frac{1}{2^{-3}}$

$\frac{x}{4}(12) - \frac{(x - 2)}{3}(12) = 8(12)$

$3x - 4x + 8 = 96$
$-x = 88$
$x = \mathbf{-88}$

21. $\frac{x}{3} - \frac{x + 2}{4} = 5$

$\frac{x}{3}(12) - \frac{(x + 2)}{4}(12) = 5(12)$

$4x - 3x - 6 = 60$
$x = \mathbf{66}$

22. $\frac{3}{a + b} - \frac{4}{b} + \frac{6}{b^2}$

$= \frac{3b^2 - 4b(a + b) + 6(a + b)}{b^2(a + b)}$

$= \frac{3b^2 - 4ab - 4b^2 + 6a + 6b}{b^2(a + b)}$

$= \frac{\mathbf{-b^2 - 4ab + 6a + 6b}}{\mathbf{b^2(a + b)}}$

23. $\frac{3}{a^2x} + \frac{2b}{a(x + a)} = \frac{3(x + a) + 2b(ax)}{a^2x(x + a)}$

$= \frac{\mathbf{3x + 3a + 2abx}}{\mathbf{a^2x(x + a)}}$

24. $\dfrac{x - \dfrac{4}{y}}{\dfrac{a}{y} + 3} = \dfrac{\dfrac{xy - 4}{y}}{\dfrac{a + 3y}{y}} \cdot \dfrac{y}{\dfrac{a + 3y}{y}}$

$= \frac{xy - 4}{y} \cdot \frac{y}{a + 3y} = \mathbf{\frac{xy - 4}{a + 3y}}$

25. $x^2 - x^0 - (x^0)^2 + ax(x - a)$
$= (-2)^2 - (-2)^0 - ((-2)^0)^2 + (4)(-2)((-2) - 4)$
$= 4 - 1 - 1 - 8(-6) = \mathbf{50}$

26. $(-2 - 3)x^0 - 2(-2)x = 3(x^0 - 2)$
$-5 + 4x = -3$
$4x = 2$
$x = \mathbf{\frac{1}{2}}$

27. $15ax + 56a + ax^2 = a(x^2 + 15x + 56)$
$= \mathbf{a(x + 7)(x + 8)}$

28. (a) $R_PT_P = R_DT_D - 90$
(b) $R_P = 30$
(c) $R_D = 30$
(d) $T_P + T_D = 9$
$T_P = 9 - T_D$
Substitute (b) and (c) into (a) and get:
(a′) $30T_P = 30T_D - 90$
Substitute (d) into (a′) and get:
(a″) $30(9 - T_D) = 30T_D - 90$
$270 - 30T_D = 30T_D - 90$
$360 = 60T_D$
$\mathbf{6} = T_D$

(d) $T_P = 9 - (6) = \mathbf{3}$

29. $\dfrac{a^2 y^{-2}}{x^4}\left(\dfrac{a^{-4} y^{-2}}{x} - \dfrac{3a^{-2} x}{y}\right)$

$= \dfrac{a^2 y^{-2} a^{-4} y^{-2}}{x^4 x} - \dfrac{a^2 y^{-2} 3a^{-2} x}{x^4 y}$

$= a^{-2} y^{-4} x^{-5} - 3y^{-3} x^{-3}$

30. $\dfrac{xxx^{-2}(y^0)(3y^{-2})^{-1}}{(2x^{-4})^2 y} = \dfrac{3^{-1} y^2}{4x^{-8} y} = \dfrac{x^8 y}{12}$

PROBLEM SET 91

1. (a) $N_P + N_N = 150$
(b) $N_P + 5N_N = 270$

$(-1)(a)\quad -N_P - N_N = -150$
$\underline{\quad(b)\quad N_P + 5N_N = 270\quad}$
$4N_N = 120$
$N_N = \textbf{30}$

(a) $N_P + (30) = 150$
$N_P = \textbf{120}$

2. (a) $N_P + 5N_N = 270$
(b) $N_P = N_N + 54$
Substitute (b) into (a) and get:
(a') $(N_N + 54) + 5N_N = 270$
$6N_N = 216$
$N_N = \textbf{36}$

(b) $N_P = (36) + 54 = \textbf{90}$

3. $\dfrac{22}{100} T_{\text{Total}} = 8800$
$\phantom{\dfrac{22}{100}}T_{\text{Total}} = 40{,}000$

$T_{\text{Total}} = N_{\text{Dejected}} + N_{\text{Cheered}}$
$N_{\text{Cheered}} = T_{\text{Total}} - N_{\text{Dejected}}$
$\phantom{N_{\text{Cheered}}} = 40{,}000 - 8800$
$\phantom{N_{\text{Cheered}}} = \textbf{31,200}$

4. $N \quad N+2 \quad N+4 \quad N+6$
$4(N + N + 6) = 7(N + 4) + 3$
$8N + 24 = 7N + 28 + 3$
$N = 7$
The desired integers are **7, 9, 11,** and **13.**

5. $\dfrac{(0.016 \times 10^{-5})(300 \times 10^6)}{(20{,}000 \times 10^4)(400 \times 10^{-8})}$

$= \dfrac{(1.6 \times 10^{-7})(3 \times 10^8)}{(2 \times 10^8)(4 \times 10^{-6})}$

$= \dfrac{1.6 \cdot 3}{2 \cdot 4} \times \dfrac{10^{-7} \cdot 10^8}{10^8 \cdot 10^{-6}} = 6 \times 10^{-2}$

6. horizontal line: $y = \pm k;\ y = -2$

7. The desired equation is $y = mx + b$.
By inspection, $b = 3$.
By inspection, the sign for m is $-$.

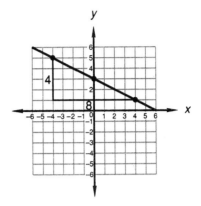

$|m| = \dfrac{4}{8} = \dfrac{1}{2}$

So $b = 3$ and $m = -\dfrac{1}{2}$: $y = -\dfrac{1}{2}x + 3$

8. $5\sqrt{5}(2\sqrt{10} - 3\sqrt{5}) = 5 \cdot 2\sqrt{5}\sqrt{5 \cdot 2} - 5 \cdot 3\sqrt{5}\sqrt{5}$
$= \textbf{50}\sqrt{\textbf{2}} - \textbf{75}$

9. $4\sqrt{7}(2\sqrt{7} - 3\sqrt{14}) = 4 \cdot 2\sqrt{7}\sqrt{7} - 4 \cdot 3\sqrt{7}\sqrt{7 \cdot 2}$
$= \textbf{56} - \textbf{84}\sqrt{\textbf{2}}$

10. $(2x^3 - 5x + 4) \div (x + 2)$

$$
\begin{array}{r}
2x^2 - 4x + 3 \\
x + 2 \overline{)\,2x^3 + 0x^2 - 5x + 4} \\
\underline{2x^3 + 4x^2} \\
-4x^2 - 5x \\
\underline{-4x^2 - 8x} \\
3x + 4 \\
\underline{3x + 6} \\
-2
\end{array}
$$

$2x^2 - 4x + 3 - \dfrac{2}{x + 2}$

11. $(3x^3 - 4) \div (x - 5)$

$$
\begin{array}{r}
3x^2 + 15x + 75 \\
x - 5 \overline{)\,3x^3 + 0x^2 + 0x - 4} \\
\underline{3x^3 - 15x^2} \\
15x^2 + 0x \\
\underline{15x^2 - 75x} \\
75x - 4 \\
\underline{75x - 375} \\
371
\end{array}
$$

$3x^2 + 15x + 75 + \dfrac{371}{x - 5}$

12. $V_{Prism} = A_{Base} \times \text{height}$

$\quad = (A_{Rectangle} + A_{Triangle}) \times \text{height}$

$\quad = \left[(10)(25) + \frac{1}{2}(20)(10) \right](10)(12) \text{ in.}^3$

$\quad = [250 + 100](120) \text{ in.}^3$

$\quad = \textbf{42,000 one-inch sugar cubes}$

$V_{Pyramid} = \frac{1}{3} V_{Prism}$

$\quad = \frac{1}{3}[A_{Base} \times \text{height}]$

$\quad = \frac{1}{3}[350 \text{ in.}^2 \times (10)(12) \text{ in.}]$

$\quad = \textbf{14,000 in.}^3$

13. {Positive rational numbers}

ADDITION: Closed. The sum of any two positive rational numbers is a positive rational number.

SUBTRACTION: Not closed. $(5) - (10) = -5$

MULTIPLICATION: Closed. The product of any two positive rational numbers is a positive rational number

DIVISION: Closed. The quotient of any two positive rational numbers is a positive rational number.

Thus the set of positive rational numbers is closed for the operations of **addition, multiplication,** and **division.**

14. $\dfrac{-b \pm \sqrt{b^2}}{2a} = \dfrac{-22 \pm \sqrt{(22)^2}}{2(11)}$

$\quad = \dfrac{-22 \pm 22}{22} = \textbf{-2, 0}$

15. Average $= \dfrac{\text{sum}}{\text{total number}} = \dfrac{396.80}{4} = \textbf{99.2}$

16. $(x - \sqrt{3}y)^2 = (x - \sqrt{3}y)(x - \sqrt{3}y)$

$\quad = \textbf{x}^2 - \textbf{2}\sqrt{\textbf{3}}\textbf{xy} + \textbf{3y}^2$

17. $\qquad 28 = x^2 - 3x$

$x^2 - 3x - 28 = 0$

$(x - 7)(x + 4) = 0$

If $x - 7 = 0$, $\textbf{x = 7}$

$28 = (7)^2 - 3(7)$

$28 = 49 - 21$

$28 = 28 \quad \text{check}$

If $x + 4 = 0$, $\textbf{x = -4}$

$28 = (-4)^2 - 3(-4)$

$28 = 16 + 12$

$28 = 28 \quad \text{check}$

18. $\qquad x^2 = 25$

$x^2 - 25 = 0$

$(x + 5)(x - 5) = 0$

If $x + 5 = 0$, $\textbf{x = -5}$

$(-5)^2 = 25$

$\quad 25 = 25 \quad \text{check}$

If $x - 5 = 0$, $\textbf{x = 5}$

$(5)^2 = 25$

$\quad 25 = 25 \quad \text{check}$

19. $\qquad x^2 - 6 = x$

$x^2 - x - 6 = 0$

$(x - 3)(x + 2) = 0$

If $x - 3 = 0$, $\textbf{x = 3}$

$(3)^2 - 6 = 3$

$\quad 9 - 6 = 3$

$\qquad 3 = 3 \quad \text{check}$

If $x + 2 = 0$, $\textbf{x = -2}$

$(-2)^2 - 6 = -2$

$\quad 4 - 6 = -2$

$\quad -2 = -2 \quad \text{check}$

20. $\qquad -x^2 - 8x = 16$

$x^2 + 8x + 16 = 0$

$(x + 4)(x + 4) = 0$

If $x + 4 = 0$, $\textbf{x = -4}$

$-(-4)^2 - 8(-4) = 16$

$\quad -16 + 32 = 16$

$\qquad 16 = 16 \quad \text{check}$

21. (a) $y = 2x - 3$

(b) $x = -4$

The first step is to graph each of these lines.

$y = 2x - 3$

x	0	1	-1
y	-3	-1	-5

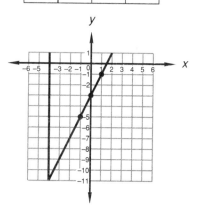

It appears that the lines cross at $x = -4$ and $y = -11$, so $\textbf{(-4, -11)}$ is the solution.

22. (a) $3x + 5y = 16$
(b) $4x - 3y = 2$

3(a) $\quad 9x + 15y = 48$
5(b) $\underline{20x - 15y = 10}$
$\quad\quad 29x \quad\quad\quad = 58$
$\quad\quad\quad\quad\quad x = 2$

(a) $3(2) + 5y = 16$
$\quad\quad\quad 5y = 10$
$\quad\quad\quad\quad y = 2$

(2, 2)

23. $x + 2 \nleq 4; \ D = \{$Positive integers$\}$
$x + 2 > 4$
$\quad\quad x > 2$

24. $4\dfrac{3}{5}x - 2^{-2} = \dfrac{1}{10}$

$\dfrac{23}{5}x = \dfrac{1}{10} + \dfrac{1}{4}$

$\dfrac{23}{5}x = \dfrac{4}{40} + \dfrac{10}{40}$

$x = \dfrac{14}{40} \cdot \dfrac{5}{23} = \dfrac{7}{92}$

25. $-(-4 - 2^0) - |-2| + \dfrac{1}{-2^{-2}} = 5 - 2 - 4 = -1$

26. (a) $R_P T_P + R_K T_K = 170$
(b) $T_P = 2$
(c) $T_K = 3$
(d) $R_P = R_K + 10$
Substitute (b) and (c) into (a) and get:
(a′) $2R_P + 3R_K = 170$
Substitute (d) into (a′) and get:
(a″) $2(R_K + 10) + 3R_K = 170$
$\quad\quad\quad 5R_K + 20 = 170$
$\quad\quad\quad\quad 5R_K = 150$
$\quad\quad\quad\quad\quad R_K = 30$

(d) $R_P = (30) + 10 = \mathbf{40}$

27. $\dfrac{2x}{3} - \dfrac{2x - 4}{5} = 7$

$\dfrac{2x}{3}(15) - \dfrac{(2x - 4)}{5}(15) = 7(15)$

$10x - 6x + 12 = 105$
$4x = 93$
$x = \dfrac{93}{4}$

28. $\dfrac{1}{a} + \dfrac{2}{a^2} + \dfrac{3}{a + x}$

$= \dfrac{a(a + x) + 2(a + x) + 3a^2}{a^2(a + x)}$

$= \dfrac{a^2 + ax + 2a + 2x + 3a^2}{a^2(a + x)}$

$= \dfrac{\mathbf{4a^2 + ax + 2a + 2x}}{\mathbf{a^2(a + x)}}$

29. $(-2x^0 - 3)2 - 3x = -2(x^0 - 2)$
$\quad\quad -10 - 3x = 2$
$\quad\quad\quad -12 = 3x$
$\quad\quad\quad \mathbf{-4} = x$

30. $\dfrac{axx^{-12}y^{-2}(a^4)^{-2}}{a^{-4}(a^2)a(a^{-4}x^2)} = \dfrac{a^{-7}x^{-11}y^{-2}}{a^{-1}a^{-4}x^2}$
$= \mathbf{a^{-2}x^{-13}y^{-2}}$

PROBLEM SET 92

1. S.A. $= 2A_{\text{Base}} + (C \times \text{height})$
$= 2\pi(24)^2 \ \text{m}^2 + [(2\pi)(24) \times 20] \ \text{m}^2$
$\approx (6{,}631.68)(100)(100) \ \text{cm}^2$
$\approx \mathbf{66{,}316{,}800 \ cm^2}$

$V_{\text{Cylinder}} = A_{\text{Base}} \times \text{height}$
$= (\pi(24)^2 \times 20)(100)(100)(100) \ \text{cm}^3$
$\approx \mathbf{36{,}172{,}800{,}000 \ cm^3}$

$V_{\text{Cone}} = \dfrac{1}{3}V_{\text{Cylinder}}$
$= \dfrac{1}{3}(36{,}172{,}800{,}000 \ \text{cm}^3)$
$= \mathbf{12{,}057{,}600{,}000 \ cm^3}$

$V_{\text{Sphere}} = \dfrac{2}{3}V_{\text{Cylinder}}$
$= \dfrac{2}{3}(A_{\text{Base}} \times \text{height})$
$= \dfrac{2}{3}(\pi(24)^2 \times 48)(100)(100)(100) \ \text{cm}^3$
$\approx \mathbf{57{,}876{,}480{,}000 \ cm^3}$

2. (a) $45N_O + 30N_F = 735$
(b) $N_F = N_O + 7$
Substitute (b) into (a) and get:
(a′) $45N_O + 30(N_O + 7) = 735$
$\quad\quad\quad 75N_O + 210 = 735$
$\quad\quad\quad\quad 75N_O = 525$
$\quad\quad\quad\quad\quad N_O = \mathbf{7}$

3. $\dfrac{23}{100}T = 1610$
$\quad\quad T = \mathbf{7000}$

4. $N \qquad N + 2 \qquad N + 4$
$4(N + N + 2) = (N + 4)(-30) - 62$
$8N + 8 = -30N - 120 - 62$
$38N = -190$
$N = -5$
The desired integers are **−5, −3,** and **−1.**

5. $\dfrac{(0.0006 \times 10^{-23})(300 \times 10^{14})}{90,000 \times 10^{25}}$

$= \dfrac{(6 \times 10^{-27})(3 \times 10^{16})}{9 \times 10^{29}} = \mathbf{2 \times 10^{-40}}$

6. (a) horizontal line: $y = \pm k$; **$y = 4$**
(b) The desired equation is $y = mx + b$.
By inspection, $b = -2$.
By inspection, the sign for m is −.

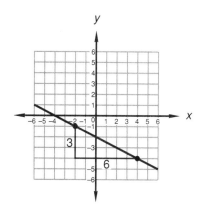

$|m| = \dfrac{3}{6} = \dfrac{1}{2}$

So $b = -2$ and $m = -\dfrac{1}{2}$: $\mathbf{y = -\dfrac{1}{2}x - 2}$

7. $3\sqrt{5}(5\sqrt{10} - 2\sqrt{5}) = 3 \cdot 5\sqrt{5}\sqrt{5 \cdot 2} - 3 \cdot 2\sqrt{5}\sqrt{5}$
$= \mathbf{75\sqrt{2} - 30}$

8. $2\sqrt{14}(3\sqrt{7} - 5\sqrt{2})$
$= 2 \cdot 3\sqrt{2 \cdot 7}\sqrt{7} - 2 \cdot 5\sqrt{7 \cdot 2}\sqrt{2}$
$= \mathbf{42\sqrt{2} - 20\sqrt{7}}$

9. $(x^2 - x - 6) \div (x + 2)$

$$
\begin{array}{r}
x - 3 \\
x + 2 \overline{)\, x^2 - x - 6} \\
\underline{x^2 + 2x} \\
-3x - 6 \\
\underline{-3x - 6} \\
0
\end{array}
$$

$\mathbf{x - 3}$

10. $(3x^3 - 1) \div (x + 4)$

$$
\begin{array}{r}
3x^2 - 12x + 48 \\
x + 4 \overline{)\, 3x^3 + 0x^2 + 0x - 1} \\
\underline{3x^3 + 12x^2} \\
-12x^2 + 0x \\
\underline{-12x^2 - 48x} \\
48x - 1 \\
\underline{48x + 192} \\
-193
\end{array}
$$

$\mathbf{3x^2 - 12x + 48 - \dfrac{193}{x + 4}}$

11. $x^2 - 12x + 35 = 0$
$(x - 7)(x - 5) = 0$

If $x - 7 = 0$, **$x = 7$**
$(7)^2 - 12(7) + 35 = 0$
$49 - 84 + 35 = 0$
$0 = 0$ check

If $x - 5 = 0$, **$x = 5$**
$(5)^2 - 12(5) + 35 = 0$
$0 = 0$ check

12. $-35 = x^2 + 12x$
$0 = x^2 + 12x + 35$
$0 = (x + 7)(x + 5)$

If $x + 7 = 0$, **$x = -7$**
$-35 = (-7)^2 + 12(-7)$
$-35 = 49 - 84$
$-35 = -35$ check

If $x + 5 = 0$, **$x = -5$**
$-35 = (-5)^2 + 12(-5)$
$-35 = 25 - 60$
$-35 = -35$ check

13. $x^2 = 12x - 32$
$x^2 - 12x + 32 = 0$
$(x - 4)(x - 8) = 0$

If $x - 4 = 0$, **$x = 4$**
$(4)^2 = 12(4) - 32$
$16 = 48 - 32$
$16 = 16$ check

If $x - 8 = 0$, **$x = 8$**
$(8)^2 = 12(8) - 32$
$64 = 96 - 32$
$64 = 64$ check

14.
$$17x = -x^2 - 60$$
$$x^2 + 17x + 60 = 0$$
$$(x + 5)(x + 12) = 0$$

If $x + 5 = 0$, $x = -5$
$$17(-5) = -(-5)^2 - 60$$
$$-85 = -25 - 60$$
$$-85 = -85 \quad \text{check}$$

If $x + 12 = 0$, $x = -12$
$$17(-12) = -(-12)^2 - 60$$
$$-204 = -144 - 60$$
$$-204 = -204 \quad \text{check}$$

15.
$$4x^2 - 9 = 0$$
$$(2x + 3)(2x - 3) = 0$$

If $2x + 3 = 0$, $x = -\dfrac{3}{2}$
$$4\left(-\dfrac{3}{2}\right)^2 - 9 = 0$$
$$9 - 9 = 0$$
$$0 = 0 \quad \text{check}$$

If $2x - 3 = 0$, $x = \dfrac{3}{2}$
$$4\left(\dfrac{3}{2}\right)^2 - 9 = 0$$
$$9 - 9 = 0$$
$$0 = 0 \quad \text{check}$$

16.
$$-49 = -9p^2$$
$$9p^2 - 49 = 0$$
$$(3p - 7)(3p + 7) = 0$$

If $3p - 7 = 0$, $p = \dfrac{7}{3}$
$$-49 = -9\left(\dfrac{7}{3}\right)^2$$
$$-49 = -49 \quad \text{check}$$

If $3p + 7 = 0$, $p = -\dfrac{7}{3}$
$$-49 = -9\left(-\dfrac{7}{3}\right)^2$$
$$-49 = -49 \quad \text{check}$$

17.
$$x^2 + 25 = -10x$$
$$x^2 + 10x + 25 = 0$$
$$(x + 5)(x + 5) = 0$$

If $x + 5 = 0$, $x = -5$
$$(-5)^2 + 25 = -10(-5)$$
$$50 = 50 \quad \text{check}$$

18.
$$x^2 - 11x + 24 = 0$$
$$(x - 8)(x - 3) = 0$$

If $x - 8 = 0$, $x = 8$
$$(8)^2 - 11(8) + 24 = 0$$
$$64 - 88 + 24 = 0$$
$$0 = 0 \quad \text{check}$$

If $x - 3 = 0$, $x = 3$
$$(3)^2 - 11(3) + 24 = 0$$
$$9 - 33 + 24 = 0$$
$$0 = 0 \quad \text{check}$$

19.
$$-9x^2 + 4 = 0$$
$$(3x - 2)(3x + 2) = 0$$

If $3x - 2 = 0$, $x = \dfrac{2}{3}$
$$-9\left(\dfrac{2}{3}\right)^2 + 4 = 0$$
$$-4 + 4 = 0$$
$$0 = 0 \quad \text{check}$$

If $3x + 2 = 0$, $x = -\dfrac{2}{3}$
$$-9\left(-\dfrac{2}{3}\right)^2 + 4 = 0$$
$$-4 + 4 = 0$$
$$0 = 0 \quad \text{check}$$

20. (a) $y = 2x - 2$
(b) $y = -x + 4$
The first step is to graph each of these lines.

$y = 2x - 2$

x	0	2	-2
y	-2	2	-6

$y = -x + 4$

x	0	3	-2
y	4	1	6

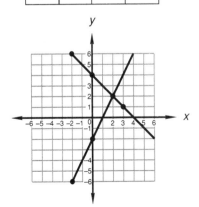

It appears that the lines cross at $x = 2$ and $y = 2$, so **(2, 2)** is the solution.

21. (a) $3x + 4y = 28$
(b) $2x - 3y = -4$

3(a) $\quad 9x + 12y = \quad 84$
4(b) $\quad \underline{8x - 12y = -16}$
$\qquad 17x \qquad = \quad 68$
$\qquad\qquad x = 4$

(b) $\quad 2(4) - 3y = -4$
$\qquad\qquad -3y = -12$
$\qquad\qquad\quad y = 4$

(4, 4)

22. $WP\left(1\dfrac{2}{5}\right) = 2\dfrac{1}{4}$

$\left(\dfrac{\cancel{5}}{\cancel{7}}\right)WP\left(\dfrac{\cancel{7}}{\cancel{5}}\right) = \dfrac{9}{4}\left(\dfrac{5}{7}\right)$

$WP = \dfrac{45}{28}$

23. $\dfrac{14}{17}(T) = 2800$
$\qquad T = \mathbf{3400}$

24. (a) $R_M T_M + 10 = R_T T_T$
(b) $R_M = 20$
(c) $R_T = 55$
(d) $T_M + T_T = 7$
$\qquad\quad T_M = 7 - T_T$
Substitute (b) and (c) into (a) and get:
(a') $20T_M + 10 = 55T_T$
Substitute (d) into (a') and get:
(a'') $\quad 20(7 - T_T) + 10 = 55T_T$
$\qquad 140 - 20T_T + 10 = 55T_T$
$\qquad\qquad\qquad\quad 150 = 75T_T$
$\qquad\qquad\qquad\quad\; 2 = T_T$

(d) $T_M = 7 - (2) = \mathbf{5}$

25. $-2(-x^0 - 3x^0) = -2(x + 5)$
$\qquad\qquad\quad 8 = -2x - 10$
$\qquad\qquad\; 18 = -2x$
$\qquad\qquad\; \mathbf{-9} = x$

26. $-3^0 - |-3^0| - 3^2 + (-3)^2 = -1 - 1 - 9 + 9$
$= \mathbf{-2}$

27. $|-x^2| + (-x)(-y) = |-(-3)^2| + (-(-3))(-4)$
$= 9 - 12 = \mathbf{-3}$

28. (a) $\dfrac{1}{-3^{-2}} = -3^2 = \mathbf{-9}$

(b) $\dfrac{1}{(-3)^{-2}} = (-3)^2 = \mathbf{9}$

(c) $-(-3)^{-2} = -\dfrac{1}{(-3)^2} = -\dfrac{1}{9}$

29. $\dfrac{\dfrac{xy}{a} + \dfrac{1}{y}}{\dfrac{x}{y} - \dfrac{1}{a}} = \dfrac{\dfrac{xy^2 + a}{ay}}{\dfrac{ax - y}{ay}} \cdot \dfrac{\dfrac{ay}{ax - y}}{\dfrac{ay}{ax - y}}$

$= \dfrac{xy^2 + a}{ay} \cdot \dfrac{ay}{ax - y} = \dfrac{\boldsymbol{xy^2 + a}}{\boldsymbol{ax - y}}$

30. $\dfrac{a^4 b^4 (2ab)^2}{(3b^{-2})^{-2}} = \dfrac{a^4 b^4 \, 4a^2 b^2}{9^{-1} b^4} = \mathbf{36a^6 b^2}$

PROBLEM SET 93

1. (a) $N_P + 5N_N = 1450$
(b) $N_P + N_N = 450$

$\qquad$ (a) $\quad N_P + 5N_N = 1450$
(-1)(b) $\underline{-N_P - \quad N_N = -450}$
$\qquad\qquad\qquad 4N_N = 1000$
$\qquad\qquad\qquad\; N_N = \mathbf{250}$

(b) $N_P + (250) = 450$
$\qquad\quad N_P = \mathbf{200}$

2. (a) $30N_I + 50N_W = 1350$
(b) $N_I = N_W + 5$
Substitute (b) into (a) and get:
(a') $30(N_W + 5) + 50N_W = 1350$
$\qquad\qquad 80N_W + 150 = 1350$
$\qquad\qquad\qquad 80N_W = 1200$
$\qquad\qquad\qquad\quad N_W = \mathbf{15}$

(b) $N_I = (15) + 5 = \mathbf{20}$

3. $\dfrac{40}{100}(T) = 1440$
$\qquad T = 3600$

$\qquad\qquad T = N_{\text{Correct}} + N_{\text{Not correct}}$
$N_{\text{Not correct}} = T - N_{\text{Correct}}$
$N_{\text{Not correct}} = 3600 - 1440$
$N_{\text{Not correct}} = \mathbf{2160}$

4. $N \qquad N + 2 \qquad N + 4 \qquad N + 6$
$\quad -(N + N + 2) = -4(N + 6) + 4$
$\qquad\quad -2N - 2 = -4N - 24 + 4$
$\qquad\qquad\quad 2N = -18$
$\qquad\qquad\qquad N = -9$
The desired integers are $\mathbf{-9, -7, -5,}$ and $\mathbf{-3.}$

5. $V_{Cylinder} = A_{Base} \times height$

$= \left[\dfrac{\pi(10)^2}{2} + \dfrac{(25)(20)}{2} \right](5)$ in.^{3}

$= (50\pi + 250)(5)$ in.^{3}

$\approx$ **2035 in.^{3}**

S.A. $= 2A_{Base} + (P \times height)$

$= 2(50\pi + 250) + (57 + 10\pi)(5)$

$\approx$ **1256 in.^{2}**

$V_{Cone} = \dfrac{1}{3}V_{Cylinder}$

$= \dfrac{1}{3}(A_{Base} \times height)$

$= \dfrac{1}{3}[(50\pi + 250) \times 5]$ in.^{3}

$\approx$ **678.$\overline{3}$ in.^{3}**

6. {Negative irrational numbers}

ADDITION: Not closed.

$(\sqrt{2} - 2) + (-\sqrt{2}) = -2$

SUBTRACTION: Not closed.

$(-\sqrt{3}) - (-\sqrt{3}) = 0$

MULTIPLICATION: Not closed. $(-\sqrt{5})(-\sqrt{5}) = 5$

DIVISION: Not closed. $\dfrac{-\sqrt{7}}{-\sqrt{7}} = 1$

Thus the set of negative irrational numbers is closed for **none** of the operations.

7. $y = -\dfrac{3}{2}x + 3$

$y = \dfrac{-3}{+2}x + 3$

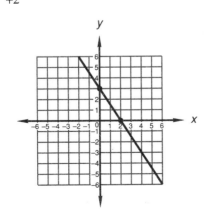

8. $y = -\dfrac{1}{2}x + 2$

$y = \dfrac{-1}{+2}x + 2$

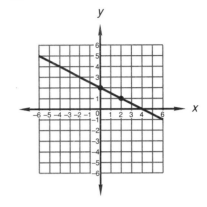

9. $\dfrac{(4000 \times 10^{-23})(0.00035 \times 10^{15})}{5000 \times 10^5}$

$= \dfrac{(4 \times 10^{-20})(3.5 \times 10^{11})}{5 \times 10^8} = \mathbf{2.8 \times 10^{-17}}$

10. (a) vertical line: $x = \pm k$; $\boldsymbol{x = 5}$

(b) The desired equation is $y = mx + b$.

By inspection, $b = 0$.

By inspection, the sign for m is $-$.

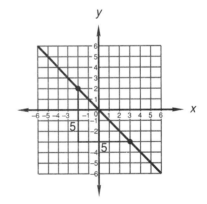

$|m| = \dfrac{5}{5} = 1$

So $b = 0$ and $m = -1$: $\boldsymbol{y = -x}$

11. $3\sqrt{2} \cdot 4\sqrt{12} - 6\sqrt{54}$

$= 3 \cdot 4\sqrt{2}\sqrt{2 \cdot 6} - 6\sqrt{3 \cdot 3 \cdot 6} = 24\sqrt{6} - 18\sqrt{6}$

$= \boldsymbol{6\sqrt{6}}$

12. $3\sqrt{2}(5\sqrt{12} - 8\sqrt{8})$

$= 3 \cdot 5\sqrt{2}\sqrt{2 \cdot 6} - 3 \cdot 8\sqrt{2}\sqrt{2 \cdot 2 \cdot 2}$

$= \boldsymbol{30\sqrt{6} - 96}$

13. $(x^3 - 3x^2 + 2x + 5) \div (x - 3)$

$$
\begin{array}{r}
x^2 + 0x + 2 \\
x - 3 \overline{\smash{)}\ x^3 - 3x^2 + 2x + 5} \\
\underline{x^3 - 3x^2} \\
2x + 5 \\
\underline{2x - 6} \\
11
\end{array}
$$

$x^2 + 2 + \dfrac{11}{x - 3}$

14. $(x^3 - 1) \div (x + 3)$

$$
\begin{array}{r}
x^2 - 3x + 9 \\
x + 3 \overline{\smash{)}\ x^3 + 0x^2 + 0x - 1} \\
\underline{x^3 + 3x^2} \\
-3x^2 + 0x \\
\underline{-3x^2 - 9x} \\
9x - 1 \\
\underline{9x + 27} \\
-28
\end{array}
$$

$x^2 - 3x + 9 - \dfrac{28}{x + 3}$

15. $x^2 - 9x + 20 = 0$
$(x - 4)(x - 5) = 0$

If $x - 4 = 0$, $x = \mathbf{4}$
$(4)^2 - 9(4) + 20 = 0$
$\qquad\qquad 0 = 0$ check

If $x - 5 = 0$, $x = \mathbf{5}$
$(5)^2 - 9(5) + 20 = 0$
$\qquad\qquad 0 = 0$ check

16. $\qquad 42 = 13x - x^2$
$x^2 - 13x + 42 = 0$
$(x - 6)(x - 7) = 0$

If $x - 6 = 0$, $x = \mathbf{6}$
$42 = 13(6) - (6)^2$
$42 = 78 - 36$
$42 = 42$ check

If $x - 7 = 0$, $x = \mathbf{7}$
$42 = 13(7) - (7)^2$
$42 = 91 - 49$
$42 = 42$ check

17. $\qquad 4x^2 - 9 = 0$
$(2x - 3)(2x + 3) = 0$

If $2x - 3 = 0$, $x = \dfrac{3}{2}$
$4\left(\dfrac{3}{2}\right)^2 - 9 = 0$
$\qquad\qquad 0 = 0$ check

If $2x + 3 = 0$, $x = -\dfrac{3}{2}$
$4\left(-\dfrac{3}{2}\right)^2 - 9 = 0$
$\qquad\qquad 0 = 0$ check

18. $\qquad 9x^2 = 4$
$9x^2 - 4 = 0$
$(3x - 2)(3x + 2) = 0$

If $3x - 2 = 0$, $x = \dfrac{2}{3}$
$9\left(\dfrac{2}{3}\right)^2 = 4$
$\qquad 4 = 4$ check

If $3x + 2 = 0$, $x = -\dfrac{2}{3}$
$9\left(-\dfrac{2}{3}\right)^2 = 4$
$\qquad 4 = 4$ check

19. (a) $y = x$

$y = \dfrac{+1}{+1}x$

(b) $y = -\dfrac{1}{2}x + 3$

$y = \dfrac{-1}{+2}x + 3$

The first step is to graph each of these lines.

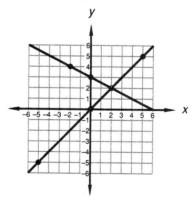

It appears that the lines cross at $x = 2$ and $y = 2$, so **(2, 2)** is the solution.

20. (a) $3x + 4y = 32$
(b) $5x - 4y = 0$

(a) $3x + 4y = 32$
(b) $\dfrac{5x - 4y = 0}{}$
$8x = 32$
$ x = 4$

(a) $3(4) + 4y = 32$
$ 4y = 20$
$ y = 5$

(4, 5)

21. $4\dfrac{2}{3}x - \dfrac{1}{5} = 3\dfrac{2}{3}$

$\dfrac{14}{3}x = \dfrac{11}{3} + \dfrac{1}{5}$

$\dfrac{14}{3}x = \dfrac{55}{15} + \dfrac{3}{15}$

$x = \dfrac{58}{15} \cdot \dfrac{3}{14} = \mathbf{\dfrac{29}{35}}$

22. $\dfrac{2\sqrt{3}}{2} \in$ **Irrationals and reals**

23. $\dfrac{4x^2 - x^2 y}{x^2} = \dfrac{x^2(4 - y)}{x^2} = \mathbf{4 - y}$

24. (a) $T_K R_K + 60 = T_M R_M$
(b) $T_K = 3$
(c) $T_M = 2$
(d) $R_K + R_M = 125$
$ R_K = 125 - R_M$
Substitute (b) and (c) into (a) and get:
(a') $3R_K + 60 = 2R_M$
Substitute (d) into (a') and get:
(a'') $3(125 - R_M) + 60 = 2R_M$
$ 375 - 3R_M + 60 = 2R_M$
$ 435 = 5R_M$
$ \mathbf{87 = R_M}$

(d) $R_K = 125 - (87) = \mathbf{38}$

25. $\dfrac{3x - 4}{2} + \dfrac{1}{5} = \dfrac{x}{10}$

$\dfrac{(3x - 4)}{2}(10) + \dfrac{1}{5}(10) = \dfrac{x}{10}(10)$

$ 15x - 20 + 2 = x$

$ 14x = 18$

$ x = \dfrac{9}{7}$

26. $\dfrac{4x^2}{y} - \dfrac{2x}{y + 4} = \dfrac{4x^2(y + 4) - 2xy}{y(y + 4)}$

$ = \dfrac{4x^2 y + 16x^2 - 2xy}{y(y + 4)}$

27. $-x^0 - x(x - y^2)$
$= -(-3)^0 - (-3)((-3) - (-4)^2) = -1 + 3(-19)$
$= \mathbf{-58}$

28. $-2(-2 - 3) - (-2^0) - 3(-3^0) - 2(-2)$
$= -2(-5) + 1 + 3 + 4 = \mathbf{18}$

29. (a) $\dfrac{1}{-3^{-3}} = -3^3 = \mathbf{-27}$

(b) $-3^{-3} = -\dfrac{1}{3^3} = -\dfrac{1}{27}$

(c) $-(-3)^{-3} = -\dfrac{1}{(-3)^3} = \dfrac{1}{27}$

30. $x^{-2}y^{-1}\left(\dfrac{x^{-1}}{y^{-1}} - \dfrac{4x^2 y^0}{(y^{-3})^2}\right)$

$= \dfrac{x^{-2}y^{-1}x^{-1}}{y^{-1}} - \dfrac{x^{-2}y^{-1}4x^2}{y^{-6}} = \mathbf{x^{-3} - 4y^5}$

PROBLEM SET 94

1. $\dfrac{(92.4)(10) + (84)(4)}{10 + 4} = \dfrac{1260}{14} = \mathbf{90}$

2. $1000\,\text{yd}^3 \times \dfrac{3\,\text{ft}}{1\,\text{yd}} \times \dfrac{3\,\text{ft}}{1\,\text{yd}} \times \dfrac{3\,\text{ft}}{1\,\text{yd}} \times \dfrac{12\,\text{in.}}{1\,\text{ft}} \times \dfrac{12\,\text{in.}}{1\,\text{ft}}$

$\times \dfrac{12\,\text{in.}}{1\,\text{ft}} \times \dfrac{2.54\,\text{cm}}{1\,\text{in.}} \times \dfrac{2.54\,\text{cm}}{1\,\text{in.}} \times \dfrac{2.54\,\text{cm}}{1\,\text{in.}}$

$\times \dfrac{1\,\text{m}}{100\,\text{cm}} \times \dfrac{1\,\text{m}}{100\,\text{cm}} \times \dfrac{1\,\text{m}}{100\,\text{cm}}$

$= \dfrac{\mathbf{1000(3)(3)(3)(12)(12)(12)(2.54)(2.54)(2.54)}}{\mathbf{(100)(100)(100)}}\,\text{m}^3$

3. $(3x + 2y)^2 = (3x + 2y)(3x + 2y)$
$= 9x^2 + 6xy + 6xy + 4y^2 = \mathbf{9x^2 + 12xy + 4y^2}$

4. (a) $L + S = 76$
(b) $L = S + 12$
Substitute (b) into (a) and get:
(a') $(S + 12) + S = 76$
$ 2S = 64$
$ S = \mathbf{32}$

(b) $L = (32) + 12 = \mathbf{44}$

5. (a) $5G + 2P = 660$
(b) $G + P = 210$

(a) $ 5G + 2P = 660$
(-2)(b) $\dfrac{-2G - 2P = -420}{}$
$ 3G = 240$
$ G = \mathbf{80}$

6. (a) $3x + y = 6$
$$y = -3x + 6$$
$$y = \frac{-3}{+1}x + 6$$

(b) $x = -y$
$$y = -x$$
$$y = \frac{-1}{+1}x$$

The first step is to graph each of these lines.

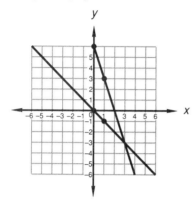

It appears that the lines cross at $x = 3$ and $y = -3$, so $(3, -3)$ is the solution.

7. (a) $y = \frac{2}{3}x - 3$
$$y = \frac{+2}{+3}x - 3$$

(b) $y = -x + 2$
$$y = \frac{-1}{+1}x + 2$$

The first step is to graph each of these lines.

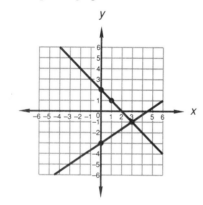

It appears that the lines cross at $x = 3$ and $y = -1$, so $(3, -1)$ is the solution.

8. $\dfrac{(3000 \times 10^{-5})(0.004 \times 10^{10})}{(200 \times 10^{14})(0.000002)}$

$= \dfrac{(3 \times 10^{-2})(4 \times 10^{7})}{(2 \times 10^{16})(2 \times 10^{-6})} = 3 \times 10^{-5}$

9. (a) The desired equation is $y = mx + b$.
By inspection, $b = 0$.
By inspection, the sign for m is $-$.

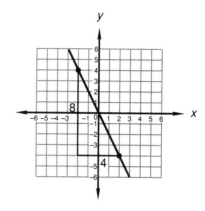

$$|m| = \frac{8}{4} = 2$$
So $b = 0$ and $m = -2$: $y = -2x$
(b) horizontal line: $y = \pm k$; $y = -3$

10. $3\sqrt{27} - 2\sqrt{3}(4\sqrt{3} - 5\sqrt{12})$
$= 3\sqrt{3 \cdot 3 \cdot 3} - 2 \cdot 4\sqrt{3}\sqrt{3}$
$+ 2 \cdot 5\sqrt{3}\sqrt{3 \cdot 2 \cdot 2}$
$= 9\sqrt{3} - 24 + 60 = 36 + 9\sqrt{3}$

11. $2\sqrt{2} \cdot 3\sqrt{3} \cdot 5\sqrt{12} = 2 \cdot 3 \cdot 5\sqrt{2}\sqrt{3}\sqrt{2 \cdot 2 \cdot 3}$
$= 180\sqrt{2}$

12. $(3x^3 - 2x - 4) \div (x + 1)$

$$\begin{array}{r} 3x^2 - 3x + 1 \\ x+1\overline{)\,3x^3 + 0x^2 - 2x - 4} \\ \underline{3x^3 + 3x^2} \\ -3x^2 - 2x \\ \underline{-3x^2 - 3x} \\ x - 4 \\ \underline{x + 1} \\ -5 \end{array}$$

$$3x^2 - 3x + 1 - \frac{5}{x + 1}$$

13. $(2x^3 - 2x^2 - 4) \div (x + 1)$

$$\begin{array}{r} 2x^2 - 4x + 4 \\ x+1\overline{)\,2x^3 - 2x^2 + 0x - 4} \\ \underline{2x^3 + 2x^2} \\ -4x^2 + 0x \\ \underline{-4x^2 - 4x} \\ 4x - 4 \\ \underline{4x + 4} \\ -8 \end{array}$$

$$2x^2 - 4x + 4 - \frac{8}{x + 1}$$

14. $2x^2 + 20x + 50 = 0$
$x^2 + 10x + 25 = 0$
$(x + 5)(x + 5) = 0$

If $x + 5 = 0$, $x = -5$
$2(-5)^2 + 20(-5) + 50 = 0$
$50 - 100 + 50 = 0$
$\qquad 0 = 0$ check

15. $\qquad 3x^2 = -33x - 90$
$3x^2 + 33x + 90 = 0$
$x^2 + 11x + 30 = 0$
$(x + 5)(x + 6) = 0$

If $x + 5 = 0$, $x = -5$
$3(-5)^2 = -33(-5) - 90$
$75 = 165 - 90$
$75 = 75$ check

If $x + 6 = 0$, $x = -6$
$3(-6)^2 = -33(-6) - 90$
$108 = 198 - 90$
$108 = 108$ check

16. $\qquad 2x^2 - 18 = 0$
$x^2 - 9 = 0$
$(x + 3)(x - 3) = 0$
If $x + 3 = 0$, $x = -3$
$2(-3)^2 - 18 = 0$
$18 - 18 = 0$
$\qquad 0 = 0$ check

If $x - 3 = 0$, $x = 3$
$2(3)^2 - 18 = 0$
$18 - 18 = 0$
$\qquad 0 = 0$ check

17. $27 - 3p^2 = 0$
$0 = p^2 - 9$
$0 = (p + 3)(p - 3)$
If $p + 3 = 0$, $p = -3$
$27 - 3(-3)^2 = 0$
$\qquad 0 = 0$ check

If $p - 3 = 0$, $p = 3$
$27 - 3(3)^2 = 0$
$\qquad 0 = 0$ check

18. (a) $y = -3x + 10$
(b) $2x + 2y = 8$
Substitute (a) into (b) and get:
(b') $2x + 2(-3x + 10) = 8$
$2x - 6x + 20 = 8$
$12 = 4x$
$3 = x$
(a) $y = -3(3) + 10 = 1$
(3, 1)

19. $\qquad \dfrac{3x + 2}{5} - \dfrac{x}{2} = 5$
$\dfrac{(3x + 2)}{5}(10) - \dfrac{x}{2}(10) = 5(10)$
$6x + 4 - 5x = 50$
$x = 46$

20. $-3x^0(-2 - 3) - (-2 - 3)4x = -2(x + 2)$
$15 + 20x = -2x - 4$
$22x = -19$
$x = -\dfrac{19}{22}$

21. $-3 \in$ **integers, rationals, and reals**

22. $\dfrac{3x^{-2}y}{m^{-3}} - \dfrac{4y^2m}{x^2ym^{-2}} + \dfrac{6y}{x^2m^{-3}}$
$= 3x^{-2}ym^3 - 4x^{-2}ym^3 + 6x^{-2}ym^3 = \mathbf{5x^{-2}ym^3}$

23. (a) $R_M T_M = R_B T_B$
(b) $R_B = 5$
(c) $R_M = 4$
(d) $T_M + T_B = 18$
$T_M = 18 - T_B$
Substitute (b) and (c) into (a) and get:
(a') $4T_M = 5T_B$
Substitute (d) into (a') and get:
(a'') $4(18 - T_B) = 5T_B$
$72 - 4T_B = 5T_B$
$72 = 9T_B$
$\mathbf{8} = T_B$

(d) $T_M = 18 - (8) = \mathbf{10}$

24. $\dfrac{x}{x + 1} + \dfrac{x^2}{x(x + 1)} = \dfrac{x^2 + x^2}{x(x + 1)}$
$= \dfrac{2x^2}{x(x + 1)} = \dfrac{2x}{x + 1}$

25. $\dfrac{a + \dfrac{x}{y}}{\dfrac{a}{y} - x} = \dfrac{\dfrac{ay + x}{y}}{\dfrac{a - xy}{y}} \cdot \dfrac{\dfrac{y}{a - xy}}{\dfrac{y}{a - xy}}$
$= \dfrac{ay + x}{y} \cdot \dfrac{y}{a - xy} = \dfrac{ay + x}{a - xy}$

26. $x + 4 \not> 2$; $D = \{$Reals$\}$
$x + 4 \leq 2$
$x \leq -2$

27. $|-x| - x^0 - x^2(x - y)$
$= |-(-2)| - (-2)^0 - (-2)^2((-2) - (-4))$
$= 2 - 1 - 4(2) = \mathbf{-7}$

28. $-|-2| - |-2^0| - (-2 - 4) = -2 - 1 + 6 = \mathbf{3}$

29. (a) $-3^{-2} = -\dfrac{1}{3^2} = -\dfrac{1}{9}$

   (b) $(-3)^{-2} = \dfrac{1}{(-3)^2} = \dfrac{1}{9}$

   (c) $-(-3)^{-2} = -\dfrac{1}{(-3)^2} = -\dfrac{1}{9}$

30. $\dfrac{x^{-2}(y^{-2})^2(y^0)^2}{xy^{-2}(x^{-2}y)^{-2}} = \dfrac{x^{-2}y^{-4}}{xy^{-2}x^4y^{-2}} = \mathbf{x^{-7}}$

PROBLEM SET 95

1. (a) $10N_D + 25N_Q = 650$
   (b) $N_Q = N_D + 5$
   Substitute (b) into (a) and get:
   (a') $10N_D + 25(N_D + 5) = 650$
   $$35N_D + 125 = 650$$
   $$35N_D = 525$$
   $$N_D = \mathbf{15}$$

   (b) $N_Q = (15) + 5 = \mathbf{20}$

2. (a) $5S + 3D = 190$
   (b) $S + D = 50$
   $$D = 50 - S$$
   Substitute (b) into (a) and get:
   (a') $5S + 3(50 - S) = 190$
   $$5S + 150 - 3S = 190$$
   $$2S = 40$$
   $$S = 20$$

   (b) $D = 50 - (20) = \mathbf{30}$

3. (a) $N_F = N_S + 90$
   (b) $N_F + N_S = 630$
   Substitute (a) into (b) and get:
   (b') $(N_S + 90) + N_S = 630$
   $$2N_S = 540$$
   $$N_S = \mathbf{270}$$

   (a) $N_F = (270) + 90 = \mathbf{360}$

4. $\dfrac{280}{100}(B) = 5600$
   $$B = \mathbf{2000}$$

5. $-x \geq 3; \quad D = \{\text{Reals}\}$
   $$x \leq -3$$

   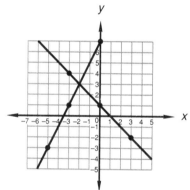

6. $\{\text{Positive integers}\}$

ADDITION:	Closed. The sum of any two positive integers is a positive integer.
SUBTRACTION:	Not Closed. $(4) - (6) = -2$
MULTIPLICATION:	Closed. The product of any two positive integers is a positive integer.
DIVISION:	Not closed. $\dfrac{1}{4}$ is not a positive integer.

Thus the set of positive integers is closed for the operations of **addition** and **multiplication.**

7. $-b \pm \sqrt{b^2 - 4ac}$

$= -(-1) \pm \sqrt{(-1)^2 - 4(-3)(4)} = 1 \pm \sqrt{49}$
$= 1 \pm 7 = \mathbf{8, -6}$

8. (a) $y = -x + 1$

   $$y = \dfrac{-1}{+1}x + 1$$
   (b) $y = 2x + 7$

   $$y = \dfrac{+2}{+1}x + 7$$
   The first step is to graph each of these lines.

It appears that the lines cross at $x = -2$ and $y = 3$, so $\mathbf{(-2, 3)}$ is the solution.

9. (a) $4x - 3y = 14$
   (b) $5x - 4y = 18$

   4(a) $\quad 16x - 12y = 56$
   (-3)(b) $\underline{-15x + 12y = -54}$
   $$\qquad\qquad x \qquad\quad = \quad 2$$

   (a) $4(2) - 3y = 14$
   $$-3y = 6$$
   $$y = -2$$
   $\mathbf{(2, -2)}$

10. $\dfrac{(0.00004 \times 10^{15})(700 \times 10^{-5})}{14{,}000 \times 10^{-21}}$

$= \dfrac{(4 \times 10^{10})(7 \times 10^{-3})}{1.4 \times 10^{-17}} = \mathbf{2 \times 10^{25}}$

11. (a) horizontal line: $y = \pm k$; $\boldsymbol{y = -3}$
(b) The desired equation is $y = mx + b$.
By inspection, $b = 3$.
By inspection, the sign for m is +.

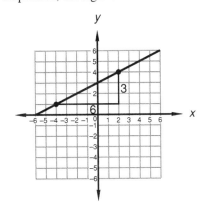

$$|m| = \frac{3}{6} = \frac{1}{2}$$

So $b = 3$ and $m = \dfrac{1}{2}$: $\boldsymbol{y = \dfrac{1}{2}x + 3}$

12. $5\sqrt{75} - 2\sqrt{108} + 5\sqrt{12}$
$= 5\sqrt{5 \cdot 5 \cdot 3} - 2\sqrt{3 \cdot 3 \cdot 3 \cdot 2 \cdot 2}$
$\quad + 5\sqrt{2 \cdot 2 \cdot 3} = 25\sqrt{3} - 12\sqrt{3} + 10\sqrt{3}$
$= \boldsymbol{23\sqrt{3}}$

13. $2\sqrt{6}(3\sqrt{6} - 2\sqrt{12}) = 2 \cdot 3\sqrt{6}\sqrt{6} - 2 \cdot 2\sqrt{6}\sqrt{6 \cdot 2}$
$= \boldsymbol{36 - 24\sqrt{2}}$

14. $(x^4 - 2x^2 - 4) \div (x + 2)$

$$
\begin{array}{r}
x^3 - 2x^2 + 2x - 4 \\
x + 2 \overline{)\, x^4 + 0x^3 - 2x^2 + 0x - 4} \\
\underline{x^4 + 2x^3} \\
-2x^3 - 2x^2 \\
\underline{-2x^3 - 4x^2} \\
2x^2 + 0x \\
\underline{2x^2 + 4x} \\
-4x - 4 \\
\underline{-4x - 8} \\
4
\end{array}
$$

$$\boldsymbol{x^3 - 2x^2 + 2x - 4 + \dfrac{4}{x + 2}}$$

15. $21 = 10x - x^2$
$x^2 - 10x + 21 = 0$
$(x - 3)(x - 7) = 0$

If $x - 3 = 0$, $\boldsymbol{x = 3}$
$21 = 10(3) - (3)^2$
$21 = 30 - 9$
$21 = 21$ check

If $x - 7 = 0$, $\boldsymbol{x = 7}$
$21 = 10(7) - (7)^2$
$21 = 70 - 49$
$21 = 21$ check

16.
$$-49 = -4x^2$$
$$4x^2 - 49 = 0$$
$$(2x + 7)(2x - 7) = 0$$

If $2x + 7 = 0$, $\boldsymbol{x = -\dfrac{7}{2}}$

$-49 = -4\left(-\dfrac{7}{2}\right)^2$
$-49 = -49$ check

If $2x - 7 = 0$, $\boldsymbol{x = \dfrac{7}{2}}$

$-49 = -4\left(\dfrac{7}{2}\right)^2$
$-49 = -49$ check

17.
$$32 = -x^2 - 12x$$
$$x^2 + 12x + 32 = 0$$
$$(x + 4)(x + 8) = 0$$

If $x + 4 = 0$, $\boldsymbol{x = -4}$
$32 = -(-4)^2 - 12(-4)$
$32 = 32$ check

If $x + 8 = 0$, $\boldsymbol{x = -8}$
$32 = -(-8)^2 - 12(-8)$
$32 = 32$ check

18.
$$\frac{4x}{3} - \frac{x + 1}{5} = 10$$
$$\frac{4x}{3}(15) - \frac{(x + 1)}{5}(15) = 10(15)$$
$$20x - 3x - 3 = 150$$
$$17x = 153$$
$$\boldsymbol{x = 9}$$

19. $3\dfrac{1}{4}x - \dfrac{2}{3} = 7\dfrac{1}{8}$

$\dfrac{13}{4}x = \dfrac{57}{8} + \dfrac{2}{3}$

$\dfrac{13}{4}x = \dfrac{171}{24} + \dfrac{16}{24}$

$x = \dfrac{187}{24} \cdot \dfrac{4}{13} = \boldsymbol{\dfrac{187}{78}}$

20. $4 \le x < 7$; $D = \{\text{Integers}\}$

$$
\begin{array}{ccccc}
\bullet & \bullet & \bullet & & \\
3 & 4 & 5 & 6 & 7
\end{array}
$$

21. $-3\dfrac{1}{3} \in$ **Rationals and reals**

22. $\dfrac{x}{x+1} + \dfrac{4}{x} = \dfrac{x^2 + 4(x+1)}{x(x+1)}$

$= \dfrac{x^2 + 4x + 4}{x(x+1)}$

23. $5x^2ym^2 - \dfrac{3xxy^{-2}}{y^{-3}m^{-1}} + \dfrac{2xmy}{y^3y}$

$= 5x^2ym^2 - 3x^2ym + 2xmy^{-3}$

24. (a) $R_HT_H - 125 = R_OT_O$
(b) $T_H = 2$
(c) $T_O = 3$
(d) $R_H + R_O = 85$
$\qquad R_H = 85 - R_O$
Substitute (b) and (c) into (a) and get:
(a′) $2R_H - 125 = 3R_O$
Substitute (d) into (a′) and get:
(a″) $2(85 - R_O) - 125 = 3R_O$
$\qquad 170 - 2R_O - 125 = 3R_O$
$\qquad\qquad 45 = 5R_O$
$\qquad\qquad 9 = R_O$

(d) $R_H = 85 - (9) = \mathbf{76}$

25. $3x^0 - 2x^0 - 3(x^0 - 2x) = -2x(4 - 3)$
$\qquad 3 - 2 - 3 + 6x = -2x$
$\qquad\qquad 8x = 2$
$\qquad\qquad x = \dfrac{1}{4}$

26. $\dfrac{\dfrac{3x}{y} - 2}{a - \dfrac{4}{y}} = \dfrac{\dfrac{3x - 2y}{y}}{\dfrac{ay - 4}{y}} \cdot \dfrac{\dfrac{y}{ay - 4}}{\dfrac{y}{ay - 4}}$

$= \dfrac{3x - 2y}{y} \cdot \dfrac{y}{ay - 4} = \dfrac{\mathbf{3x - 2y}}{\mathbf{ay - 4}}$

27. $\dfrac{3xy - 9xy^2}{3xy} = \dfrac{3xy(1 - 3y)}{3xy} = \mathbf{1 - 3y}$

28. (a) $-2^{-3} = -\dfrac{1}{2^3} = -\dfrac{1}{8}$

(b) $(-2)^{-3} = \dfrac{1}{(-2)^3} = -\dfrac{1}{8}$

(c) $\dfrac{1}{-(-2)^{-3}} = -(-2)^3 = 8$

29. $-2^0[(-3 - 5)(-2 - 1)] - 3^0 = -[(-8)(-3)] - 1$
$= \mathbf{-25}$

30. $\dfrac{4x^2(x^{-2})^0 xx^{-4}}{2(3x^{-2})^0(x^2)^{-2}} = \dfrac{4x^{-1}}{2x^{-4}} = \mathbf{2x^3}$

PROBLEM SET 96

1. Average $= \dfrac{12,000.16}{4} = \mathbf{3000.04}$

2. $10,000 \text{ yd}^3 \times \dfrac{3 \text{ ft}}{1 \text{ yd}} \times \dfrac{3 \text{ ft}}{1 \text{ yd}} \times \dfrac{3 \text{ ft}}{1 \text{ yd}} \times \dfrac{12 \text{ in.}}{1 \text{ ft}}$

$\times \dfrac{12 \text{ in.}}{1 \text{ ft}} \times \dfrac{12 \text{ in.}}{1 \text{ ft}} \times \dfrac{2.54 \text{ cm}}{1 \text{ in.}} \times \dfrac{2.54 \text{ cm}}{1 \text{ in.}}$

$\times \dfrac{2.54 \text{ cm}}{1 \text{ in.}} \times \dfrac{1 \text{ m}}{100 \text{ cm}} \times \dfrac{1 \text{ m}}{100 \text{ cm}} \times \dfrac{1 \text{ m}}{100 \text{ cm}}$

$= \dfrac{10,000(3)(3)(3)(12)(12)(12)(2.54)(2.54)(2.54)}{(100)(100)(100)} \text{ m}^3$

3. $T_P = 3; \ T_F = 7; \ R_P = R_F + 40;$
$R_PT_P = R_FT_F$

$3(R_F + 40) = 7R_F$
$3R_F + 120 = 7R_F$
$\qquad 120 = 4R_F$
$\qquad R_F = \mathbf{30 \text{ miles per hour}}$

$R_P = (30) + 40 = \mathbf{70 \text{ miles per hour}}$

4. $R_R = 10; \ R_W = 4; \ T_R + T_W = 14;$
$R_RT_R = R_WT_W$

$10(14 - T_W) = 4T_W$
$140 - 10T_W = 4T_W$
$\qquad 140 = 14T_W$
$\qquad 10 = T_W$

$D_R = D_W = (4)(10) = \mathbf{40 \text{ km}}$

5. $WN = (0.38)(50) = \mathbf{19}$

6. $p - (-p) - 5(p - 3) - (2p - 5) = 3(p + 2p)$
$\qquad p + p - 5p + 15 - 2p + 5 = 9p$
$\qquad\qquad 20 = 14p$
$\qquad\qquad \dfrac{10}{7} = p$

7. $-4x + 4 \geq 8; \ D = \{\text{Reals}\}$
$\qquad -4x \geq 4$
$\qquad\qquad x \leq -1$

8. (a) $y = -2x + 4$

$y = \dfrac{-2}{+1}x + 4$

(b) $y = -2$

The first step is to graph each of these lines.

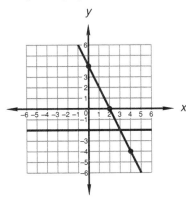

It appears that the lines cross at $x = 3$ and $y = -2$, so $(3, -2)$ is the solution.

9. (a) $3x + y = 20$

(b) $2x - 3y = -5$

3(a) $9x + 3y = 60$

  (b) $\underline{2x - 3y = -5}$

  $11x \qquad = 55$

  $x = 5$

(a) $3(5) + y = 20$

  $y = 5$

(5, 5)

10. $\dfrac{0.000030 \times 10^{-18}}{(5000 \times 10^{-14})(300 \times 10^{5})}$

$= \dfrac{3 \times 10^{-23}}{(5 \times 10^{-11})(3 \times 10^{7})} = \mathbf{2 \times 10^{-20}}$

11. (a) vertical line: $x = \pm k$; $\mathbf{x = -3}$

(b) The desired equation is $y = mx + b$.

By inspection, $b = 2$.

By inspection, the sign for m is +.

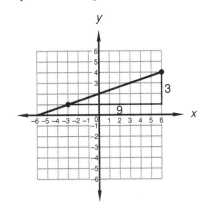

$|m| = \dfrac{3}{9} = \dfrac{1}{3}$

So $b = 2$ and $m = \dfrac{1}{3}$: $\mathbf{y = \dfrac{1}{3}x + 2}$

12. $3\sqrt{45} - 2\sqrt{180} + 2\sqrt{80}$

$= 3\sqrt{3 \cdot 3 \cdot 5} - 2\sqrt{3 \cdot 3 \cdot 2 \cdot 2 \cdot 5}$

$\quad + 2\sqrt{2 \cdot 2 \cdot 2 \cdot 2 \cdot 5}$

$= 9\sqrt{5} - 12\sqrt{5} + 8\sqrt{5} = \mathbf{5\sqrt{5}}$

13. $3\sqrt{2}(4\sqrt{20} - 3\sqrt{2})$

$= 3 \cdot 4\sqrt{2}\sqrt{2 \cdot 2 \cdot 5} - 3 \cdot 3\sqrt{2}\sqrt{2}$

$= \mathbf{24\sqrt{10} - 18}$

14. $(x^3 - 4) \div (x - 5)$

$$
\begin{array}{r}
x^2 + 5x + 25 \\
x - 5 \overline{)\, x^3 + 0x^2 + 0x - 4} \\
\underline{x^3 - 5x^2} \\
5x^2 + 0x \\
\underline{5x^2 - 25x} \\
25x - 4 \\
\underline{25x - 125} \\
121
\end{array}
$$

$\mathbf{x^2 + 5x + 25 + \dfrac{121}{x - 5}}$

15. $x^2 = -6x - 8$

$x^2 + 6x + 8 = 0$

$(x + 2)(x + 4) = 0$

If $x + 2 = 0$, $\mathbf{x = -2}$

$(-2)^2 = -6(-2) - 8$

$4 = 12 - 8$

$4 = 4$ check

If $x + 4 = 0$, $\mathbf{x = -4}$

$(-4)^2 = -6(-4) - 8$

$16 = 24 - 8$

$16 = 16$ check

16. $9 = 4x^2$

$0 = 4x^2 - 9$

$0 = (2x + 3)(2x - 3)$

If $2x + 3 = 0$, $x = -\dfrac{3}{2}$

$9 = 4\left(-\dfrac{3}{2}\right)^2$

$9 = 9$ check

If $2x - 3 = 0$, $x = \dfrac{3}{2}$

$9 = 4\left(\dfrac{3}{2}\right)^2$

$9 = 9$ check

17.
$$x^2 = -12x - 32$$
$$x^2 + 12x + 32 = 0$$
$$(x + 4)(x + 8) = 0$$

If $x + 4 = 0$, $x = -4$
$$(-4)^2 = -12(-4) - 32$$
$$16 = 48 - 32$$
$$16 = 16 \quad \text{check}$$

If $x + 8 = 0$, $x = -8$
$$(-8)^2 = -12(-8) - 32$$
$$64 = 96 - 32$$
$$64 = 64 \quad \text{check}$$

18.
$$\frac{x}{5} - \frac{4 + x}{7} = 5$$
$$\frac{x}{5}(35) - \frac{(4 + x)}{7}(35) = 5(35)$$
$$7x - 20 - 5x = 175$$
$$2x = 195$$
$$x = \frac{195}{2}$$

19. $2\frac{1}{8}x - 3\frac{1}{4} = 2\frac{1}{16}$
$$\frac{17}{8}x = \frac{33}{16} + \frac{13}{4}$$
$$\frac{17}{8}x = \frac{33}{16} + \frac{52}{16}$$
$$x = \frac{85}{16} \cdot \frac{8}{17} = \frac{5}{2}$$

20. $WF\left(\frac{5}{6}\right) = 7\frac{2}{3}$
$$\left(\frac{6}{5}\right)WF\left(\frac{5}{6}\right) = \frac{23}{3}\left(\frac{6}{5}\right)$$
$$WF = \frac{46}{5}$$

21. False $\{\text{Rationals}\} \subset \{\text{Reals}\}$

22. (a) $R_W T_W + 200 = R_R T_R$
(b) $R_W = 40$
(c) $R_R = 60$
(d) $T_W + T_R = 10$
$$T_W = 10 - T_R$$
Substitute (b) and (c) into (a) and get:
(a') $40T_W + 200 = 60T_R$
Substitute (d) into (a') and get:
(a'') $40(10 - T_R) + 200 = 60T_R$
$$400 - 40T_R + 200 = 60T_R$$
$$600 = 100T_R$$
$$6 = T_R$$
(d) $T_W = 10 - (6) = 4$

23. $\dfrac{2x}{5} + \dfrac{3x + 5}{6x} = \dfrac{2x(6x) + 5(3x + 5)}{30x}$
$$= \frac{12x^2 + 15x + 25}{30x}$$

24. $\dfrac{\dfrac{3a}{b} - 2b}{b - \dfrac{4}{b}} = \dfrac{\dfrac{3a - 2b^2}{b}}{\dfrac{b^2 - 4}{b}} \cdot \dfrac{\dfrac{b}{b^2 - 4}}{\dfrac{b}{b^2 - 4}}$
$$= \frac{3a - 2b^2}{b} \cdot \frac{b}{b^2 - 4} = \frac{3a - 2b^2}{b^2 - 4}$$

25. $\dfrac{4 + 4k}{4} = \dfrac{4(1 + k)}{4} = 1 + k$

26. $|-x^2| - |x| + x(x - y^0)$
$$= |-(-3)^2| - |-3| + (-3)((-3) - 4^0)$$
$$= 9 - 3 - 3(-4) = 18$$

27. $-3^0 - [(-3 + 5) - (-2 - 5)] = -1 - [2 + 7]$
$$= -10$$

28. (a) $-2^{-2} = -\dfrac{1}{2^2} = -\dfrac{1}{4}$

(b) $\dfrac{1}{-2^{-2}} = -2^2 = -4$

(c) $-(-2)^{-2} = -\dfrac{1}{(-2)^2} = -\dfrac{1}{4}$

(d) $\sqrt[7]{-128} = \sqrt[7]{(-2)^7} = -2$

29. $\left(\dfrac{x^4 y}{a^2} - \dfrac{x^{-3}y^2}{ya^{-4}}\right)\dfrac{x^{-4}y}{a^{-2}}$
$$= \frac{x^4 y x^{-4} y}{a^2 a^{-2}} - \frac{x^{-3}y^2 x^{-4}y}{ya^{-4}a^{-2}} = y^2 - x^{-7}y^2 a^6$$

30. $V_{\text{Prism}} = A_{\text{Base}} \times \text{height}$
$$= (A_{\text{Rectangle}} + A_{\text{Triangle}}) \times \text{height}$$
$$= \left[\left((10)(31) + \frac{(20)(10)}{2}\right) \times 100\right] \text{cm}^3$$
$$= (410)(100) \text{ cm}^3 = \textbf{41,000 cm}^3$$

S.A. $= 2A_{\text{Base}} + (P \times \text{height})$
$$= 2(410) \text{ cm}^2 + [(94.4 \times 100)] \text{ cm}^2$$
$$= [820 + 9440] \text{ cm}^2$$
$$= \textbf{10,260 cm}^2$$

$V_{\text{Pyramid}} = \dfrac{1}{3}V_{\text{Prism}}$
$$= \frac{1}{3}(410)(100) \text{ cm}^3$$
$$= \textbf{13,666.}\overline{\textbf{6}} \textbf{ cm}^3$$

PROBLEM SET 97

1. $R_G = 12$; $R_S = 8$; $T_S = T_G + 5$

$R_G T_G = R_S T_S$

$12T_G = 8(T_G + 5)$
$12T_G = 8T_G + 40$
$4T_G = 40$
$T_G = \mathbf{10 \ hr}$

$T_S = (10) + 5 = \mathbf{15 \ hr}$

2. $R_C = 30$; $R_W = 4$; $T_C + T_W = 17$

$R_C T_C = R_W T_W$

$30(17 - T_W) = 4T_W$
$510 - 30T_W = 4T_W$
$510 = 34T_W$
$T_W = \mathbf{15 \ hr}$

$R_W T_W = (4)(15) = \mathbf{60 \ miles}$

3. (a) $3A + 2K = 209$
(b) $A + K = 77$

$$\begin{array}{r} \text{(a)} \quad 3A + 2K = 209 \\ (-2)\text{(b)} \quad -2A - 2K = -154 \\ \hline A = 55 \end{array}$$

(b) $(55) + K = 77$
$K = \mathbf{22}$

4. $\dfrac{20}{100}(T) = 300$
$T = 1500$

$T = F + G$
$G = T - F$
$\quad = 1500 - 300 = \mathbf{1200}$

5. $a(b + c) = ab + ac$

6. $a + (b + c) = (a + b) + c$

7. Reciprocal

8. $-m^3 - 11m^2 - 24m = -m(m^2 + 11m + 24)$
$= \mathbf{-m(m + 3)(m + 8)}$

9. $-4(x - 2)(-2) + 3(x - 4) = 2x(4 - 2^0)$
$8x - 16 + 3x - 12 = 6x$
$5x = 28$
$x = \dfrac{\mathbf{28}}{\mathbf{5}}$

10. $-x + 4 \leq 2$; $D = \{\text{Integers}\}$
$-x \leq -2$
$x \geq 2$

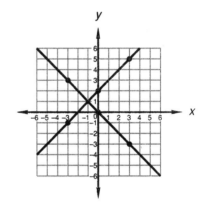

11. (a) $y = x + 2$

$y = \dfrac{+1}{+1}x + 2$

(b) $y = -x$

$y = \dfrac{-1}{+1}x$

The first step is to graph each of these lines.

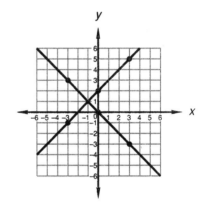

It appears that the lines cross at $x = -1$ and $y = 1$, so $\mathbf{(-1, 1)}$ is the solution.

12. (a) $5x - 2y = 18$
(b) $3x + y = 24$

$$\begin{array}{r} \text{(a)} \quad 5x - 2y = 18 \\ (2)\text{(b)} \quad 6x + 2y = 48 \\ \hline 11x = 66 \\ x = 6 \end{array}$$

(b) $3(6) + y = 24$
$y = 6$

$\mathbf{(6, 6)}$

13. $\dfrac{(0.00042 \times 10^{-15})(300,000)}{(180,000 \times 10^{-14})(7000 \times 10^{-23})}$

$= \dfrac{(4.2 \times 10^{-19})(3 \times 10^5)}{(1.8 \times 10^{-9})(7 \times 10^{-20})} = \mathbf{1 \times 10^{15}}$

14. (a) horizontal line: $y = \pm k$; $y = -2$

(b) The desired equation is $y = mx + b$.

By inspection, $b = \dfrac{3}{2}$.

By inspection, the sign for m is $-$.

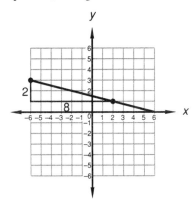

$|m| = \dfrac{2}{8} = \dfrac{1}{4}$

So $b = \dfrac{3}{2}$ and $m = -\dfrac{1}{4}$: $y = -\dfrac{1}{4}x + \dfrac{3}{2}$

15. $3\sqrt{2} \cdot 4\sqrt{3} \cdot 4\sqrt{6} - 3\sqrt{2}$

$= 3 \cdot 4 \cdot 4\sqrt{2}\sqrt{3}\sqrt{3 \cdot 2} - 3\sqrt{2} = \mathbf{288 - 3\sqrt{2}}$

16. $3\sqrt{2}(5\sqrt{12} - 6\sqrt{36})$

$= 3 \cdot 5\sqrt{2}\sqrt{2 \cdot 2 \cdot 3} - 3 \cdot 6\sqrt{2}\sqrt{2 \cdot 3 \cdot 3 \cdot 2}$

$= \mathbf{30\sqrt{6} - 108\sqrt{2}}$

17. $(x^4 - x - 4) \div (x - 1)$

$$
\begin{array}{r}
x^3 + x^2 + x \\
x - 1 \overline{)\, x^4 + 0x^3 + 0x^2 - x - 4} \\
\underline{x^4 - x^3} \\
x^3 + 0x^2 \\
\underline{x^3 - x^2} \\
x^2 - x \\
\underline{x^2 - x} \\
0 - 4
\end{array}
$$

$x^3 + x^2 + x - \dfrac{4}{x - 1}$

18. $24 = -x^2 - 10x$

$x^2 + 10x + 24 = 0$

$(x + 4)(x + 6) = 0$

If $x + 4 = 0$, $x = -4$

$24 = -(-4)^2 - 10(-4)$

$24 = -16 + 40$

$24 = 24$ check

If $x + 6 = 0$, $x = -6$

$24 = -(-6)^2 - 10(-6)$

$24 = -36 + 60$

$24 = 24$ check

19.
$$-4 + 9x^2 = 0$$
$$9x^2 - 4 = 0$$
$$(3x + 2)(3x - 2) = 0$$

If $3x + 2 = 0$, $x = -\dfrac{2}{3}$

$-4 + 9\left(-\dfrac{2}{3}\right)^2 = 0$

$0 = 0$ check

If $3x - 2 = 0$, $x = \dfrac{2}{3}$

$-4 + 9\left(\dfrac{2}{3}\right)^2 = 0$

$0 = 0$ check

20.
$$\dfrac{3x}{2} - \dfrac{x - 5}{6} = 3$$
$$\dfrac{3x}{2}(6) - \dfrac{(x - 5)}{6}(6) = 3(6)$$
$$9x - x + 5 = 18$$
$$8x = 13$$
$$x = \dfrac{13}{8}$$

21.
$$3\dfrac{2}{5}x - \dfrac{1}{10} = \dfrac{1}{20}$$
$$\dfrac{17}{5}x = \dfrac{1}{20} + \dfrac{2}{20}$$
$$x = \dfrac{3}{20} \cdot \dfrac{5}{17} = \dfrac{3}{68}$$

22. $\dfrac{p}{p + 4} - \dfrac{p - 2}{p}$

$= \dfrac{p^2 - (p - 2)(p + 4)}{p(p + 4)}$

$= \dfrac{p^2 - p^2 + 2p - 4p + 8}{p(p + 4)}$

$= \dfrac{-2p + 8}{p(p + 4)}$

23. $\dfrac{xy - \dfrac{1}{y}}{\dfrac{x}{y} - 4} = \dfrac{\dfrac{xy^2 - 1}{y}}{\dfrac{x - 4y}{y}} \cdot \dfrac{\dfrac{y}{x - 4y}}{\dfrac{y}{x - 4y}}$

$= \dfrac{xy^2 - 1}{x - 4y}$

24. $WF\left(20\dfrac{1}{3}\right) = 15\dfrac{2}{5}$

$WF = \dfrac{77}{5} \cdot \dfrac{3}{61}$

$WF = \dfrac{231}{305}$

25. $\frac{5\sqrt{2}}{7} \in$ **Irrationals and reals**

26. $-|x^0| - (x - y)(y - x)$
$= -|(-4)^0| - ((-4) - (-5))((-5) - (-4))$
$= -1 - (1)(-1) = \mathbf{0}$

27. $-2^0 - 2[(-3 - 2) - (-2)] - [(-3 + 2) - (-2)]$
$= -1 - 2[-5 + 2] - [-1 + 2] = -1 + 6 - 1$
$= \mathbf{4}$

28. (a) $\dfrac{1}{-3^{-2}} = -3^2 = \mathbf{-9}$

(b) $\dfrac{1}{-(-3)^{-2}} = -(-3)^2 = \mathbf{-9}$

(c) $-(-2)^{-2} = -\dfrac{1}{(-2)^2} = \mathbf{-\dfrac{1}{4}}$

29. $x^2 y^2 \left(\dfrac{x^{-2}}{y^{-2}} + 4x^4 y^{-2} \right)$

$= \dfrac{x^2 y^2 x^{-2}}{y^{-2}} + x^2 y^2 4 x^4 y^{-2} = \mathbf{y^4 + 4x^6}$

30. (a) $a(b + c) = \mathbf{ab + ac}$

(b) $\mathbf{+2}$

(c) $\mathbf{-\dfrac{1}{b}}$

PROBLEM SET 98

1. $R_C T_C = R_H T_H$; $R_C = 300$;
$R_H = 400$; $T_C + T_H = 7$

$\begin{array}{c}\longrightarrow D_C \\ \hline \longleftarrow \\ D_H\end{array}$

$300 T_C = 400(7 - T_C)$
$300 T_C = 2800 - 400 T_C$
$700 T_C = 2800$
$\quad T_C = \mathbf{4 \ minutes}$

$R_C T_C = 300(4) = \mathbf{1200 \ cm}$

2. $R_G T_G = R_B T_B$; $R_B = R_G + 11$;
$T_G = 4$; $T_B = 3$

$\begin{array}{c}\longrightarrow D_G \\ \hline \longleftarrow \\ D_B\end{array}$

$4 R_G = 3(R_G + 11)$
$4 R_G = 3 R_G + 33$
$\quad R_G = \mathbf{33 \ mph}$

$R_B = (33) + 11 = \mathbf{44 \ mph}$

3. $\dfrac{WP}{100}(460) = 92$

$\qquad WP = \mathbf{20\%}$

4. (a) $N_B + N_G = 179$
(b) $N_B = N_G + 13$
Substitute (b) into (a) and get:
(a') $(N_G + 13) + N_G = 179$
$\qquad\qquad 2N_G = 166$
$\qquad\qquad\; N_G = \mathbf{83}$

(b) $N_B = (83) + 13 = \mathbf{96}$

5. (a) $a(bc) = (ab)c$
(b) $a + b = b + a$

6. $\dfrac{1}{N} = -\dfrac{1}{9}$
$\quad N = -9$
$-9 + (-(-9)) = 0$
$\quad N = \mathbf{9}$

7. **Associative property of addition**

8. $\dfrac{8}{13}(T) = 400$
$\qquad T = \mathbf{650}$

9. $-2(3x - 4^0) + 3x - 2^0 = -(x - 3^2)$
$\quad -6x + 2 + 3x - 1 = -x + 9$
$\qquad\qquad\qquad -8 = 2x$
$\qquad\qquad\qquad \mathbf{-4} = x$

10. $-x - 3 \not> 2$; $D = \{\text{Reals}\}$
$\quad -x - 3 \leq 2$
$\qquad -x \leq 5$
$\qquad\; x \geq -5$

$\begin{array}{ccccccc} & | & | & \bullet\!\!-\!\!-\!\!-\!\!\!\longrightarrow \\ -7 & -6 & -5 & -4 & -3 \end{array}$

11. (a) $y = 2x - 4$

$\quad y = \dfrac{+2}{+1}x - 4$

(b) $y = -x + 2$

$\quad y = \dfrac{-1}{+1}x + 2$

The first step is to graph each of these lines.

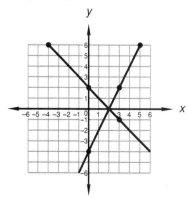

It appears that the lines cross at $x = 2$ and $y = 0$, so $\mathbf{(2, 0)}$ is the solution.

12. (a) $3x + 5y = -14$
(b) $-2x + y = 5$

$\begin{array}{ll} 2(a) & 6x + 10y = -28 \\ 3(b) & \underline{-6x + 3y = 15} \\ & 13y = -13 \\ & y = -1 \end{array}$

(b) $-2x + (-1) = 5$
$ -2x = 6$
$ x = -3$

(−3, −1)

13. $\dfrac{(0.000004)(0.003 \times 10^{21})}{(20,000 \times 10^{8})(0.002 \times 10^{15})}$

$= \dfrac{(4 \times 10^{-6})(3 \times 10^{18})}{(2 \times 10^{12})(2 \times 10^{12})} = \mathbf{3 \times 10^{-12}}$

14. (a) vertical line: $x = \pm k$; $\mathbf{x = -5}$
(b) The desired equation is $y = mx + b$.
By inspection, $b = 0$.
By inspection, the sign for m is −.

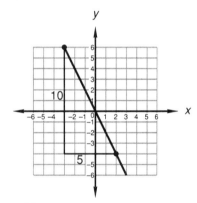

$|m| = \dfrac{10}{5} = 2$
So $b = 0$ and $m = -2$: $\mathbf{y = -2x}$

15. $3\sqrt{6} \cdot 2\sqrt{5} - \sqrt{120} = 3 \cdot 2\sqrt{6}\sqrt{5} - \sqrt{2 \cdot 2 \cdot 30}$
$= 6\sqrt{30} - 2\sqrt{30} = \mathbf{4\sqrt{30}}$

16. $4\sqrt{12}(3\sqrt{2} - 4\sqrt{3})$
$= 4 \cdot 3\sqrt{6} \cdot 2\sqrt{2} - 4 \cdot 4\sqrt{2 \cdot 2 \cdot 3}\sqrt{3}$
$= \mathbf{24\sqrt{6} - 96}$

17. $(3x^3 - 4) \div (x + 3)$

$\begin{array}{r} 3x^2 - 9x + 27 \\ x + 3 \overline{\smash{)}\ 3x^3 + 0x^2 + 0x - 4} \\ \underline{3x^3 + 9x^2} \\ -9x^2 + 0x \\ \underline{-9x^2 - 27x} \\ 27x - 4 \\ \underline{27x + 81} \\ -85 \end{array}$

$\mathbf{3x^2 - 9x + 27 - \dfrac{85}{x + 3}}$

18. $ 40 = -x^2 - 14x$
$x^2 + 14x + 40 = 0$
$(x + 4)(x + 10) = 0$

If $x + 4 = 0$, $\mathbf{x = -4}$
$40 = -(-4)^2 - 14(-4)$
$40 = -16 + 56$
$40 = 40$ check

If $x + 10 = 0$, $\mathbf{x = -10}$
$40 = -(-10)^2 - 14(-10)$
$40 = -100 + 140$
$40 = 40$ check

19. $2 > x > -3$; $D = \{\text{Reals}\}$

$\begin{array}{ccccccccc} & \circ & & & & & & \bullet & \\ \hline -4 & -3 & -2 & -1 & 0 & 1 & 2 & 3 \end{array}$

20. $\dfrac{x - 5}{7} + \dfrac{x}{4} = \dfrac{1}{2}$

$\dfrac{(x - 5)}{7}(28) + \dfrac{x}{4}(28) = \dfrac{1}{2}(28)$
$4x - 20 + 7x = 14$
$11x = 34$
$x = \mathbf{\dfrac{34}{11}}$

21. $3\dfrac{1}{8}x - 2\dfrac{1}{2} = \dfrac{1}{8}$

$\dfrac{25}{8}x = \dfrac{1}{8} + \dfrac{5}{2}$
$\dfrac{25}{8}x = \dfrac{1}{8} + \dfrac{20}{8}$
$x = \dfrac{21}{8} \cdot \dfrac{8}{25} = \mathbf{\dfrac{21}{25}}$

22. $(3x + 3y)^2 = (3x + 3y)(3x + 3y)$
$= \mathbf{9x^2 + 18xy + 9y^2}$

23. **False** $\{\text{Wholes}\} \not\subset \{\text{Naturals}\}$

24. $\dfrac{x}{ya^2} + \dfrac{xa}{a^2y^2} = \mathbf{\dfrac{xy + xa}{a^2y^2}}$

25. $\dfrac{k + \dfrac{k}{y}}{y + \dfrac{a}{y}} = \dfrac{\dfrac{ky + k}{y}}{\dfrac{y^2 + a}{y}} \cdot \dfrac{\dfrac{y}{y^2 + a}}{\dfrac{y}{y^2 + a}}$

$= \mathbf{\dfrac{ky + k}{y^2 + a}}$

26. $-y^0(-y^2 - 4y) - ay$
$= -(-2)^0(-(-2)^2 - 4(-2)) - (-5)(-2)$
$= -(-4 + 8) - 10 = \mathbf{-14}$

27. $-2^0[(-3 - 4^0) - (-2 - 3^0) - 2^2]$
$= -[(-4) - (-3) - 4] = \mathbf{5}$

28. (a) $\dfrac{1}{-3^{-3}} = -3^3 = \mathbf{-27}$

(b) $\dfrac{1}{-(-3)^{-3}} = -(-3)^3 = \mathbf{27}$

(c) $-(-3)^{-3} = \dfrac{1}{-(-3)^3} = \dfrac{1}{27}$

(d) $\sqrt[3]{-64} = \sqrt[3]{(-4)^3} = \mathbf{-4}$

29. $\dfrac{(-4x^{-2})^2}{(-2y^{-2})^2 x} = \dfrac{16x^{-4}}{4y^{-4}x} = 4y^4x^{-5}$

30. $\dfrac{x^3 - 4x}{x^2 + 7x + 10} \div \dfrac{x^2 - 2x}{x^2 - 25}$

$= \dfrac{x(x^2 - 4)}{x^2 + 7x + 10} \cdot \dfrac{x^2 - 25}{x^2 - 2x}$

$= \dfrac{x(x + 2)(x - 2)}{(x + 5)(x + 2)} \cdot \dfrac{(x + 5)(x - 5)}{x(x - 2)}$

$= \mathbf{x - 5}$

PROBLEM SET 99

1. $D_1 + D_2 = 700;$
$R_1T_1 + R_2T_2 = 700$
$R_1 = R_2 + 30; \ T_1 = T_2 = 10$

$(R_2 + 30)10 + R_2(10) = 700$
$10R_2 + 300 + 10R_2 = 700$
$20R_2 = 400$
$R_2 = \mathbf{20 \ mph}$

$R_1 = (20) + 30 = \mathbf{50 \ mph}$

2. (a) **0**
(b) **1**
(c) **−9** reciprocal is multiplicative inverse

3. $93 = \dfrac{7(91) + 3(F)}{7 + 3}$
$930 = 637 + 3F$
$293 = 3F$
$\mathbf{97.67} = F$

4. (a) $5P + 7B = 1140$
(b) $P + B = 192$

$\begin{array}{r} \text{(a)} \quad 5P + 7B = 1140 \\ (-5)\text{(b)} \ \underline{-5P - 5B = -960} \\ 2B = 180 \\ B = \mathbf{90} \end{array}$

(b) $P + (90) = 192$
$P = \mathbf{102}$

5. $\dfrac{63}{100}(T) = 2520$
$T = \mathbf{4000}$

6. $\dfrac{4x + 12}{x^2 + 11x + 30} \div \dfrac{x^3 - 4x^2 - 21x}{4x^2 + 20x}$

$= \dfrac{4x + 12}{x^2 + 11x + 30} \cdot \dfrac{4x^2 + 20x}{x(x^2 - 4x - 21)}$

$= \dfrac{4(x + 3)}{(x + 6)(x + 5)} \cdot \dfrac{4x(x + 5)}{x(x - 7)(x + 3)}$

$= \dfrac{\mathbf{16}}{\mathbf{(x + 6)(x - 7)}}$

7. $\dfrac{x^2 + 11x + 24}{x^2 + 3x} \div \dfrac{x^2 + 13x + 40}{4x^2 + 20x}$

$= \dfrac{x^2 + 11x + 24}{x^2 + 3x} \cdot \dfrac{4x^2 + 20x}{x^2 + 13x + 40}$

$= \dfrac{(x + 8)(x + 3)}{x(x + 3)} \cdot \dfrac{4x(x + 5)}{(x + 5)(x + 8)} = \mathbf{4}$

8. $\dfrac{7}{16}(T) = 700$
$T = 1600$

$T = D + U$
$D = T - U$
$= 1600 - 700 = \mathbf{900}$

9. $-p^0(p - 4) - (-p^0)p + 3^0(p - 2) = -p - 6^0$
$-p + 4 + p + p - 2 = -p - 1$
$2p = -3$
$p = -\dfrac{3}{2}$

10. $-4 \le x < 1; \ D = \{\text{Integers}\}$

11. (a) $y = x$

$y = \dfrac{+1}{+1}x$

(b) $x = -3$

The first step is to graph each of these lines.

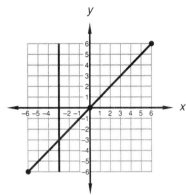

It appears that the lines cross at $x = -3$ and $y = -3$, so $(-3, -3)$ is the solution.

12. (a) $y - 2x = 4$

(b) $2y - x = -1$

$$
\begin{array}{rl}
(-2)(a) & -2y + 4x = -8 \\
(b) & \underline{2y - x = -1} \\
& 3x = -9 \\
& x = -3
\end{array}
$$

(a) $y - 2(-3) = 4$

$y = -2$

$(-3, -2)$

13. $\dfrac{(0.00035 \times 10^{15})(200{,}000)}{(1000 \times 10^{-45})(0.00007)}$

$= \dfrac{(3.5 \times 10^{11})(2 \times 10^{5})}{(1 \times 10^{-42})(7 \times 10^{-5})} = \mathbf{1 \times 10^{63}}$

14. (a) horizontal line: $y = \pm k$; $\mathbf{y = -2}$

(b) The desired equation is $y = mx + b$.

By inspection, $b = 3$.

By inspection, the sign for m is +.

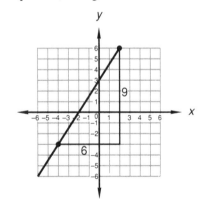

$|m| = \dfrac{9}{6} = \dfrac{3}{2}$

So $b = 3$ and $m = \dfrac{3}{2}$: $y = \dfrac{3}{2}x + 3$

15. $4\sqrt{3} \cdot 5\sqrt{6} + \sqrt{5} \cdot 2 = 4 \cdot 5\sqrt{3}\sqrt{3 \cdot 2} + 2\sqrt{5}$

$= \mathbf{60\sqrt{2} + 2\sqrt{5}}$

16. $4\sqrt{12}(3\sqrt{2} - 3\sqrt{12})$

$= 4 \cdot 3\sqrt{6} \cdot 2\sqrt{2} - 4 \cdot 3\sqrt{12}\sqrt{12} = \mathbf{24\sqrt{6} - 144}$

17. $(2x^3 + 5x^2 - 1) \div (2x + 1)$

$$
\begin{array}{r}
x^2 + 2x - 1 \\
2x + 1 \overline{)\ 2x^3 + 5x^2 + 0x - 1} \\
\underline{2x^3 + \ x^2} \\
4x^2 + 0x \\
\underline{4x^2 + 2x} \\
-2x - 1 \\
\underline{-2x - 1} \\
0
\end{array}
$$

$\mathbf{x^2 + 2x - 1}$

18. $\qquad x^2 = 7x + 30$

$x^2 - 7x - 30 = 0$

$(x - 10)(x + 3) = 0$

If $x - 10 = 0$, $\mathbf{x = 10}$

$(10)^2 = 7(10) + 30$

$100 = 70 + 30$

$100 = 100$ check

If $x + 3 = 0$, $\mathbf{x = -3}$

$(-3)^2 = 7(-3) + 30$

$9 = -21 + 30$

$9 = 9$ check

19. $100 = 9p^2$

$0 = 9p^2 - 100$

$0 = (3p - 10)(3p + 10)$

If $3p - 10 = 0$, $\boldsymbol{p = \dfrac{10}{3}}$

$100 = 9\left(\dfrac{10}{3}\right)^2$

$100 = 100$ check

If $3p + 10 = 0$, $\boldsymbol{p = -\dfrac{10}{3}}$

$100 = 9\left(-\dfrac{10}{3}\right)^2$

$100 = 100$ check

20. $\dfrac{x - 7}{4} - \dfrac{x}{2} = \dfrac{1}{8}$

$\dfrac{(x - 7)}{4}(8) - \dfrac{x}{2}(8) = \dfrac{1}{8}(8)$

$2x - 14 - 4x = 1$

$-2x = 15$

$x = -\dfrac{15}{2}$

21. $5\dfrac{1}{6}x + 2\dfrac{1}{4} = \dfrac{3}{8}$

$\qquad \dfrac{31}{6}x = \dfrac{3}{8} - \dfrac{18}{8}$

$\qquad\quad x = -\dfrac{15}{8} \cdot \dfrac{6}{31}$

$\qquad\quad x = -\dfrac{45}{124}$

22. $\dfrac{a}{x^2} + \dfrac{a^2}{x^3 y} + \dfrac{a^3}{x(x + y)}$

$= \dfrac{axy(x + y) + a^2(x + y) + a^3 x^2 y}{x^3 y(x + y)}$

$= \dfrac{ax^2 y + axy^2 + a^2 x + a^2 y + a^3 x^2 y}{x^3 y(x + y)}$

23. $\dfrac{1 + \dfrac{1}{y}}{y - \dfrac{1}{y}} = \dfrac{\dfrac{y + 1}{y}}{\dfrac{y^2 - 1}{y}} \cdot \dfrac{\dfrac{y}{y^2 - 1}}{\dfrac{y}{y^2 - 1}} = \dfrac{y + 1}{y^2 - 1}$

$= \dfrac{y + 1}{(y + 1)(y - 1)} = \dfrac{1}{y - 1}$

24. $WF\left(\dfrac{7}{8}\right) = 3\dfrac{1}{4}$

$\left(\dfrac{8}{7}\right)WF\left(\dfrac{7}{8}\right) = \dfrac{13}{4}\left(\dfrac{8}{7}\right)$

$\qquad\qquad WF = \dfrac{26}{7}$

25. $0.037 \in$ **Rationals and reals**

26. $ay^2 - y(-y + a^0)$

$= (-4)(-3)^2 - (-3)(-(-3) + (-4)^0)$

$= -36 + 3(4) = \mathbf{-24}$

27. $-3[(-2^0 - 5^0) - 2 - (4 - 6)(-2)]$

$= -3[-2 - 2 - 4] = \mathbf{24}$

28. (a) $\dfrac{4x - 4}{4} = \dfrac{4(x - 1)}{4} = \mathbf{x - 1}$

(b) $-(-2)^{-3} = \dfrac{1}{-(-2)^3} = \dfrac{1}{8}$

29. $4x^2 y^{-1}\left(\dfrac{p^0 y}{x^2} - 3x^{-2}y^4\right)$

$= \dfrac{4x^2 y^{-1} y}{x^2} - 4x^2 y^{-1} 3x^{-2} y^4 = \mathbf{4 - 12y^3}$

30. $V_{Cyl.} = A_{Base} \times \text{height}$

$= \left[\dfrac{\pi(10)^2}{2} + (11)(10) + \dfrac{\pi(5)^2}{2}\right](24)$

$\approx [306.25](24)$

$\approx \mathbf{7350\ in.^3}$

$S.A. = 2A_{Base} + (P \times \text{height})$

$= 2[306.25] + [(22 + 15\pi)(24)]$

$\approx 612.5 + 1658.4$

$\approx \mathbf{2270.9\ in.^2}$

$V_{Cone} = \dfrac{1}{3}V_{Cylinder}$

$= \dfrac{1}{3}(306.25 \times 24)\ in.^3$

$= \mathbf{2450\ in.^3}$

PROBLEM SET 100

1. $R_B T_B + R_L T_L = 340$; $R_B = 30$;
$R_L = 40$; $T_B = T_L + 2$

$30(T_L + 2) + 40T_L = 340$
$30T_L + 60 + 40T_L = 340$
$\qquad\qquad 70T_L = 280$
$\qquad\qquad\quad T_L = 4$

5 p.m. + 4 hr = **9 p.m.**

2. $R_A T_A = R_B T_B$; $R_A = 30$; $R_B = 60$;
$T_A = T_B + 2$

$30(T_B + 2) = 60T_B$
$30T_B + 60 = 60T_B$
$\qquad\quad 60 = 30T_B$
$\qquad\quad\ 2 = T_B$

11 a.m. + 2 hr = **1 p.m.**

3. $R_R T_R = R_W T_W$; $R_R = 8$; $R_W = 3$;
$T_R + T_W = 11$
$\qquad T_R = 11 - T_W$

$8(11 - T_W) = 3T_W$
$88 - 8T_W = 3T_W$
$\qquad\quad 88 = 11T_W$
$\qquad\quad\ 8 = T_W$

$R_W T_W = 8(3) = \mathbf{24\ km}$

4. (a) $N_Q + N_{HD} = 190$

(b) $25N_Q + 50N_{HD} = 7250$

$(-25)(a)$ $-25N_Q - 25N_{HD} = -4750$

(b) $\dfrac{25N_Q + 50N_{HD} = 7250}{}$

$25N_{HD} = 2500$

$N_{HD} = \mathbf{100}$

(a) $N_Q + (100) = 190$

$N_Q = \mathbf{90}$

5. $\dfrac{85}{100}(S) = 289$

$S = \mathbf{340}$

6. $\dfrac{x^3 + 2x^2 - 15x}{x^2 + 5x} \div \dfrac{x^3 - 6x^2 + 9x}{x^2 - 3x}$

$= \dfrac{x^3 + 2x^2 - 15x}{x^2 + 5x} \cdot \dfrac{x^2 - 3x}{x^3 - 6x^2 + 9x}$

$= \dfrac{x(x^2 + 2x - 15)}{x(x + 5)} \cdot \dfrac{x(x - 3)}{x(x^2 - 6x + 9)}$

$= \dfrac{\cancel{x}(x - 3)(x + 5)}{\cancel{x}(x + 5)} \cdot \dfrac{\cancel{x}(x - 3)}{\cancel{x}(x - 3)(x - 3)} = \mathbf{1}$

7. (a) $p^2 = 49$

$p = \mathbf{\pm 7}$

(b) $p^2 = 39$

$p = \mathbf{\pm\sqrt{39}}$

(c) $k^2 = 11$

$k = \mathbf{\pm\sqrt{11}}$

8. $\dfrac{3}{10}(T) = 1200$

$T = \mathbf{4000}$

$T = A + N$

$A = T - N$

$= 4000 - 1200 = \mathbf{2800}$

9. $m - m^0(m - 4) - (-2)m + (-2)(m - 4^0)$

$= m - 6$

$m - m + 4 + 2m - 2m + 2 = m - 6$

$6 = m - 6$

$\mathbf{12} = m$

10. $-4 - x \not> -2$; $D = \{\text{Negative integers}\}$

$-4 - x \le -2$

$-x \le 2$

$x \ge -2$

11. (a) $y = 2x$

$y = \dfrac{+2}{+1}x$

(b) $x = -1$

The first step is to graph each of these lines.

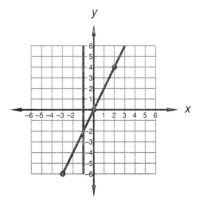

It appears that the lines cross at $x = -1$ and $y = -2$, so $\mathbf{(-1, -2)}$ is the solution.

12. (a) $3x + 5y = -13$

(b) $2x - 3y = 23$

$3(a)$ $9x + 15y = -39$

$5(b)$ $\dfrac{10x - 15y = 115}{}$

$19x = 76$

$x = 4$

(a) $3(4) + 5y = -13$

$5y = -25$

$y = -5$

$\mathbf{(4, -5)}$

13. $\dfrac{(42{,}000{,}000)(0.0001 \times 10^{-5})}{(7000 \times 10^{14})(200{,}000 \times 10^{-8})}$

$= \dfrac{(4.2 \times 10^7)(1 \times 10^{-9})}{(7 \times 10^{17})(2 \times 10^{-3})} = \mathbf{3 \times 10^{-17}}$

14. (a) vertical line: $x = \pm k$; $\mathbf{x = -5}$

(b) The desired equation is $y = mx + b$.

By inspection, $b = 3$.

By inspection, the sign for m is $-$.

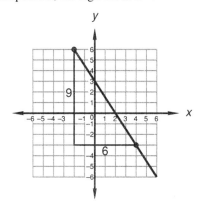

$|m| = \dfrac{9}{6} = \dfrac{3}{2}$

So $b = 3$ and $m = -\dfrac{3}{2}$: $\mathbf{y = -\dfrac{3}{2}x + 3}$

15. $4\sqrt{2} \cdot 3\sqrt{3} \cdot 5\sqrt{6} = 4 \cdot 3 \cdot 5\sqrt{2}\sqrt{3}\sqrt{3 \cdot 2} = \mathbf{360}$

16. $3\sqrt{2}(2\sqrt{2} - 3\sqrt{8})$
$= 3 \cdot 2\sqrt{2}\sqrt{2} - 3 \cdot 3\sqrt{2}\sqrt{2 \cdot 2 \cdot 2} = 12 - 36$
$= \mathbf{-24}$

17. $(x^3 - x^2 - 2) \div (x + 1)$

$$
\begin{array}{r}
x^2 - 2x + 2 \\
x + 1 \overline{)\ x^3 - x^2 + 0x - 2} \\
\underline{x^3 + x^2} \\
-2x^2 + 0x \\
\underline{-2x^2 - 2x} \\
2x - 2 \\
\underline{2x + 2} \\
-4
\end{array}
$$

$$\mathbf{x^2 - 2x + 2 - \frac{4}{x + 1}}$$

18. $-56 = 15x + x^2$
$0 = x^2 + 15x + 56$
$0 = (x + 7)(x + 8)$

If $x + 7 = 0$, $\mathbf{x = -7}$
$-56 = 15(-7) + (-7)^2$
$-56 = -105 + 49$
$-56 = -56$ check

If $x + 8 = 0$, $\mathbf{x = -8}$
$-56 = 15(-8) + (-8)^2$
$-56 = -120 + 64$
$-56 = -56$ check

19. $-81 + 4x^2 = 0$
$4x^2 - 81 = 0$
$(2x + 9)(2x - 9) = 0$

If $2x + 9 = 0$, $\mathbf{x = -\dfrac{9}{2}}$

$-81 + 4\left(-\dfrac{9}{2}\right)^2 = 0$
$-81 + 81 = 0$
$0 = 0$ check

If $2x - 9 = 0$, $\mathbf{x = \dfrac{9}{2}}$

$-81 + 4\left(\dfrac{9}{2}\right)^2 = 0$
$-81 + 81 = 0$
$0 = 0$ check

20. $\dfrac{k - 4}{2} - \dfrac{k + 6}{3} = 5$

$\dfrac{(k - 4)}{2}(6) - \dfrac{(k + 6)}{3}(6) = 5(6)$
$3k - 12 - 2k - 12 = 30$
$\mathbf{k = 54}$

21. $3\dfrac{1}{3}x - \dfrac{1}{6} = \dfrac{5}{12}$

$\dfrac{10}{3}x = \dfrac{5}{12} + \dfrac{2}{12}$

$x = \dfrac{7}{12} \cdot \dfrac{3}{10}$

$x = \dfrac{7}{40}$

22. $\dfrac{4}{x} + \dfrac{x + 4}{x - 3} = \dfrac{4(x - 3) + x(x + 4)}{x(x - 3)}$

$= \dfrac{4x - 12 + x^2 + 4x}{x(x - 3)}$

$= \dfrac{x^2 + 8x - 12}{x(x - 3)}$

23. $-x - 4 \geq 2$; $D = \{\text{Integers}\}$
$-x \geq 6$
$x \leq -6$

$-8 \quad -7 \quad -6 \quad -5 \quad -4$

24. $WF\left(7\dfrac{1}{8}\right) = 5\dfrac{1}{4}$

$\left(\dfrac{8}{57}\right)WF\left(\dfrac{57}{8}\right) = \dfrac{\overset{7}{\cancel{21}}}{\underset{}{\cancel{4}}}\left(\dfrac{\overset{2}{\cancel{8}}}{\underset{19}{\cancel{57}}}\right)$

$WF = \dfrac{14}{19}$

25. $\dfrac{4\sqrt{2}}{5} \in$ **Irrationals and reals**

26. $-y - y^0(y - a) = -(-2) - (-2)^0((-2) - (-5))$
$= 2 - (-2 + 5) = \mathbf{-1}$

27. $-(-3)^0[(-3 - 2^0)(-2 - 3)] = -[(-4)(-5)]$
$= \mathbf{-20}$

28. (a) $\dfrac{ax + a^2x^2}{ax} = \dfrac{ax(1 + ax)}{ax} = \mathbf{1 + ax}$

  (b) $-(-3)^{-2} = \dfrac{1}{-(-3)^2} = \mathbf{-\dfrac{1}{9}}$

29. $\dfrac{2x^2y^2}{xy^{-1}} + \dfrac{5xy}{y^{-2}} = 2xy^3 + 5xy^3 = \mathbf{7xy^3}$

30. $-N = 7$
$N = -7$
$\dfrac{1}{N} = -\dfrac{1}{7}$

PROBLEM SET 101

1. $(-4 + (-N))(-3) + 6 = 2N$
$$12 + 3N + 6 = 2N$$
$$N = -18$$

2. $N \quad N + 1 \quad N + 2 \quad N + 3$
$$4(N + N + 3) + 1 = 9(N + 2)$$
$$8N + 12 + 1 = 9N + 18$$
$$-5 = N$$
The desired integers are **−5, − 4, −3**, and **−2**.

3. $\dfrac{20}{100}(T) = 32$
$$T = 160$$

4. $R_WT_W = R_DT_D$; $R_W = 60$;
$R_D = 50$; $T_W + 1 = T_D$

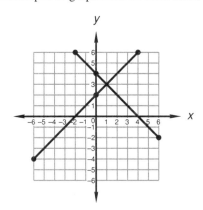

$$60T_W = 50(T_W + 1)$$
$$60T_W = 50T_W + 50$$
$$10T_W = 50$$
$$T_W = 5 \text{ hr}$$

$$T_D = (5) + 1 = 6 \text{ hr}$$
$$R_WT_W = 60(5) = 300 \text{ miles}$$

5. (a) $5N_F + 10N_T = 9000$
(b) $N_F + N_T = 1250$

$$
\begin{array}{rl}
\text{(a)} & 5N_F + 10N_T = \ \ 9000 \\
(-5)\text{(b)} & -5N_F - \ \ 5N_T = -6250 \\
\hline
& 5N_T = \ \ 2750 \\
& N_T = 550
\end{array}
$$

(b) $N_F + (550) = 1250$
$$N_F = 700$$

6. $\dfrac{x^2 + x - 20}{x^2 + 6x - 16} \div \dfrac{x^2 - 2x - 8}{x^2 + 10x + 16}$

$= \dfrac{x^2 + x - 20}{x^2 + 6x - 16} \cdot \dfrac{x^2 + 10x + 16}{x^2 - 2x - 8}$

$= \dfrac{(x - 4)(x + 5)}{(x - 2)(x + 8)} \cdot \dfrac{(x + 2)(x + 8)}{(x - 4)(x + 2)} = \dfrac{x + 5}{x - 2}$

7. $\dfrac{(1)96 + (2)R_2}{1 + 2} = 120$
$$96 + 2R_2 = 360$$
$$2R_2 = 264$$
$$R_2 = 132$$

8. Convert 1 cubic mile to cubic kilometers:

$1 \text{ mi}^3 \times \dfrac{5280 \text{ ft}}{1 \text{ mi}} \times \dfrac{5280 \text{ ft}}{1 \text{ mi}} \times \dfrac{5280 \text{ ft}}{1 \text{ mi}} \times \dfrac{12 \text{ in.}}{1 \text{ ft}}$

$\times \dfrac{12 \text{ in.}}{1 \text{ ft}} \times \dfrac{12 \text{ in.}}{1 \text{ ft}} \times \dfrac{2.54 \text{ cm}}{1 \text{ in.}} \times \dfrac{2.54 \text{ cm}}{1 \text{ in.}}$

$\times \dfrac{2.54 \text{ cm}}{1 \text{ in.}} \times \dfrac{1 \text{ m}}{100 \text{ cm}} \times \dfrac{1 \text{ m}}{100 \text{ cm}} \times \dfrac{1 \text{ m}}{100 \text{ cm}}$

$\times \dfrac{1 \text{ km}}{1000 \text{ m}} \times \dfrac{1 \text{ km}}{1000 \text{ m}} \times \dfrac{1 \text{ km}}{1000 \text{ m}}$

$= \dfrac{(5280)^3 (12)^3 (2.54)^3}{(100)^3 (1000)^3} \text{ km}^3$

9. $k^2 + 4^2 = 6^2$
$$k^2 + 16 = 36$$
$$k^2 = 20$$
$$k^2 = (\sqrt{20})^2$$
$$k = \sqrt{20}$$
$$k = 2\sqrt{5}$$

10. $-(-3)k^0 - 3^0k + (-2)(2 - k) - (-3)(k + 2) = 0$
$$3 - k - 4 + 2k + 3k + 6 = 0$$
$$4k = -5$$
$$k = -\dfrac{5}{4}$$

11. (a) $y = x + 2$
$$y = \dfrac{+1}{+1}x + 2$$
(b) $y = -x + 4$
$$y = \dfrac{-1}{+1}x + 4$$
The first step is to graph each of these lines.

It appears that the lines cross at $x = 1$ and $y = 3$, so
(1, 3) is the solution.

12. $\dfrac{(36{,}000 \times 10^{-5})(400{,}000)}{(0.0006 \times 10^{-4})(600 \times 10^5)}$

$= \dfrac{(3.6 \times 10^{-1})(4 \times 10^5)}{(6 \times 10^{-8})(6 \times 10^7)} = 4 \times 10^4$

13. (a) vertical line: $x = \pm k$; $x = -2$

(b) The desired equation is $y = mx + b$.

By inspection, $b = -2$.

By inspection, the sign for m is +.

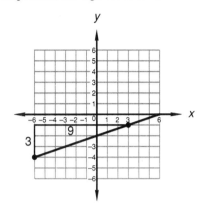

$$|m| = \frac{3}{9} = \frac{1}{3}$$

So $b = -2$ and $m = \frac{1}{3}$: $\mathbf{y = \frac{1}{3}x - 2}$

14. $3\sqrt{2} \cdot 5\sqrt{3} + 5\sqrt{54}$

$= 3 \cdot 5\sqrt{2}\sqrt{3} + 5\sqrt{3 \cdot 3 \cdot 6}$

$= 15\sqrt{6} + 15\sqrt{6} = \mathbf{30\sqrt{6}}$

15. $5\sqrt{2}(3\sqrt{6} - 2\sqrt{36})$

$= 5 \cdot 3\sqrt{2}\sqrt{2 \cdot 3} - 5 \cdot 2\sqrt{2}\sqrt{6 \cdot 6}$

$= \mathbf{30\sqrt{3} - 60\sqrt{2}}$

16. $\qquad 100 = 25x - x^2$

$x^2 - 25x + 100 = 0$

$(x - 5)(x - 20) = 0$

If $x - 5 = 0$, $\mathbf{x = 5}$

$100 = 25(5) - (5)^2$

$100 = 125 - 25$

$100 = 100 \quad$ check

If $x - 20 = 0$, $\mathbf{x = 20}$

$100 = 25(20) - (20)^2$

$100 = 500 - 400$

$100 = 100 \quad$ check

17. $(x^3 - x) \div (x + 2)$

$$
\begin{array}{r}
x^2 - 2x + 3 \\
x + 2 \overline{)\ x^3 + 0x^2 - x + 0} \\
\underline{x^3 + 2x^2} \\
-2x^2 - x \\
\underline{-2x^2 - 4x} \\
3x + 0 \\
\underline{3x + 6} \\
-6
\end{array}
$$

$$x^2 - 2x + 3 - \frac{6}{x + 2}$$

18. $\qquad \dfrac{x}{4} - \dfrac{x - 2}{7} = 1$

$\dfrac{x}{4}(28) - \dfrac{(x - 2)}{7}(28) = 1(28)$

$\qquad 7x - 4x + 8 = 28$

$\qquad\qquad\qquad 3x = 20$

$\qquad\qquad\qquad\quad x = \dfrac{\mathbf{20}}{\mathbf{3}}$

19. $4\dfrac{1}{3}x + 2\dfrac{1}{4} = 7\dfrac{1}{2}$

$\dfrac{13}{3}x = \dfrac{15}{2} - \dfrac{9}{4}$

$\dfrac{13}{3}x = \dfrac{30}{4} - \dfrac{9}{4}$

$x = \dfrac{21}{4} \cdot \dfrac{3}{13} = \dfrac{\mathbf{63}}{\mathbf{52}}$

20. $\dfrac{5}{k} + \dfrac{k + 3}{k + 5} = \dfrac{5(k + 5) + k(k + 3)}{k(k + 5)}$

$= \dfrac{5k + 25 + k^2 + 3k}{k(k + 5)}$

$= \dfrac{\mathbf{k^2 + 8k + 25}}{\mathbf{k(k + 5)}}$

21. $\dfrac{\dfrac{p}{k} - 4}{k - \dfrac{1}{k}} = \dfrac{\dfrac{p - 4k}{k}}{\dfrac{k^2 - 1}{k}} \cdot \dfrac{\dfrac{k}{k^2 - 1}}{\dfrac{k}{k^2 - 1}}$

$= \dfrac{\mathbf{p - 4k}}{\mathbf{k^2 - 1}}$

22. $WF\left(3\dfrac{1}{8}\right) = \dfrac{1}{3}$

$WF\left(\dfrac{25}{8}\right) = \dfrac{1}{3}$

$WF = \dfrac{\mathbf{8}}{\mathbf{75}}$

23. **False** $\quad \{\text{Reals}\} \not\subset \{\text{Integers}\}$

24. $\dfrac{-b \pm \sqrt{b^2 - 4ac}}{2a}$

$= \dfrac{-5 \pm \sqrt{5^2 - 4(2)(2)}}{2(2)} = \dfrac{-5 \pm \sqrt{9}}{4}$

$= \dfrac{-5 \pm 3}{4} = \mathbf{-2, -\dfrac{1}{2}}$

25. $-(-3)^0 - 3^0 - 3^2 - (4 - 6)$

$= -1 - 1 - 9 + 2 = \mathbf{-9}$

26. (a) $\dfrac{-3 - 3x}{3} = \dfrac{3(-1 - x)}{3}$

$= \mathbf{-1 - x}$ **or** $\mathbf{-(1 + x)}$

(b) $\dfrac{-2^2}{-2^{-2}} = -2^2(-2^2) = -4(-4) = \mathbf{16}$

27. $\dfrac{x^{-2}}{a^2}\left(x^2a^2y^0 - \dfrac{4x^4y^2}{a^2}\right)$

$= \dfrac{x^{-2}x^2a^2}{a^2} - \dfrac{x^{-2}4x^4y^2}{a^2a^2} = \mathbf{1 - 4x^2y^2a^{-4}}$

28. $(2m + 2p)^2 = (2m + 2p)(2m + 2p)$

$= \mathbf{4m^2 + 8mp + 4p^2}$

29. **Commutative property of addition**

30. $V_{\text{Cylinder}} = A_{\text{Base}} \times \text{height}$

$= [(10)(10) + 25\pi]\ \text{m}^2 \times \dfrac{50}{100}\ \text{m}$

$\approx (178.5)(0.5)\ \text{m}^3 \approx \mathbf{89.25\ m^3}$

S.A. $= 2A_{\text{Base}} + (P \times \text{height})$

$= 2(178.5)\ \text{m}^2 + \left[(20 + 10\pi)\left(\dfrac{50}{100}\right)\right]\text{m}^2$

$\approx 357\ \text{m}^2 + 25.7\ \text{m}^2$

$\approx \mathbf{382.7\ m^2}$

$V_{\text{Cone}} = \dfrac{1}{3}V_{\text{Cylinder}}$

$= \dfrac{1}{3}(89.25)\ \text{m}^3 = \mathbf{29.75\ m^3}$

PROBLEM SET 102

1. $(2(-N) + 7)3 = 3(-N) + 42$

$-6N + 21 = -3N + 42$

$-3N = 21$

$N = \mathbf{-7}$

2. $N \qquad N + 2 \qquad N + 4 \qquad N + 6$

$(N + N + 4)3 = 5(N + 6) + 10$

$6N + 12 = 5N + 30 + 10$

$N = 28$

The desired integers are **28, 30, 32,** and **34**.

3. $WN = \dfrac{350}{100}(180)$

$WN = \mathbf{630}$

4. $R_ST_S + R_JT_J = 332;\ R_S = 60;$

$R_J = 46;\ T_S = T_J + 2$

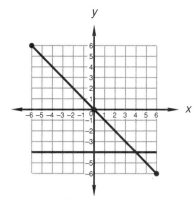

$D_S \qquad D_J$

$60(T_J + 2) + 46T_J = 332$

$60T_J + 120 + 46T_J = 332$

$106T_J = 212$

$T_J = 2$

2 p.m. + 2 hr = **4 p.m.**

5. $\dfrac{120}{100}(B) = 48$

$B = \mathbf{40\ hr}$

6. $p^2 + 8^2 = 10^2$

$p^2 + 64 = 100$

$p = \sqrt{36}$

$p = \mathbf{6}$

7. $D^2 = 6^2 + 2^2$

$D^2 = 36 + 4$

$D = \sqrt{40}$

$D = \mathbf{2\sqrt{10}}$

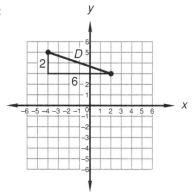

8. $x = \dfrac{\sqrt{b^2 - 4ac}}{} = \sqrt{11^2 - 4(5)(2)}$

$= \sqrt{121 - 40} = \sqrt{81} = \mathbf{9}$

9. $\dfrac{x^2 + 2x}{4x + 12} \div \dfrac{x^2 - 2x - 8}{x^2 - x - 12}$

$= \dfrac{x^2 + 2x}{4x + 12} \cdot \dfrac{x^2 - x - 12}{x^2 - 2x - 8}$

$= \dfrac{x(x + 2)}{4(x + 3)} \cdot \dfrac{(x + 3)(x - 4)}{(x - 4)(x + 2)} = \dfrac{1}{4}x$

10. $\dfrac{(0.00042 \times 10^{-8})(15,000)}{(5000 \times 10^7)(0.0021 \times 10^{14})}$

$= \dfrac{(4.2 \times 10^{-12})(1.5 \times 10^4)}{(5 \times 10^{10})(2.1 \times 10^{11})} = \mathbf{6 \times 10^{-30}}$

11. $-2k^0 - 4k + 6(-k - 2^0) - (-5k)$

$= -(2 - 5)k - 4k$

$-2 - 4k - 6k - 6 + 5k = 3k - 4k$

$-4k = 8$

$k = \mathbf{-2}$

12. (a) $y = -x$ \qquad (b) $y = -4$

$y = \dfrac{-1}{+1}x$

It appears that the lines cross at $x = 4$ and $y = -4$, so $(\mathbf{4, -4})$ is the solution.

13. (a) horizontal line: $y = \pm k$; $\mathbf{y = 3}$

(b) The desired equation is $y = mx + b$.

By inspection, $b = -1$.

By inspection, the sign for m is $-$.

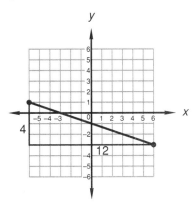

$|m| = \dfrac{4}{12} = \dfrac{1}{3}$

So $b = -1$ and $m = -\dfrac{1}{3}$: $\mathbf{y = -\dfrac{1}{3}x - 1}$

14. $4\sqrt{50} - 3\sqrt{8} + 2\sqrt{3}\sqrt{6}$
$= 4\sqrt{5 \cdot 5 \cdot 2} - 3\sqrt{2 \cdot 2 \cdot 2} + 2\sqrt{3}\sqrt{3 \cdot 2}$
$= 20\sqrt{2} - 6\sqrt{2} + 6\sqrt{2} = \mathbf{20\sqrt{2}}$

15. $3\sqrt{2}(6\sqrt{6} - 4\sqrt{12})$
$= 3 \cdot 6\sqrt{2}\sqrt{2 \cdot 3} - 3 \cdot 4\sqrt{2}\sqrt{2 \cdot 6}$
$= \mathbf{36\sqrt{3} - 24\sqrt{6}}$

16.
$$-14 = -x^2 - 5x$$
$$x^2 + 5x - 14 = 0$$
$$(x - 2)(x + 7) = 0$$

If $x - 2 = 0$, $\mathbf{x = 2}$
$-14 = -(2)^2 - 5(2)$
$-14 = -4 - 10$
$-14 = -14$ check

If $x + 7 = 0$, $\mathbf{x = -7}$
$-14 = -(-7)^2 - 5(-7)$
$-14 = -49 + 35$
$-14 = -14$ check

17. $(x^3 + 6x^2 + 6x + 5) \div (x + 5)$

$$
\begin{array}{r}
x^2 + x + 1 \\
x + 5 \overline{)\ x^3 + 6x^2 + 6x + 5} \\
\underline{x^3 + 5x^2} \\
x^2 + 6x \\
\underline{x^2 + 5x} \\
x + 5 \\
\underline{x + 5} \\
0
\end{array}
$$

$\mathbf{x^2 + x + 1}$

18.
$$\frac{y}{3} - \frac{y - 2}{5} = 3$$
$$\frac{y}{3}(15) - \frac{(y - 2)}{5}(15) = 3(15)$$
$$5y - 3y + 6 = 45$$
$$2y = 39$$
$$y = \mathbf{\frac{39}{2}}$$

19.
$$4\frac{7}{8}p + \frac{2}{5} = \frac{3}{10}$$
$$\frac{39}{8}p = \frac{3}{10} - \frac{4}{10}$$
$$p = -\frac{1}{10} \cdot \frac{8}{39} = \mathbf{-\frac{4}{195}}$$

20. $\dfrac{6}{m} + \dfrac{4m}{m + 5} = \dfrac{6(m + 5) + 4m^2}{m(m + 5)}$

$= \dfrac{6m + 30 + 4m^2}{m(m + 5)} = \mathbf{\dfrac{4m^2 + 6m + 30}{m(m + 5)}}$

21. $WF\left(7\dfrac{1}{4}\right) = \dfrac{5}{8}$

$\left(\dfrac{\cancel{4}}{29}\right)WF\left(\dfrac{\cancel{29}}{\cancel{4}}\right) = \dfrac{5}{\underset{2}{\cancel{8}}}\left(\dfrac{\cancel{4}}{29}\right)$

$WF = \mathbf{\dfrac{5}{58}}$

22. $\dfrac{3x - \dfrac{1}{y}}{\dfrac{2x}{y} - 4} = \dfrac{\dfrac{3xy - 1}{y}}{\dfrac{2x - 4y}{y}} \cdot \dfrac{\dfrac{y}{2x - 4y}}{\dfrac{y}{2x - 4y}}$

$= \mathbf{\dfrac{3xy - 1}{2x - 4y}}$

23. $-0.061 \in$ **Rationals and reals**

24. $-x^0a(a - x^0) - a^2$
$= -(-2)^0(-4)((-4) - (-2)^0) - (-4)^2$
$= 4(-5) - 16 = \mathbf{-36}$

25. $-2 - 2^0(-3 - 2) - (-4 + 6)(-5^0 + 2) - 2^2$
$\quad - \sqrt[5]{-243}$
$= -2 + 5 - (2)(1) - 4 - \sqrt[5]{(-3)^5}$
$= 3 - 6 + 3 = \mathbf{0}$

26. (a) $\dfrac{5x^2 - 5x}{5x} = \dfrac{5x(x - 1)}{5x} = \mathbf{x - 1}$

(b) $\dfrac{-3^0}{-3^{-2}} = 3^0(3^2) = \mathbf{9}$

27. Reciprocal

28. $\dfrac{2xxxx}{x^{11}} - 3x^{-7} + \dfrac{4a^0}{x^7} = 2x^{-7} - 3x^{-7} + 4x^{-7}$

$= 3x^{-7}$

29. $-x + 2 \not< 3; \ D = \{\text{Integers}\}$

$-x + 2 \geq 3$

$-x \geq 1$

$x \leq -1$

```
  ←———•———•———•———|———|——→
     -3  -2  -1   0   1
```

30. **Distributive property**

PROBLEM SET 103

1. $R_ST_S + R_PT_P = 490; \ R_S = 20;$

$R_P = 35; \ T_S + T_P = 17$

$T_S = 17 - T_P$

$20(17 - T_P) + 35T_P = 490$

$340 - 20T_P + 35T_P = 490$

$15T_P = 150$

$T_P = \textbf{10 hr}$

2. $R_JT_J = R_RT_R; \ R_J = R_R + 10;$

$T_J = 8; \ T_R = 10$

$8(R_R + 10) = 10R_R$

$8R_R + 80 = 10R_R$

$80 = 2R_R$

$R_R = \textbf{40 km/hr}$

$R_J = (40) + 10 = \textbf{50 km/hr}$

3. $N \quad N + 2 \quad N + 4 \quad N + 6$

$6(N + N + 6) = 8(-N - 4) + 108$

$12N + 36 = -8N - 32 + 108$

$20N = 40$

$N = 2$

The desired integers are **2, 4, 6,** and **8**.

4. (a) $N_H + N_E = 3000$

(b) $N_H = 3N_E + 1800$

Substitute (b) into (a) and get:

(a′) $(3N_E + 1800) + N_E = 3000$

$4N_E = 1200$

$N_E = \textbf{300}$

(b) $N_H = 3(300) + 1800 = \textbf{2700}$

5. $\dfrac{77}{100}(T) = 3465$

$T = \textbf{4500}$

6. $s + x + n = (s + x) + n \quad$ associative

$= (x + s) + n \quad$ commutative

$= x + (s + n) \quad$ associative

$= x + (n + s) \quad$ commutative

$= x + n + s \quad$ removed parentheses

7. $\dfrac{N_A}{9} = \$90{,}000$

$N_A = \$810{,}000$

$\$1{,}500{,}000 = A + N_A$

$A = \$1{,}500{,}000 - N_A$

$A = \$1{,}500{,}000 - \$810{,}000$

$A = \textbf{\$690{,}000}$

8. $10 \text{ km}^3 \times \dfrac{1000 \text{ m}}{1 \text{ km}} \times \dfrac{1000 \text{ m}}{1 \text{ km}} \times \dfrac{1000 \text{ m}}{1 \text{ km}}$

$\times \dfrac{100 \text{ cm}}{1 \text{ m}} \times \dfrac{100 \text{ cm}}{1 \text{ m}} \times \dfrac{100 \text{ cm}}{1 \text{ m}} \times \dfrac{1 \text{ in.}}{2.54 \text{ cm}}$

$\times \dfrac{1 \text{ in.}}{2.54 \text{ cm}} \times \dfrac{1 \text{ in.}}{2.54 \text{ cm}} \times \dfrac{1 \text{ ft}}{12 \text{ in.}} \times \dfrac{1 \text{ ft}}{12 \text{ in.}}$

$\times \dfrac{1 \text{ ft}}{12 \text{ in.}} \times \dfrac{1 \text{ mi}}{5280 \text{ ft}} \times \dfrac{1 \text{ mi}}{5280 \text{ ft}} \times \dfrac{1 \text{ mi}}{5280 \text{ ft}}$

$= \dfrac{10(1000)^3(100)^3}{(2.54)^3(12)^3(5280)^3} \text{ mi}^3$

9. $5^2 + d^2 = 7^2$

$25 + d^2 = 49$

$d^2 = 24$

$d = \sqrt{24}$

$d = \textbf{2}\sqrt{\textbf{6}}$

10. $D^2 = 2^2 + 6^2$

$D^2 = 4 + 36$

$D^2 = 40$

$D = \sqrt{40}$

$D = \textbf{2}\sqrt{\textbf{10}}$

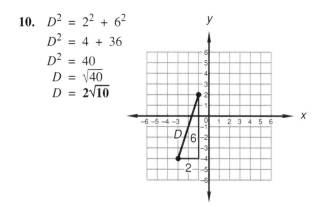

11. $\dfrac{x^2 + 5x + 6}{-x^2 - 3x} \div \dfrac{x^2 + 7x + 10}{x^3 + 8x^2 + 15x}$

$= \dfrac{x^2 + 5x + 6}{-x^2 - 3x} \cdot \dfrac{x^3 + 8x^2 + 15x}{x^2 + 7x + 10}$

$= \dfrac{(x + 2)(x + 3)}{x(-1)(x + 3)} \cdot \dfrac{x(x + 5)(x + 3)}{(x + 5)(x + 2)} = -x - 3$

12. $-3(-2 - p) - p^0(-4) - 2^0(-5p - 6)$
$= -3 - (-2p)$
$6 + 3p + 4 + 5p + 6 = -3 + 2p$
$6p = -19$
$$p = -\frac{19}{6}$$

13. (a) $y = -2x - 3$
$$y = \frac{-2}{+1}x - 3$$
(b) $x = 2$
The first step is to graph each of these lines.

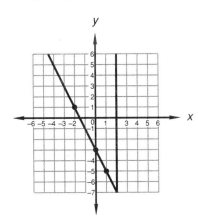

It appears that the lines cross at $x = 2$ and $y = -7$, so $(2, -7)$ is the solution.

14. $\dfrac{(0.000075)(200 \times 10^{-15})}{(0.025 \times 10^{45})(300 \times 10^{-23})}$

$= \dfrac{(7.5 \times 10^{-5})(2 \times 10^{-13})}{(2.5 \times 10^{43})(3 \times 10^{-21})} = \mathbf{2 \times 10^{-40}}$

15. (a) horizontal line: $y = \pm k$; $\mathbf{y = -3\dfrac{1}{2}}$

(b) The desired equation is $y = mx + b$.
By inspection, $b = 3$.
By inspection, the sign for m is $-$.

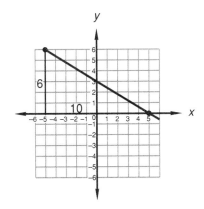

$$|m| = \frac{6}{10} = \frac{3}{5}$$

So $b = 3$ and $m = -\dfrac{3}{5}$: $\mathbf{y = -\dfrac{3}{5}x + 3}$

16. $5\sqrt{75} \cdot 2\sqrt{3} + 7\sqrt{3} \cdot 2\sqrt{6}$
$= 5 \cdot 2\sqrt{5 \cdot 5} \cdot 3\sqrt{3} + 7 \cdot 2\sqrt{3}\sqrt{3 \cdot 2}$
$= \mathbf{150 + 42\sqrt{2}}$

17. $4\sqrt{6}(3\sqrt{6} - 2\sqrt{2}) = 4 \cdot 3\sqrt{6}\sqrt{6} - 4 \cdot 2\sqrt{3} \cdot 2\sqrt{2}$
$= \mathbf{72 - 16\sqrt{3}}$

18. $50 = x^2 + 5x$
$0 = x^2 + 5x - 50$
$0 = (x - 5)(x + 10)$

If $x - 5 = 0$, $\mathbf{x = 5}$
$50 = (5)^2 + 5(5)$
$50 = 25 + 25$
$50 = 50$ check

If $x + 10 = 0$, $\mathbf{x = -10}$
$50 = (-10)^2 + 5(-10)$
$50 = 100 - 50$
$50 = 50$ check

19. $(2x^3 + x^2 - 3x) \div (2x + 3)$

$$
\begin{array}{r}
x^2 - x \\
2x + 3 \overline{)\ 2x^3 + x^2 - 3x + 0} \\
\underline{2x^3 + 3x^2} \\
-2x^2 - 3x \\
\underline{-2x^2 - 3x} \\
0
\end{array}
$$

$x^2 - x$

20. $\dfrac{x}{4} - \dfrac{x - 5}{8} = 2$
$\dfrac{x}{4}(8) - \dfrac{(x - 5)}{8}(8) = 2(8)$
$2x - x + 5 = 16$
$x = \mathbf{11}$

21. $7\dfrac{1}{2}x - 4\dfrac{1}{3} = 14\dfrac{1}{8}$
$\dfrac{15}{2}x = \dfrac{113}{8} + \dfrac{13}{3}$
$\dfrac{15}{2}x = \dfrac{339}{24} + \dfrac{104}{24}$
$x = \dfrac{443}{24} \cdot \dfrac{2}{15}$
$x = \mathbf{\dfrac{443}{180}}$

22. $\dfrac{4}{x} + \dfrac{6x + 2}{x^2} + \dfrac{3}{x(x + 1)}$

$= \dfrac{4x(x + 1) + (6x + 2)(x + 1) + 3x}{x^2(x + 1)}$

$= \dfrac{4x^2 + 4x + 6x^2 + 8x + 2 + 3x}{x^2(x + 1)}$

$= \dfrac{\mathbf{10x^2 + 15x + 2}}{\mathbf{x^2(x + 1)}}$

23. $\dfrac{x + \dfrac{x}{y}}{y - \dfrac{1}{y}} = \dfrac{\dfrac{xy + x}{y}}{\dfrac{y^2 - 1}{y}} \cdot \dfrac{\dfrac{y}{y^2 - 1}}{\dfrac{y}{y^2 - 1}} = \dfrac{xy + x}{y^2 - 1}$

$= \dfrac{x\,(y + 1)}{(y + 1)(y - 1)} = \dfrac{x}{y - 1}$

24. $WF\left(14\dfrac{1}{8}\right) = 7\dfrac{3}{5}$

$\left(\dfrac{8}{113}\right)WF\left(\dfrac{113}{8}\right) = \dfrac{38}{5}\left(\dfrac{8}{113}\right)$

$WF = \dfrac{304}{565}$

25. $(3\sqrt{2} - 5) \in$ **Irrationals and reals**

26. $-p^0 - p^2(p - a^0) - ap + |-ap|$
$= -(-4)^0 - (-4)^2((-4) - (-3)^0) - (-3)(-4)$
$\quad + |-(-3)(-4)|$
$= -1 - 16(-5) - 12 + 12 = \textbf{79}$

27. (a) $\dfrac{4xym + 4x^2ym^2}{4xym} = \dfrac{4xym(1 + xm)}{4xym}$
$= \textbf{1 + } \textit{\textbf{xm}}$

(b) $\dfrac{-5^0}{-2^{-4}} = 5^0(2^4) = \textbf{16}$

28. $4x^2y\left(\dfrac{x^{-2}}{4y} - \dfrac{5x^3y^{-3}}{a^{-4}}\right)$
$= \dfrac{4x^2yx^{-2}}{4y} - \dfrac{4x^2y5x^3y^{-3}}{a^{-4}} = \textbf{1 - } \textbf{20}\textit{\textbf{x}}^\textbf{5}\textit{\textbf{y}}^{\textbf{-2}}\textit{\textbf{a}}^\textbf{4}$

29. $-3^0[(-3^2 + 4)(-2^2 - 2) - (-2) + 4] - \sqrt[3]{(-2)^3}$
$= -[(-5)(-6) + 6] + 2 = -36 + 2 = \textbf{-34}$

30. $x^2 - 13 = \sqrt{9}$
$x^2 = 13 + 3$
$x^2 = 16$
$x^2 = (\sqrt{16})^2$
$x = \pm\textbf{4}$

PROBLEM SET 104

1. $R_FT_F + 500 = R_JT_J;\ R_J = 250;$
$R_F = 230;\ T_J = T_F$

$D_F \ \longrightarrow \ 500$

$D_J \ \longrightarrow$

$230T_J + 500 = 250T_J$
$500 = 20T_J$
$T_J = \textbf{25 minutes}$

2. Convert 25,000 cubic meters to cubic miles.

$25{,}000\ m^3 \times \dfrac{100\ cm}{1\ m} \times \dfrac{100\ cm}{1\ m} \times \dfrac{100\ cm}{1\ m}$

$\times \dfrac{1\ in.}{2.54\ cm} \times \dfrac{1\ in.}{2.54\ cm} \times \dfrac{1\ in.}{2.54\ cm} \times \dfrac{1\ ft}{12\ in.}$

$\times \dfrac{1\ ft}{12\ in.} \times \dfrac{1\ ft}{12\ in.} \times \dfrac{1\ mi}{5280\ ft} \times \dfrac{1\ mi}{5280\ ft}$

$\times \dfrac{1\ mi}{5280\ ft} = \dfrac{25{,}000(100)^3}{(2.54)^3(12)^3(5280)^3}\ mi^3$

3. $x^2 - 20 = 380$
$x^2 = 400$
$x^2 = (\sqrt{400})^2$
$x = \pm\textbf{20}$

4. (a) $N_N + N_Q = 450$
(b) $5N_N + 25N_Q = 6250$

$(-5)(a)\ -5N_N - 5N_Q = -2250$
$(b)\ \ \underline{\ \ 5N_N + 25N_Q = \ \ 6250}$
$20N_Q = \ \ 4000$
$N_Q = \textbf{200}$

(a) $N_N + (200) = 450$
$N_N = \textbf{250}$

5. $\dfrac{66}{100}(T) = 3300$
$T = \textbf{5000}$

6. $-x - 3 < 2;\ D = \{\text{Reals}\}$
$-x < 5$
$x > -5$

$\overset{\hspace{3.2cm}\circ\longrightarrow}{\underset{-7\ \ -6\ \ -5\ \ -4\ \ -3}{\rule{5cm}{0.4pt}}}$

7. $d^2 = 4^2 + 7^2$
$d^2 = 16 + 49$
$d^2 = 65$
$d = \sqrt{65}$

8. $a^2 + 9^2 = 12^2$
$a^2 + 81 = 144$
$a^2 = 63$
$a = \sqrt{63}$
$a = 3\sqrt{7}$

9. $f^2 + 3^2 = 7^2$
$f^2 + 9 = 49$
$f^2 = 40$
$f = \sqrt{40}$
$f = 2\sqrt{10}$

10. $D^2 = 5^2 + 3^2$
$D^2 = 25 + 9$
$D^2 = 34$
$D = \sqrt{34}$

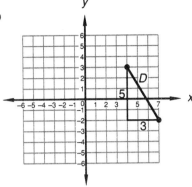

11. $\dfrac{x^2 + 11x + 28}{-x^2 + 5x} \div \dfrac{x^2 + x - 12}{x^3 - 3x^2 - 10x}$

$= \dfrac{(x + 4)(x + 7)}{x(-1)(x - 5)} \cdot \dfrac{x(x - 5)(x + 2)}{(x + 4)(x - 3)}$

$= -\dfrac{(x + 7)(x + 2)}{x - 3}$

12. $-x - (-3)(x - 5) - 2^0(2x + 3) = 5x - 7 - 7^0$
$-x + 3x - 15 - 2x - 3 = 5x - 8$
$-10 = 5x$
$x = -2$

13. (a) $y = x - 4$

$y = \dfrac{+1}{+1}x - 4$

(b) $y = -x + 2$

$y = \dfrac{-1}{+1}x + 2$

The first step is to graph each of these lines.

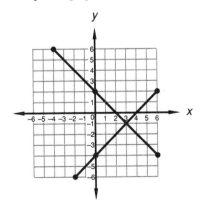

It appears that the lines cross at $x = 3$ and $y = -1$, so $(3, -1)$ is the solution.

14. $\dfrac{(22{,}000 \times 10^{-7})(500)}{(0.0011)(0.002 \times 10^{14})}$

$= \dfrac{(2.2 \times 10^{-3})(5 \times 10^2)}{(1.1 \times 10^{-3})(2 \times 10^{11})} = 5 \times 10^{-9}$

15. (a) horizontal line: $y = \pm k$; $\mathbf{y = 4}$
(b) The desired equation is $y = mx + b$.
By inspection, $b = -3$.
By inspection, the sign for m is $-$.

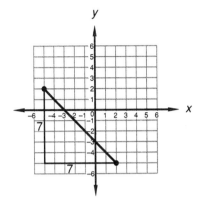

$|m| = \dfrac{7}{7} = 1$

So $b = -3$ and $m = -1$: $\mathbf{y = -x - 3}$

16. $3\sqrt{2} \cdot 4\sqrt{3} \cdot 5\sqrt{12} + 2\sqrt{8}$
$= 3 \cdot 4 \cdot 5\sqrt{2}\sqrt{3}\sqrt{2 \cdot 3 \cdot 2} + 2\sqrt{2 \cdot 2 \cdot 2}$
$= 360\sqrt{2} + 4\sqrt{2} = \mathbf{364\sqrt{2}}$

17. $3\sqrt{2}(5\sqrt{2} - 4\sqrt{42})$
$= 3 \cdot 5\sqrt{2}\sqrt{2} - 3 \cdot 4\sqrt{2}\sqrt{2 \cdot 21} = \mathbf{30 - 24\sqrt{21}}$

18. $81 = 4x^2$
$0 = 4x^2 - 81$
$0 = (2x + 9)(2x - 9)$

If $2x + 9 = 0$, $x = -\dfrac{9}{2}$

$81 = 4\left(-\dfrac{9}{2}\right)^2$
$81 = 81$ check

If $2x - 9 = 0$, $x = \dfrac{9}{2}$

$81 = 4\left(\dfrac{9}{2}\right)^2$
$81 = 81$ check

19. $(x^3 - 4) \div (x - 4)$

$$
\begin{array}{r}
x^2 + 4x + 16 \\
x - 4 \overline{\smash{)}\ x^3 + 0x^2 + 0x - 4} \\
\underline{x^3 - 4x^2} \\
4x^2 + 0x \\
\underline{4x^2 - 16x} \\
16x - 4 \\
\underline{16x - 64} \\
60
\end{array}
$$

$x^2 + 4x + 16 + \dfrac{60}{x - 4}$

20.
$$\frac{p}{6} - \frac{p+2}{4} = \frac{1}{3}$$
$$\frac{p}{6}(12) - \frac{(p+2)}{4}(12) = \frac{1}{3}(12)$$
$$2p - 3p - 6 = 4$$
$$-p = 10$$
$$p = \mathbf{-10}$$

21.
$$7\frac{1}{9}p + 3\frac{1}{3} = 2\frac{1}{6}$$
$$\frac{64}{9}p = \frac{13}{6} - \frac{10}{3}$$
$$\frac{64}{9}p = \frac{13}{6} - \frac{20}{6}$$
$$p = -\frac{7}{6} \cdot \frac{9}{64}$$
$$p = -\frac{\mathbf{21}}{\mathbf{128}}$$

22.
$$\frac{x}{x+4} + \frac{3}{x} - \frac{x+2}{x^2}$$
$$= \frac{x^3 + 3x(x+4) - (x+2)(x+4)}{x^2(x+4)}$$
$$= \frac{\mathbf{x^3 + 2x^2 + 6x - 8}}{\mathbf{x^2(x+4)}}$$

23.
$$\frac{\frac{1}{a}+4}{a^2+\frac{4}{a}} = \frac{\frac{1+4a}{a}}{\frac{a^3+4}{a}} \cdot \frac{\frac{a^3+4}{a}}{\frac{a^3+4}{a}}$$
$$= \frac{\mathbf{1+4a}}{\mathbf{a^3+4}}$$

24.
$$7\frac{3}{8} = WF(21)$$
$$\left(\frac{1}{21}\right)\frac{59}{8} = WF(\cancel{21})\left(\frac{1}{\cancel{21}}\right)$$
$$\frac{\mathbf{59}}{\mathbf{168}} = WF$$

25. **True** {Integers} ⊂ {Reals}

26. $-p^2 - p^0 + p(-p+a)$
$$= -(-3)^2 - (-3)^0 + (-3)(-(-3)+4)$$
$$= -9 - 1 - 3(7) = \mathbf{-31}$$

27. (a) $\dfrac{-2p^2a^2 - p^2a}{-p^2a} = \dfrac{-p^2a(2a+1)}{-p^2a}$
$$= \mathbf{2a+1}$$

(b) $\dfrac{-3^2}{-(-3)^{-2}} = 3^2(-3)^2 = \mathbf{81}$

28. $-2^0 - 2[(-3-3^0)(-2+6)] = -1 - 2[(-4)(4)]$
$$= \mathbf{31}$$

29. $\dfrac{1}{(2x)^{-2}y^{-6}} - \dfrac{3x^4}{x^2y^{-6}} - 2x^2y^6$
$$= 4x^2y^6 - 3x^2y^6 - 2x^2y^6 = \mathbf{-x^2y^6}$$

30. $a + c + x = (a+c) + x$ associative
$$= (c+a) + x \quad \text{commutative}$$
$$= c + (a+x) \quad \text{associative}$$
$$= c + (x+a) \quad \text{commutative}$$
$$= (c+x) + a \quad \text{associative}$$
$$= (x+c) + a \quad \text{commutative}$$
$$= x + c + a \quad \text{removed parentheses}$$

Problem Set 105

1. $R_E T_E = R_A T_A + 60$; $R_E = 60$;
$T_E = 6$; $T_A = 4$

$$60(6) = 4R_A + 60$$
$$360 = 4R_A + 60$$
$$300 = 4R_A$$
$$R_A = \mathbf{75\ mph}$$

2. $\dfrac{70}{100}(T) = 28$
$$T = \mathbf{40}$$

3. $R_W T_W = R_B T_B$; $R_W = R_B + 2$;
$T_W = 60$; $T_B = 100$

$$(R_B + 2)(60) = 100R_B$$
$$60R_B + 120 = 100R_B$$
$$120 = 40R_B$$
$$R_B = 3$$
$$D_B = R_B T_B = (3)(100) = \mathbf{300\ miles}$$

4. $5(N + (-8)) = 2(-N) + 9$
$$5N - 40 = -2N + 9$$
$$7N = 49$$
$$N = \mathbf{7}$$

5. (a) $7N_R + 3N_W = 130$
(b) $N_R + N_W = 30$

(a) $7N_R + 3N_W = 130$
(−3)(b) $\underline{-3N_R - 3N_W = -90}$
$$4N_R \quad\quad = \quad 40$$
$$N_R = \mathbf{10}$$

(b) $(10) + N_W = 30$
$$N_W = \mathbf{20}$$

6. $N \quad\quad N+1 \quad\quad N+2 \quad\quad N+3$
$$5(N + 1 + N + 2) + 6 = 7N$$
$$10N + 15 + 6 = 7N$$
$$3N = -21$$
$$N = -7$$
The desired integers are $\mathbf{-7, -6, -5,}$ and $\mathbf{-4}$.

7. $g^2 + 3^2 = 8^2$
   $g^2 + 9 = 64$
   $g^2 = 55$
   $g = \sqrt{55}$

8. $D^2 = 4^2 + 8^2$
   $D^2 = 16 + 64$
   $D^2 = 80$
   $D = \sqrt{80}$
   $D = 4\sqrt{5}$

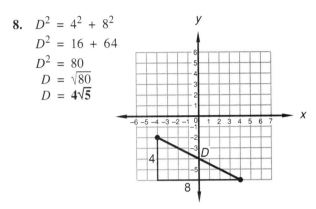

9. $\dfrac{4x^2 + 8x}{x^2 + 8x + 12} \div \dfrac{4x^2 - 16x}{x^2 + 3x - 18}$

$= \dfrac{\cancel{4x}(x + 2)}{(x + 2)(x + 6)} \cdot \dfrac{(x - 3)(x + 6)}{\cancel{4x}(x - 4)}$

$= \dfrac{x - 3}{x - 4}$

10. $(-3)x^0 - (-2x) - 4(x - 4) - (2 - x)$
   $= 3^0(x - 4)$
   $-3 + 2x - 4x + 16 - 2 + x = x - 4$
   $15 = 2x$
   $x = \dfrac{15}{2}$

11. (a) $y = -2x$
   $y = \dfrac{-2}{+1}x$
   (b) $y = -4$
   The first step is to graph each of these lines.

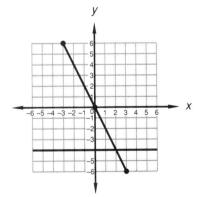

It appears that the lines cross at $x = 2$ and $y = -4$, so $(2, -4)$ is the solution.

12. $\dfrac{(1200 \times 10^{-42})(300 \times 10^{14})}{(0.004 \times 10^5)(3000 \times 10^{-20})}$

$= \dfrac{(1.2 \times 10^{-39})(3 \times 10^{16})}{(4 \times 10^2)(3 \times 10^{-17})} = \mathbf{3 \times 10^{-9}}$

13. (a) vertical line: $x = \pm k$: $\mathbf{x = 4}$
   (b) The desired equation is $y = mx + b$.
   By inspection, $b = 1$.
   By inspection, the sign for m is +.

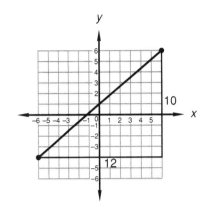

$|m| = \dfrac{10}{12} = \dfrac{5}{6}$

So $b = 1$ and $m = \dfrac{5}{6}$: $y = \dfrac{5}{6}x + 1$

14. $x = \sqrt{b^2 - 4ac} = \sqrt{12^2 - 4(2)(10)}$
   $= \sqrt{64} = 8$

15. $\{-1, 0, 1\}$

ADDITION:	Not closed. $1 + 1 = 2$
SUBTRACTION:	Not closed. $1 - (-1) = 2$
MULTIPLICATION:	Closed. The product of any combination of the numbers $-1, 0, 1$ is one of these numbers.
DIVISION:	Not closed. $-1 \div 0$ is not defined.

Thus the set $\{-1, 0, 1\}$ is closed for the operation of **multiplication**.

16. $4\sqrt{50,000} + 3\sqrt{5,000,000}$
   $= 4\sqrt{5 \cdot 10,000} + 3\sqrt{5 \cdot 1,000,000}$
   $= 400\sqrt{5} + 3000\sqrt{5}$
   $= \mathbf{3400\sqrt{5}}$

17. $-4 < x \leq 2$; $D = \{\text{Integers}\}$

$$\overset{\bullet\ \ \bullet\ \ \bullet\ \ \ \ \ \bullet\ \ \bullet}{\underset{-4\ -3\ -2\ -1\ \ \ 0\ \ \ 1\ \ \ 2\ \ \ 3}{\vdash\!\!\!+\!\!\!+\!\!\!+\!\!\!+\!\!\!+\!\!\!+\!\!\!+\!\!\!\dashv}}$$

18. $64 = 16x - x^2$
   $x^2 - 16x + 64 = 0$
   $(x - 8)(x - 8) = 0$

   If $x - 8 = 0$, $\mathbf{x = 8}$
   $64 = 16(8) - (8)^2$
   $64 = 128 - 64$
   $64 = 64$ check

19. $(x^4 + x^3 + 2x + 2) \div (x + 1)$

$$
\begin{array}{r}
x^3 + 2 \\
x + 1 \overline{\smash{)}\, x^4 + x^3 + 0x^2 + 2x + 2} \\
\underline{x^4 + x^3 } \\
2x + 2 \\
\underline{2x + 2} \\
0
\end{array}
$$

$x^3 + 2$

20.
$$\frac{k}{7} - \frac{k-4}{3} = 2$$
$$\frac{k}{7}(21) - \frac{(k-4)}{3}(21) = 2(21)$$
$$3k - 7k + 28 = 42$$
$$-4k = 14$$
$$k = -\frac{7}{2}$$

21. $3\frac{1}{4}k - 2\frac{1}{2} = \frac{3}{4}$
$$\frac{13}{4}k = \frac{3}{4} + \frac{5}{2}$$
$$\frac{13}{4}k = \frac{3}{4} + \frac{10}{4}$$
$$k = \frac{13}{4} \cdot \frac{4}{13} = 1$$

22. $\dfrac{4}{x^2} + \dfrac{x+4}{x} - \dfrac{3x+2}{x+1}$

$$= \frac{4(x+1) + x(x+4)(x+1)}{x^2(x+1)}$$

$$- \frac{(3x+2)x^2}{x^2(x+1)}$$

$$= \frac{4x + 4 + x^3 + 5x^2}{x^2(x+1)}$$

$$+ \frac{4x - 3x^3 - 2x^2}{x^2(x+1)}$$

$$= \frac{-2x^3 + 3x^2 + 8x + 4}{x^2(x+1)}$$

23. $\dfrac{\frac{1}{x} - 4}{y - \frac{1}{x}} = \dfrac{\frac{1-4x}{x}}{\frac{xy-1}{x}} \cdot \dfrac{\frac{x}{xy-1}}{\frac{x}{xy-1}} = \dfrac{1-4x}{xy-1}$

24. $2\dfrac{1}{5} = WF\left(28\dfrac{1}{10}\right)$

$$\left(\frac{\overset{2}{\cancel{10}}}{281}\right)\frac{11}{\cancel{5}} = WF\left(\frac{\cancel{281}}{\cancel{10}}\right)\left(\frac{\cancel{10}}{\cancel{281}}\right)$$

$$\frac{22}{281} = WF$$

25. $0.0003\sqrt{2} \in$ **Irrationals and reals**

26. $p^2 - p^0(-p^2 - p - x)$
$$= (-4)^2 - (-4)^0(-(-4)^2 - (-4) - (-2))$$
$$= 16 - (-16 + 6) = \mathbf{26}$$

27. $\dfrac{pa - pa^2}{pa} = \dfrac{pa(1-a)}{pa} = \mathbf{1 - a}$

28. $\dfrac{-2^{-2}}{(-2)^2} = \dfrac{-1}{2^2(-2)^2} = -\dfrac{1}{16}$

29. $-3^2 - 2^0 - 2[(-2-3) - (-4-6)]$
$$= -9 - 1 - 2[-5 + 10] = \mathbf{-20}$$

30. $\dfrac{x^2a}{a^2}\left(\dfrac{a}{x^2} - \dfrac{x^2a}{a^2x}\right) = \dfrac{x^2aa}{a^2x^2} - \dfrac{x^2ax^2a}{a^2a^2x}$
$$= \mathbf{1 - x^3a^{-2}}$$

PROBLEM SET 106

1. $R_BT_B + 40 = R_LT_L$; $R_L = 10$;
$R_B = 6$; $T_L = T_B$

$$6T_L + 40 = 10T_L$$
$$40 = 4T_L$$
$$T_L = \mathbf{10 \ sec}$$

2. $\dfrac{73}{100}(T) = 511$
$$T = \mathbf{700}$$

3. $R_RT_R = R_WT_W$; $R_R = 6$; $R_W = 8$;
$T_R = T_W + 2$

$$6(T_W + 2) = 8T_W$$
$$6T_W + 12 = 8T_W$$
$$12 = 2T_W$$
$$T_W = \mathbf{6 \ hr}$$

$$T_R = (6) + 2 = \mathbf{8 \ hr}$$

4. $N \qquad N+2 \qquad N+4 \qquad N+6$
$$5(N + N + 2) + 5 = 19(N + 6)$$
$$10N + 10 + 5 = 19N + 114$$
$$-9N = 99$$
$$N = -11$$
The desired integers are **−11, −9, −7,** and **−5.**

5. (a) $P_1 + P_2 = 60$

(b) $P_1 = 4P_2 + 10$

Substitute (b) into (a) and get:

(a') $(4P_2 + 10) + P_2 = 60$

$$5P_2 = 50$$
$$P_2 = \textbf{10 ft}$$

(b) $P_1 = 4(10) + 10 = \textbf{50 ft}$

6. Round:

(a) $104.062\overset{\downarrow}{\textcircled{5}}3527$

104.0625

(b) $\textcircled{4}13.0\overset{\downarrow}{\overline{5}}527$

400

7. $s^2 + 4^2 = 6^2$

$$s^2 + 16 = 36$$
$$s^2 = 20$$
$$s = \sqrt{20}$$
$$s = \textbf{2}\sqrt{\textbf{5}}$$

8. $D^2 = 2^2 + 2^2$

$$D^2 = 4 + 4$$
$$D^2 = 8$$
$$D = \sqrt{8}$$
$$D = \textbf{2}\sqrt{\textbf{2}}$$

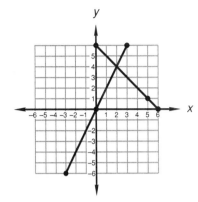

9. $\dfrac{x^2 + 8x + 15}{x^2 + 3x} \div \dfrac{x^2 + 3x - 10}{x^3 - 6x^2 + 8x}$

$$= \dfrac{(x+3)(x+5)}{x(x+3)} \cdot \dfrac{x(x-4)(x-2)}{(x+5)(x-2)}$$

$$= \textbf{\textit{x}} - \textbf{4}$$

10. $-2x - 3(x - 2^0) + 2x(-3 - 4^0) = x^0 - 4x - 2$

$$-2x - 3x + 3 - 8x = -4x - 1$$
$$4 = 9x$$
$$x = \dfrac{\textbf{4}}{\textbf{9}}$$

11. (a) $y = 2x$

$$y = \dfrac{+2}{+1}x$$

(b) $y = -x + 6$

$$y = \dfrac{-1}{+1}x + 6$$

The first step is to graph each of these lines.

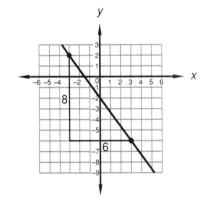

It appears that the lines cross at $x = 2$ and $y = 4$, so **(2, 4)** is the solution.

12. $\dfrac{(400 \times 10^5)(0.0008 \times 10^{14})}{(20{,}000 \times 10^{-30})(0.00002)}$

$$= \dfrac{(4 \times 10^7)(8 \times 10^{10})}{(2 \times 10^{-26})(2 \times 10^{-5})} = \textbf{8} \times \textbf{10}^{\textbf{48}}$$

13. (a) vertical line: $x = \pm k$; $\boldsymbol{x = 5}$

(b) The desired equation is $y = mx + b$.

By inspection, $b = -2$.

By inspection, the sign for m is $-$.

$|m| = \dfrac{8}{6} = \dfrac{4}{3}$

So $b = -2$ and $m = -\dfrac{4}{3}$: $y = -\dfrac{\textbf{4}}{\textbf{3}}\textbf{\textit{x}} - \textbf{2}$

14. $3\sqrt{30{,}000} - 9\sqrt{300} + 3\sqrt{2} \cdot 5\sqrt{6}$

$$= 3\sqrt{3 \cdot 10{,}000} - 9\sqrt{3 \cdot 100} + 3 \cdot 5\sqrt{2}\sqrt{2 \cdot 3}$$
$$= 300\sqrt{3} - 90\sqrt{3} + 30\sqrt{3}$$
$$= \textbf{240}\sqrt{\textbf{3}}$$

15. $3\sqrt{2}(4\sqrt{8} - 3\sqrt{12})$

$$= 3 \cdot 4\sqrt{2}\sqrt{2 \cdot 2 \cdot 2} - 3 \cdot 3\sqrt{2}\sqrt{2 \cdot 6}$$
$$= \textbf{48} - \textbf{18}\sqrt{\textbf{6}}$$

16. (a) $\dfrac{1}{N} = -\dfrac{1}{101}$

$\qquad N = -101$

$\qquad$ **101**

(b) Associative property of addition

17. $-2 \geq -2x + 2;\ D = \{\text{Integers}\}$

$\qquad -4 \geq -2x$

$\qquad\ \ 2 \leq x$

18. $\qquad\qquad 35 = -12x - x^2$

$x^2 + 12x + 35 = 0$

$(x + 7)(x + 5) = 0$

If $x + 5 = 0,\ x = -5$

$35 = -12(-5) - (-5)^2$

$35 = 60 - 25$

$35 = 35\quad$ check

If $x + 7 = 0,\ x = -7$

$35 = -12(-7) - (-7)^2$

$35 = 84 - 49$

$35 = 35\quad$ check

19. $(x^3 + 12x + 5) \div (x + 2)$

$$
\begin{array}{r}
x^2 - 2x + 16 \\
x + 2 \overline{) x^3 + 0x^2 + 12x + 5} \\
\underline{x^3 + 2x^2} \qquad\qquad\ \\
-2x^2 + 12x \quad\ \\
\underline{-2x^2 - 4x} \quad\ \\
16x + 5 \\
\underline{16x + 32} \\
-27
\end{array}
$$

$x^2 - 2x + 16 - \dfrac{27}{x + 2}$

20. $\qquad\qquad \dfrac{x}{4} - \dfrac{x + 2}{6} = 4$

$\dfrac{x}{4}(12) - \dfrac{(x + 2)}{6}(12) = 4(12)$

$\qquad\qquad 3x - 2x - 4 = 48$

$\qquad\qquad\qquad\qquad x = 52$

21. $5\dfrac{1}{2}m + \dfrac{3}{8} = \dfrac{1}{16}$

$\qquad \dfrac{11}{2}m = \dfrac{1}{16} - \dfrac{3}{8}$

$\qquad \dfrac{11}{2}m = \dfrac{1}{16} - \dfrac{6}{16}$

$\qquad\quad m = -\dfrac{5}{16} \cdot \dfrac{2}{11}$

$\qquad\quad m = -\dfrac{5}{88}$

22. $\dfrac{4}{x^2} - \dfrac{x + 3}{4x} - \dfrac{2x}{x + 1}$

$= \dfrac{16(x + 1) - x(x + 3)(x + 1) - 8x^3}{4x^2(x + 1)}$

$= \dfrac{16x + 16 - x^3 - 4x^2 - 3x - 8x^3}{4x^2(x + 1)}$

$= \dfrac{-9x^3 - 4x^2 + 13x + 16}{4x^2(x + 1)}$

23. $\dfrac{\dfrac{ay}{x} - 4}{\dfrac{1}{x} + 5} = \dfrac{\dfrac{ay - 4x}{x}}{\dfrac{1 + 5x}{x}} \cdot \dfrac{\dfrac{x}{1 + 5x}}{\dfrac{x}{1 + 5x}}$

$= \dfrac{ay - 4x}{1 + 5x}$

24. $\qquad 3\dfrac{1}{11} = WF(22)$

$\left(\dfrac{1}{22}\right)\overset{17}{\underset{11}{\dfrac{34}{11}}} = WF(22)\left(\dfrac{1}{22}\right)$

$\qquad \dfrac{17}{121} = WF$

25. $\dfrac{3 + 4\sqrt{2}}{5} \in$ **Irrationals and reals**

26. $-p^2 - p^0(-p + x)$

$= -(-2)^2 - (-2)^0(-(-2) + (-4))$

$= -4 - (2 - 4) = -2$

27. $\dfrac{x^2 - ax^2}{x^2} = \dfrac{x^2(1 - a)}{x^2} = 1 - a$

28. $\dfrac{(4x)^2(y^{-2})^2 xx^2 y}{(2x)^2(y^2)^2 x^0 yx^2} = \dfrac{16x^2 y^{-4} x^3 y}{4x^2 y^4 yx^2}$

$= \dfrac{16x^5 y^{-3}}{4x^4 y^5} = 4xy^{-8}$

29. $\dfrac{-3^{-2}}{3} = -\dfrac{1}{(3)^2(3)} = -\dfrac{1}{27}$

30. $-2^2 - 2[(-3-2)(-5-4)][-3^0(-2-5)]$
$= -4 - 2[45][7] = \mathbf{-634}$

Problem Set 107

1. $R_R T_R = R_W T_W;\ R_R = 6;\ R_W = 3;$
$T_R + T_W = 6$
$\qquad T_R = 6 - T_W$

$6(6 - T_W) = 3T_W$
$36 - 6T_W = 3T_W$
$\qquad 36 = 9T_W$
$\qquad T_W = 4$

$R_W T_W = 3(4) = \mathbf{12\ km}$

2. (a) $4N_H + 6N_C = 540$
(b) $N_H + N_C = 100$

$\begin{array}{r} \text{(a)} \quad 4N_H + 6N_C = 540 \\ (-6)\text{(b)} \quad -6N_H - 6N_C = -600 \\ \hline -2N_H = -60 \\ N_H = \mathbf{30} \end{array}$

3. $R_R T_R + 500 = R_W T_W;$
$R_W = 40;\ R_R = 20;\ T_R = T_W$

$20T_W + 500 = 40T_W$
$\qquad 500 = 20T_W$
$\qquad T_W = \mathbf{25\ sec}$

4. $\dfrac{73}{100}(P) = 438$
$\qquad P = \mathbf{600}$

5. $N \qquad N+2 \qquad N+4 \qquad N+6$
$-6(N + 2 + N + 6) + 8 = 11(-N - 4)$
$\qquad -12N - 48 + 8 = -11N - 44$
$\qquad\qquad\qquad 4 = N$
The desired integers are **4, 6, 8,** and **10.**

6. $abxy = ab(xy) \qquad$ associative
$\qquad = ab(yx) \qquad$ commutative
$\qquad = a(by)x \qquad$ associative
$\qquad = a(yb)x \qquad$ commutative
$\qquad = (ay)bx \qquad$ associative
$\qquad = (ya)bx \qquad$ commutative
$\qquad = yabx \qquad$ removed parentheses

7. $x = \dfrac{\sqrt{b^2 - 4ac}}{2a} = \dfrac{\sqrt{7^2 - 9(5)}}{2(5)} = \dfrac{\sqrt{4}}{10}$
$\quad = \dfrac{1}{5}$

8. Estimate:
$\sqrt{0.003266 \times 10^{-18}} = \sqrt{3.27 \times 10^{-21}}$
$= \sqrt{3.27}\sqrt{10}\sqrt{10^{-22}} = (1.6)(3.1) \times 10^{-11}$
Using the table:
$\sqrt{0.003266 \times 10^{-18}} = \sqrt{3.27 \times 10^{-21}}$
$= \sqrt{3.27}\sqrt{10}\sqrt{10^{-22}}$
$= \mathbf{(1.80831)(3.16228) \times 10^{-11}}$

9. $k^2 + 9^2 = 11^2$
$k^2 + 81 = 121$
$\qquad k^2 = 40$
$\qquad k = \sqrt{40}$
$\qquad k = \mathbf{2\sqrt{10}}$

10. $D^2 = 5^2 + 6^2$
$D^2 = 25 + 36$
$D^2 = 61$
$\ D = \mathbf{\sqrt{61}}$

11. $\dfrac{x^3 + 12x^2 + 35x}{4x^2 + 8x} \div \dfrac{x^2 + 15x + 50}{4x + 8}$
$= \dfrac{x(x + 7)(x + 5)}{4x(x + 2)} \cdot \dfrac{4(x + 2)}{(x + 5)(x + 10)}$
$= \dfrac{x + 7}{x + 10}$

12. $3x - 2^0(x - 4) + 3(2x + 5) = 7 + x^0$
$3x - x + 4 + 6x + 15 = 8$
$\qquad\qquad\qquad 8x = -11$
$\qquad\qquad\qquad x = -\dfrac{11}{8}$

13. (a) $y = 2x + 4$

$y = \dfrac{+2}{+1}x + 4$

(b) $y = -2x$

$y = \dfrac{-2}{+1}x$

The first step is to graph each of these lines.

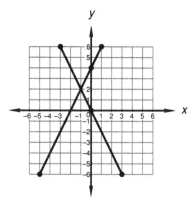

It appears that the lines cross at $x = -1$ and $y = 2$, so **(−1, 2)** is the solution.

14. $\dfrac{(30,000)(0.000005)}{(1500 \times 10^{-5})(10,000)}$

$= \dfrac{(3 \times 10^{4})(5 \times 10^{-6})}{(1.5 \times 10^{-2})(1 \times 10^{4})} = \mathbf{1 \times 10^{-3}}$

15. (a) horizontal line: $y = \pm k$; $\mathbf{y = 3}$

(b) The desired equation is $y = mx + b$.

By inspection, $b = -3$.

By inspection, the sign for m is +.

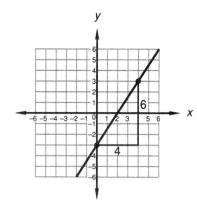

$|m| = \dfrac{6}{4} = \dfrac{3}{2}$

So $b = -3$ and $m = \dfrac{3}{2}$: $\mathbf{y = \dfrac{3}{2}x - 3}$

16. $4\sqrt{20,000} = 4\sqrt{2 \cdot 10,000} = \mathbf{400\sqrt{2}}$

17. $4\sqrt{3} \cdot 5\sqrt{2} - 2\sqrt{2}(3\sqrt{2} - 2\sqrt{12})$

$= 4 \cdot 5\sqrt{3}\sqrt{2} - 2 \cdot 3\sqrt{2}\sqrt{2} + 2 \cdot 2\sqrt{2}\sqrt{2 \cdot 6}$

$= 20\sqrt{6} - 12 + 8\sqrt{6} = \mathbf{28\sqrt{6} - 12}$

18. $2 \le x < 5$; $D = \{$Positive integers$\}$

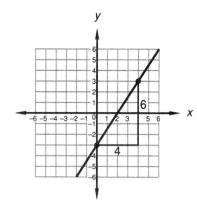

19. $70 = x^2 + 3x$

$0 = x^2 + 3x - 70$

$0 = (x - 7)(x + 10)$

If $x - 7 = 0$, $\boldsymbol{x = 7}$

$70 = (7)^2 + 3(7)$

$70 = 49 + 21$

$70 = 70$ check

If $x + 10 = 0$, $\boldsymbol{x = -10}$

$70 = (-10)^2 + 3(-10)$

$70 = 100 - 30$

$70 = 70$ check

20. $\dfrac{2x}{3} - \dfrac{x + 4}{7} = 2$

$\dfrac{2x}{3}(21) - \dfrac{(x + 4)}{7}(21) = 2(21)$

$14x - 3x - 12 = 42$

$11x = 54$

$x = \dfrac{\mathbf{54}}{\mathbf{11}}$

21. $3\dfrac{1}{4}p + 3\dfrac{1}{4} = 7\dfrac{1}{8}$

$\dfrac{13}{4}p = \dfrac{57}{8} - \dfrac{13}{4}$

$\dfrac{13}{4}p = \dfrac{57}{8} - \dfrac{26}{8}$

$p = \dfrac{31}{8} \cdot \dfrac{4}{13}$

$p = \dfrac{\mathbf{31}}{\mathbf{26}}$

22. $\dfrac{4}{x^2} - \dfrac{3x + 2}{x + 1} + \dfrac{5}{x}$

$= \dfrac{4(x + 1) - (3x + 2)x^2 + 5x(x + 1)}{x^2(x + 1)}$

$= \dfrac{4x + 4 - 3x^3 - 2x^2 + 5x^2 + 5x}{x^2(x + 1)}$

$= \dfrac{\mathbf{-3x^3 + 3x^2 + 9x + 4}}{\mathbf{x^2(x + 1)}}$

23. $\dfrac{\dfrac{mx}{4} + 1}{\dfrac{1}{4} + a} = \dfrac{\dfrac{mx + 4}{4}}{\dfrac{1 + 4a}{4}} \cdot \dfrac{\dfrac{4}{1 + 4a}}{\dfrac{4}{1 + 4a}}$

$= \dfrac{\mathbf{mx + 4}}{\mathbf{1 + 4a}}$

24. **False** $\{$Integers$\} \not\subset \{$Naturals$\}$

25. $-p - p(-p - ap)$
$= -(-5) - (-5)(-(-5) - (-4)(-5))$
$= 5 + 5(5 - 20) = \mathbf{-70}$

26. $\dfrac{4 - 4x}{4} = \dfrac{4(1 - x)}{4} = \mathbf{1 - x}$

27. $\dfrac{-2^{-2}}{-2^2} = \dfrac{1}{2^2 2^2} = \dfrac{\mathbf{1}}{\mathbf{16}}$

28. $-2\big[|4 - 2| - (5 - 3)(-2 - 4^0)\big] - \sqrt[3]{-125}$
$= -2[2 + 6] - \sqrt[3]{(-5)^3} = \mathbf{-11}$

29. $\dfrac{a^{-3}y^{-2}}{x}\left(\dfrac{xa^3}{y^2} - \dfrac{2ay}{x}\right)$
$= \dfrac{a^{-3}y^{-2}xa^3}{xy^2} - \dfrac{a^{-3}y^{-2}2ay}{xx}$
$= \mathbf{y^{-4} - 2a^{-2}y^{-1}x^{-2}}$

30. 40.373737③737
40.3737374

PROBLEM SET 108

1. $R_M T_M = R_F T_F + 40;\; R_F = 46$
$R_M = 54;\; T_M = T_F$

$40 \quad \xrightarrow{D_F}$
$\xrightarrow{\quad D_M\quad}$

$54T_M = 46T_M + 40$
$8T_M = 40$
$T_M = \mathbf{5\ sec}$

2. $N \quad N + 2 \quad N + 4$
$4N = 16(N + 4 + 2)$
$4N = 16N + 96$
$-12N = 96$
$N = -8$
The desired integers are $\mathbf{-8, -6,}$ and $\mathbf{-4.}$

3. $R_W T_W + R_B T_B = 20;$
$R_W = 5;\; R_B = 15;$
$T_B + T_W = 2$
$\qquad T_W = 2 - T_B$

$\xrightarrow{D_W}\xrightarrow{D_B}$

$5(2 - T_B) + 15T_B = 20$
$10 - 5T_B + 15T_B = 20$
$\qquad\qquad 10T_B = 10$
$\qquad\qquad\quad T_B = 1$

$D_B = R_B T_B = 15(1) = \mathbf{15\ miles}$

4. $\dfrac{80}{100}(T) = 384$
$\qquad T = \mathbf{480}$

5. (a) $N_O + 10N_T = 6750$
(b) $N_O = N_T + 150$
Substitute (b) into (a) and get:
(a′) $(N_T + 150) + 10N_T = 6750$
$\qquad\qquad\quad 11N_T = 6600$
$\qquad\qquad\qquad N_T = \mathbf{600}$

(b) $N_O = (600) + 150$
$\quad N_O = \mathbf{750}$

6. Estimate:
$\sqrt{108{,}052 \times 10^{-10}} = \sqrt{1.08 \times 10^{-5}}$
$= \sqrt{1.08 \times 10 \times 10^{-6}} = \sqrt{1.08}\sqrt{10}\sqrt{10^{-6}}$
$= (1)(3.1)(10^{-3})$
Approximate with tablets:
$\sqrt{108{,}052 \times 10^{-10}} = \sqrt{1.08}\sqrt{10}\sqrt{10^{-6}}$
$= \mathbf{(1.03923)(3.16228) \times 10^{-3}}$

7. $a^2 = 4^2 + 8^2$
$a^2 = 16 + 64$
$a^2 = 80$
$a = \sqrt{80}$
$a = \mathbf{4\sqrt{5}}$

8. $D^2 = 5^2 + 8^2$
$D^2 = 25 + 64$
$D^2 = 89$
$D = \sqrt{89}$

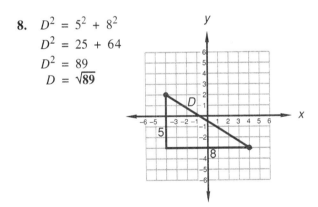

9. $\dfrac{x^3 + 11x^2 + 24x}{x^2 + 10x + 21} \div \dfrac{4x^2 + 32x}{4x + 40}$
$= \dfrac{x(x^2 + 11x + 24)}{x^2 + 10x + 21} \cdot \dfrac{4x + 40}{4x^2 + 32x}$
$= \dfrac{x(x + 3)(x + 8)}{(x + 7)(x + 3)} \cdot \dfrac{4(x + 10)}{4x(x + 8)}$
$= \dfrac{\mathbf{x + 10}}{\mathbf{x + 7}}$

10. $-2x(4 - 3^0) - (2x - 5) + 3x - 2 = -2^0 x$
$-6x - 2x + 5 + 3x - 2 = -x$
$3 = 4x$
$x = \dfrac{\mathbf{3}}{\mathbf{4}}$

11. (a) $y = -2x$

$y = \dfrac{-2}{+1}x$

(b) $y = -2$

The first step is to graph each of these lines.

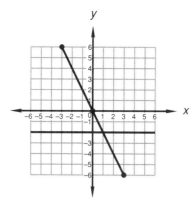

It appears that the lines cross at $x = 1$ and $y = -2$, so $(1, -2)$ is the solution.

12. $\dfrac{(4000 \times 10^{-40})(0.0003 \times 10^{-21})}{(20,000)(3000 \times 10^{-14})}$

$= \dfrac{(4 \times 10^{-37})(3 \times 10^{-25})}{(2 \times 10^{4})(3 \times 10^{-11})} = \mathbf{2 \times 10^{-55}}$

13. (a) horizontal line: $y = \pm k$; $\mathbf{y = -2}$

(b) The desired equation is $y = mx + b$.

By inspection, $b = 0$.

By inspection, the sign for m is $-$.

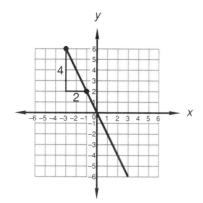

$|m| = \dfrac{4}{2} = 2$

So $b = 0$ and $m = -2$: $\mathbf{y = -2x}$

14. $2\sqrt{60,000} = 2\sqrt{6 \cdot 10,000} = \mathbf{200\sqrt{6}}$

15. $4\sqrt{5} \cdot 2\sqrt{3} + 5\sqrt{3}(\sqrt{3} + 2\sqrt{5})$

$= 4 \cdot 2\sqrt{5}\sqrt{3} + 5\sqrt{3}\sqrt{3} + 5 \cdot 2\sqrt{3}\sqrt{5}$

$= 8\sqrt{15} + 15 + 10\sqrt{15}$

$= \mathbf{18\sqrt{15} + 15}$

16. $-4 - x \not< 2$; $D = \{\text{Reals}\}$

$-4 - x \geq 2$

$-x \geq 6$

$x \leq -6$

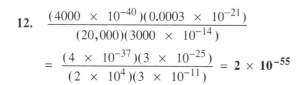

17. $-81 + 4x^2 = 0$

$4x^2 - 81 = 0$

$(2x + 9)(2x - 9) = 0$

If $2x + 9 = 0$, $\mathbf{x = -\dfrac{9}{2}}$

$-81 + 4\left(-\dfrac{9}{2}\right)^2 = 0$

$-81 + 81 = 0$

$0 = 0$ check

If $2x - 9 = 0$, $\mathbf{x = \dfrac{9}{2}}$

$-81 + 4\left(\dfrac{9}{2}\right)^2 = 0$

$-81 + 81 = 0$

$0 = 0$ check

18. $\dfrac{5x}{3} - \dfrac{x - 5}{2} = 14$

$\dfrac{5x}{3}(6) - \dfrac{(x - 5)}{2}(6) = 14(6)$

$10x - 3x + 15 = 84$

$7x = 69$

$x = \dfrac{69}{7}$

19. $4\dfrac{1}{8}p - \dfrac{3}{4} = 2\dfrac{1}{4}$

$\dfrac{33}{8}p = \dfrac{9}{4} + \dfrac{3}{4}$

$p = \dfrac{12}{4} \cdot \dfrac{8}{33}$

$p = \dfrac{8}{11}$

20. $V_{Cyl.} = A_{Base} \times \text{height}$

$= \frac{1}{2}\left[\pi(10)^2 + \pi(5)^2 + \pi(5)^2\right](3) \text{ cm}^3$

$\approx [235.5](3) \text{ cm}^3$

$\approx (706.5)\left(\frac{1}{100}\right)\left(\frac{1}{100}\right)\left(\frac{1}{100}\right) \text{ m}^3$

$\approx \mathbf{7.07 \times 10^{-4} \text{ m}^3}$

S.A. $= 2A_{Base} + (P \times \text{height})$

$= 2(235.5) \text{ cm}^2 + \left[(10\pi + 2\pi(5)) \times 3\right] \text{cm}^2$

$\approx 471 \text{ cm}^2 + (62.8)(3) \text{ cm}^2$

$\approx (659.4)\left(\frac{1}{100}\right)\left(\frac{1}{100}\right) \text{ m}^2$

$\approx \mathbf{6.6 \times 10^{-2} \text{ m}^2}$

$V_{Cone} = \frac{1}{3}V_{Cylinder}$

$= \frac{1}{3}(7.07 \times 10^{-4} \text{ m}^3)$

$= \mathbf{2.36 \times 10^{-4} \text{ m}^3}$

21. {Negative irrational numbers}
ADDITION: Not closed.
$(\sqrt{2} - 2) + (-\sqrt{2}) = -2$
SUBTRACTION: Not closed. $-\sqrt{7} - (-\sqrt{7}) = 0$
MULTIPLICATION: Not closed. $(-\sqrt{5})(-\sqrt{5}) = 5$
DIVISION: Not closed. $-\sqrt{3} \div (-\sqrt{3}) = 1$
The set of negative irrational numbers is not closed for any of the operations.

22. $\dfrac{p}{x^2 - 9} + \dfrac{2x}{x^2 - 3x}$

$= \dfrac{p}{(x + 3)(x - 3)} + \dfrac{2x}{x(x - 3)}$

$= \dfrac{px + 2x(x + 3)}{x(x + 3)(x - 3)} = \dfrac{x(p + 2x + 6)}{x(x^2 - 9)}$

$= \dfrac{\mathbf{p + 2x + 6}}{\mathbf{x^2 - 9}}$

23. $4^2 \in$ **Naturals, wholes, integers, rationals, and reals**

24. $\dfrac{-4x^2 - 8x^2a}{-4x^2} = \dfrac{-4x^2(1 + 2a)}{-4x^2} = \mathbf{1 + 2a}$

25. $\dfrac{-3^{-2}}{(-3)^2} = -\dfrac{1}{3^2(-3)^2} = -\dfrac{\mathbf{1}}{\mathbf{81}}$

26. $\dfrac{\dfrac{5p}{x} - 4}{\dfrac{3}{x} - x} = \dfrac{\dfrac{5p - 4x}{x}}{\dfrac{3 - x^2}{x}} \cdot \dfrac{\dfrac{x}{3 - x^2}}{\dfrac{x}{3 - x^2}}$

$= \dfrac{\mathbf{5p - 4x}}{\mathbf{3 - x^2}}$

27. $-x - xk(x - k) = -(-4) - (-4)(5)((-4) - 5)$
$= 4 + 20(-9) = \mathbf{-176}$

28. $\dfrac{x^2a(x^2a)(x^{-2})^2 x^0 xa^2}{(a^{-3})^2 ax^{-2}x^4x} = \dfrac{xa^4}{a^{-5}x^3} = \mathbf{x^{-2}a^9}$

29. $2^2[-(-2^0 - 3)(-2 + 5) + 3] = 4[-(-4)(3) + 3]$
$= 4(15) = \mathbf{60}$

30. 7.1851851$\overset{\downarrow}{\circled{8}}$5
7.18518519

PROBLEM SET 109

1. $R_AT_A + R_RT_R = 38$; $R_A = 3$;
$R_R = 5$; $T_A = T_R + 2$

$3(T_R + 2) + 5T_R = 38$
$3T_R + 6 + 5T_R = 38$
$8T_R = 32$
$T_R = 4$

$T_R = 2 \text{ p.m.} + 4 \text{ hr} = \mathbf{6 \text{ p.m.}}$

2. (a) $N_P + 5N_N = 2950$
(b) $N_P = N_N + 10$
Substitute (b) into (a) and get:
(a') $(N_N + 10) + 5N_N = 2950$
$6N_N = 2940$
$N_N = \mathbf{490}$

3. $\dfrac{88}{100}(T) = 4224$
$T = \mathbf{4800}$

4. $N \quad N + 1 \quad N + 2 \quad N + 3$
$5(-N) = -3(N + 2 + N + 3) + 5$
$-5N = -6N - 15 + 5$
$N = -10$
The desired integers are **−10, −9, −8,** and **−7.**

5. (a) $N_R + N_W = 52$

(b) $N_R = 2N_W + 16$

Substitute (b) into (a) and get:

(a') $(2N_W + 16) + N_W = 52$

$$3N_W = 36$$

$$N_W = \mathbf{12}$$

(b) $N_R = 2(12) + 16 = \mathbf{40}$

6. Estimate:

$$\sqrt{8{,}372{,}150 \times 10^{-15}} = \sqrt{8.37 \times 10^{-9}}$$

$$= \sqrt{8.37 \times 10 \times 10^{-10}} = \sqrt{8.37}\sqrt{10}\sqrt{10^{-10}}$$

$$= (2.9)(3.1)(10^{-5})$$

Approximate with tables:

$$\sqrt{8{,}372{,}150 \times 10^{-15}} = \sqrt{8.37 \times 10^{-9}}$$

$$= \sqrt{8.37 \times 10 \times 10^{-10}} = \sqrt{8.37}\sqrt{10}\sqrt{10^{-10}}$$

$$= \mathbf{(2.89310)(3.16228) \times 10^{-5}}$$

7. $p^2 = 5^2 + 11^2$

$p^2 = 25 + 121$

$p^2 = 146$

$p = \sqrt{\mathbf{146}}$

8. $D^2 = 1^2 + 2^2$

$D^2 = 5$

$D = \sqrt{\mathbf{5}}$

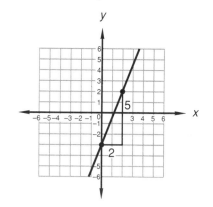

9. $\dfrac{x^3 + x^2 - 12x}{x^2 + 4x} \div \dfrac{x^2 - 11x + 24}{x^2 + 2x - 80}$

$= \dfrac{x(x^2 + x - 12)}{x^2 + 4x} \cdot \dfrac{x^2 + 2x - 80}{x^2 - 11x + 24}$

$= \dfrac{\cancel{x}\cancel{(x-3)}\cancel{(x+4)}}{\cancel{x}\cancel{(x+4)}} \cdot \dfrac{\cancel{(x-8)}(x+10)}{\cancel{(x-8)}\cancel{(x-3)}}$

$= \mathbf{x + 10}$

10. $(-x) - 3^0(x - 7) = -(-x - 5)$

$-x - x + 7 = x + 5$

$2 = 3x$

$x = \dfrac{\mathbf{2}}{\mathbf{3}}$

11. (a) $x = 2$

(b) $y = -\dfrac{1}{2}x + 6$

$y = \dfrac{-1}{+2}x + 6$

The first step is to graph each of these lines.

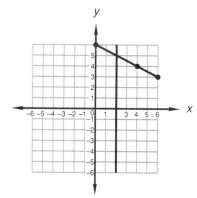

It appears that the lines cross at $x = 2$ and $y = 5$, so **(2, 5)** is the solution.

12. $\dfrac{(0.0004 \times 10^{15})(0.06 \times 10^{41})}{(30{,}000{,}000)(400 \times 10^{-21})}$

$= \dfrac{(4 \times 10^{11})(6 \times 10^{39})}{(3 \times 10^{7})(4 \times 10^{-19})} = \mathbf{2 \times 10^{62}}$

13. (a) vertical line: $x = \pm k$; $x = \mathbf{-4}$

(b) The desired equation is $y = mx + b$.

By inspection, $b = -3$.

By inspection, the sign for m is $+$.

$|m| = \dfrac{5}{2}$

So $b = -3$ and $m = \dfrac{5}{2}$: $y = \dfrac{5}{2}x - 3$

14. $3\sqrt{6{,}000{,}000} - 5\sqrt{60{,}000} + 2\sqrt{3}(3\sqrt{2} - 5\sqrt{3})$

$= 3\sqrt{6 \cdot 1{,}000{,}000} - 5\sqrt{6 \cdot 10{,}000} + 6\sqrt{3}\sqrt{2}$

$\quad - 2 \cdot 5\sqrt{3}\sqrt{3}$

$= 3000\sqrt{6} - 500\sqrt{6} + 6\sqrt{6} - 30 = \mathbf{2506\sqrt{6} - 30}$

15. $-80 = x^2 + 18x$

$\quad\ \ 0 = x^2 + 18x + 80$

$\quad\ \ 0 = (x + 8)(x + 10)$

If $x + 8 = 0$, $\boldsymbol{x = -8}$

$-80 = (-8)^2 + 18(-8)$

$-80 = 64 - 144$

$-80 = -80$ check

If $x + 10 = 0$, $\boldsymbol{x = -10}$

$-80 = (-10)^2 + 18(-10)$

$-80 = 100 - 180$

$-80 = -80$ check

16. $V_{Cylinder} = A_{Base} \times height$

$\quad = \left[\dfrac{\pi(5)^2}{2} + \dfrac{(8)(6)}{2}\right](3)(100)\ cm^3$

$\quad \approx (63.25)(300)\ cm^3$

$\quad \approx \boldsymbol{18{,}975\ cm^3}$

S.A. $= 2A_{Base} + (P \times height)$

$\quad = 2(63.25)\ cm^2 + [(14 + 5\pi) \times 300]\ cm^2$

$\quad \approx \boldsymbol{9036.5\ cm^2}$

$V_{Cone} = \dfrac{1}{3}V_{Cylinder}$

$\quad\ = \dfrac{1}{3}(18{,}975)\ cm^3 = \boldsymbol{6325\ cm^3}$

17. $x = \dfrac{\sqrt{b^2 - 4ac}}{2a} = \dfrac{\sqrt{(13)^2 - 4(10)\left(\dfrac{5}{8}\right)}}{2(10)}$

$= \dfrac{\sqrt{169 - 25}}{20} = \dfrac{\sqrt{144}}{20} = \dfrac{12}{20} = \boldsymbol{\dfrac{3}{5}}$

18. $-|x| + 3 > 0$; $D = \{Integers\}$

$\quad -|x| > -3$

$\quad\ \ |x| < 3$

19. $\dfrac{4}{x - 4} + \dfrac{5}{x^2 - 16}$

$= \dfrac{4}{x - 4} + \dfrac{5}{(x + 4)(x - 4)}$

$= \dfrac{4(x + 4) + 5}{(x + 4)(x - 4)} = \dfrac{4x + 16 + 5}{x^2 - 16}$

$= \boldsymbol{\dfrac{4x + 21}{x^2 - 16}}$

20. $\dfrac{4}{x^2 + 2x + 1} + \dfrac{3x}{x + 1}$

$= \dfrac{4}{(x + 1)(x + 1)} + \dfrac{3x}{x + 1}$

$= \dfrac{4 + 3x(x + 1)}{(x + 1)(x + 1)} = \dfrac{4 + 3x^2 + 3x}{x^2 + 2x + 1}$

$= \boldsymbol{\dfrac{3x^2 + 3x + 4}{x^2 + 2x + 1}}$

21. $\dfrac{5x}{2} - \dfrac{x - 3}{5} = 7$

$\dfrac{5x}{2}(10) - \dfrac{(x - 3)}{5}(10) = 7(10)$

$25x - 2x + 6 = 70$

$23x = 64$

$x = \boldsymbol{\dfrac{64}{23}}$

22. $4\dfrac{1}{5}k + 2\dfrac{1}{4} = 7\dfrac{1}{8}$

$\dfrac{21}{5}k = \dfrac{57}{8} - \dfrac{9}{4}$

$\dfrac{21}{5}k = \dfrac{57}{8} - \dfrac{18}{8}$

$k = \dfrac{39}{8} \cdot \dfrac{5}{21}$

$k = \boldsymbol{\dfrac{65}{56}}$

23. $-x^0 - x^2 - x(-x + y)$

$= -(-4)^0 - (-4)^2 - (-4)(-(-4) + (-3))$

$= -1 - 16 + 4(1) = \boldsymbol{-13}$

24. $\dfrac{-3x - 9x^2}{-3x} = \dfrac{-3x(1 + 3x)}{-3x} = \boldsymbol{1 + 3x}$

25. $\dfrac{-3^0 - 4^0}{-2^{-2}} = (-1 - 1)(-2^2) = \boldsymbol{8}$

26. $\dfrac{4 + \dfrac{y}{x^2}}{y^2 + \dfrac{y}{x^2}} = \dfrac{\dfrac{4x^2 + y}{x^2}}{\dfrac{x^2y^2 + y}{x^2}} \cdot \dfrac{\dfrac{x^2}{x^2y^2 + y}}{\dfrac{x^2}{x^2y^2 + y}}$

$= \boldsymbol{\dfrac{4x^2 + y}{x^2y^2 + y}}$

27. $0.0013 \in$ **Rationals and reals**

28. $\dfrac{3x^2y^{-2}}{a^{-2}}\left(\dfrac{x^2y}{a} - \dfrac{4x^{-5}y^{-3}}{a^5}\right)$

$= \dfrac{3x^2y^{-2}x^2y}{a^{-2}a} - \dfrac{3x^2y^{-2}4x^{-5}y^{-3}}{a^{-2}a^5}$

$= \boldsymbol{3x^4y^{-1}a - 12x^{-3}y^{-5}a^{-3}}$

29. $-3^0[(-2 - 2^0) - (-5 + 6^0)] - \sqrt[3]{-64}$
$= -[(-3 + 4)] - (-4) = \mathbf{3}$

30. 0 is the additive identity, so $(-42)(0) = \mathbf{0}$.

PROBLEM SET 110

1. $\dfrac{130}{100} \times N_M = 260$

$N_M = \dfrac{260}{130} \times 100 = \mathbf{200}$

Total $= N_M + N_B = (200) + (260) = \mathbf{460}$

2. $R_{F1}T_{F1} + R_{F2}T_{F2} = 52;$
$R_{F1} = 3;\ R_{F2} = 4;$
$T_{F1} + T_{F2} = 15$
$\qquad T_{F2} = 15 - T_{F1}$

$3T_{F1} + 4(15 - T_{F1}) = 52$
$3T_{F1} + 60 - 4T_{F1} = 52$
$\qquad\qquad T_{F1} = \mathbf{8\ hr}$

3. $R_W T_W = R_T T_T;\ R_W = 2;\ R_T = 4;$
$T_W = T_T + 2$

$2(T_T + 2) = 4T_T$
$2T_T + 4 = 4T_T$
$4 = 2T_T$
$2 = T_T$

$R_T T_T = 4(2) = \mathbf{8\ miles}$

4. $(N + 10)5 = 7(-N) + 2$
$5N + 50 = -7N + 2$
$12N = -48$
$N = \mathbf{-4}$

5. (a) $10N_C + 20N_D = 350$
(b) $N_C + N_D = 25$

$\quad$ (a) $\quad 10N_C + 20N_D = \ \ 350$
(-10)(b) $\underline{-10N_C - 10N_D = -250}$
$\qquad\qquad\quad 10N_D = \ \ 100$
$\qquad\qquad\qquad N_D = \mathbf{10}$

(b) $N_C + (10) = 25$
$\qquad N_C = \mathbf{15}$

6. hr 1 = \$5,
hr 2 + hr 3 + hr 4 + hr 5 + hr 6 = \$5
5(\$1) + \$1 + \$1 + \$1 + \$1 + \$1 = **\$10**

7. $\dfrac{1}{N} = -7$

$N = -\dfrac{1}{7}$

Multiplicative identity is **1**.

8. $\dfrac{p - 4}{p} = \dfrac{16}{5p} - \dfrac{1}{5}$

$\dfrac{(p - 4)}{p}(5p) = \dfrac{16}{5p}(5p) - \dfrac{1}{5}(5p)$

$5p - 20 = 16 - p$
$6p = 36$
$p = \mathbf{6}$

9. $\dfrac{3}{4n} = \dfrac{3}{n + 3}$

$(4n)(n + 3)\dfrac{3}{4n} = (4n)(n + 3)\dfrac{3}{n + 3}$

$3n + 9 = 12n$
$9 = 9n$
$n = \mathbf{1}$

10. $-|x| + 4 > -2;\ D = \{\text{Integers}\}$
$-|x| > -6$
$|x| < 6$

11. $-|x| - 4 > -2;\ D = \{\text{Reals}\}$
$-|x| > 2$
$|x| < -2$
No real numbers

12. $p^2 + 4^2 = 6^2$
$p^2 + 16 = 36$
$p^2 = 20$
$p = \sqrt{20}$
$p = \mathbf{2\sqrt{5}}$

13. $\dfrac{x^2 + 10x + 25}{x^2 + 5x} \div \dfrac{x^2 + 8x + 15}{x^3 + x^2 - 6x}$

$= \dfrac{x^2 + 10x + 25}{x(x + 5)} \cdot \dfrac{x(x^2 + x - 6)}{x^2 + 8x + 15}$

$= \dfrac{(x + 5)(x + 5)}{x(x + 5)} \cdot \dfrac{x(x + 3)(x - 2)}{(x + 5)(x + 3)}$

$= \mathbf{\textit{x} - 2}$

14. (a) $y = x - 2$

$y = \dfrac{+1}{+1}x - 2$

(b) $y = -\dfrac{1}{2}x + 1$

$y = \dfrac{-1}{+2}x + 1$

The first step is to graph each of these lines.

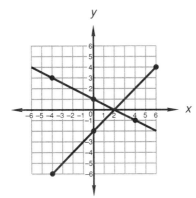

It appears that the lines cross at $x = 2$ and $y = 0$, so **(2, 0)** is the solution.

15. (a) horizontal line: $y = \pm k$; **$y = 4$**

(b) The desired equation is $y = mx + b$.

By inspection, $b = -3$.

By inspection, the sign for m is $-$.

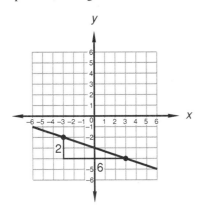

$|m| = \dfrac{2}{6} = \dfrac{1}{3}$

So $b = -3$ and $m = -\dfrac{1}{3}$: **$y = -\dfrac{1}{3}x - 3$**

16. $4\dfrac{1}{2}x + \dfrac{1}{2} = \dfrac{3}{4}$

$\dfrac{9}{2}x = \dfrac{3}{4} - \dfrac{1}{2}$

$\dfrac{9}{2}x = \dfrac{3}{4} - \dfrac{2}{4}$

$x = \dfrac{1}{4} \cdot \dfrac{2}{9}$

$x = \dfrac{1}{18}$

17. (a) $\dfrac{3x - 3x^2}{3x} = \dfrac{3x(1 - x)}{3x} = \mathbf{1 - x}$

(b) $\dfrac{-4^{-2}}{-(-2)^{-2}} = \dfrac{(-2)^2}{4^2} = \dfrac{4}{16} = \dfrac{1}{4}$

18. $\dfrac{a^2 + \dfrac{1}{a}}{ax + \dfrac{b}{a}} = \dfrac{\dfrac{a^3 + 1}{a}}{\dfrac{a^2x + b}{a}} \cdot \dfrac{\dfrac{a}{a^2x + b}}{\dfrac{a}{a^2x + b}}$

$= \dfrac{a^3 + 1}{a^2x + b}$

19. $(-2)\left[(-2 + 5) + (-2 - 3^0)\right] = -2(3 - 3) = \mathbf{0}$

20. $\dfrac{4}{a - 2} + \dfrac{6a}{a^2 - 4}$

$= \dfrac{4}{a - 2} + \dfrac{6a}{(a + 2)(a - 2)}$

$= \dfrac{4(a + 2) + 6a}{(a + 2)(a - 2)} = \dfrac{4a + 8 + 6a}{a^2 - 4}$

$= \dfrac{\mathbf{10a + 8}}{\mathbf{a^2 - 4}}$

21. $\dfrac{5}{x + 4} - \dfrac{3}{x^2 + 2x - 8}$

$= \dfrac{5}{x + 4} - \dfrac{3}{(x + 4)(x - 2)}$

$= \dfrac{5(x - 2) - 3}{x^2 + 2x - 8} = \dfrac{5x - 10 - 3}{x^2 + 2x - 8}$

$= \dfrac{\mathbf{5x - 13}}{\mathbf{x^2 + 2x - 8}}$

22. Estimate:

$\sqrt{417{,}530 \times 10^{20}} = \sqrt{4.18 \times 10^{25}}$

$= \sqrt{4.18 \times 10 \times 10^{24}} = \sqrt{4.18}\sqrt{10}\sqrt{10^{24}}$

$= (2.1)(3.1)(10^{12})$

Approximate:

$\sqrt{417{,}530 \times 10^{20}} = \sqrt{4.18 \times 10^{25}}$

$= \sqrt{4.18 \times 10 \times 10^{24}} = \sqrt{4.18}\sqrt{10}\sqrt{10^{24}}$

$= \mathbf{(2.04450)(3.16228) \times 10^{12}}$

23. Estimate:

$\sqrt{417{,}530 \times 10^{-60}} = \sqrt{4.18 \times 10^{-55}}$

$= \sqrt{4.18 \times 10 \times 10^{-56}}$

$= \sqrt{4.18}\sqrt{10}\sqrt{10^{-56}} = (2.1)(3.1)(10^{-28})$

Approximate:

$\sqrt{417{,}530 \times 10^{-60}} = \sqrt{4.18 \times 10^{-55}}$

$= \sqrt{4.18 \times 10 \times 10^{-56}}$

$= \sqrt{4.18}\sqrt{10}\sqrt{10^{-56}}$

$= \mathbf{(2.04450)(3.16228) \times 10^{-28}}$

24. $3\sqrt{2} \cdot 4\sqrt{3} - 4\sqrt{60,000} + 2\sqrt{3}(3\sqrt{2} - \sqrt{3})$
$= 3 \cdot 4\sqrt{2}\sqrt{3} - 4\sqrt{6 \cdot 10,000} + 2 \cdot 3\sqrt{3}\sqrt{2}$
$\quad - 2 \cdot 1\sqrt{3}\sqrt{3} = 12\sqrt{6} - 400\sqrt{6} + 6\sqrt{6} - 6$
$= \mathbf{-382\sqrt{6} - 6}$

25. $(x^3 - 4) \div (x + 7)$

$$
\begin{array}{r}
x^2 - 7x + 49 \\
x + 7 \overline{\smash{)}\; x^3 + 0x^2 + 0x - 4} \\
\underline{x^3 + 7x^2} \\
-7x^2 + 0x \\
\underline{-7x^2 - 49x} \\
49x - 4 \\
\underline{49x + 343} \\
-347
\end{array}
$$

$$x^2 - 7x + 49 - \frac{347}{x + 7}$$

26. $\qquad 4x^2 - 81 = 0$
$\quad (2x + 9)(2x - 9) = 0$

If $2x + 9 = 0$, $x = -\dfrac{9}{2}$

$4\left(-\dfrac{9}{2}\right)^2 - 81 = 0$
$\qquad 81 - 81 = 0$
$\qquad\qquad\quad 0 = 0 \quad$ check

If $2x - 9 = 0$, $x = \dfrac{9}{2}$

$4\left(\dfrac{9}{2}\right)^2 - 81 = 0$
$\qquad 81 - 81 = 0$
$\qquad\qquad\quad 0 = 0 \quad$ check

27. $WF\left(2\dfrac{1}{4}\right) = \dfrac{7}{8}$

$\quad WF\left(\dfrac{9}{4}\right) = \dfrac{7}{8}$

$\qquad WF = \dfrac{7}{18}$

28. $\dfrac{4\sqrt{2}}{5} \in$ **Irrationals and reals**

29. $-x - x^2 + (-x)^3(x - y)$
$= -(-3) - (-3)^2 + (-(-3))^3((-3) - (-5))$
$= 3 - 9 + 27(2) = \mathbf{48}$

30. $\dfrac{x}{y} + \dfrac{3x^2 y}{y^2 x} - \dfrac{4x^0 x x^2 y^{-2}}{(x)^2 y y^{-2}}$
$= xy^{-1} + 3xy^{-1} - 4xy^{-1} = \mathbf{0}$

PROBLEM SET 111

1. (a) $422G + 4C = 2122$
(b) $G + C = 8$
$\qquad C = 8 - G$
Substitute (b) into (a) and get:
(a′) $422G + 4(8 - G) = 2122$
$\qquad 422G + 32 - 4G = 2122$
$\qquad\qquad\qquad 418G = 2090$
$\qquad\qquad\qquad\quad G = \mathbf{5 \ grams}$

2. $N \qquad N + 2 \qquad N + 4$
$\quad 4(N) + 14 = 2(2 + N + 4)$
$\quad\; 4N + 14 = 2N + 12$
$\qquad\quad 2N = -2$
$\qquad\quad\; N = -1$
The desired integers are **–1, 1,** and **3.**

3. $\dfrac{30}{100}(T) = 81,150$
$\qquad\quad T = \mathbf{270,500}$

4. $R_M T_M = R_H T_H$; $R_M = 8$; $R_H = 16$;
$T_M = T_H + 4$

$\quad 8(T_H + 4) = 16T_H$
$\quad 8T_H + 32 = 16T_H$
$\qquad\quad\; 32 = 8T_H$
$\qquad\quad\; T_H = \mathbf{4 \ hr}$

5. $R_T T_T = R_G T_G$; $R_T = R_G + 55$;
$T_T = 4$; $T_G = 48$

$\quad (R_G + 55)4 = R_G(48)$
$\quad 4R_G + 220 = 48R_G$
$\qquad\quad\; 220 = 44R_G$
$\qquad\quad\; R_G = 5$

$R_G T_G = 5(48) = \mathbf{240 \ miles}$

6. $\qquad \dfrac{1 + m}{m} - \dfrac{3}{m} = 0$
$\quad \dfrac{(1 + m)}{m}(m) - \dfrac{3}{m}(m) = 0$
$\qquad\qquad 1 + m - 3 = 0$
$\qquad\qquad\qquad\quad m = \mathbf{2}$

7. $\qquad\qquad \dfrac{3}{4x} = \dfrac{2}{x + 5}$
$\quad \dfrac{3}{4x}(x + 5)(4x) = \dfrac{2}{(x + 5)}(x + 5)(4x)$
$\qquad\quad 3x + 15 = 8x$
$\qquad\qquad\quad 15 = 5x$
$\qquad\qquad\quad\; 3 = x$

8.
$$\frac{x}{5} - \frac{3 + x}{7} = 0$$
$$\frac{x}{5}(35) - \frac{(3 + x)}{7}(35) = 0$$
$$7x - 15 - 5x = 0$$
$$2x = 15$$
$$x = \frac{15}{2}$$

9.
$$\frac{2}{x} - \frac{3}{x - 1} = 0$$
$$\frac{2}{x}(x)(x - 1) - \frac{3}{x - 1}(x)(x - 1) = 0$$
$$2x - 2 - 3x = 0$$
$$-2 = x$$

10.
$$\frac{a}{n} - m + \frac{5k}{x} = y$$
$$\frac{a}{n}(nx) - m(nx) + \frac{5k}{x}(nx) = y(nx)$$
$$ax - mnx + 5kn = ynx$$
$$ax = ynx + mnx - 5kn$$
$$ax = n(yx + mx - 5k)$$
$$\frac{ax}{yx + mx - 5k} = n$$

11.
$$\frac{2c}{a} - x = \frac{b}{d}$$
$$\frac{2c}{a}(ad) - x(ad) = \frac{b}{d}(ad)$$
$$2cd - xad = ba$$
$$d(2c - xa) = ba$$
$$d = \frac{ba}{2c - xa}$$

12.
$abxy = (ab)xy$ associative
$= (ba)xy$ commutative
$= b(ax)y$ associative
$= b(xa)y$ commutative
$= (bx)ay$ associative
$= (xb)ay$ commutative
$= xb(ay)$ associative
$= xb(ya)$ commutative
$= xbya$ removed parentheses

13. $x = \dfrac{-b \pm \sqrt{b^2 - 4ac}}{2a}$
$$= \frac{-(3) \pm \sqrt{3^2 - 4(2)(-2)}}{2(2)} = \frac{-3 \pm 5}{4}$$
$$= \frac{1}{2}, -2$$

14. $\dfrac{4}{x^2 - 4} + \dfrac{3x}{x - 2}$
$$= \frac{4}{(x + 2)(x - 2)} + \frac{3x(x + 2)}{(x + 2)(x - 2)}$$
$$= \frac{4 + 3x^2 + 6x}{x^2 - 4} = \frac{3x^2 + 6x + 4}{x^2 - 4}$$

15. $\dfrac{7}{x + 5} - \dfrac{2x}{x^2 - 25}$
$$= \frac{7(x - 5)}{(x + 5)(x - 5)} - \frac{2x}{(x + 5)(x - 5)}$$
$$= \frac{7x - 35 - 2x}{x^2 - 25} = \frac{5x - 35}{x^2 - 25}$$

16. Estimate:
$$\sqrt{714,200 \times 10^{-15}} = \sqrt{7.14 \times 10^{-10}}$$
$$= \sqrt{7.14}\sqrt{10^{-10}} = (2.5)(10^{-5})$$
Approximate:
$$\sqrt{714,200 \times 10^{-15}} = \sqrt{7.14 \times 10^{-10}}$$
$$= \sqrt{7.14}\sqrt{10^{-10}} = 2.67208 \times 10^{-5}$$

17. $D^2 = 4^2 + 6^2$
$D^2 = 16 + 36$
$D^2 = 52$
$D = \sqrt{52}$
$D = 2\sqrt{13}$

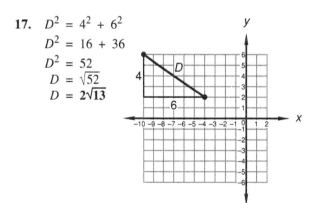

18. $2x^0(x - 2) - 3x - 4 - [-(-2)] - 7^0 = -2x - 4$
$$2x - 4 - 3x - 4 - 2 - 1 = -2x - 4$$
$$-x - 11 = -2x - 4$$
$$x = 7$$

19. $\dfrac{(21,000 \times 10^{50})(0.0006 \times 10^{15})}{(0.007 \times 10^{20})(9000 \times 10^{-40})}$
$$= \frac{(2.1 \times 10^{54})(6 \times 10^{11})}{(7 \times 10^{17})(9 \times 10^{-37})} = 2 \times 10^{84}$$

20.
$$63 = -x^2 - 16x$$
$$x^2 + 16x + 63 = 0$$
$$(x + 7)(x + 9) = 0$$

If $x + 7 = 0$, $x = -7$
$$63 = -(-7)^2 - 16(-7)$$
$$63 = -49 + 112$$
$$63 = 63 \quad \text{check}$$

If $x + 9 = 0$, $x = -9$
$$63 = -(-9)^2 - 16(-9)$$
$$63 = -81 + 144$$
$$63 = 63 \quad \text{check}$$

21. $4\sqrt{20,000} - 15\sqrt{8} + 3\sqrt{2}(4\sqrt{2} - 5)$
$$= 4\sqrt{2 \cdot 10,000} - 15\sqrt{4 \cdot 2} + 3 \cdot 4\sqrt{2}\sqrt{2}$$
$$- 5 \cdot 3\sqrt{2} = 400\sqrt{2} - 30\sqrt{2} + 24 - 15\sqrt{2}$$
$$= \mathbf{355\sqrt{2} + 24}$$

22. $\dfrac{3}{x - 5} + \dfrac{2}{x} + \dfrac{7}{x^2 - 25}$
$$= \frac{3x(x + 5) + 2(x^2 - 25) + 7x}{x(x + 5)(x - 5)}$$
$$= \frac{3x^2 + 15x + 2x^2 - 50 + 7x}{x(x^2 - 25)}$$
$$= \frac{\mathbf{5x^2 + 22x - 50}}{\mathbf{x(x^2 - 25)}}$$

23. $\dfrac{-x}{x + 5} - \dfrac{3x}{x^2 + 3x - 10}$
$$= \frac{-x(x - 2) - 3x}{(x + 5)(x - 2)} = \frac{-x^2 + 2x - 3x}{x^2 + 3x - 10}$$
$$= \frac{\mathbf{-x^2 - x}}{\mathbf{x^2 + 3x - 10}}$$

24. $-x^2 - x(xy - xy^2)$
$$= -(-2)^2 - (-2)((-2)(-3) - (-2)(-3)^2)$$
$$= -4 + 2(6 + 18) = \mathbf{44}$$

25. $\dfrac{(x^2)^{-2} yyx^{-2}}{(x^2 y^{-2})^{-3}} = \dfrac{x^{-4} y^2 x^{-2}}{x^{-6} y^6} = \mathbf{y^{-4}}$

26. $-|x| - 2 < -4$; $D = \{\text{Reals}\}$
$$-|x| < -2$$
$$|x| > 2$$

27. $-x + 2 \leq 7$; $D = \{\text{Integers}\}$
$$-x \leq 5$$
$$x \geq -5$$

28. (a) $\dfrac{4x^2 ay - 4xay}{4xay} = \dfrac{4xay(x - 1)}{4xay} = \mathbf{x - 1}$

(b) $\dfrac{-2^{-2}}{-(-2^0)^{-3}} = \dfrac{-(-1)^3}{-2^2} = \mathbf{-\dfrac{1}{4}}$

29. $\dfrac{4x^{-2}}{a^2}\left(\dfrac{x^2}{4a^{-2}} - \dfrac{2x^{-2}}{a^4}\right)$
$$= \frac{4x^{-2}x^2}{a^2 4a^{-2}} - \frac{4x^{-2} 2x^{-2}}{a^2 a^4} = \mathbf{1 - 8x^{-4}a^{-6}}$$

30. $V_{\text{Remain}} = V_{\text{Cylinder}} - V_{\text{Prism}}$
$$= [A_{\text{Cylinder base}} - A_{\text{Prism base}}] \times \text{length}$$
$$= \left[\pi(9)^2 - \frac{6(6)}{2}\right](10) \text{ m}^3$$
$$\approx [236.34](10) \text{ m}^3$$
$$\approx \mathbf{2363.4 \text{ m}^3}$$

PROBLEM SET 112

1. $R_P T_P + R_F T_F = 440$; $R_P = 70$;
$R_F = 30$; $T_P = T_F + 2$

$$70(T_F + 2) + 30T_F = 440$$
$$70T_F + 140 + 30T_F = 440$$
$$100T_F = 300$$
$$T_F = 3$$
$$T_F = 8 \text{ a.m.} + 3 \text{ hr} = \mathbf{11 \text{ a.m.}}$$

2. $R_S T_S = R_C T_C$; $R_S = 30$; $R_C = 50$;
$T_S = T_C + 2$

$$30(T_C + 2) = 50T_C$$
$$30T_C + 60 = 50T_C$$
$$60 = 20T_C$$
$$T_C = \mathbf{3 \text{ hr}}$$

3. (a) $10N_D + 25N_Q = 955$

(b) $N_D + N_Q = 64$

$$\begin{array}{r} \text{(a)} \quad 10N_D + 25N_Q = 955 \\ (-10)\text{(b)} \quad -10N_D - 10N_Q = -640 \\ \hline 15N_Q = 315 \\ N_Q = \mathbf{21} \end{array}$$

(b) $N_D + (21) = 64$
$$N_D = \mathbf{43}$$

4. $N \qquad N + 2 \qquad N + 4$
$$(-7)(5 + N + 2) = 5(-N - 4) + 11$$
$$-7N - 49 = -5N - 20 + 11$$
$$-40 = 2N$$
$$N = -20$$
The desired integers are **−20, −18,** and **−16.**

5. $\frac{17}{100}(T) = 3825$

$\quad\quad T = \textbf{22,500}$

6. Graph the points to find the slope.

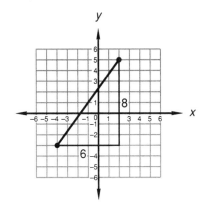

$m = \frac{8}{6} = \frac{4}{3}$

$y = \frac{4}{3}x + b$

Use the point $(2, 5)$ for x and y.

$5 = \frac{4}{3}(2) + b$

$\frac{15}{3} = \frac{8}{3} + b$

$b = \frac{7}{3}$

$\boldsymbol{y = \frac{4}{3}x + \frac{7}{3}}$

7. $-N = \frac{2}{3}$

$N = -\frac{2}{3}$

$\frac{1}{N} = \frac{1}{-\frac{2}{3}} = \boldsymbol{-\frac{3}{2}}$

8. $V_{\text{Walls}} = V_{\text{Outer cylinder}} - V_{\text{Inner cylinder}}$

$= [A_{\text{Outer cylinder}} - A_{\text{Inner cylinder}}](\text{height})$

$= [\pi(8)^2 - \pi(6)^2](3) \text{ m}^3$

$= [28\pi](3) \text{ m}^3$

$\approx \textbf{263.76 m}^3$

9. $\frac{2 + x}{4} + \frac{x}{2} = 5$

$\frac{(2 + x)}{4}(4) + \frac{x}{2}(4) = 5(4)$

$2 + x + 2x = 20$

$3x = 18$

$x = \textbf{6}$

10. $\frac{9}{4x} = \frac{5}{x + 11}$

$\frac{9}{4x}(4x)(x + 11) = \frac{5}{x + 11}(4x)(x + 11)$

$9x + 99 = 20x$

$99 = 11x$

$x = \textbf{9}$

11. $\frac{12}{x} + \frac{1}{4x} = 7$

$\frac{12}{x}(4x) + \frac{1}{4x}(4x) = 7(4x)$

$48 + 1 = 28x$

$49 = 28x$

$x = \boldsymbol{\frac{7}{4}}$

12. $\frac{x}{y} + \frac{1}{m} = p$

$\frac{x}{y}(ym) + \frac{1}{m}(ym) = p(ym)$

$xm + y = pym$

$xm = pym - y$

$xm = y(pm - 1)$

$y = \boldsymbol{\frac{xm}{pm - 1}}$

13. $\frac{k}{m} + \frac{1}{c} = x$

$\frac{k}{m}(mc) + \frac{1}{c}(mc) = x(mc)$

$kc + m = xmc$

$m = xmc - kc$

$m = c(xm - k)$

$c = \boldsymbol{\frac{m}{xm - k}}$

14. $\frac{1}{b} + \frac{k}{x} = y$

$\frac{1}{b}(bx) + \frac{k}{x}(bx) = y(bx)$

$x + kb = ybx$

$x = ybx - kb$

$x = b(yx - k)$

$b = \boldsymbol{\frac{x}{yx - k}}$

15. $\frac{1}{m} + \frac{b}{c} = \frac{x}{y}$

$\frac{1}{m}(mcy) + \frac{b}{c}(mcy) = \frac{x}{y}(mcy)$

$cy + bmy = xmc$

$cy = xmc - bmy$

$cy = m(xc - by)$

$m = \boldsymbol{\frac{cy}{xc - by}}$

16. $\dfrac{4}{x^2 - 25} - \dfrac{x}{x - 5} = \dfrac{4 - x(x + 5)}{(x + 5)(x - 5)}$

$= \dfrac{4 - x^2 - 5x}{x^2 - 25} = \dfrac{\mathbf{4 - 5x - x^2}}{\mathbf{x^2 - 25}}$

17. $\dfrac{3x}{x^2 - x - 6} - \dfrac{3}{x - 3}$

$= \dfrac{3x - 3(x + 2)}{(x + 2)(x - 3)} = \dfrac{3x - 3x - 6}{x^2 - x - 6}$

$= \dfrac{\mathbf{-6}}{\mathbf{x^2 - x - 6}}$

18. Estimate:

$\sqrt{0.000325 \times 10^{-41}} = \sqrt{3.25 \times 10^{-45}}$

$= \sqrt{3.25 \times 10 \times 10^{-46}} = \sqrt{3.25}\sqrt{10}\sqrt{10^{-46}}$

$= (1.8)(3.1)(10^{-23})$

Approximate:

$\sqrt{0.000325 \times 10^{-41}} = \sqrt{3.25 \times 10^{-45}}$

$= \sqrt{3.25 \times 10 \times 10^{-46}} = \sqrt{3.25}\sqrt{10}\sqrt{10^{-46}}$

$= \mathbf{(1.80278)(3.16228) \times 10^{-23}}$

19. $D^2 = 5^2 + 9^2$

$D^2 = 25 + 81$

$D^2 = 106$

$D = \mathbf{\sqrt{106}}$

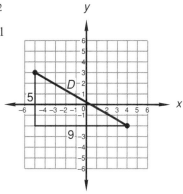

20. $-3^0(x - 4) - 2x - (-2x) - [-(-3)] + 5^0$

$\quad = 2(-x + 2)$

$-x + 4 - 2x + 2x - 3 + 1 = -2x + 4$

$\qquad\qquad -x + 2 = -2x + 4$

$\qquad\qquad\qquad x = \mathbf{2}$

21. $\dfrac{(35,000 \times 10^{-40})(300 \times 10^{15})}{(0.007 \times 10^{15})(15,000,000)}$

$= \dfrac{(3.5 \times 10^{-36})(3 \times 10^{17})}{(7 \times 10^{12})(1.5 \times 10^7)} = \mathbf{1 \times 10^{-38}}$

22. $\dfrac{(y^{-2})^0 y^0 y^2 yyx(xy)^2}{y^2 y^{-2}(y^2)^{-2} axy} = \dfrac{y^4 xx^2 y^2}{y^{-4} axy} = \mathbf{x^2 y^9 a^{-1}}$

23. $3\sqrt{30,000} - 5\sqrt{27} + 5\sqrt{3}(2\sqrt{3} - 2)$

$= 3\sqrt{3 \cdot 10,000} - 5\sqrt{9 \cdot 3} + 5 \cdot 2\sqrt{3}\sqrt{3}$

$\quad - 2 \cdot 5\sqrt{3} = 300\sqrt{3} - 15\sqrt{3} + 30 - 10\sqrt{3}$

$= \mathbf{275\sqrt{3} + 30}$

24. (a) $\dfrac{6x + 6}{6} = \dfrac{6(x + 1)}{6} = \mathbf{x + 1}$

(b) $\dfrac{-3^{-2}}{(-2)^2} = -\dfrac{1}{3^2(-2)^2} = \mathbf{-\dfrac{1}{36}}$

25. $-56 = 15x + x^2$

$\quad 0 = x^2 + 15x + 56$

$\quad 0 = (x + 7)(x + 8)$

If $x + 7 = 0$, $x = \mathbf{-7}$

$-56 = 15(-7) + (-7)^2$

$-56 = -105 + 49$

$-56 = -56$ check

If $x + 8 = 0$, $x = \mathbf{-8}$

$-56 = 15(-8) + (-8)^2$

$-56 = -120 + 64$

$-56 = -56$ check

26. $-x^2 - x(xy - y) = -(-3)^2 - (-3)((-3)(4) - 4)$

$= -9 + 3(-12 - 4) = \mathbf{-57}$

27. $-|x| - 4 > 2$; $D = \{\text{Reals}\}$

$\quad -|x| > 6$

$\quad |x| < -6$

No real numbers

28. $\dfrac{x^2 y^3 a^2}{a^{-2}} + \dfrac{a^5 ay^4}{a^2 yx^{-2}} - \dfrac{4a^2 y^5}{y^{-2} x^{-2}}$

$= x^2 y^3 a^4 + x^2 y^3 a^4 - 4x^2 y^7 a^2$

$= \mathbf{2x^2 y^3 a^4 - 4x^2 y^7 a^2}$

29. $\dfrac{4x^2 y^{-2}}{a^2}\left(\dfrac{x^{-2} y^{-2}}{a^{-2}} + \dfrac{3xy^{-2}}{a^2}\right)$

$= \dfrac{4x^2 y^{-2} x^{-2} y^{-2}}{a^2 a^{-2}} + \dfrac{4x^2 y^{-2} 3xy^{-2}}{a^2 a^2}$

$= \mathbf{4y^{-4} + 12x^3 y^{-4} a^{-4}}$

30. $\overset{\downarrow}{④}5,732.\overline{654}$

50,000

PROBLEM SET 113

1. $R_M T_M = R_P T_P$; $R_M = 2$; $R_P = 13$;

$T_M + T_P = 15$

$\qquad T_P = 15 - T_M$

$\quad 2T_M = 13(15 - T_M)$

$\quad 2T_M = 195 - 13T_M$

$\ 15T_M = 195$

$\quad\ T_M = 13$

$R_M T_M = 2(13) = \mathbf{26\ miles}$

2. $R_W T_W = R_C T_C$; $R_W = 4$; $R_C = 2$;
$$T_W = 120 - T_C$$

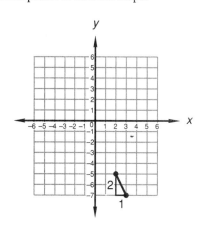

$$4(120 - T_C) = 2T_C$$
$$480 - 4T_C = 2T_C$$
$$480 = 6T_C$$
$$T_C = 80$$
$$R_C T_C = 2(80) = \textbf{160 miles}$$

3. (a) $50N_{50} + 100N_{100} = 260,000$
(b) $N_{50} + N_{100} = 5100$

$$\begin{array}{rl}
\text{(a)} & 50N_{50} + 100N_{100} = 260,000 \\
(-50)\text{(b)} & -50N_{50} - 50N_{100} = -255,000 \\
\hline
& 50N_{100} = 5000 \\
& N_{100} = \textbf{100}
\end{array}$$

(b) $N_{50} + (100) = 5100$
$$N_{50} = \textbf{5000}$$

4. $\dfrac{WP}{100}(20,000) = 4000$
$$WP = \textbf{20\%}$$

5. $N \quad N + 1 \quad N + 2 \quad N + 3$
$$(-7)(N + N + 2) = 12(-N - 3) + 4$$
$$-14N - 14 = -12N - 36 + 4$$
$$-2N = -18$$
$$N = 9$$
The desired integers are **9, 10, 11,** and **12.**

6. Graph the points to find the slope.

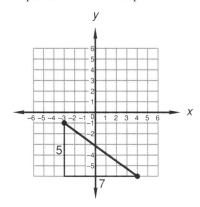

$$m = -\frac{5}{7}$$
$$y = -\frac{5}{7}x + b$$
Use the point $(-3, -1)$ for x and y.
$$-1 = -\frac{5}{7}(-3) + b$$
$$b = -\frac{22}{7}$$
$$y = -\frac{5}{7}x - \frac{22}{7}$$

7. Graph the points to find the slope.

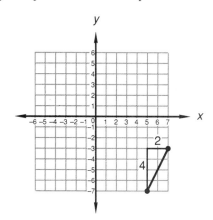

$$m = -\frac{2}{1} = -2$$
$$y = -2x + b$$
Use the point $(2, -5)$ for x and y.
$$-5 = -2(2) + b$$
$$b = -1$$
$$y = -2x - 1$$

8. Graph the points to find the slope.

$$m = \frac{4}{2} = 2$$
$$y = 2x + b$$
Use the point $(5, -7)$ for x and y.
$$-7 = 2(5) + b$$
$$b = -17$$
$$y = 2x - 17$$

9. (a) function: domain is specified and there is exactly one image for every member of the domain
(b) function: every x coordinate has only one y coordinate
(c) not a function: every $x > -3$ coordinate has two y coordinates
(d) function: every member of the domain has only one image
(e) not a function: 5 has two images
(f) function: every member of the domain has only one image

10. {Positive odd integers}

ADDITION: Not closed. (3) + (5) = 8

SUBTRACTION: Not closed. (7) − (1) = 6

MULTIPLICATION: Closed. The product of any two positive odd integers is a positive odd integer.

DIVISION: Not closed. $\dfrac{11}{9}$ is not a positive odd integer.

Thus the set of positive odd integers is closed for the operation of **multiplication.**

11. (a) vertical line: $x = \pm k$; $\boldsymbol{x = -3}$

(b) The desired equation is $y = mx + b$.

By inspection, $b = 6$.

By inspection, the slope for m is −.

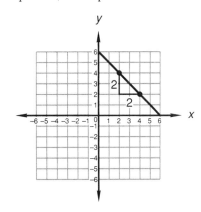

$|m| = \dfrac{2}{2} = 1$

So $b = 6$ and $m = -1$: $\boldsymbol{y = -x + 6}$

12.
$$\frac{4}{x} - \frac{2}{x-4} = 0$$
$$\frac{4}{x}(x)(x-4) - \frac{2}{x-4}(x)(x-4) = 0$$
$$4x - 16 - 2x = 0$$
$$2x = 16$$
$$x = \boldsymbol{8}$$

13.
$$\frac{x}{4} - \frac{x+6}{5} = 1$$
$$\frac{x}{4}(20) - \frac{(x+6)}{5}(20) = 1(20)$$
$$5x - 4x - 24 = 20$$
$$x = \boldsymbol{44}$$

14.
$$\frac{a}{b} + \frac{1}{c} = d$$
$$\frac{a}{b}(bc) + \frac{1}{c}(bc) = d(bc)$$
$$ac + b = dbc$$
$$ac = dbc - b$$
$$ac = b(dc - 1)$$
$$b = \boldsymbol{\frac{ac}{dc - 1}}$$

15.
$$\frac{a}{x} - \frac{1}{c} = \frac{b}{d}$$
$$\frac{a}{x}(xcd) - \frac{1}{c}(xcd) = \frac{b}{d}(xcd)$$
$$acd - xd = bxc$$
$$acd - bxc = xd$$
$$c(ad - bx) = xd$$
$$c = \boldsymbol{\frac{xd}{ad - bx}}$$

16.
$$\frac{p}{x} + \frac{1}{c} = k$$
$$\frac{p}{x}(xc) + \frac{1}{c}(xc) = k(xc)$$
$$pc + x = kxc$$
$$x = kxc - pc$$
$$x = c(kx - p)$$
$$c = \boldsymbol{\frac{x}{kx - p}}$$

17.
$$\frac{4}{x^2 - 9} - \frac{3}{x+3} = \frac{4 - 3(x-3)}{(x+3)(x-3)}$$
$$= \frac{4 - 3x + 9}{x^2 - 9} = \boldsymbol{\frac{13 - 3x}{x^2 - 9}}$$

18.
$$\frac{5}{x+2} - \frac{3x}{x^2 + 5x + 6}$$
$$= \frac{5(x+3) - 3x}{(x+2)(x+3)} = \frac{5x + 15 - 3x}{x^2 + 5x + 6}$$
$$= \boldsymbol{\frac{2x + 15}{x^2 + 5x + 6}}$$

19. Estimate:
$$\sqrt{0.0052 \times 10^{-7}} = \sqrt{5.2 \times 10^{-10}}$$
$$= \sqrt{5.2}\sqrt{10^{-10}} = (2.1)(10^{-5})$$

Approximate:
$$\sqrt{0.0052 \times 10^{-7}} = \sqrt{5.2 \times 10^{-10}}$$
$$= \sqrt{5.2}\sqrt{10^{-10}} = \boldsymbol{2.28035 \times 10^{-5}}$$

20. $|x| - 3 > 4$; $D = \{$Negative reals$\}$

    $|x| > 7$

$$\xleftarrow{\quad\quad\!\!\!\overset{\displaystyle\circ}{\quad}\quad\quad}$$
$$-9 \quad -8 \quad -7 \quad -6 \quad -5$$

21. $-(-2x + 4) - 3^0(3 - 3x) - (-2) = 4(3 - x^0)$

    $2x - 4 - 3 + 3x + 2 = 8$

               $5x = 13$

                 $x = \boldsymbol{\dfrac{13}{5}}$

22. $\dfrac{(42,000 \times 10^{46})(5000 \times 10^{-20})}{(0.00007 \times 10^{21})(0.0006 \times 10^{-14})}$

$= \dfrac{(4.2 \times 10^{50})(5 \times 10^{-17})}{(7 \times 10^{16})(6 \times 10^{-18})} = \mathbf{5 \times 10^{34}}$

23. $\dfrac{x^2 + 6x + 9}{x^2 + 3x} \div \dfrac{x^3 + 5x^2 + 6x}{x^2 + 2x}$

$= \dfrac{x^2 + 6x + 9}{x^2 + 3x} \cdot \dfrac{x^2 + 2x}{x^3 + 5x^2 + 6x}$

$= \dfrac{\cancel{(x + 3)}(x + 3)}{\cancel{x}(x + 3)} \cdot \dfrac{\cancel{x}\cancel{(x + 2)}}{\cancel{x}(x + 2)(x + 3)}$

$= \dfrac{1}{x}$

24. $k^2 = 2^2 + 4^2$

$k^2 = 4 + 16$

$k^2 = 20$

$k = \sqrt{20}$

$k = \mathbf{2\sqrt{5}}$

25. $\sqrt{50,000} - 25\sqrt{125} + 5\sqrt{5}(\sqrt{5} - 5)$

$= \sqrt{5 \cdot 10,000} - 25\sqrt{5 \cdot 25} + 5\sqrt{5}\sqrt{5} - 5 \cdot 5\sqrt{5}$

$= 100\sqrt{5} - 125\sqrt{5} + 25 - 25\sqrt{5}$

$= \mathbf{-50\sqrt{5} + 25}$

26. $\dfrac{xa + \dfrac{1}{a}}{\dfrac{x}{a} + a} = \dfrac{\dfrac{xa^2 + 1}{a}}{\dfrac{x + a^2}{a}} \cdot \dfrac{\dfrac{a}{x + a^2}}{\dfrac{a}{x + a^2}}$

$= \dfrac{xa^2 + 1}{x + a^2}$

27. $-2^0[(-2 + 3)(-2 - 4) - (-2 - 5)]$

$= -[(1)(-6) - (-7)] = \mathbf{-1}$

28. $4\sqrt{3} \in$ **Irrationals and reals**

29. $4\dfrac{1}{5}m + \dfrac{3}{4} = \dfrac{7}{8}$

$\dfrac{21}{5}m = \dfrac{7}{8} - \dfrac{3}{4}$

$\dfrac{21}{5}m = \dfrac{7}{8} - \dfrac{6}{8}$

$m = \dfrac{1}{8} \cdot \dfrac{5}{21}$

$m = \mathbf{\dfrac{5}{168}}$

30. (a) $y = x - 2$

$y = \dfrac{+1}{+1}x - 2$

(b) $y = -x + 2$

$y = \dfrac{-1}{+1}x + 2$

The first step is to graph each of these lines.

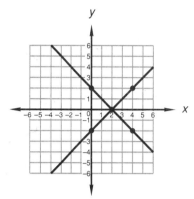

It appears that the lines cross at $x = 2$ and $y = 0$, so **(2, 0)** is the solution.

PROBLEM SET 114

1. $R_B T_B + 30 = R_N T_N$; $R_N = 2R_B$;
$T_N = T_B = 6$

$6R_B + 30 = 2R_B(6)$

$30 = 6R_B$

$R_B = \mathbf{5 \text{ mph}}$

2. $R_F T_F + 20 = R_E T_E$; $R_F = 40$;
$R_E = 60$; $T_F = T_E + 2$

$40(T_E + 2) + 20 = 60T_E$

$40T_E + 80 + 20 = 60T_E$

$100 = 20T_E$

$T_E = 5$

$T_E = 11$ a.m. $+ 5$ hr $= \mathbf{4 \text{ p.m.}}$

3. $\dfrac{40}{100}(T) = 3000$

$T = \mathbf{7500}$

$WN = \dfrac{60}{100}(7500)$

$WN = \mathbf{4500}$

4. $15,400 = P_P - \dfrac{23}{100}P_P$

$15,400 = \dfrac{77}{100}P_P$

$\mathbf{\$20,000} = P_P$

5. $N \qquad N + 1 \qquad N + 2$

$-7(N + N + 2) = 10(-N - 1) + 12$

$-14N - 14 = -10N - 10 + 12$

$-4N = 16$

$N = -4$

The desired integers are **−4, −3,** and **−2.**

6. $x = \dfrac{-b \pm \sqrt{b^2 - 4ac}}{2a}$

$= \dfrac{-(-3) \pm \sqrt{(-3)^2 - 4(-2)(2)}}{2(-2)}$

$= \dfrac{3 \pm \sqrt{9 + 16}}{-4} = \dfrac{3 \pm 5}{-4} = \mathbf{-2, \dfrac{1}{2}}$

7. (a) $f(x) = x + 2$

$f(2) = (2) + 2 = \mathbf{4}$

(b) $g(x) = x^2 + 4$

$g(0.6) = (0.6)^2 + 4 = \mathbf{4.36}$

(c) $\varnothing(x) = 3x + 5$

$\varnothing(x) = 3\left(\dfrac{1}{4}\right) + 5 = \dfrac{\mathbf{23}}{\mathbf{4}}$

8. $\dfrac{7x + 2}{x + 3} - \dfrac{x}{x^2 - 9}$

$= \dfrac{(7x + 2)(x - 3) - x}{(x + 3)(x - 3)}$

$= \dfrac{\mathbf{7x^2 - 20x - 6}}{\mathbf{x^2 - 9}}$

9. $-105(1) = \mathbf{-105}$

10. Graph the points to find the slope.

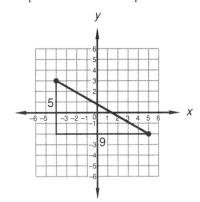

$m = -\dfrac{5}{9}$

$y = -\dfrac{5}{9}x + b$

Use the point $(5, -2)$ for x and y.

$-2 = -\dfrac{5}{9}(5) + b$

$b = \dfrac{7}{9}$

$\mathbf{y = -\dfrac{5}{9}x + \dfrac{7}{9}}$

11. Graph the points to find the slope.

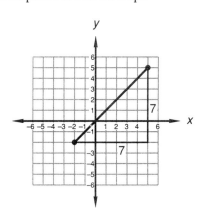

$m = \dfrac{7}{7} = 1$

$y = x + b$

Use the point $(5, 5)$ for x and y.

$5 = 5 + b$

$b = 0$

$\mathbf{y = x}$

12. Graph the points to find the slope.

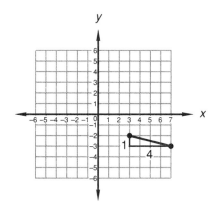

$m = -\dfrac{1}{4}$

$y = -\dfrac{1}{4}x + b$

Use the point $(3, -2)$ for x and y.

$-2 = -\dfrac{1}{4}(3) + b$

$b = -\dfrac{5}{4}$

$\mathbf{y = -\dfrac{1}{4}x - \dfrac{5}{4}}$

13. (a) function: every element in the domain has only one image

(b) function: every element in the domain has only one image

(c) function: every element in the domain has only one image

(d) function: every x coordinate has only one y coordinate

(e) function: every x coordinate has only one y coordinate

14. Range = $\{d, e\}$; Domain = $\{a, b, c\}$

15. **(a)** function: every element in the domain has only one image
(b) function: every element in the domain has only one image
(c) not a function: (-3) has three images

16. $\quad \dfrac{y}{3} + \dfrac{1}{4} = 2y$

$$\dfrac{y}{3}(12) + \dfrac{1}{4}(12) = 2y(12)$$
$$4y + 3 = 24y$$
$$3 = 20y$$
$$y = \dfrac{3}{20}$$

17. $\qquad \dfrac{4}{p} - \dfrac{3}{p-4} = 0$

$$\dfrac{4}{p}(p)(p-4) - \dfrac{3}{p-4}(p)(p-4) = 0$$
$$4p - 16 - 3p = 0$$
$$p = \mathbf{16}$$

18. $\qquad \dfrac{a}{c} + \dfrac{1}{x} = k$

$$\dfrac{a}{c}(xc) + \dfrac{1}{x}(xc) = k(xc)$$
$$ax + c = ckx$$
$$c = ckx - ax$$
$$c = x(ck - a)$$
$$x = \dfrac{c}{ck - a}$$

19. $11^2 = f^2 + 7^2$
$f^2 = 121 - 49$
$f^2 = 72$
$f = \sqrt{72}$
$f = \mathbf{6\sqrt{2}}$

20. $\dfrac{x^2 + 5x + 6}{x^3 + 7x^2 + 10x} \div \dfrac{x^3 + 11x^2 + 24x}{x^2 + 2x - 15}$

$= \dfrac{x^2 + 5x + 6}{x^3 + 7x^2 + 10x} \cdot \dfrac{x^2 + 2x - 15}{x^3 + 11x^2 + 24x}$

$= \dfrac{\cancel{(x+2)}\cancel{(x+3)}}{x\cancel{(x+5)}\cancel{(x+2)}} \cdot \dfrac{\cancel{(x+5)}(x-3)}{x(x+8)\cancel{(x+3)}}$

$= \dfrac{x-3}{x^3 + 8x^2}$

21. **(a)** $y = 2x + 2$

$$y = \dfrac{+2}{+1}x + 2$$

(b) $y = -x - 1$

$$y = \dfrac{-1}{+1}x - 1$$

The first step is to graph each of these lines.

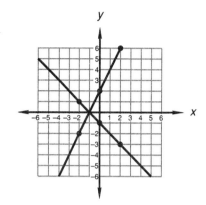

It appears that the lines cross at $x = -1$ and $y = 0$, so $(\mathbf{-1, 0})$ is the solution.

22. **(a)** horizontal line: $y = \pm k$; $y = \mathbf{-4}$
(b) The desired equation is $y = mx + b$.
By inspection, $b = 0$.
By inspection, the sign for m is $-$.

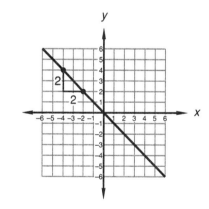

$|m| = \dfrac{2}{2} = 1$
So $b = 0$ and $m = -1$: $y = \mathbf{-x}$

23. $\dfrac{\dfrac{a}{x^2} - \dfrac{x}{a}}{\dfrac{x}{a} - \dfrac{1}{x^2}} = \dfrac{\dfrac{a^2 - x^3}{ax^2}}{\dfrac{x^3 - a}{ax^2}} \cdot \dfrac{\dfrac{ax^2}{x^3 - a}}{\dfrac{ax^2}{x^3 - a}}$

$= \dfrac{a^2 - x^3}{ax^2} \cdot \dfrac{ax^2}{x^3 - a}$

$= \dfrac{a^2 - x^3}{x^3 - a}$

24. $(x^3 + 5) \div (x - 2)$

$$
\begin{array}{r}
x^2 + 2x + 4 \\
x - 2 \overline{\smash{)}\ x^3 + 0x^2 + 0x + 5} \\
\underline{x^3 - 2x^2} \\
2x^2 + 0x \\
\underline{2x^2 - 4x} \\
4x + 5 \\
\underline{4x - 8} \\
13
\end{array}
$$

$$x^2 + 2x + 4 + \dfrac{13}{x - 2}$$

25. $-3[(-2^0 - 3) - (-5 + 7)(-2^2 + 3)]$
$\qquad - [(-6^0 - 2) + \sqrt[3]{-64}]$
$= -3[-4 - (2)(-1)] - [-3 - 4] = 6 + 7 = \mathbf{13}$

26. $WF\left(\dfrac{3}{5}\right) = 1\dfrac{1}{3}$

$\qquad WF = \left(\dfrac{4}{3}\right)\left(\dfrac{5}{3}\right)$

$\qquad WF = \dfrac{\mathbf{20}}{\mathbf{9}}$

27. $-x^0 - x^2(x - xy)$
$= -(-3)^0 - (-3)^2((-3) - (-3)(2))$
$= -1 - 9(-3 + 6) = \mathbf{-28}$

28. $\dfrac{x^2 yya}{y^{-2}x^4} + \dfrac{3x^{-2}yy^{-5}y^9}{a^{-1}yxx^{-1}} - \dfrac{3x^2 yyy^3 a}{x^2 yay^{-4}}$
$= x^{-2}y^4 a + 3x^{-2}y^4 a - 3y^8 = \mathbf{4x^{-2}y^4 a - 3y^8}$

29. $0.002\sqrt{3} \in$ **Irrationals and reals**

30. $4 - |x| < 3; \ D = \{\text{Integers}\}$
$\qquad 1 < |x|$

PROBLEM SET 115

1. $R_R T_R = R_T T_T; \ R_R = 20; \ R_T = 8;$
$T_R + T_T = 14$
$\qquad T_T = 14 - T_R$

$20T_R = 8(14 - T_R)$
$20T_R = 112 - 8T_R$
$28T_R = 112$
$\quad T_R = 4$

$R_R T_R = 20(4) = \mathbf{80 \ miles}$

2. $R_S T_S + 36 = R_E T_E; \ R_E = 2R_S;$
$T_S = T_E = 3$

$\qquad 3R_S + 36 = 2R_S(3)$
$\qquad\qquad 36 = 3R_S$
$\qquad\qquad R_S = 12$

$R_E = 2(12) = \mathbf{24 \ mph}$

3. $\dfrac{60}{100}P_P = P_P - 20$

$\qquad 20 = \dfrac{40}{100}P_P$
$\qquad \mathbf{\$50} = P_P$

4. (a) $10N_D + 25N_Q = 7500$
(b) $N_D = N_Q + 400$
Substitute (b) into (a) and get:
(a') $10(N_Q + 400) + 25N_Q = 7500$
$\qquad 10N_Q + 4000 + 25N_Q = 7500$
$\qquad\qquad\qquad\qquad 35N_Q = 3500$
$\qquad\qquad\qquad\qquad\quad N_Q = \mathbf{100}$

(b) $N_D = (100) + 400$
$\qquad N_D = \mathbf{500}$

5. $N \qquad N + 2 \qquad N + 4$
$-7(N + N + 4) = 11(-N - 2) + 27$
$\qquad -14N - 28 = -11N - 22 + 27$
$\qquad\qquad -3N = 33$
$\qquad\qquad\quad N = -11$
The desired integers are $\mathbf{-11, -9,}$ and $\mathbf{-7.}$

6. $x = \dfrac{-b \pm \sqrt{b^2 - 4ac}}{2a}$

$\quad = \dfrac{-(-6) \pm \sqrt{(-6)^2 - 4(4)(-4)}}{2(4)}$

$\quad = \dfrac{6 \pm \sqrt{36 + 64}}{8} = \dfrac{6 \pm 10}{8} = \mathbf{2, -\dfrac{1}{2}}$

7. Diameter of base $= 10$ m
L.S.A. $=$ Circumference $\times$ height
$\qquad = 2\pi(5)$ m $\times 10$ m
$\qquad \approx \mathbf{314 \ m^2}$

8. Graph the points to find the slope.

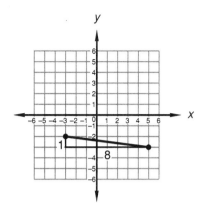

$$m = -\frac{1}{8}$$

$$y = -\frac{1}{8}x + b$$

Use the point $(5, -3)$ for x and y.

$$-3 = -\frac{1}{8}(5) + b$$

$$b = -\frac{19}{8}$$

$$\mathbf{y = -\frac{1}{8}x - \frac{19}{8}}$$

9. Graph the points to find the slope.

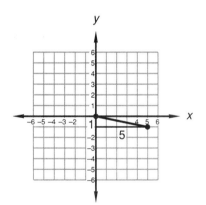

$$m = -\frac{1}{5}$$

$$y = -\frac{1}{5}x + b$$

Use the point $(0, 0)$ for x and y.

$$0 = -\frac{1}{5}(0) + b$$

$$b = 0$$

$$\mathbf{y = -\frac{1}{5}x}$$

10. $k(x) = x + 4$
   $k(4) = (4) + 4 = \mathbf{8}$

11. $p(x) = x^2 + 5$
   $p(4) = \varnothing$ because 4 is not in the domain

12. **(a)** function: every element in the domain has only one image
   (b) not a function: 3 has two images
   (c) function: every element in the domain has only one image
   (d) function: every x coordinate has only one y coordinate

13. Domain = $\{a, b, c\}$; Range = $\{4, 5\}$

14. **(a)** function: every element in the domain has only one image
   (b) function: every element in the domain has only one image
   (c) not a function: -7 has two images

15. $\dfrac{7}{y}(y)(y - 2) + \dfrac{3}{y - 2}(y)(y - 2) = 0$

$$7y - 14 + 3y = 0$$

$$10y = 14$$

$$y = \frac{7}{5}$$

16. $\dfrac{y}{7} - \dfrac{3}{4} = \dfrac{2y}{5}$

$$\frac{y}{7}(140) - \frac{3}{4}(140) = \frac{2y}{5}(140)$$

$$20y - 105 = 56y$$

$$-105 = 36y$$

$$y = -\frac{35}{12}$$

17. $\dfrac{a}{c} - \dfrac{1}{x} = b$

$$\frac{a}{c}(cx) - \frac{1}{x}(cx) = b(cx)$$

$$ax - c = bcx$$

$$ax = bcx + c$$

$$ax = c(bx + 1)$$

$$c = \frac{ax}{bx + 1}$$

18. $2 - |x| \geq -2$; $D = \{\text{Negative integers}\}$
   $4 \geq |x|$

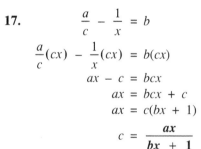

19. $D^2 = 1^2 + 8^2$
   $D^2 = 1 + 64$
   $D = \sqrt{65}$

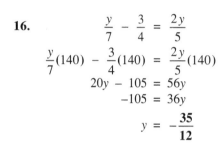

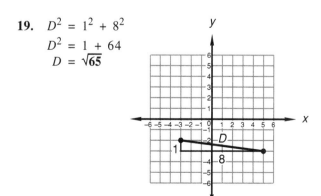

20. $x^0 - 3x(2 - 4^0) - (-3) - 2(x - 3)$
$= 3x - (-4)$
$1 - 3x + 3 - 2x + 6 = 3x + 4$
$6 = 8x$
$$x = \frac{3}{4}$$

21. $\dfrac{(30{,}000 \times 10^{-42})(7000 \times 10^{15})}{(0.00021 \times 10^{14})(1000 \times 10^{-23})}$

$= \dfrac{(3 \times 10^{-38})(7 \times 10^{18})}{(2.1 \times 10^{10})(1 \times 10^{-20})} = 1 \times 10^{-9}$

22. $\dfrac{(2x)^{-2} y^2 x^2 y^4 y}{y^0 (x^{-4}) y^2 y^{-2} y (x^{-4})^{-2}} = \dfrac{x^{-2} y^2 x^2 y^4 y}{4 x^{-4} y^2 y^{-2} y x^8}$

$= \dfrac{y^7}{4x^4 y} = \dfrac{y^6}{4x^4}$

23. $4\sqrt{50{,}000} - 3\sqrt{125} = 4\sqrt{5 \cdot 10{,}000} - 3\sqrt{25 \cdot 5}$
$= 400\sqrt{5} - 15\sqrt{5} = 385\sqrt{5}$

24. $\dfrac{-3 - 3x}{-3} = \dfrac{-3(1 + x)}{-3} = 1 + x$

25. $\dfrac{-2^{-2}}{(-2^0)^{-2}} = -\dfrac{(-1)^2}{2^2} = -\dfrac{1}{4}$

26. $80 = -x^2 + 18x$
$x^2 - 18x + 80 = 0$
$(x - 8)(x - 10) = 0$

If $x - 8 = 0$, $x = 8$
$80 = -(8)^2 + 18(8)$
$80 = -64 + 144$
$80 = 80$ check

If $x - 10 = 0$, $x = 10$
$80 = -(10)^2 + 18(10)$
$80 = -100 + 180$
$80 = 80$ check

27. $-x^3 - x^2 - x(x^0 - yx)$
$= -(-4)^3 - (-4)^2 - (-4)((-4)^0 - 3(-4))$
$= 64 - 16 + 4(1 + 12) = 48 + 52 = 100$

28. $-4 - |x| \le -4$
$0 \le |x|$
All real numbers

29. $\dfrac{x^{-3}}{y^2}\left(\dfrac{y^2}{x^3} - \dfrac{3y^{-3}}{x^{-2}}\right) = \dfrac{x^{-3}y^2}{y^2 x^3} - \dfrac{x^{-3} 3 y^{-3}}{y^2 x^{-2}}$
$= x^{-6} - 3x^{-1}y^{-5}$

30. $0.00\overset{\downarrow}{\underset{}{(3)}}18$
0.003

PROBLEM SET 116

1. $R_R T_R = R_T T_T$; $R_R = 8$; $R_T = 6$;
$T_R + T_T = 7$
$T_T = 7 - T_R$

$8T_R = 6(7 - T_R)$
$8T_R = 42 - 6T_R$
$14T_R = 42$
$T_R = 3$

$R_R T_R = 8(3) = $ **24 miles**

2. $R_N T_N + R_S T_S = 880$; $R_N = 40$;
$R_S = 60$; $T_N = T_S + 2$

$40(T_S + 2) + 60T_S = 880$
$40T_S + 80 + 60T_S = 880$
$100T_S = 800$
$T_S = 8$

$T_S = 6$ a.m. $+ 8$ hr $= $ **2 p.m.**

3. (a) $3N_S + 5N_L = 475$
(b) $N_S + N_L = 125$

$\quad$ (a) $\quad 3N_S + 5N_L = 475$
(-3)(b) $\underline{-3N_S - 3N_L = -375}$
$\qquad\qquad\quad 2N_L = 100$
$\qquad\qquad\quad\; N_L = $ **50**

(b) $N_S + (50) = 125$
$\qquad N_S = $ **75**

4. $\dfrac{WP}{100}(2500) = 300$
$WP = $ **12 percent**

5. $N \qquad N + 2 \qquad N + 4$
$-3(N + 2(N + 4)) + 3 = 8(-N - 2)$
$-3(N + 2N + 8) + 3 = -8N - 16$
$-9N - 24 + 3 = -8N - 16$
$-5 = N$
The desired integers are **−5, −3,** and **−1.**

6. $\dfrac{13}{18} = \dfrac{N_B}{2610}$

$N_B = \mathbf{1885}$

$N_M = 2610 - N_B = 2610 - 1885 = \mathbf{725}$

7. Graph the points to find the slope.

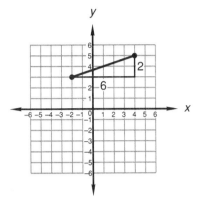

$m = \dfrac{2}{6} = \dfrac{1}{3}$

$y = \dfrac{1}{3}x + b$

Use the point $(4, 5)$ for x and y.

$5 = \dfrac{1}{3}(4) + b$

$b = \dfrac{11}{3}$

$\boldsymbol{y = \dfrac{1}{3}x + \dfrac{11}{3}}$

8. $2x + 3y = 7$

$3y = -2x + 7$

$y = -\dfrac{2}{3}x + \dfrac{7}{3}$

Since parallel lines have the same slope:

$y = -\dfrac{2}{3}x + b$

Use the point $(-2, 3)$ for x and y.

$3 = -\dfrac{2}{3}(-2) + b$

$b = \dfrac{5}{3}$

$\boldsymbol{y = -\dfrac{2}{3}x + \dfrac{5}{3}}$

9. $x = \dfrac{-b \pm \sqrt{b^2 - 4ac}}{2a}$

$= \dfrac{-(7) \pm \sqrt{7^2 - 4(36)\left(-\dfrac{1}{2}\right)}}{2(36)}$

$= \dfrac{-7 \pm \sqrt{49 + 72}}{72} = \dfrac{-7 \pm 11}{72}$

$= \boldsymbol{\dfrac{1}{18}, -\dfrac{1}{4}}$

10. (a) $a + (b + c) = (a + b) + c$

(b) $ab = ba$

11. (a) $f(2) = \varnothing$ because 2 is not in the domain

(b) $p(2) = (2) + 5 = \mathbf{7}$

12. (a) not a function: 6 has two images

(**b**) function: every element in the domain has only one image

(**c**) function: every x coordinate has only one y coordinate

(d) not a function: 4 has two images

(**e**) function: every element in the domain has only one image

13. Range $= \{\boldsymbol{p, 5}\}$

14. $\dfrac{5x}{3} - \dfrac{1}{3} = \dfrac{2x}{5}$

$\dfrac{5x}{3}(15) - \dfrac{1}{3}(15) = \dfrac{2x}{5}(15)$

$25x - 5 = 6x$

$19x = 5$

$x = \boldsymbol{\dfrac{5}{19}}$

15. $\dfrac{x - 2}{3x} = \dfrac{4}{x} - \dfrac{1}{5}$

$\dfrac{x - 2}{3x}(15x) = \dfrac{4}{x}(15x) - \dfrac{1}{5}(15x)$

$5x - 10 = 60 - 3x$

$8x = 70$

$x = \boldsymbol{\dfrac{35}{4}}$

16. $\dfrac{k}{m} - \dfrac{1}{c} + \dfrac{x}{y} = p$

$\dfrac{k}{m}(mcy) - \dfrac{1}{c}(mcy) + \dfrac{x}{y}(mcy) = p(mcy)$

$kcy - my + xmc = pmcy$

$kcy + xmc - pmcy = my$

$c(ky + xm - pmy) = my$

$c = \boldsymbol{\dfrac{my}{ky + xm - pmy}}$

17. Estimate: $\sqrt{0.000178563 \times 10^{-13}}$

$= \sqrt{1.79 \times 10^{-17}} = \sqrt{1.79 \times 10 \times 10^{-18}}$

$= \sqrt{1.79}\sqrt{10}\sqrt{10^{-18}} = (1.3)(3.1)(10^{-9})$

Approximate: $\sqrt{0.000178563 \times 10^{-13}}$

$= \sqrt{1.79 \times 10^{-17}} = \sqrt{1.79 \times 10 \times 10^{-18}}$

$= \sqrt{1.79}\sqrt{10}\sqrt{10^{-18}}$

$= \boldsymbol{(1.33791)(3.16228) \times 10^{-9}}$

18. $D^2 = 2^2 + 6^2$

$D^2 = 4 + 36$

$D = \sqrt{40}$

$D = \mathbf{2\sqrt{10}}$

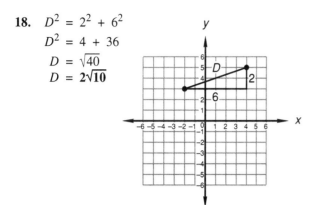

19. $-x^0 - (2x - 5) + x - (-3^2) - 2$

$= 3x(4^0 - 2) - 2^2$

$-1 - 2x + 5 + x + 9 - 2 = -3x - 4$

$2x = -15$

$x = -\dfrac{\mathbf{15}}{\mathbf{2}}$

20. $\dfrac{(21{,}000 \times 10^{-42})(7{,}000{,}000)}{(0.0003 \times 10^{-21})(700 \times 10^{15})}$

$= \dfrac{(2.1 \times 10^{-38})(7 \times 10^6)}{(3 \times 10^{-25})(7 \times 10^{17})} = \mathbf{7 \times 10^{-25}}$

21. $\dfrac{x(x^{-2}y)^{-2}(x^{-2}y)x^{-2}ya^2x}{(xy^{-2})^{-2}x^{-2}y^{-4}yy^3x^2}$

$= \dfrac{xx^4y^{-2}x^{-2}yx^{-2}ya^2x}{x^{-2}y^4x^{-2}y^{-4}yy^3x^2} = \dfrac{x^2a^2}{x^{-2}y^4} = \mathbf{x^4a^2y^{-4}}$

22. $\sqrt{150{,}000} + 2\sqrt{3} \cdot 5\sqrt{5} + 2\sqrt{15}(\sqrt{15} - 3)$

$= \sqrt{15 \cdot 10{,}000} + 10\sqrt{15} + 30 - 6\sqrt{15}$

$= 100\sqrt{15} + 4\sqrt{15} + 30 = \mathbf{104\sqrt{15} + 30}$

23. $\dfrac{6xy + 6xy^2}{6xy} = \dfrac{6xy(1 + y)}{6xy} = \mathbf{1 + y}$

24. $\dfrac{-3^{-2}}{-(-3)^{-3}} = \dfrac{(-3)^3}{3^2} = \mathbf{-3}$

25. $120 = -22x - x^2$

$x^2 + 22x + 120 = 0$

$(x + 10)(x + 12) = 0$

If $x + 10 = 0$, $\mathbf{x = -10}$

$120 = -22(-10) - (-10)^2$

$120 = 220 - 100$

$120 = 120$ check

If $x + 12 = 0$, $\mathbf{x = -12}$

$120 = -22(-12) - (-12)^2$

$120 = 264 - 144$

$120 = 120$ check

26. $-x^0 - x^2 - xy(x - y)$

$= -(-3)^0 - (-3)^2 - (-3)(4)((-3) - 4)$

$= -1 - 9 + 12(-7)$

$= \mathbf{-94}$

27. $-3 - |x| \le -3$; $D = \{\text{Integers}\}$

$\qquad 0 \le |x|$

All integer numbers

28. $\dfrac{4x^{-2}}{yx}\left(\dfrac{x^3}{y} - \dfrac{3y^3}{x^3}\right) = \dfrac{4x^{-2}x^3}{yxy} - \dfrac{4x^{-2}3y^3}{yxx^3}$

$= \mathbf{4y^{-2} - 12x^{-6}y^2}$

29. $V_{\text{Cyl.}} = A_{\text{Base}} \times \text{height}$

$= \left[\dfrac{\pi(12)^2}{2} + 17(12) + \dfrac{11(12)}{2}\right](4) \text{ cm}^3$

$\approx [496.08](4) \text{ cm}^3$

$\approx (1984.32)\left(\dfrac{1}{100}\right)\left(\dfrac{1}{100}\right)\left(\dfrac{1}{100}\right) \text{ m}^3$

$\approx \mathbf{1.98 \times 10^{-3} \text{ m}^3}$

S.A. $= 2A_{\text{Base}} + (P \times \text{height})$

$= 2(496.08) + [(57 + \sqrt{265} + 12\pi)(4)]$

$\approx 992.16 + 443.84$

$\approx \mathbf{1436 \text{ cm}^2}$

$V_{\text{Cone}} = \dfrac{1}{3}V_{\text{Cylinder}}$

$= \dfrac{1}{3}(1.98 \times 10^{-3} \text{ m}^3)$

$= \mathbf{6.61 \times 10^{-4} \text{ m}^3}$

30. Convert 26,000 square miles to square kilometers:

$26{,}000 \text{ mi}^2 \times \dfrac{5280 \text{ ft}}{1 \text{ mi}} \times \dfrac{5280 \text{ ft}}{1 \text{ mi}} \times \dfrac{12 \text{ in.}}{1 \text{ ft}}$

$\times \dfrac{12 \text{ in.}}{1 \text{ ft}} \times \dfrac{2.54 \text{ cm}}{1 \text{ in.}} \times \dfrac{2.54 \text{ cm}}{1 \text{ in.}} \times \dfrac{1 \text{ m}}{100 \text{ cm}}$

$\times \dfrac{1 \text{ m}}{100 \text{ cm}} \times \dfrac{1 \text{ km}}{1000 \text{ m}} \times \dfrac{1 \text{ km}}{1000 \text{ m}}$

$= \dfrac{26{,}000(5280)(5280)(12)(12)(2.54)(2.54)}{(100)(100)(1000)(1000)} \text{ km}^2$

Problem Set 117

1. $\dfrac{7}{11} = \dfrac{N_R}{3102}$
$N_R = \mathbf{1974}$

2. $R_W T_W = R_R T_R$; $R_W = 2$; $R_R = 10$;
$T_W + T_R = 18$
$\qquad T_W = 18 - T_R$

$2(18 - T_R) = 10 T_R$
$36 - 2T_R = 10 T_R$
$\qquad 36 = 12 T_R$
$\qquad T_R = 3$

$R_R T_R = 10(3) = \mathbf{30\ miles}$

3. $R_R T_R + 6 = R_B T_B$;
$T_R = T_B = 3$; $R_B = 10$

$3R_R + 6 = 10(3)$
$\qquad 3R_R = 24$
$\qquad R_R = \mathbf{8\ mph}$

4. (a) $N_R + N_G = 178$
(b) $N_R = N_G + 8$
Substitute (b) into (a) and get:
(a') $(N_G + 8) + N_G = 178$
$\qquad\qquad 2N_G = 170$
$\qquad\qquad N_G = \mathbf{85}$

5. (a) $400N_G + 3N_P = 21{,}013$
(b) $N_G + N_P = 123$

$\qquad$ (a) $\quad 400N_G + 3N_P = 21{,}013$
(-3)(b) $\quad \underline{-3N_G - 3N_P = \ -369}$
$\qquad\qquad 397N_G \qquad\ \ = 20{,}644$
$\qquad\qquad\qquad N_G = \mathbf{52}$

(b) $(52) + N_P = 123$
$\qquad\qquad N_P = \mathbf{71}$

6. Graph the points to find the slope.

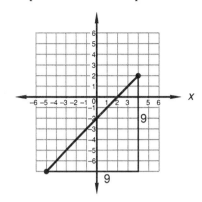

$m = \dfrac{9}{9} = 1$
$y = x + b$
Use the point $(4, 2)$ for x and y.
$2 = 4 + b$
$b = -2$
$\mathbf{y = x - 2}$

7. (a) $\quad f(x) = x + 3$
$\qquad f(-2) = (-2) + 3 = \mathbf{1}$
(b) $\quad g(x) = x - 4$
$\qquad g(-2) = (-2) - 4 = \mathbf{-6}$

8. $a(b + c) = ab + ac$

9. $\dfrac{10(94) + 10(76)}{10 + 10} = \dfrac{1700}{20} = \mathbf{85}$

10. $\sqrt{x^2 + 11} - 9 = 0$
$\qquad \sqrt{x^2 + 11} = 9$
$\qquad\quad x^2 + 11 = 81$
$\qquad\qquad\ x^2 = 70$
$\qquad\qquad\ x = \mathbf{\pm\sqrt{70}}$

Check $\sqrt{70}$:
$\sqrt{\left(\sqrt{70}\right)^2 + 11} - 9 = 0$
$\qquad\qquad \sqrt{81} - 9 = 0$
$\qquad\qquad\quad 9 - 9 = 0 \quad$ check

Check $-\sqrt{70}$:
$\sqrt{\left(-\sqrt{70}\right)^2 + 11} - 9 = 0$
$\qquad\qquad \sqrt{81} - 9 = 0$
$\qquad\qquad\quad 9 - 9 = 0 \quad$ check

11. $\sqrt{x} = 5\sqrt{2}$
$\quad x = \mathbf{50}$

Check: $\sqrt{50} = 5\sqrt{2}$
$\qquad\quad 5\sqrt{2} = 5\sqrt{2}$ check

12. $\dfrac{x}{3} - \dfrac{2+x}{5} = -3$

$\dfrac{x}{3}(15) - \dfrac{(2+x)}{5}(15) = -3(15)$

$5x - 6 - 3x = -45$

$2x = -39$

$x = -\dfrac{\mathbf{39}}{\mathbf{2}}$

13. $\dfrac{4}{x+3} - \dfrac{2}{2x} = 0$

$\dfrac{4}{x+3}(x+3)(2x) - \dfrac{2}{2x}(x+3)(2x) = 0$

$8x - 2x - 6 = 0$

$6x = 6$

$x = \mathbf{1}$

14. $\dfrac{x}{y} - \dfrac{1}{c} - d = k$

$\dfrac{x}{y}(cy) - \dfrac{1}{c}(cy) - d(cy) = k(cy)$

$xc - y - dcy = kcy$

$xc = kcy + y + dcy$

$xc = y(kc + dc + 1)$

$y = \dfrac{xc}{\mathbf{kc + dc + 1}}$

15. $c^2 + 5^2 = 9^2$

$c^2 = 81 - 25$

$c^2 = 56$

$c = \sqrt{56}$

$c = \mathbf{2\sqrt{14}}$

16. $\dfrac{x^2 - 25}{x^2 - 12x + 35} \div \dfrac{x^2 + x - 6}{x^2 - 4x - 21}$

$= \dfrac{x^2 - 25}{x^2 - 12x + 35} \cdot \dfrac{x^2 - 4x - 21}{x^2 + x - 6}$

$= \dfrac{(x+5)(x-5)}{(x-5)(x-7)} \cdot \dfrac{(x-7)(x+3)}{(x+3)(x-2)}$

$= \dfrac{\mathbf{x + 5}}{\mathbf{x - 2}}$

17. (a) $y = 3x$

$\quad y = \dfrac{+3}{+1}x$

(b) $y = -x + 4$

$\quad y = \dfrac{-1}{+1}x + 4$

The first step is to graph each of these lines.

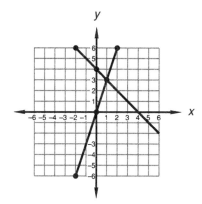

It appears that the lines cross at $x = 1$ and $y = 3$, so $\mathbf{(1, 3)}$ is the solution.

18. (a) horizontal line: $y = \pm k$; $\mathbf{y = -4}$

(b) The desired equation is $y = mx + b$.
By inspection, $b = 2$.
By inspection, the sign for m is $+$.

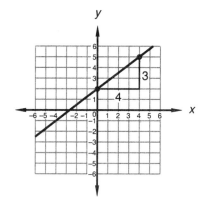

$|m| = \dfrac{3}{4}$

So $b = 2$ and $m = \dfrac{3}{4}$: $\mathbf{y = \dfrac{3}{4}x + 2}$

19. $\dfrac{\dfrac{x}{yz} - \dfrac{1}{z^2}}{\dfrac{a}{z} - \dfrac{3}{yz^2}} = \dfrac{\dfrac{xz - y}{yz^2}}{\dfrac{ayz - 3}{yz^2}} \cdot \dfrac{\dfrac{yz^2}{ayz - 3}}{\dfrac{yz^2}{ayz - 3}}$

$= \dfrac{\mathbf{xz - y}}{\mathbf{ayz - 3}}$

20. $(2x^3 + 3x^2 + 5x + 4) \div (x - 1)$

$$
\begin{array}{r}
2x^2 + 5x + 10 \\
x - 1 \overline{\smash{)}\ 2x^3 + 3x^2 + 5x + 4} \\
\underline{2x^3 - 2x^2} \\
5x^2 + 5x \\
\underline{5x^2 - 5x} \\
10x + 4 \\
\underline{10x - 10} \\
14
\end{array}
$$

$$2x^2 + 5x + 10 + \dfrac{14}{x - 1}$$

21. $-[(-2^0)(-3^2) - (-7 - 2) - \sqrt[5]{-32}\,]$
$\qquad - [-3(-5 + 7)]$
$= -(9 + 9 + 2) - (-6) = \mathbf{-14}$

22.
$$WF\left(2\frac{1}{8}\right) = 3\frac{4}{5}$$
$$WF\left(\frac{17}{8}\right)\left(\frac{8}{17}\right) = \frac{19}{5}\left(\frac{8}{17}\right)$$
$$WF = \frac{\mathbf{152}}{\mathbf{85}}$$

23. $-x^3 + (-x)^2 - x^2 - x(x - xy^2)$
$= -(-3)^3 + (-(-3))^2 - (-3)^2$
$\qquad - (-3)((-3) - (-3)(-2)^2)$
$= 27 + 9 - 9 + 3(-3 + 12) = \mathbf{54}$

24. $-3x^2yy^{-2} + \dfrac{2x^2}{y} - \dfrac{3xy^{-1}}{x^{-1}} + \dfrac{4x^3x^{-1}}{y}$
$= -3x^2y^{-1} + 2x^2y^{-1} - 3x^2y^{-1} + 4x^2y^{-1} = \mathbf{0}$

25. $\dfrac{3\sqrt{2}}{5} \in$ **Irrationals and reals**

26. $2\dfrac{1}{8}x + \dfrac{1}{4} = \dfrac{7}{8}$
$$\frac{17}{8}x = \frac{7}{8} - \frac{2}{8}$$
$$x = \frac{5}{8} \cdot \frac{8}{17}$$
$$x = \frac{\mathbf{5}}{\mathbf{17}}$$

27. $\dfrac{x}{y^{-2}x} - \dfrac{3}{y^3x^2} - \dfrac{2}{x + y}$
$= \dfrac{y^2(y^3x^3 + y^4x^2)}{y^3x^2(x + y)} - \dfrac{3(x + y)}{y^3x^2(x + y)}$
$\qquad - \dfrac{2(y^3x^2)}{y^3x^2(x + y)}$
$= \dfrac{y^5x^3 + y^6x^2 - 3x - 3y - 2y^3x^2}{y^3x^3 + y^4x^2}$

28. $\dfrac{3x + 2}{x - 4} - \dfrac{2x}{x^2 - 16}$
$= \dfrac{(3x + 2)(x + 4) - 2x}{(x + 4)(x - 4)}$
$= \dfrac{3x^2 + 14x + 8 - 2x}{x^2 - 16}$
$= \dfrac{\mathbf{3x^2 + 12x + 8}}{\mathbf{x^2 - 16}}$

29. $0.037474\overset{\downarrow}{\textcircled{7}}4$
0.0374747

30. $x = \dfrac{-b \pm \sqrt{b^2 - 4ac}}{2a}$

$= \dfrac{-(-9) \pm \sqrt{(-9)^2 - 4(21)\left(-\dfrac{3}{4}\right)}}{2(21)}$

$= \dfrac{9 \pm \sqrt{81 + 63}}{42} = \dfrac{9 \pm 12}{42} = \mathbf{-\dfrac{1}{14}, \dfrac{1}{2}}$

PROBLEM SET 118

1. $\dfrac{2}{9} = \dfrac{N_D}{774}$
$N_D = \mathbf{172}$

2. $R_RT_R = R_JT_J$; $R_R = 14$; $R_J = 7$;
$T_R + T_J = 3$
$\qquad T_J = 3 - T_R$

$\begin{aligned}
D_R &\\
\xleftarrow{\quad} &\xrightarrow{\quad}\\
D_J&
\end{aligned}$

$14T_R = 7(3 - T_R)$
$14T_R = 21 - 7T_R$
$21T_R = 21$
$\quad T_R = 1$

$R_RT_R = 14(1) = \mathbf{14\ miles}$

3. $N \qquad N + 2 \qquad N + 4 \qquad N + 6$
$-5(N + N + 6) = 6(-(N + 4 + N + 6)) + 10$
$\qquad -10N - 30 = -12N - 60 + 10$
$\qquad\qquad 2N = -20$
$\qquad\qquad N = -10$
The desired integers are $\mathbf{-10, -8, -6,}$ and $\mathbf{-4.}$

4. (a) $\dfrac{L}{S} = \dfrac{3}{1}$
$\qquad L = 3S$
(b) $L + S = 40$
Substitute (a) into (b) and get:
(b') $(3S) + S = 40$
$\qquad 4S = 40$
$\qquad S = \mathbf{10\ ft}$

(a) $L = 3(10) = \mathbf{30\ ft}$

5. $\dfrac{19}{100}(T) = 855$

$T = \mathbf{4500}$

6. Since parallel lines have the same slope:

$y = -\dfrac{1}{2}x + b$

Use the point $(5, -2)$ for x and y.

$-2 = -\dfrac{1}{2}(5) + b$

$b = \dfrac{1}{2}$

$\boldsymbol{y = -\dfrac{1}{2}x + \dfrac{1}{2}}$

7. (a) horizontal line: $y = \pm k$; $\mathbf{y = 4}$

(b) The desired equation is $y = mx + b$.
By inspection, $b = -1$.
By inspection, the sign for m is $-$.

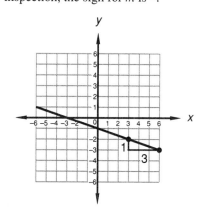

$|m| = \dfrac{1}{3}$

So $b = -1$ and $m = -\dfrac{1}{3}$: $\boldsymbol{y = -\dfrac{1}{3}x - 1}$

8. (a) function: every element in the domain has only one image
(b) not a function: 7 has two images
(c) function: every x coordinate has only one y coordinate
(d) not a function: every x coordinate has two y coordinates
(e) function: every element in the domain has only one image
(f) function: every element in the domain has only one image
(g) not a function: 4 has two images

9. $\sqrt{x-1} - 4 = 0$

$\sqrt{x-1} = 4$

$x - 1 = 16$

$x = \mathbf{17}$

Check: $\sqrt{17-1} - 4 = 0$

$4 - 4 = 0$ true

10. $\sqrt{3x} + 4 = 7$

$\sqrt{3x} = 3$

$3x = 9$

$x = \mathbf{3}$

Check: $\sqrt{3 \cdot 3} + 4 = 7$

$3 + 4 = 7$ true

11. $5\sqrt{2x} = 4$

$\sqrt{2x} = \dfrac{4}{5}$

$2x = \dfrac{16}{25}$

$x = \dfrac{\mathbf{8}}{\mathbf{25}}$

Check: $5\sqrt{2 \cdot \dfrac{8}{25}} = 4$

$5\left(\dfrac{4}{5}\right) = 4$ true

12. $m = \dfrac{y_2 - y_1}{x_2 - x_1} = \dfrac{-3 - 4}{5 - (-2)} = \dfrac{-7}{7} = \mathbf{-1}$

$m = \dfrac{4 - (-3)}{-2 - 5} = \dfrac{7}{-7} = \mathbf{-1}$

13. $\dfrac{2x}{3} - \dfrac{x-2}{5} + x = 7$

$\dfrac{2x}{3}(15) - \dfrac{(x-2)}{5}(15) + x(15) = 7(15)$

$10x - 3x + 6 + 15x = 105$

$22x = 99$

$x = \dfrac{\mathbf{9}}{\mathbf{2}}$

14. $\dfrac{x-2}{2x} - \dfrac{3}{x} = -\dfrac{1}{5}$

$\dfrac{(x-2)}{2x}(10x) - \dfrac{3}{x}(10x) = -\dfrac{1}{5}(10x)$

$5x - 10 - 30 = -2x$

$7x = 40$

$x = \dfrac{\mathbf{40}}{\mathbf{7}}$

15. $\dfrac{x}{y} + \dfrac{m}{n} - \dfrac{1}{c} = k$

$\dfrac{x}{y}(ncy) + \dfrac{m}{n}(ncy) - \dfrac{1}{c}(ncy) = k(ncy)$

$xnc + mcy - ny = kncy$

$xnc = kncy + ny - mcy$

$xnc = y(knc + n - mc)$

$\boldsymbol{y = \dfrac{xnc}{knc + n - mc}}$

16. Estimate: $\sqrt{0.00052843 \times 10^{40}}$

$= \sqrt{5.28 \times 10^{36}} = \sqrt{5.28}\sqrt{10^{36}}$

$= (2.3)(10^{18})$

Approximate: $\sqrt{0.00052843 \times 10^{40}}$

$= \sqrt{5.28 \times 10^{36}} = \sqrt{5.28}\sqrt{10^{36}}$

$= \mathbf{2.29783 \times 10^{18}}$

17. $D^2 = 9^2 + 8^2$

$D^2 = 81 + 64$

$D = \mathbf{\sqrt{145}}$

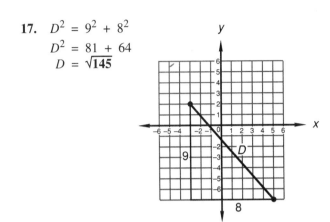

18. $-3(x - 4^0) - (-2) - 3(-x - y^0) = 3(x - 2^2)$

$-3x + 3 + 2 + 3x + 3 = 3x - 12$

$20 = 3x$

$x = \mathbf{\dfrac{20}{3}}$

19. $\dfrac{(5000 \times 10^{-15})(30,000 \times 10^{41})}{(6000 \times 10^{-14})(0.000025 \times 10^{-50})}$

$= \dfrac{(5 \times 10^{-12})(3 \times 10^{45})}{(6 \times 10^{-11})(2.5 \times 10^{-55})} = \mathbf{1 \times 10^{99}}$

20. $\dfrac{x^{-2}(x^{-4}x)^3}{x^{-3}x^0xx^{-2}} = \dfrac{x^{-2}x^{-9}}{x^{-4}} = \mathbf{x^{-7}}$

21. $\sqrt{2} \cdot 3\sqrt{12} + 2\sqrt{3} \cdot \sqrt{2} - 2\sqrt{6}(4\sqrt{6} - \sqrt{24})$

$= 3\sqrt{2}\sqrt{2 \cdot 6} + 2\sqrt{3}\sqrt{2} - 2 \cdot 4\sqrt{6}\sqrt{6}$

$+ 2\sqrt{6}\sqrt{6 \cdot 4} = 6\sqrt{6} + 2\sqrt{6} - 48 + 24$

$= \mathbf{8\sqrt{6} - 24}$

22. $\dfrac{4x + 4}{4} = \dfrac{4(x + 1)}{4} = \mathbf{x + 1}$

23. $\left(\dfrac{-3^{-2}}{3^{-3}}\right)^{-2} = \left(\dfrac{3^3}{-3^2}\right)^{-2} = \left(\dfrac{27}{-9}\right)^{-2} = (-3)^{-2}$

$= \dfrac{1}{(-3)^2} = \mathbf{\dfrac{1}{9}}$

24. $84 = -19x - x^2$

$x^2 + 19x + 84 = 0$

$(x + 7)(x + 12) = 0$

If $x + 7 = 0$, $x = \mathbf{-7}$

$84 = -19(-7) - (-7)^2$

$84 = 133 - 49$

$84 = 84$ check

If $x + 12 = 0$, $x = \mathbf{-12}$

$84 = -19(-12) - (-12)^2$

$84 = 228 - 144$

$84 = 84$ check

25. $-xy(y - x^0) - x^2 - x^0$

$= -(-3)(-5)((-5) - (-3)^0) - (-3)^2 - (-3)^0$

$= -15(-6) - 9 - 1 = \mathbf{80}$

26. $4 - |x| - 2 \geq 4$; $D = \{\text{Reals}\}$

$-2 \geq |x|$

No real numbers

27. $xy^2\left[\dfrac{y^{-2}}{x} - \dfrac{3x^0x}{(y^{-3})^2}\right] = \dfrac{xy^2y^{-2}}{x} - \dfrac{xy^2\,3x^0x}{(y^{-3})^2}$

$= \mathbf{1 - 3x^2y^8}$

28. **False**; $\{\text{Reals}\} \not\subset \{\text{Integers}\}$

29. $\dfrac{\dfrac{a}{x^2y} - \dfrac{1}{y^2}}{\dfrac{bc}{x^2y^2} - 1} = \dfrac{\dfrac{ay - x^2}{x^2y^2}}{\dfrac{bc - x^2y^2}{x^2y^2}} \cdot \dfrac{\dfrac{x^2y^2}{bc - x^2y^2}}{\dfrac{x^2y^2}{bc - x^2y^2}}$

$= \mathbf{\dfrac{ay - x^2}{bc - x^2y^2}}$

30. $WF\left(3\dfrac{1}{8}\right) = \dfrac{2}{3}$

$WF\left(\dfrac{25}{8}\right)\left(\dfrac{8}{25}\right) = \dfrac{2}{3}\left(\dfrac{8}{25}\right)$

$WF = \mathbf{\dfrac{16}{75}}$

31. $abcd = (ab)cd$ associative

$= (ba)cd$ commutative

$= ba(cd)$ associative

$= ba(dc)$ commutative

$= b(ad)c$ associative

$= b(da)c$ commutative

$= bdac$ removed parentheses

PROBLEM SET 119

1. $R_W T_W + R_R T_R = 66$; $R_W = 3$;
$R_R = 15$; $T_R = 2T_W$

$$|\!\!\overset{D_W}{\underset{}{\longmapsto}}\,\overset{D_R}{\longrightarrow}\!\!|$$

$3T_W + 30T_W = 66$
$33T_W = 66$
$T_W = 2$

$T_R = 2(2) = \textbf{4 hr}$

2. $R_S T_S + R_N T_N = 880$;
$R_S = 20$; $R_N = 60$;
$T_S = T_N + 4$

$$|\!\!\overset{D_S}{\underset{}{\longleftarrow}}\,\overset{D_N}{\bullet\longrightarrow}\!\!|$$

$20(T_N + 4) + 60T_N = 880$
$80T_N + 80 = 880$
$80T_N = 800$
$T_N = 10$

$T_S = 4$ p.m. $+ 10$ hr $= \textbf{2 a.m.}$

3. (a) $2N_R + 7N_C = 259$
(b) $N_R + N_C = 52$

(a) $2N_R + 7N_C = 259$
(-2)(b) $\underline{-2N_R - 2N_C = -104}$
$5N_C = 155$
$N_C = \textbf{31}$

(b) $N_R + (31) = 52$
$N_R = \textbf{21}$

4. $\dfrac{5}{8} = \dfrac{N_R}{968}$
$N_R = \textbf{605}$
$N_M = 968 - N_R = 968 - (605) = \textbf{363}$

5. $\dfrac{63}{100}(T) = 4788$
$T = \textbf{7600}$

6. $m = \dfrac{y_2 - y_1}{x_2 - x_1} = \dfrac{-3 - 2}{7 - 4} = -\dfrac{5}{3}$
$y = -\dfrac{5}{3}x + b$
Use the point $(4, 2)$ for x and y.
$2 = -\dfrac{5}{3}(4) + b$
$b = \dfrac{26}{3}$
$y = -\dfrac{5}{3}x + \dfrac{26}{3}$

7. $f\left(\dfrac{1}{2}\right) = \left(\dfrac{1}{2}\right)^2 + 4 = \dfrac{\textbf{17}}{\textbf{4}}$

8. $7\sqrt{x} = 14\sqrt{2}$
$\sqrt{x} = 2\sqrt{2}$
$x = \textbf{8}$

Check: $7\sqrt{8} = 14\sqrt{2}$
$14\sqrt{2} = 14\sqrt{2}$ true

9. $\sqrt{x - 3} = 5$
$x - 3 = 25$
$x = \textbf{28}$

Check: $\sqrt{28 - 3} = 5$
$5 = 5$ true

10. $\sqrt{x} + 2 = 7$
$\sqrt{x} = 5$
$x = \textbf{25}$

Check: $\sqrt{25} + 2 = 7$
$5 + 2 = 7$ true

11. **Inconsistent;** because they have no common solution.

12. $\dfrac{4x}{3} - \dfrac{x + 2}{5} = 7$
$\dfrac{4x}{3}(15) - \dfrac{(x + 2)}{5}(15) = 7(15)$
$20x - 3x - 6 = 105$
$17x = 111$
$x = \dfrac{\textbf{111}}{\textbf{17}}$

13. $\dfrac{p - 3}{p} = \dfrac{5}{3p} - \dfrac{1}{4}$
$\dfrac{(p - 3)}{p}(12p) = \dfrac{5}{3p}(12p) - \dfrac{1}{4}(12p)$
$12p - 36 = 20 - 3p$
$15p = 56$
$p = \dfrac{\textbf{56}}{\textbf{15}}$

14. $\dfrac{k}{x} - \dfrac{1}{c} + p = m$
$\dfrac{k}{x}(xc) - \dfrac{1}{c}(xc) + p(xc) = m(xc)$
$kc - x + pxc = mxc$
$kc = mxc + x - pxc$
$kc = x(mc + 1 - pc)$
$x = \dfrac{\textbf{kc}}{\textbf{1 + mc - pc}}$

15. $b^2 + 4^2 = 7^2$
$b^2 = 33$
$b = \sqrt{\textbf{33}}$

16. $\dfrac{x^4 + 7x^3 + 12x^2}{x^2 - 16}$

$\quad \div \dfrac{x^4 - 2x^3 - 15x^2}{x^2 - 9x + 20}$

$= \dfrac{x^4 + 7x^3 + 12x^2}{x^2 - 16}$

$\quad \cdot \dfrac{x^2 - 9x + 20}{x^4 - 2x^3 - 15x^2}$

$= \dfrac{x^2(x + 4)(x + 3)}{(x + 4)(x - 4)} \cdot \dfrac{(x - 4)(x - 5)}{x^2(x - 5)(x + 3)} = 1$

17. (a) $y = -x - 2$

$\quad y = \dfrac{-1}{+1}x - 2$

(b) $y = \dfrac{1}{2}x + 1$

$\quad y = \dfrac{+1}{+2}x + 1$

The first step is to graph each of these lines.

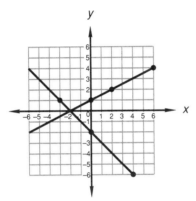

It appears that the lines cross at $x = -2$ and $y = 0$, so **(–2, 0)** is the solution.

18. (a) vertical line: $x = \pm k$; **$x = 5$**

(b) The desired equation is $y = mx + b$.
By inspection, $b = -4$.
By inspection, the sign for m is –.

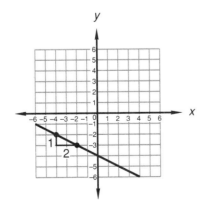

$|m| = \dfrac{1}{2}$

So $b = -4$ and $m = -\dfrac{1}{2}$: $\; y = -\dfrac{1}{2}x - 4$

19. $\dfrac{\dfrac{x}{y^2 a} - \dfrac{a}{y^2}}{\dfrac{p}{y} - \dfrac{3}{ay^2}} = \dfrac{\dfrac{x - a^2}{ay^2}}{\dfrac{pay - 3}{ay^2}} \cdot \dfrac{\dfrac{ay^2}{pay - 3}}{\dfrac{ay^2}{pay - 3}}$

$\quad = \dfrac{x - a^2}{pay - 3}$

20. $(x^3 - 2x^2 - 5) \div (x - 1)$

$$
\begin{array}{r}
x^2 - x - 1 \\
x - 1 \overline{\smash{)}\, x^3 - 2x^2 + 0x - 5} \\
\underline{x^3 - x^2} \\
-x^2 + 0x \\
\underline{-x^2 + x} \\
-x - 5 \\
\underline{-x + 1} \\
-6
\end{array}
$$

$x^2 - x - 1 - \dfrac{6}{x - 1}$

21. $WF\left(\dfrac{5}{16}\right) = 14\dfrac{3}{8}$

$\quad WF\left(\dfrac{5}{16}\right)\left(\dfrac{16}{5}\right) = \dfrac{115}{8}\left(\dfrac{16}{5}\right)$

$\quad\quad\quad WF = 46$

22. $-2^0 - (-2^0) - [(-3 - 2) - (-5 + 7)]$

$\quad = -1 + 1 - (-5 - 2) = 7$

23. $-x^0 - x^2 - x^3 + xy(x - xy)$

$\quad = -(-3)^0 - (-3)^2 - (-3)^3$

$\quad\quad + (-3)(2)((-3) - (-3)(2))$

$\quad = -1 - 9 + 27 - 6(3) = -1$

24. $-3 \in$ **Integers, rationals, and reals**

25. $\quad\quad x^2 + 40 = -22x$

$\quad x^2 + 22x + 40 = 0$

$\quad (x + 2)(x + 20) = 0$

If $x + 2 = 0$, $x = -2$

$(-2)^2 + 40 = -22(-2)$

$\quad 4 + 40 = 44 \quad$ check

If $x + 20 = 0$, $x = -20$

$(-20)^2 + 40 = -22(-20)$

$\quad 400 + 40 = 440 \quad$ check

26. $x^2y - \dfrac{3x^3y}{x} + \dfrac{2x^4y^2}{yx^{-2}} + \dfrac{5x^2}{y^{-1}}$

$\quad = x^2y - 3x^2y + 2x^6y + 5x^2y = \mathbf{3x^2y + 2x^6y}$

27. $\dfrac{x}{y^2} + \dfrac{2x^2}{xy^2} - \dfrac{x^2}{y - 1}$

$= \dfrac{x(y - 1) + 2x(y - 1) - x^2y^2}{y^2(y - 1)}$

$= \dfrac{xy - x + 2xy - 2x - x^2y^2}{y^2(y - 1)}$

$= \dfrac{\mathbf{3xy - 3x - x^2y^2}}{\mathbf{y^2(y - 1)}}$

28. $\dfrac{4x - 2}{x - 3} - \dfrac{x + 3}{x^2 - 9} = \dfrac{4x - 2}{x - 3}$

$\quad - \dfrac{x + 3}{(x + 3)(x - 3)} = \dfrac{4x - 2 - 1}{x - 3}$

$= \dfrac{\mathbf{4x - 3}}{\mathbf{x - 3}}$

29. $32.0758158\textcircled{1}5$
$\quad \overset{\downarrow}{}$
32.07581582

30. $\dfrac{1}{N} = -\dfrac{1}{5}$
$\quad N = \mathbf{-5}$

PROBLEM SET 120

1. $R_H T_H = R_M T_M + 60$;
$R_H = 17$; $T_H = T_M = 20$

$17(20) = 20R_M + 60$
$\quad 280 = 20R_M$
$\quad R_M = \mathbf{14\ mph}$

2. $R_W T_W = R_R T_R$; $R_W = 4$; $R_R = 24$;
$T_W + T_R = 14$
$\quad T_W = 14 - T_R$

$4(14 - T_R) = 24T_R$
$\quad 56 = 28T_R$
$\quad T_R = 2$

$R_R T_R = 24(2) = \mathbf{48\ miles}$

3. $3(13 - N) + 11 = 2N$
$\quad 39 - 3N + 11 = 2N$
$\quad\quad\quad\quad 50 = 5N$
$\quad\quad\quad\quad N = \mathbf{10}$

4. $120 = P_P - \dfrac{20}{100}P_P$

$120 = \dfrac{80}{100}P_P$
$150 = P_P$

$M_D = \dfrac{10}{100}(150) = 15$
$S_P = P_P - M_D = 150 - 15 = \mathbf{\$135}$

5. (a) $7N_P + 6N_A = 346$
(b) $N_P = N_A + 29$
Substitute (b) into (a) and get:
(a′) $7(N_A + 29) + 6N_A = 346$
$\quad 7N_A + 203 + 6N_A = 346$
$\quad\quad\quad\quad 13N_A = 143$
$\quad\quad\quad\quad N_A = \mathbf{11}$

(b) $N_P = (11) + 29 = \mathbf{40}$

6. $y = -\dfrac{1}{7}x + b$
Use the point $(-3, 2)$ for x and y.
$2 = -\dfrac{1}{7}(-3) + b$
$b = \dfrac{11}{7}$
$\mathbf{y = -\dfrac{1}{7}x + \dfrac{11}{7}}$

7. (a) function
(b) not a function
(c) not a function
(d) function
(e) not a function
(f) not a function
(g) function

8. $4\sqrt{y} = 20$
$\quad \sqrt{y} = 5$
$\quad y = \mathbf{25}$

Check: $4\sqrt{25} = 20$
$\quad\quad\quad 20 = 20$

9. $\sqrt{x - 4} - 5 = 0$
$\quad \sqrt{x - 4} = 5$
$\quad x - 4 = 25$
$\quad\quad x = \mathbf{29}$

Check: $\sqrt{29 - 4} - 5 = 0$
$\quad\quad\quad 5 - 5 = 0$
$\quad\quad\quad 0 = 0$

10. $0 \le x + 6 < 11$; $D = \{$Reals$\}$
$\quad -6 \le x < 5$

11. $x < -1$ or $x \geq 5$; $D = \{$Integers$\}$

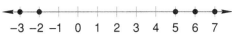

$$-3\ -2\ -1\ \ 0\ \ 1\ \ 2\ \ 3\ \ 4\ \ 5\ \ 6\ \ 7$$

12. $\{$Negative odd integers$\}$

ADDITION: Not closed. $(-1) + (-3) = -4$

SUBTRACTION: Not closed. $(-5) - (-7) = 2$

MULTIPLICATION: Not closed. $(-9)(-11) = 99$

DIVISION: Not closed. $\dfrac{(-5)}{(-3)}$ is not a negative odd integer.

Thus, the set of negative odd integers is not closed for any of the operations.

13.
$$\frac{x}{4} - \frac{x-2}{3} = 7$$
$$\frac{x}{4}(12) - \frac{(x-2)}{3}(12) = 7(12)$$
$$3x - 4x + 8 = 84$$
$$-x = 76$$
$$x = -76$$

14.
$$\frac{p-5}{p} = \frac{5}{3p} - \frac{1}{5}$$
$$\frac{(p-5)}{p}(15p) = \frac{5}{3p}(15p) - \frac{1}{5}(15p)$$
$$15p - 75 = 25 - 3p$$
$$18p = 100$$
$$p = \frac{50}{9}$$

15.
$$\frac{a}{x} - \frac{1}{c} = \frac{1}{d}$$
$$\frac{a}{x}(xcd) - \frac{1}{c}(xcd) = \frac{1}{d}(xcd)$$
$$acd - xd = xc$$
$$acd = xc + xd$$
$$acd = x(c + d)$$
$$x = \frac{acd}{c+d}$$

16. Estimate:
$$\sqrt{0.0004168521 \times 10^{-30}} = \sqrt{4.17 \times 10^{-34}}$$
$$= \sqrt{4.17}\sqrt{10^{-34}} = (2.01)(10^{-17})$$

Approximate:
$$\sqrt{0.0004168521 \times 10^{-30}} = \sqrt{4.17 \times 10^{-34}}$$
$$= \sqrt{4.17}\sqrt{10^{-34}} = \mathbf{2.04206 \times 10^{-17}}$$

17.
$$D^2 = 9^2 + 8^2$$
$$D^2 = 81 + 64$$
$$D^2 = 145$$
$$D = \sqrt{145}$$

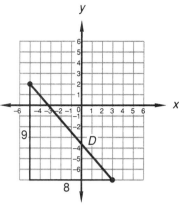

18. $p - 3p^0 - 2(p - 4^0) - (-3) - 2 = -3^0(2 - p)$
$$p - 3 - 2p + 2 + 3 - 2 = -2 + p$$
$$2 = 2p$$
$$p = \mathbf{1}$$

19.
$$\frac{(2000 \times 10^{15})(0.0004 \times 10^{21})}{(4000 \times 10^{-23})(1000 \times 10^{14})}$$
$$= \frac{(2 \times 10^{18})(4 \times 10^{17})}{(4 \times 10^{-20})(1 \times 10^{17})} = \mathbf{2 \times 10^{38}}$$

20.
$$\frac{3(x^{-2}y)^{-3}x^{-3}y^0y^2}{(x^{-3}y^{-2})^{-2}xx^0} = \frac{3x^6y^{-3}y^2x^{-3}}{x^6y^4x}$$
$$= \mathbf{3x^{-4}y^{-5}}$$

21. $2\sqrt{800} - 3\sqrt{18} = 2\sqrt{2 \cdot 400} - 3\sqrt{2 \cdot 9}$
$$= 40\sqrt{2} - 9\sqrt{2} = \mathbf{31\sqrt{2}}$$

22. $4\sqrt{2}(5\sqrt{2} - 2\sqrt{12}) = 4 \cdot 5\sqrt{2}\sqrt{2} - 4 \cdot 2\sqrt{2}\sqrt{2}\sqrt{6}$
$$= \mathbf{40 - 16\sqrt{6}}$$

23.
$$\frac{4x^2 - 4x}{4x} = \frac{4x(x-1)}{4x} = \mathbf{x - 1}$$

24.
$$\frac{-3^{-3}(-3)^{-2}}{3^{-2}} = \frac{3^2}{-3^3(-3)^2} = \mathbf{-\frac{1}{27}}$$

25. $45 = x^2 + 4x$
$$0 = x^2 + 4x - 45$$
$$0 = (x - 5)(x + 9)$$

If $x - 5 = 0$, $x = 5$
$$45 = (5)^2 + 4(5)$$
$$45 = 45$$

If $x + 9 = 0$, $x = -9$
$$45 = (-9)^2 + 4(-9)$$
$$45 = 45$$

26. $-x - ab(x - b^0) = -(-3) - 4(-5)((-3) - (-5)^0)$
$$= 3 + 20(-3 - 1) = \mathbf{-77}$$

27. $-4 - |x| \le -4;$ $D = \{$Reals$\}$

$\quad\quad -|x| \le 0$

$\quad\quad\;\; |x| \ge 0$

All real numbers.

28. $\dfrac{x^{-2}a^2}{y}\left(\dfrac{ya^{-2}}{x^{-2}} - \dfrac{3x^{-2}a^2}{y}\right)$

$\quad = \dfrac{x^{-2}a^2 ya^{-2}}{yx^{-2}} - \dfrac{x^{-2}a^2\, 3x^{-2}a^2}{yy}$

$\quad = \mathbf{1 - 3a^4x^{-4}y^{-2}}$

29. $47\overset{\downarrow}{\textcircled{8}},325.0\overline{63}$

$\quad$ **478,000**

30. $x = \dfrac{-b \pm \sqrt{b^2 - 4ac}}{2a}$

$\quad = \dfrac{-(-1) \pm \sqrt{(-1)^2 - 4\left(-\frac{1}{2}\right)\left(\frac{15}{2}\right)}}{2\left(-\frac{1}{2}\right)}$

$\quad = \dfrac{1 \pm \sqrt{1 + 15}}{-1} = \dfrac{1 \pm 4}{-1} = \mathbf{-5, 3}$

PROBLEM SET 121

1. $\dfrac{WP}{100}(1200) = 900$

$\quad\quad WP = \mathbf{75 \text{ percent}}$

2. $R_N T_N + R_S T_S = 580;$ $R_N = 50;$ $\quad\overset{D_S\quad D_N}{\vdash\!\!-\!\!\bullet\!\!-\!\!\dashv}$

$\quad R_S = 45;$ $T_N = T_S + 4$

$\quad\quad 50(T_S + 4) + 45T_S = 580$

$\quad\quad 50T_S + 200 + 45T_S = 580$

$\quad\quad\quad\quad\quad\;\; 95T_S = 380$

$\quad\quad\quad\quad\quad\quad\; T_S = \mathbf{4 \text{ hr}}$

3. $R_W T_W = R_R T_R;$ $R_W = 5;$ $R_R = 30;$

$\quad T_W + T_R = 21$

$\quad\quad\quad T_R = 21 - T_W$

$\quad\quad 5T_W = 30(21 - T_W)$

$\quad\quad 35T_W = 630$

$\quad\quad\; T_W = 18$

$\quad R_W T_W = 5(18) = \mathbf{90 \text{ km}}$

4. $\dfrac{11}{13} = \dfrac{N_H}{195}$

$\quad N_H = \mathbf{165}$

5. (a) $5N_F + 20N_T = 1075$

$\quad$ (b) $N_F + N_T = 176$

$\quad\quad\quad\text{(a)}\quad\;\; 5N_F + 20N_T = 1075$

$\quad(-5)\text{(b)}\;\; \underline{-5N_F - 5N_T = -880}$

$\quad\quad\quad\quad\quad\quad\;\; 15N_T = \quad 195$

$\quad\quad\quad\quad\quad\quad\quad\; N_T = \mathbf{13}$

$\quad$ (b) $N_F + (13) = 176$

$\quad\quad\quad\quad N_F = \mathbf{163}$

6. **Yes**

7. Since parallel lines have the same slope:

$\quad y = -\dfrac{2}{3}x + 5$

$\quad$ Use the point $(-2, -3)$ for x and y.

$\quad (-3) = -\dfrac{2}{3}(-2) + b$

$\quad\quad b = -\dfrac{13}{3}$

$\quad y = -\dfrac{2}{3}x - \dfrac{13}{3}$

8. (a) horizontal line: $y = \pm k;$ $\mathbf{y = -2}$

$\quad$ (b) The desired equation is $y = mx + b$.

$\quad\quad$ By inspection, $b = 0$.

$\quad\quad$ By inspection, the sign for m is $-$.

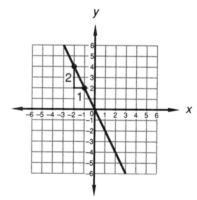

$\quad |m| = \dfrac{2}{1} = 2$

$\quad$ So $b = 0$ and $m = -2$: $\mathbf{y = -2x}$

9. $g\left(\dfrac{1}{2}\right) = \varnothing$ because $\dfrac{1}{2} \notin \{$Integers$\}$

10. $2\sqrt{x} - 4 = 3$

$\quad\quad 2\sqrt{x} = 7$

$\quad\quad\;\; \sqrt{x} = \dfrac{7}{2}$

$\quad\quad\quad\; x = \dfrac{49}{4}$

$\quad$ Check: $2\sqrt{\dfrac{49}{4}} - 4 = 3$

$\quad\quad\quad\quad\quad 7 - 4 = 3$

$\quad\quad\quad\quad\quad\quad\; 3 = 3 \quad$ true

11. $\sqrt{x + 5} - 3 = 2$

$\qquad \sqrt{x + 5} = 5$

$\qquad x + 5 = 25$

$\qquad x = \mathbf{20}$

Check: $\sqrt{20 + 5} - 3 = 2$

$\qquad\qquad 5 - 3 = 2$

$\qquad\qquad 2 = 2 \quad$ true

12. $4 \le x - 3 < 6;\ D = \{\text{Integers}\}$

$7 \le x < 9$

```
  —+——•——•——+——+—
   6   7   8   9  10
```

13. $x + 2 < 5$ or $x + 2 \ge 6;\ D = \{\text{Reals}\}$

$x < 3$ or $\qquad x \ge 4$

```
◄——+——+——○——+——•——+——►
   1   2   3   4   5   6
```

14. $V_{\text{Prism}} = A_{\text{Base}} \times \text{height}$

$\qquad = \left[\dfrac{18(28)}{2} + 40(2) + 10(2)\right](2)(3) \text{ ft}^3$

$\qquad = [352](6) \text{ ft}^3$

$\qquad = \mathbf{2112 \text{ ft}^3}$

S.A. $= 2A_{\text{Base}} + (P \times \text{height})$

$\qquad = 2[352] \text{ ft}^2 + [(94 + 2\sqrt{277}) \times (2)(3)] \text{ ft}^2$

$\qquad = (704 + 763.72) \text{ ft}^2$

$\qquad = \mathbf{1467.72 \text{ ft}^2}$

15. $1{,}000{,}000 \, \cancel{m^3} \cdot \dfrac{100 \, \cancel{cm}}{1 \, \cancel{m}} \cdot \dfrac{100 \, \cancel{cm}}{1 \, \cancel{m}} \cdot \dfrac{100 \, \cancel{cm}}{1 \, \cancel{m}}$

$\cdot \dfrac{1 \, \cancel{in.}}{2.54 \, \cancel{cm}} \cdot \dfrac{1 \, \cancel{in.}}{2.54 \, \cancel{cm}} \cdot \dfrac{1 \, \cancel{in.}}{2.54 \, \cancel{cm}} \cdot \dfrac{1 \, \cancel{ft}}{12 \, \cancel{in.}}$

$\cdot \dfrac{1 \, \cancel{ft}}{12 \, \cancel{in.}} \cdot \dfrac{1 \, \cancel{ft}}{12 \, \cancel{in.}} \cdot \dfrac{1 \, \text{mi}}{5280 \, \cancel{ft}} \cdot \dfrac{1 \, \text{mi}}{5280 \, \cancel{ft}} \cdot \dfrac{1 \, \text{mi}}{5280 \, \cancel{ft}}$

$= \dfrac{1{,}000{,}000(100)^3}{(2.54)^3(12)^3(5280)^3} \text{ mi}^3$

16. $a + x + y + m$

$= a + (x + y) + m \qquad$ associative

$= a + (y + x) + m \qquad$ commutative

$= a + y + (x + m) \qquad$ associative

$= a + y + (m + x) \qquad$ commutative

$= (a + y) + m + x \qquad$ associative

$= (y + a) + m + x \qquad$ commutative

$= y + a + m + x \qquad$ removed parentheses

17. (a) $(2 - 3\sqrt{12})(3 + 2\sqrt{12})$

$\qquad = 6 - 18\sqrt{3} + 8\sqrt{3} - 72 = \mathbf{-66 - 10\sqrt{3}}$

(b) $(\sqrt{2}a - \sqrt{3}p)^2 = (\sqrt{2}a - \sqrt{3}p)(\sqrt{2}a - \sqrt{3}p)$

$\qquad = \mathbf{2a^2 - 2\sqrt{6}ap + 3p^2}$

18. $\dfrac{k - 5}{k} = \dfrac{1}{5k} - \dfrac{1}{5}$

$\dfrac{(k - 5)}{k}(5k) = \dfrac{1}{5k}(5k) - \dfrac{1}{5}(5k)$

$\qquad 5k - 25 = 1 - k$

$\qquad\qquad 6k = 26$

$\qquad\qquad k = \dfrac{\mathbf{13}}{\mathbf{3}}$

19. $\dfrac{a}{b} + \dfrac{x}{m} - \dfrac{1}{c} = p$

$\dfrac{a}{b}(bmc) + \dfrac{x}{m}(bmc) - \dfrac{1}{c}(bmc) = p(bmc)$

$amc + xbc - bm = pbmc$

$\qquad\qquad xbc = pbmc + bm - amc$

$\qquad\qquad xbc = m(pbc + b - ac)$

$\qquad\qquad m = \dfrac{\boldsymbol{xbc}}{\boldsymbol{pbc + b - ac}}$

20. (a) $y = -x + 3$

$\qquad y = \dfrac{-1}{+1}x + 3$

(b) $y = -2$

The first step is to graph each of these lines.

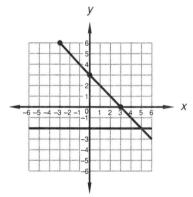

It appears that the lines cross at $x = 5$ and $y = -2$, so $\mathbf{(5, -2)}$ is the solution.

21. $\dfrac{\dfrac{xy}{a^2} - \dfrac{1}{a}}{\dfrac{1}{a} + \dfrac{x^2 y}{a^2}} = \dfrac{\dfrac{xy - a}{a^2}}{\dfrac{a + x^2 y}{a^2}} \cdot \dfrac{\dfrac{a^2}{a + x^2 y}}{\dfrac{a^2}{a + x^2 y}}$

$= \dfrac{\boldsymbol{xy - a}}{\boldsymbol{a + x^2 y}}$

22. $(x^3 - 2x - 4) \div (x + 2)$

$$
\begin{array}{r}
x^2 - 2x + 2 \\
x + 2 \overline{)\, x^3 + 0x^2 - 2x - 4} \\
\underline{x^3 + 2x^2} \\
-2x^2 - 2x \\
\underline{-2x^2 - 4x} \\
2x - 4 \\
\underline{2x + 4} \\
-8
\end{array}
$$

$x^2 - 2x + 2 - \dfrac{8}{x + 2}$.

23. $WF\left(3\dfrac{1}{7}\right) = \dfrac{3}{8}$

$\qquad WF = \dfrac{3}{8}\left(\dfrac{7}{22}\right)$

$\qquad WF = \dfrac{21}{176}$

24. $-3\sqrt{2} \in$ **Irrationals and reals**

25. $-[(-3 - 2)(-2) - 3^0(-3)] - [(-2^0 - 3^2)$
$\quad - (-2 - 4)] = -[10 + 3] - [-10 + 6]$
$= \mathbf{-9}$

26. $-y^2 - y^0 - y(xy - y)$
$= -(-3)^2 - (-3)^0 - (-3)(4(-3) - (-3))$
$= -9 - 1 + 3(-9)$
$= \mathbf{-37}$

27. $3\dfrac{1}{8}m + 2\dfrac{1}{4} = \dfrac{3}{8}$

$\qquad \dfrac{25}{8}m = \dfrac{3}{8} - \dfrac{9}{4}$

$\qquad \dfrac{25}{8}m = \dfrac{3}{8} - \dfrac{18}{8}$

$\qquad m = -\dfrac{15}{8} \cdot \dfrac{8}{25}$

$\qquad m = -\dfrac{3}{5}$

28. $\dfrac{5x + 2}{x - 3} - \dfrac{2x + 2}{x^2 - 9}$

$= \dfrac{(5x + 2)(x + 3) - (2x + 2)}{(x + 3)(x - 3)}$

$= \dfrac{5x^2 + 17x + 6 - 2x - 2}{x^2 - 9}$

$= \dfrac{5x^2 + 15x + 4}{x^2 - 9}$

29. $-2 < x \le 2$; $D = \{\text{Reals}\}$

30. $-|x| + 2 \ge -1$; $D = \{\text{Positive integers}\}$
$\qquad 3 \ge |x|$

PROBLEM SET 122

1. $R_R T_R = R_r T_r$; $R_R = 8$; $R_r = 20$;
$T_R + T_r = 7$
$\qquad T_R = 7 - T_r$

$8(7 - T_r) = 20T_r$
$\qquad 56 = 28T_r$
$\qquad T_r = 2$

$R_r T_r = 20(2) = \mathbf{40\ km}$

2. $D = kT$
$90 = k(9)$
$k = 10$

$D = 10T$
$D = 10(5)$
$D = \mathbf{50\ km}$

3. $M = kV$
$42 = k(7)$
$k = 6$

$M = 6V$
$63 = 6V$

$V = \dfrac{21}{2}$ **liters** (or 10.5 liters)

4. (a) $50N_R + 40N_W = 1230$
(b) $N_R + N_W = 27$

$\qquad$ (a) $\quad 50N_R + 40N_W = 1230$
(-40)(b) $\underline{-40N_R - 40N_W = -1080}$
$\qquad\qquad 10N_R = 150$
$\qquad\qquad\quad N_R = \mathbf{15}$

(b) $(15) + N_W = 27$
$\qquad\quad N_W = \mathbf{12}$

5. $x = \dfrac{-b \pm \sqrt{b^2 - 4ac}}{2a}$

$= \dfrac{-(\pm\sqrt{3}) \pm \sqrt{3 - 4(3)\left(\dfrac{1}{4}\right)}}{2(3)}$

$= \dfrac{\pm\sqrt{3} \pm \sqrt{3 - 3}}{6} = \pm\dfrac{\sqrt{3}}{6}$

6. Since parallel lines have the same slope:
$y = 2x + b$
Use the point $(-2, -5)$ for x and y.
$-5 = 2(-2) + b$
$b = -1$
$y = 2x - 1$

7. **(a)** function   **(c)** not a function
(b) function   **(d)** function

8. $2\sqrt{x} + 2 = 5$
$2\sqrt{x} = 3$
$\sqrt{x} = \dfrac{3}{2}$
$x = \dfrac{9}{4}$

Check: $2\sqrt{\dfrac{9}{4}} + 2 = 5$
$3 + 2 = 5$
$5 = 5$

9. $\sqrt{x - 4} - 2 = 6$
$\sqrt{x - 4} = 8$
$x - 4 = 64$
$x = 68$

Check: $\sqrt{68 - 4} - 2 = 6$
$8 - 2 = 6$
$6 = 6$

10. $-2 \leq x + 5 < 3$; $D = \{\text{Reals}\}$
$-7 \leq x < -2$

$-8\ -7\ -6\ -5\ -4\ -3\ -2\ -1$

11. $(2 + \sqrt{3})(4 - 5\sqrt{12}) = 8 + 4\sqrt{3} - 20\sqrt{3} - 30$
$= -22 - 16\sqrt{3}$

12. $(2 + \sqrt{2})(4 - 3\sqrt{8}) = 8 + 4\sqrt{2} - 12\sqrt{2} - 12$
$= -4 - 8\sqrt{2}$

13. $(5 + \sqrt{6})(2 - 3\sqrt{24}) = 10 + 2\sqrt{6} - 30\sqrt{6} - 36$
$= -26 - 28\sqrt{6}$

14. $\dfrac{x}{4} - \dfrac{x - 3}{2} = \dfrac{1}{5}$

$\dfrac{x}{4}(20) - \dfrac{(x - 3)}{2}(20) = \dfrac{1}{5}(20)$
$5x - 10x + 30 = 4$
$26 = 5x$
$x = \dfrac{26}{5}$

15. $\dfrac{m - 2}{m} = \dfrac{1}{2m} - \dfrac{1}{3}$

$\dfrac{(m - 2)}{m}(6m) = \dfrac{1}{2m}(6m) - \dfrac{1}{3}(6m)$
$6m - 12 = 3 - 2m$
$8m = 15$
$m = \dfrac{15}{8}$

16. $\dfrac{x}{a} - \dfrac{1}{k} = \dfrac{m}{c}$

$\dfrac{x}{a}(akc) - \dfrac{1}{k}(akc) = \dfrac{m}{c}(akc)$
$xkc - ac = mak$
$xkc = mak + ac$
$xkc = a(mk + c)$
$a = \dfrac{xkc}{mk + c}$

17. Estimate: $\sqrt{0.000416852 \times 10^{-13}}$
$= \sqrt{4.17 \times 10^{-17}} = \sqrt{4.17 \times 10 \times 10^{-18}}$
$= (2.04)(3.1)(10^{-9})$

Table: $\sqrt{0.000416852 \times 10^{-13}}$
$= \sqrt{4.17 \times 10^{-17}} = \sqrt{4.17 \times 10 \times 10^{-18}}$
$= (2.04206)(3.16228) \times 10^{-9}$

18. $D^2 = 9^2 + 8^2$
$D^2 = 145$
$D = \sqrt{145}$

19. $3x^0 - 2(-x - 5) - (-3) + 2(x - 5)$
$= -2(x + 3^0)$
$3 + 2x + 10 + 3 + 2x - 10 = -2x - 2$
$6x = -8$
$x = -\dfrac{4}{3}$

20. $\dfrac{(35,000 \times 10^{-41})(700 \times 10^{14})}{(7000 \times 10^{21})(0.00005 \times 10^{15})}$

$= \dfrac{(3.5 \times 10^{-37})(7 \times 10^{16})}{(7 \times 10^{24})(5 \times 10^{10})} = \mathbf{7 \times 10^{-56}}$

21. $\dfrac{(x^{-2})^{-3}(x^{-2}y^2)}{x^2yy^0(x^0y)^{-2}} = \dfrac{x^6x^{-2}y^2}{x^2yy^{-2}} = \mathbf{x^2y^3}$

22. $(3 + 3\sqrt{2})(4 - \sqrt{2}) = 12 + 12\sqrt{2} - 3\sqrt{2} - 6$
$= \mathbf{6 + 9\sqrt{2}}$

23. $2\sqrt{5}(\sqrt{5} - 2\sqrt{75}) = \mathbf{10 - 20\sqrt{15}}$

24. $\dfrac{2x^2yz - 2x^2yz^2}{2x^2yz} = \dfrac{2x^2yz(1 - z)}{2x^2yz} = \mathbf{1 - z}$

25. $\dfrac{3^{-2}}{-2^{-3}} = \dfrac{-2^3}{3^2} = -\dfrac{\mathbf{8}}{\mathbf{9}}$

26. $\qquad -8 = -x^2 + 7x$
$x^2 - 7x - 8 = 0$
$(x - 8)(x + 1) = 0$

If $x - 8 = 0$, $x = \mathbf{8}$
$-8 = -(8)^2 + 7(8)$
$-8 = -8$

If $x + 1 = 0$, $x = \mathbf{-1}$
$-8 = -(-1)^2 + 7(-1)$
$-8 = -8$

27. $-x^2 - x^0 - x^3 + xy(y - xy)$
$= -(-3)^2 - (-3)^0 - (-3)^3$
$\quad + (-3)(-4)((-4) - (-3)(-4))$
$= -9 - 1 + 27 + 12(-16) = \mathbf{-175}$

28. $-3 - |-x| \geq -2$; $D = \{\text{Integers}\}$
$\qquad -|-x| \geq 1$
$\qquad |-x| \leq -1$
$\qquad |x| \leq -1$
No integers

29. $\dfrac{a^{-2}x}{y}\left(\dfrac{ya^2}{x} - \dfrac{4x^2y}{a^2}\right)$

$= \dfrac{a^{-2}xya^2}{yx} - \dfrac{a^{-2}x4x^2y}{ya^2} = \mathbf{1 - 4x^3a^{-4}}$

30. $4.060\overset{\downarrow}{\underset{}{\textcircled{6}}}0$
4.0606

PROBLEM SET 123

1. $R = \dfrac{k}{T}$

$100 = \dfrac{k}{5}$
$\quad k = 500$

$R = \dfrac{500}{T}$

$125 = \dfrac{500}{T}$
$\quad T = \mathbf{4\ hr}$

2. $1,000,000\ \cancel{\text{yd}}^3 \cdot \dfrac{3\ \cancel{\text{ft}}}{1\ \cancel{\text{yd}}} \cdot \dfrac{3\ \cancel{\text{ft}}}{1\ \cancel{\text{yd}}} \cdot \dfrac{3\ \cancel{\text{ft}}}{1\ \cancel{\text{yd}}} \cdot \dfrac{12\ \text{in.}}{1\ \cancel{\text{ft}}}$

$\cdot \dfrac{12\ \text{in.}}{1\ \cancel{\text{ft}}} \cdot \dfrac{12\ \text{in.}}{1\ \cancel{\text{ft}}} \cdot \dfrac{2.54\ \cancel{\text{cm}}}{1\ \cancel{\text{in.}}} \cdot \dfrac{2.54\ \cancel{\text{cm}}}{1\ \cancel{\text{in.}}} \cdot \dfrac{2.54\ \cancel{\text{cm}}}{1\ \cancel{\text{in.}}}$

$\cdot \dfrac{1\ \cancel{\text{m}}}{100\ \cancel{\text{cm}}} \cdot \dfrac{1\ \cancel{\text{m}}}{100\ \cancel{\text{cm}}} \cdot \dfrac{1\ \cancel{\text{m}}}{100\ \cancel{\text{cm}}} \cdot \dfrac{1\ \text{km}}{1000\ \cancel{\text{m}}} \cdot \dfrac{1\ \text{km}}{1000\ \cancel{\text{m}}}$

$\cdot \dfrac{1\ \text{km}}{1000\ \cancel{\text{m}}}$

$= \dfrac{\mathbf{1,000,000(3)^3(12)^3(2.54)^3}}{\mathbf{(100)^3(1000)^3}}\ \mathbf{km^3}$

3. $N_G = kN_B$
$21 = k(3)$
$\ k = 7$

$N_G = 7N_B$
$N_G = 7(5)$
$N_G = \mathbf{35}$

4. $P = kA$
$40 = k(120)$
$\ k = \dfrac{1}{3}$

$P = \dfrac{A}{3}$

$500 = \dfrac{A}{3}$
$\ A = \mathbf{1500}$

5. $\dfrac{4}{9} = \dfrac{A_c}{1278}$
$A_c = \mathbf{568}$

6. $y = -\dfrac{1}{5}x + b$
Use the point $(-2, -3)$ for x and y.

$-3 = -\dfrac{1}{5}(-2) + b$

$b = -\dfrac{17}{5}$

$y = -\dfrac{1}{5}x - \dfrac{17}{5}$

7. **(a), (c), (d)**
(b) is not a function because y has two images

8. $\sqrt{x} - 4 = 2$
$\sqrt{x} = 6$
$x = \mathbf{36}$
Check: $\sqrt{36} - 4 = 2$
$6 - 4 = 2$
$2 = 2$

9. $\sqrt{x - 5} - 3 = 2$
$\sqrt{x - 5} = 5$
$x - 5 = 25$
$x = \mathbf{30}$
Check: $\sqrt{30 - 5} - 3 = 2$
$\sqrt{25} - 3 = 2$
$5 - 3 = 2$
$2 = 2$

10. $x + 2 \geq 5$ or $x + 3 \leq 0$; $D = \{\text{Integers}\}$
$x \geq 3$ or $x \leq -3$

$$-4\ -3\ -2\ -1\quad 0\quad 1\quad 2\quad 3\quad 4$$

11. $(4 - 3\sqrt{2})(2 + 6\sqrt{2}) = 8 - 6\sqrt{2} + 24\sqrt{2} - 36$
$= \mathbf{-28 + 18\sqrt{2}}$

12. $(2 - \sqrt{5})(3 - 2\sqrt{5}) = 6 - 3\sqrt{5} - 4\sqrt{5} + 10$
$= \mathbf{16 - 7\sqrt{5}}$

13. $(3 - \sqrt{3})(2 - 2\sqrt{3}) = 6 - 2\sqrt{3} - 6\sqrt{3} + 6$
$= \mathbf{12 - 8\sqrt{3}}$

14.
$$\frac{x}{4} - \frac{x - 5}{7} = 2$$
$$\frac{x}{4}(28) - \frac{(x - 5)}{7}(28) = 2(28)$$
$$7x - 4x + 20 = 56$$
$$3x = 36$$
$$x = \mathbf{12}$$

15.
$$\frac{m + 5}{m} = \frac{3}{2m} - \frac{2}{5}$$
$$\frac{(m + 5)}{m}(10m) = \frac{3}{2m}(10m) - \frac{2}{5}(10m)$$
$$10m + 50 = 15 - 4m$$
$$14m = -35$$
$$m = -\frac{\mathbf{5}}{\mathbf{2}}$$

16.
$$\frac{x}{y} - m + \frac{1}{c} = k$$
$$\frac{x}{y}(yc) - m(yc) + \frac{1}{c}(yc) = k(yc)$$
$$xc - myc + y = kyc$$
$$xc = kyc + myc - y$$
$$xc = y(kc + mc - 1)$$
$$y = \frac{xc}{kc + mc - 1}$$

17. $k^2 + 5^2 = 8^2$
$k^2 = 64 - 25$
$k^2 = 39$
$k = \mathbf{\sqrt{39}}$

18. $\dfrac{x^5 - 5x^4}{x^2 - 25} \div \dfrac{x^4 + 4x^3 - 32x^2}{x^2 + x - 20}$

$= \dfrac{x^4(x - 5)}{(x + 5)(x - 5)} \cdot \dfrac{(x + 5)(x - 4)}{x^2(x - 4)(x + 8)}$

$= \dfrac{x^2}{x + 8}$

19. (a) $y = \dfrac{1}{2}x - 2$

$y = \dfrac{+1}{+2}x - 2$

(b) $x = -4$
The first step is to graph each of these lines.

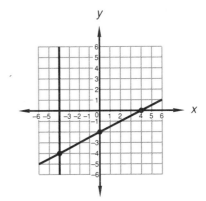

It appears that the lines cross at $x = -4$ and $y = -4$, so $\mathbf{(-4, -4)}$ is the solution.

20. (a) horizontal line: $y = \pm k$; $\mathbf{y = 5}$
(b) The desired equation is $y = mx + b$.
By inspection, $b = -2$.
By inspection, the sign for m is $-$.

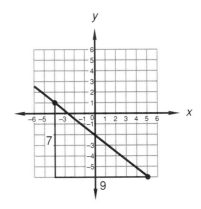

$|m| = \dfrac{7}{9}$

So $b = -2$ and $m = -\dfrac{7}{9}$: $y = -\dfrac{7}{9}x - 2$

21. $\dfrac{a + \dfrac{a}{x}}{\dfrac{1}{x} + a^2} = \dfrac{\dfrac{ax + a}{x}}{\dfrac{1 + a^2x}{x}} \cdot \dfrac{\dfrac{x}{1 + a^2x}}{\dfrac{x}{1 + a^2x}}$

$= \dfrac{ax + a}{1 + a^2x}$

22. $(x^3 - 2) \div (x^2 - 1)$

$$x^2 - 1 \overline{\smash{\big)}\ \begin{array}{l} x \\ x^3 + 0x^2 + 0x - 2 \\ \underline{x^3 + 0x^2 - x} \\ x - 2 \end{array}}$$

$x + \dfrac{x - 2}{x^2 - 1}$

23. $-2^0(-3^0 - 5)[(7 - 2^2)(-3 - 4^0) - (-2)][-(-2)]$
$= 6[3(-4) + 2](2) = \mathbf{-120}$

24. $+1 - |x| \le -1;\ D = \{\text{Positive integers}\}$
$\qquad 2 \le |x|$

25. $-1 < x + 2 \le 1;\ D = \{\text{Reals}\}$
$\qquad -3 < x \le -1$

26. $-p^0 - (p^0)^2 - p^2 - p^3 - p(p - y)$
$= -(-3)^0 - ((-3)^0)^2 - (-3)^2 - (-3)^3$
$\quad - (-3)((-3) - 2)$
$= -1 - 1 - 9 + 27 - 15 = \mathbf{1}$

27. $x^2yz^{-1} + \dfrac{3y}{x^{-2}z} - \dfrac{4yx^2}{z} + 2y^2x^2z^{-1}$
$= x^2yz^{-1} + 3x^2yz^{-1} - 4x^2yz^{-1} + 2x^2y^2z^{-1}$
$= \mathbf{2x^2y^2z^{-1}}$

28. $3\dfrac{1}{6}p + \dfrac{1}{4} = \dfrac{7}{8}$

$\qquad \dfrac{19}{6}p = \dfrac{7}{8} - \dfrac{1}{4}$

$\qquad \dfrac{19}{6}p = \dfrac{7}{8} - \dfrac{2}{8}$

$\qquad\qquad p = \dfrac{5}{8} \cdot \dfrac{6}{19}$

$\qquad\qquad p = \mathbf{\dfrac{15}{76}}$

29. $\dfrac{3x - 2}{x - 3} - \dfrac{2x + 5}{x^2 - 9}$

$= \dfrac{(3x - 2)(x + 3) - (2x + 5)}{(x + 3)(x - 3)}$

$= \dfrac{3x^2 - 2x + 9x - 6 - 2x - 5}{x^2 - 9}$

$= \dfrac{\mathbf{3x^2 + 5x - 11}}{\mathbf{x^2 - 9}}$

PROBLEM SET 124

1. $P = \dfrac{k}{D}$

$500 = \dfrac{k}{6}$

$\quad k = 3000$

$P = \dfrac{3000}{D}$

$P = \dfrac{3000}{10}$

$P = \mathbf{300}$

2. $R_hT_h = R_HT_H;\ R_h = 5;\ R_H = 2;$
$T_h + T_H = 28$
$\qquad T_H = 28 - T_h$

$5T_h = 2(28 - T_h)$
$5T_h = 56 - 2T_h$
$7T_h = 56$
$\ T_h = 8$

$R_hT_h = 5(8) = \mathbf{40\ miles}$

3. $A_{11} = \$700(1 + 0.09)^{11}$
$A_{11} = \$700(1.09)^{11}$
$A_{11} = \$700(2.580426)$
$A_{11} = \mathbf{\$1806.30}$
Interest: $\$1806.30 - \$700 = \mathbf{\$1106.30}$

4. $R_x = R_0y^x$
$R_{24} = 1000(4)^{24}$
$R_{24} = 1000(2.81 \times 10^{14})$
$R_{24} = \mathbf{2.81 \times 10^{17}}$

5. $\dfrac{3}{17} = \dfrac{90}{N_B}$

$N_B = \dfrac{90(17)}{3}$

$N_B = \mathbf{510}$

6. (a) vertical line: $x = \pm k$; $x = 3$

(b) The desired equation is $y = mx + b$.

By inspection, $b = 0$.

By inspection, the sign for m is $-$.

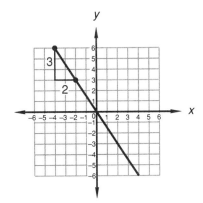

$|m| = \dfrac{3}{2}$

So $b = 0$ and $m = -\dfrac{3}{2}$: $y = -\dfrac{3}{2}x$

7. (a), (d)

(b) is not a function because -2 has three images

(c) is not a function because -2 has two images

8. $\sqrt{x - 7} + 4 = 9$

$\sqrt{x - 7} = 5$

$x - 7 = 25$

$x = 32$

Check: $\sqrt{32 - 7} + 4 = 9$

$\sqrt{25} + 4 = 9$

$5 + 4 = 9$

$9 = 9$

9. $x + 4 > 7$ or $x - 2 \le 0$; $D = \{$Reals$\}$

$x > 3$ or $x \le 2$

$$\begin{array}{ccccccc} & 0 & 1 & 2 & 3 & 4 & 5 \end{array}$$

10. $(4 + 3\sqrt{5})(1 - \sqrt{5}) = 4 + 3\sqrt{5} - 4\sqrt{5} - 15$

$= -11 - \sqrt{5}$

11. $(3 + 2\sqrt{2})(3 - \sqrt{2}) = 9 + 6\sqrt{2} - 3\sqrt{2} - 4$

$= 5 + 3\sqrt{2}$

12. $(5 + \sqrt{2})(2 - 4\sqrt{2}) = 10 + 2\sqrt{2} - 20\sqrt{2} - 8$

$= 2 - 18\sqrt{2}$

13. $3\sqrt[5]{-32} = (3)(-2) = -6$

14. $5\sqrt{18} = 5\sqrt{9 \cdot 2} = 15\sqrt{2}$

15. $2\sqrt{63} = 2\sqrt{9 \cdot 7} = 6\sqrt{7}$

16. $6\sqrt{50} = 6\sqrt{25 \cdot 2} = 30\sqrt{2}$

17. $A_{\text{Shaded}} = A_{\text{Trapezoid}} - A_{\text{Circle}}$

$= \left[\dfrac{12(4)}{2} + \dfrac{6(4)}{2} \right] \text{ft}^2 - \pi(2)^2 \text{ ft}^2$

$= (36 - 4\pi) \text{ ft}^2$

$\approx \textbf{23.44 ft}^2$

18. $160,000 \, \text{m}^3 \cdot \dfrac{100 \text{ cm}}{1 \text{ m}} \cdot \dfrac{100 \text{ cm}}{1 \text{ m}} \cdot \dfrac{100 \text{ cm}}{1 \text{ m}}$

$\cdot \dfrac{1 \text{ in.}}{2.54 \text{ cm}} \cdot \dfrac{1 \text{ in.}}{2.54 \text{ cm}} \cdot \dfrac{1 \text{ in.}}{2.54 \text{ cm}}$

$= \dfrac{(160,000)(100)(100)(100)}{(2.54)(2.54)(2.54)} \text{ in.}^3$

19. $\dfrac{p + 8}{3p} = \dfrac{5}{2p} + \dfrac{1}{4}$

$\dfrac{(p + 8)}{3p}(12p) = \dfrac{5}{2p}(12p) + \dfrac{1}{4}(12p)$

$4p + 32 = 30 + 3p$

$p = \textbf{-2}$

20. $\dfrac{p}{m} - \dfrac{x}{z} + a = k$

$\dfrac{p}{m}(mz) - \dfrac{x}{z}(mz) + a(mz) = k(mz)$

$pz - xm + amz = kmz$

$pz + amz - kmz = xm$

$z(p + am - km) = xm$

$z = \dfrac{xm}{p + am - km}$

21. $\dfrac{\dfrac{mp^2}{x} - \dfrac{z}{x^2}}{\dfrac{y}{x^2} - \dfrac{5a}{x}} = \dfrac{\dfrac{mp^2 x - z}{x^2}}{\dfrac{y - 5ax}{x^2}} \cdot \dfrac{\dfrac{x^2}{y - 5ax}}{\dfrac{x^2}{y - 5ax}}$

$= \dfrac{mp^2 x - z}{y - 5ax}$

22. $(7x^3 - 2x - 2) \div (x + 2)$

$$\begin{array}{r} 7x^2 - 14x + 26 \\ x + 2 \enclose{longdiv}{7x^3 + 0x^2 - 2x - 2} \\ \underline{7x^3 + 14x^2} \\ -14x^2 - 2x \\ \underline{-14x^2 - 28x} \\ 26x - 2 \\ \underline{26x + 52} \\ -54 \end{array}$$

$7x^2 - 14x + 26 - \dfrac{54}{x + 2}$

23. $-3[(-3^0 - 3)^2(-3^3 - 3) - (-3)] - \sqrt[3]{-27}$

$= -3[16(-30) + 3] - (-3) = \textbf{1434}$

24. $-xy - y^x - x\left(\dfrac{y}{x}\right)$

$$= -(-2)(-3) - (-3)^{-2} - (-2)\left(\dfrac{-3}{-2}\right)$$

$$= -6 - \dfrac{1}{9} + 3 = -\dfrac{28}{9}$$

25. $4\dfrac{1}{2}x + \dfrac{3}{5} = \dfrac{1}{4}$

$$\dfrac{9}{2}x = \dfrac{1}{4} - \dfrac{3}{5}$$

$$\dfrac{9}{2}x = \dfrac{5}{20} - \dfrac{12}{20}$$

$$x = -\dfrac{7}{20} \cdot \dfrac{2}{9}$$

$$x = -\dfrac{7}{90}$$

26. Since parallel lines have the same slope:

$$y = -\dfrac{1}{4}x + b$$

Use the point $(4, -1)$ for x and y.

$$-1 = -\dfrac{1}{4}(4) + b$$

$$b = 0$$

$$y = -\dfrac{1}{4}x$$

27. $m = \dfrac{4 - (-1)}{-1 - 4} = \dfrac{5}{-5} = -1$

$$y = -x + b$$

Use the point $(4, -1)$ for x and y.

$$-1 = -1(4) + b$$

$$b = 3$$

$$y = -x + 3$$

28. $y = -3x + b$

Use the point $(-1, -1)$ for x and y.

$$-1 = -3(-1) + b$$

$$b = -4$$

$$y = -3x - 4$$

29. $y = -3x - 1$

$$y = \dfrac{-3}{+1}x - 1$$

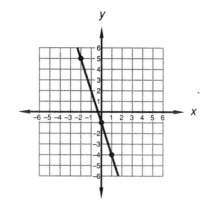

30. Check: $x = -1$

$$4(-1)^2 + 3(-1) - 1 = 0$$

$$4 - 3 - 1 = 0$$

$$4 - 4 = 0$$

$$0 = 0$$

Check: $x = \dfrac{1}{4}$

$$4\left(\dfrac{1}{4}\right)^2 + 3\left(\dfrac{1}{4}\right) - 1 = 0$$

$$\dfrac{1}{4} + \dfrac{3}{4} - \dfrac{4}{4} = 0$$

$$\dfrac{4}{4} - \dfrac{4}{4} = 0$$

$$0 = 0$$

Yes; both make the statement **true**

PROBLEM SET 125

1. $P = \dfrac{k}{V}$

$$10 = \dfrac{k}{150}$$

$$k = 1500$$

$$P = \dfrac{1500}{V}$$

$$3 = \dfrac{1500}{V}$$

$$V = \textbf{500 liters}$$

2. $A = \dfrac{k}{W}$

$$10 = \dfrac{k}{300}$$

$$k = 3000$$

$$A = \dfrac{3000}{W}$$

$$A = \dfrac{3000}{150}$$

$$A = \textbf{20}$$

3. (a) $5N_N + 10N_D = 270$

(b) $N_N + N_D = 34$

$$
\begin{array}{r}
\text{(a)} \quad 5N_N + 10N_D = 270 \\
\text{(-5)(b)} \quad -5N_N - 5N_D = -170 \\
\hline
5N_D = 100 \\
N_D = \textbf{20}
\end{array}
$$

(b) $N_N + (20) = 34$

$$N_N = \textbf{14}$$

4. $R_R T_R = R_W T_W$; $R_R = 7$; $R_W = 3$;
   $T_R + T_W = 20$
   $ T_W = 20 - T_R$

D_R
D_W

   $7T_R = 3(20 - T_R)$
   $7T_R = 60 - 3T_R$
   $10T_R = 60$
   $T_R = 6$

   $R_R T_R = 7(6) =$ **42 miles**

5. $N_x = N_0(2)^x$
   $N_{30} = 17(2)^{30}$
   $N_{30} = 17(1073741824)$ or $17(1.0737 \times 10^9)$
   $N_{30} =$ **18,253,611,008** or 1.825×10^{10}

6. $x < -5$
   Test: $(-6, 0)$
   $-6 < -5$ true

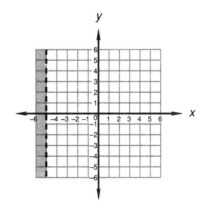

7. $p(-2) = (-2)^2 + 2(-2) + 5$
   $p(-2) = 4 - 4 + 5$
   $p(-2) =$ **5**

8. $-2\sqrt{x} + 4 = -1$
   $-2\sqrt{x} = -5$
   $\sqrt{x} = \dfrac{5}{2}$
   $\phantom{-2-2\sqrt{}}x = \dfrac{25}{4}$

   Check: $-2\sqrt{\dfrac{25}{4}} + 4 = -1$
   $-2\left(\dfrac{5}{2}\right) + 4 = -1$
   $-5 + 4 = -1$
   $-1 = -1$

9. $2\sqrt{p + 2} - 4 = 3$
   $2\sqrt{p + 2} = 7$
   $\sqrt{p + 2} = \dfrac{7}{2}$
   $p + 2 = \dfrac{49}{4}$
   $p = \dfrac{\mathbf{41}}{\mathbf{4}}$

   Check: $2\sqrt{\dfrac{41}{4} + 2} - 4 = 3$
   $2\sqrt{\dfrac{49}{4}} - 4 = 3$
   $2\left(\dfrac{7}{2}\right) - 4 = 3$
   $7 - 4 = 3$
   $3 = 3$

10. $4 \le x + 3 < 7$; $D = \{\text{Integers}\}$
   $1 \le x < 4$

   0 1 2 3 4 5

11. $(3 + 2\sqrt{2})(5 - 3\sqrt{2}) = 15 + 10\sqrt{2} - 9\sqrt{2} - 12$
   $= \mathbf{3 + \sqrt{2}}$

12. $(4 + \sqrt{3})(2 - 4\sqrt{3}) = 8 + 2\sqrt{3} - 16\sqrt{3} - 12$
   $= \mathbf{-4 - 14\sqrt{3}}$

13. $(2 + \sqrt{8})(3 - 2\sqrt{2}) = 6 + 6\sqrt{2} - 4\sqrt{2} - 8$
   $= \mathbf{-2 + 2\sqrt{2}}$

14. $\dfrac{2x}{5} - \dfrac{x + 4}{2} = 3$
   $\dfrac{2x}{5}(10) - \dfrac{(x + 4)}{2}(10) = 3(10)$
   $4x - 5x - 20 = 30$
   $\mathbf{-50} = x$

15. $\dfrac{k - 3}{2k} = \dfrac{3}{6k} - \dfrac{1}{4}$
   $\dfrac{(k - 3)}{2k}(12k) = \dfrac{3}{6k}(12k) - \dfrac{1}{4}(12k)$
   $6k - 18 = 6 - 3k$
   $9k = 24$
   $k = \dfrac{\mathbf{8}}{\mathbf{3}}$

16. $\dfrac{x}{m} - \dfrac{c}{d} = d$
   $\dfrac{x}{m}(md) - \dfrac{c}{d}(md) = d(md)$
   $xd - cm = d^2 m$
   $xd = d^2 m + cm$
   $xd = m(d^2 + c)$
   $m = \dfrac{\mathbf{xd}}{\mathbf{d^2 + c}}$

17. Estimate:

$$\sqrt{0.0001234567 \times 10^{-15}} = \sqrt{1.23 \times 10^{-19}}$$

$$= \sqrt{1.23 \times 10 \times 10^{-20}} = (1.1)(3.1)(10^{-10})$$

Tables:

$$\sqrt{0.0001234567 \times 10^{-15}} = \sqrt{1.23 \times 10^{-19}}$$

$$= \sqrt{1.23 \times 10 \times 10^{-20}}$$

$$= \mathbf{(1.10905)(3.16228) \times 10^{-10}}$$

18. $D^2 = 4^2 + 7^2$
   $D^2 = 16 + 49$
   $D^2 = 65$
   $D = \mathbf{\sqrt{65}}$

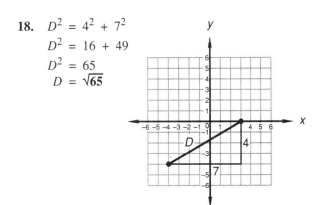

19. $-(-3)x^0 - (-2)(x - 4) = -3(-x^0)$
   $3 + 2x - 8 = 3$
   $2x = 8$
   $x = \mathbf{4}$

20. $\dfrac{(21{,}000 \times 10^{-40})(5000 \times 10^{-20})}{(0.00003 \times 10^{15})(0.0007 \times 10^{28})}$

$$= \dfrac{(2.1 \times 10^{-36})(5 \times 10^{-17})}{(3 \times 10^{10})(7 \times 10^{24})} = \mathbf{5 \times 10^{-88}}$$

21. $\dfrac{4x^2y^{-2}(x^2)^{-2}y^2xy}{(2x^0)^2x^2y^{-2}(xy)} = \dfrac{4x^2x^{-4}}{4\,x^2y^{-2}} = \mathbf{y^2x^{-4}}$

22. $3\sqrt{2} \cdot \sqrt{3} - 5\sqrt{24} + 3\sqrt{54} = 3\sqrt{6} - 10\sqrt{6} + 9\sqrt{6}$
   $= \mathbf{2\sqrt{6}}$

23. $3\sqrt{2}(\sqrt{2} - 4\sqrt{8}) = 6 - 48 = \mathbf{-42}$

24. $\dfrac{xy - 4xy^2}{xy} = \dfrac{xy(1 - 4y)}{xy} = \mathbf{1 - 4y}$

25. $\dfrac{-2^{-4}}{(-2)^{-3}} = \dfrac{(-2)^3}{-2^4} = \mathbf{\dfrac{1}{2}}$

26. $45 = x^2 - 4x$
   $0 = x^2 - 4x - 45$
   $0 = (x - 9)(x + 5)$
   If $x - 9 = 0$, $x = \mathbf{9}$
   $45 = (9)^2 - 4(9)$
   $45 = 45$
   If $x + 5 = 0$, $x = \mathbf{-5}$
   $45 = (-5)^2 - 4(-5)$
   $45 = 45$

27. $xy - a - ya(y - a)$
   $= (-2)(-5) - (-1) - (-5)(-1)((-5) - (-1))$
   $= 10 + 1 - 5(-4)$
   $= \mathbf{31}$

28. $4 \geq |x|$; $D = \{\text{Positive integers}\}$

├──┼──●──●──●──●──┼──
0   1   2   3   4   5

29. $\dfrac{3ax}{y}\left(\dfrac{y}{3ax} - \dfrac{a^{-1}x}{3y}\right) = \dfrac{3axy}{y3ax} - \dfrac{3axa^{-1}x}{y3y}$

$$= \mathbf{1 - x^2y^{-2}}$$

30. $4 \in \{\text{Naturals}\}$ **True**

PROBLEM SET 126

1. $R = \dfrac{k}{T}$

   $10 = \dfrac{k}{100}$
   $k = 1000$

   $R = \dfrac{1000}{T}$
   $R = \dfrac{1000}{25}$
   $R = \mathbf{40\ rpm}$

2. $R_ET_E = R_CT_C$; $R_E = 2$; $R_C = 10$;
   $T_E + T_C = 18$
   $\qquad T_E = 18 - T_C$

   $2(18 - T_C) = 10T_C$
   $\qquad 36 = 12T_C$
   $\qquad 3 = T_C$

   $R_CT_C = 10(3) = \mathbf{30\ km}$

3. $\$3.60 = P_B - \dfrac{40}{100}P_B$

   $\$3.60 = \dfrac{60}{100}P_B$
   $\quad P_B = \mathbf{\$6}$

4. (a) $15N_C + 50N_E = 550$
   (b) $N_C = N_E + 15$
   Substitute (b) into (a) and get:
   (a') $15(N_E + 15) + 50N_E = 550$
   $\qquad\qquad 65N_E + 225 = 550$
   $\qquad\qquad\qquad 65N_E = 325$
   $\qquad\qquad\qquad\quad N_E = \mathbf{5}$

   (b) $N_C = (5) + 15 = \mathbf{20}$

5. $A_{20} = \$1100(1 + 0.06)^{20}$
    $A_{20} = \$1100(3.20713547221)$
    $A_{20} = \mathbf{\$3527.85}$

    $I = \$3527.85 - \$1100$
    $I = \mathbf{\$2427.85}$

6. (a) horizontal line: $y = \pm k$; $\mathbf{y = 3}$
    (b) The desired equation is $y = mx + b$.
        By inspection, $b = 0$.
        By inspection the sign for m is +.

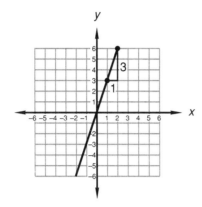

    $|m| = \dfrac{3}{1} = 3$
    So $b = 0$ and $m = 3$: $\mathbf{y = 3x}$

7. **(a), (c), (d)**
    (b) is not a function because -5 has two images.

8. $\sqrt{x - 3} - 2 = 5$
    $\sqrt{x - 3} = 7$
    $x - 3 = 49$
    $x = \mathbf{52}$

    Check: $\sqrt{52 - 3} - 2 = 5$
    $\sqrt{49} - 2 = 5$
    $7 - 2 = 5$
    $5 = 5$

9. $x + 2 > 6$ or $x - 3 \le -6$; $D = \{\text{Reals}\}$
    $x > 4$ or $x \le -3$

    ```
    ←——●—+—+—+—+—+—+—○—→
      -4 -3 -2 -1  0  1  2  3  4  5
    ```

10. $(3 + 2\sqrt{2})(2 - 4\sqrt{2}) = 6 + 4\sqrt{2} - 12\sqrt{2} - 16$
    $= \mathbf{-10 - 8\sqrt{2}}$

11. $(2 + 3\sqrt{3})(2 - \sqrt{3}) = 4 + 6\sqrt{3} - 2\sqrt{3} - 9$
    $= \mathbf{-5 + 4\sqrt{3}}$

12. $(3 + \sqrt{5})(2 - 4\sqrt{5}) = 6 + 2\sqrt{5} - 12\sqrt{5} - 20$
    $= \mathbf{-14 - 10\sqrt{5}}$

13. $\dfrac{2 + 3\sqrt{6}}{\sqrt{2}} \cdot \dfrac{\sqrt{2}}{\sqrt{2}} = \dfrac{2\sqrt{2} + 6\sqrt{3}}{2}$
    $= \mathbf{\sqrt{2} + 3\sqrt{3}}$

14. $\sqrt{\dfrac{2}{5}} = \dfrac{\sqrt{2}}{\sqrt{5}} \cdot \dfrac{\sqrt{5}}{\sqrt{5}} = \dfrac{\sqrt{10}}{5}$

15. $\sqrt{\dfrac{3}{7}} = \dfrac{\sqrt{3}}{\sqrt{7}} \cdot \dfrac{\sqrt{7}}{\sqrt{7}} = \dfrac{\sqrt{21}}{7}$

16. $\dfrac{4 + 2\sqrt{10}}{\sqrt{5}} \cdot \dfrac{\sqrt{5}}{\sqrt{5}} = \dfrac{4\sqrt{5} + 10\sqrt{2}}{5}$

17. $A_{\text{Shaded}} = A_{\text{Rectangle}} + A_{\text{Triangle}} - A_{\text{Circle}}$
    $= \left[(40)(7) + \dfrac{(24)(12)}{2} - \pi(7)^2 \right] \text{m}^2$
    $= (424 - 49\pi) \text{ m}^2$
    $\approx \mathbf{270.14 \text{ m}^2}$

18. $145{,}000 \text{ in.}^3 \times \dfrac{2.54 \text{ cm}}{1 \text{ in.}} \times \dfrac{2.54 \text{ cm}}{1 \text{ in.}} \times \dfrac{2.54 \text{ cm}}{1 \text{ in.}}$
    $\times \dfrac{1 \text{ m}}{100 \text{ cm}} \times \dfrac{1 \text{ m}}{100 \text{ cm}} \times \dfrac{1 \text{ m}}{100 \text{ cm}}$
    $= \dfrac{(145{,}000)(2.54)(2.54)(2.54)}{(100)(100)(100)} \text{ m}^3$

19. $\dfrac{m + 2}{2m} = \dfrac{7}{3m} + \dfrac{2}{5}$
    $\dfrac{(m + 2)}{2m}(30m) = \dfrac{7}{3m}(30m) + \dfrac{2}{5}(30m)$
    $15m + 30 = 70 + 12m$
    $3m = 40$
    $m = \dfrac{\mathbf{40}}{\mathbf{3}}$

20. $\dfrac{a}{x} - \dfrac{m}{c} + b = k$
    $\dfrac{a}{x}(xc) - \dfrac{m}{c}(xc) + b(xc) = k(xc)$
    $ac - mx + bxc = kxc$
    $ac + bxc - kxc = mx$
    $c(a + bx - kx) = mx$
    $c = \dfrac{\mathbf{mx}}{\mathbf{a + bx - kx}}$

21. $\dfrac{\dfrac{ax^2}{y} - \dfrac{x}{y^2}}{\dfrac{p}{y^2} - \dfrac{3k}{y}} = \dfrac{\dfrac{ax^2 y - x}{y^2}}{\dfrac{p - 3ky}{y^2}} \cdot \dfrac{\dfrac{y^2}{p - 3ky}}{\dfrac{y^2}{p - 3ky}}$
    $= \dfrac{\mathbf{ax^2 y - x}}{\mathbf{p - 3ky}}$

22. $(4x^3 - 2x^2 + 4) \div (x + 2)$

$$
\begin{array}{r}
4x^2 - 10x + 20 \\
x + 2 \overline{\smash{\big)}\ 4x^3 - 2x^2 + 0x + 4} \\
\underline{4x^3 + 8x^2} \\
-10x^2 + 0x \\
\underline{-10x^2 - 20x} \\
20x + 4 \\
\underline{20x + 40} \\
-36
\end{array}
$$

$$4x^2 - 10x + 20 - \frac{36}{x + 2}$$

23. $-2[(-2^0 - 2^2)(-2^3 - 2) + (-2)][-(-3)(-2^2)]$
$= -2[(-5)(-10) - 2][-12] = \mathbf{1152}$

24. $-xy - y^2 - y^0(x - y)$
$= -3(-2) - (-2)^2 - (-2)^0(3 - (-2))$
$= 6 - 4 - 5 = \mathbf{-3}$

25. $3\frac{1}{5}k + \frac{2}{3} = \frac{1}{9}$

$$\frac{16}{5}k = \frac{1}{9} - \frac{6}{9}$$

$$k = -\frac{5}{9} \cdot \frac{5}{16}$$

$$k = -\frac{\mathbf{25}}{\mathbf{144}}$$

26. Since parallel lines have the same slope:
$y = -3x + b$
Use the point $(5, -2)$ for x and y.
$-2 = -3(5) + b$
$b = 13$
$\mathbf{y = -3x + 13}$

27. $m = \dfrac{2 - (-3)}{-5 - 4} = -\dfrac{5}{9}$

$y = -\dfrac{5}{9}x + b$

Use the point $(-5, 2)$ for x and y.

$2 = -\dfrac{5}{9}(-5) + b$

$b = -\dfrac{7}{9}$

$\mathbf{y = -\dfrac{5}{9}x - \dfrac{7}{9}}$

28. $y = -5x + b$
Use the point $(-4, -3)$ for x and y.
$-3 = -5(-4) + b$
$b = -23$
$\mathbf{y = -5x - 23}$

29. $y \le -x - 3$
Test: use $(-4, -3)$
$-3 \le -(-4) - 3$
$-3 \le 1$ true

30. $x = \dfrac{1}{4}$:

$$8\left(\frac{1}{4}\right)^2 + 2\left(\frac{1}{4}\right) - 1 = 0$$

$$\frac{8}{16} + \frac{2}{4} - 1 = 0$$

$$\frac{1}{2} + \frac{1}{2} - 1 = 0$$

$$1 - 1 = 0$$

$$0 = 0$$

$x = -\dfrac{1}{2}$:

$$8\left(-\frac{1}{2}\right)^2 + 2\left(-\frac{1}{2}\right) - 1 = 0$$

$$\frac{8}{4} - \frac{2}{2} - 1 = 0$$

$$2 - 1 - 1 = 0$$

$$2 - 2 = 0$$

$$0 = 0$$

yes, both $\dfrac{1}{4}$ and $-\dfrac{1}{2}$ make the equation **true.**

PROBLEM SET 127

1. $Y = kF$
$2000 = k(500)$
$k = 4$

$Y = 4F$
$Y = 4(400)$
$Y = \mathbf{1600\ tons}$

2. $\dfrac{7}{12} = \dfrac{N_B}{2160}$
$N_B = \mathbf{1260\ boys}$

$N_G = 2160 - 1260$
$N_G = \mathbf{900\ girls}$

3. $R_5 = (10{,}000)(2)^5$
$R_5 = (10{,}000)(32)$
$R_5 = \mathbf{320{,}000}$

4. $y > x$
Test: use $(0, 4)$
$4 > 0$ true

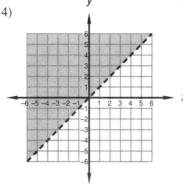

5. $y < -1$
Test: use $(2, -4)$
$-4 < -1$ true

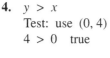

6. $m = 5(-1)^2 + 2(-1) - 3 = 5 - 2 - 3 = \mathbf{0}$

7. $m = 5\left(\dfrac{3}{5}\right)^2 + 2\left(\dfrac{3}{5}\right) - 3 = \dfrac{45}{25} + \dfrac{6}{5} - 3$
$= \mathbf{0}$

8. $x = \dfrac{-b \pm \sqrt{b^2 - 4ac}}{2a}$

$= \dfrac{-2 \pm \sqrt{2^2 - 4(5)(-3)}}{2(5)}$

$= \dfrac{-2 \pm \sqrt{4 + 60}}{10} = \dfrac{-2 \pm 8}{10} = \mathbf{-1, \dfrac{3}{5}}$

9. $3x^2 - 14x - 5$
try $(3x + 1)(x - 5)$, middle term is $-14x$
$\mathbf{(3x + 1)(x - 5)}$

10. $2x^2 + 8 + 10x = 2x^2 + 10x + 8$
$= 2(x^2 + 5x + 4)$
try $2(x + 1)(x + 4)$, middle term is $5x$
$\mathbf{2(x + 4)(x + 1)}$

11. $18 - 15x + 2x^2 = 2x^2 - 15x + 18$
try $(2x - 3)(x - 6)$, middle term is $-15x$
$\mathbf{(2x - 3)(x - 6)}$

12. $-15 + 7x + 2x^2 = 2x^2 + 7x - 15$
try $(2x - 3)(x + 5)$, middle term is $7x$
$\mathbf{(2x - 3)(x + 5)}$

13. $8x - 24 + 2x^2 = 2x^2 + 8x - 24$
$= 2(x^2 + 4x - 12)$
try $2(x - 2)(x + 6)$, middle term is $4x$
$\mathbf{2(x - 2)(x + 6)}$

14. $2x^2 - 24 - 8x = 2x^2 - 8x - 24$
$= 2(x^2 - 4x - 12)$
try $2(x + 2)(x - 6)$, middle term is $-4x$
$\mathbf{2(x + 2)(x - 6)}$

15. $2x^2 - 6x + 4 = 2(x^2 - 3x + 2)$
try $2(x - 2)(x - 1)$, middle term is $-3x$
$\mathbf{2(x - 2)(x - 1)}$

16. $2x^2 - 18 + 9x = 2x^2 + 9x - 18$
try $(2x - 3)(x + 6)$, middle term is $9x$
$\mathbf{(2x - 3)(x + 6)}$

17. $2x^2 + 4 + 6x = 2x^2 + 6x + 4$
$= 2(x^2 + 3x + 2)$
try $2(x + 2)(x + 1)$, middle term is $3x$
$\mathbf{2(x + 2)(x + 1)}$

18. $3x^2 - 7 - 20x = 3x^2 - 20x - 7$
try $(3x + 1)(x - 7)$, middle term is $-20x$
$\mathbf{(3x + 1)(x - 7)}$

19. $3x^2 - 8 - 23x = 3x^2 - 23x - 8$
try $(3x + 1)(x - 8)$, middle term is $-23x$
$\mathbf{(3x + 1)(x - 8)}$

20. $4 - 7x + 3x^2 = 3x^2 - 7x + 4$
try $(3x - 4)(x - 1)$, middle term is $-7x$
$\mathbf{(3x - 4)(x - 1)}$

21. $(4\sqrt{2} + 2)(3\sqrt{2} - 4) = 24 + 6\sqrt{2} - 16\sqrt{2} - 8$
$= \mathbf{16 - 10\sqrt{2}}$

22. $(2\sqrt{3} + 4)(5\sqrt{6} - 2)$
$= \mathbf{30\sqrt{2} + 20\sqrt{6} - 4\sqrt{3} - 8}$

23. $\sqrt{\dfrac{3}{7}} = \dfrac{\sqrt{3}}{\sqrt{7}} \cdot \dfrac{\sqrt{7}}{\sqrt{7}} = \dfrac{\sqrt{21}}{7}$

24. $\sqrt{\dfrac{5}{8}} = \dfrac{\sqrt{5}}{\sqrt{8}} = \dfrac{\sqrt{5}}{2\sqrt{2}} \cdot \dfrac{\sqrt{2}}{\sqrt{2}} = \dfrac{\sqrt{10}}{4}$

25. $\dfrac{2 + \sqrt{3}}{\sqrt{5}} \cdot \dfrac{\sqrt{5}}{\sqrt{5}} = \dfrac{2\sqrt{5} + \sqrt{15}}{5}$

26. $\dfrac{4 + \sqrt{2}}{\sqrt{3}} \cdot \dfrac{\sqrt{3}}{\sqrt{3}} = \dfrac{4\sqrt{3} + \sqrt{6}}{3}$

27. $3 - |x| \geq 1$; $D = \{\text{Reals}\}$
$2 \geq |x|$

-3 -2 -1 0 1 2 3

28. $V_{Remain} = V_{Rect solid} - V_{Right prism}$
$= [A_{Rect base} - A_{Right base}] \times length$
$= \left[(20)(20) - \dfrac{(18)(18)}{2}\right](2)(12) \text{ in.}^3$
$= \textbf{5712 in.}^3$

29. $R_1T_1 = R_2T_2;\ R_1 = 3;\ R_2 = 9;$
$T_1 + T_2 = 16$
$\qquad T_1 = 16 - T_2$

$3(16 - T_2) = 9T_2$
$\qquad 48 = 12T_2$
$\qquad T_2 = 4$

$R_2T_2 = 9(4) = \textbf{36 miles}$

30. Since parallel lines have the same slope:
$y = -2x + b$
Use the point $(4, -3)$ for x and y.
$-3 = -2(4) + b$
$\quad b = 5$
$\textbf{\textit{y}} = \textbf{--2\textit{x}} + \textbf{5}$

PROBLEM SET 128

1. $P = \dfrac{k}{V}$

$15 = \dfrac{k}{20}$

$k = 300$

$P = \dfrac{300}{V}$

$P = \dfrac{300}{10}$

$P = \textbf{30}\ \dfrac{\textbf{lb}}{\textbf{in.}^2}$

2. $P = kT$
$1000 = k(250)$
$\quad k = 4$

$P = 4T$
$P = 4(1000)$

$P = \textbf{4000}\ \dfrac{\textbf{lb}}{\textbf{in.}^2}$

3. $\dfrac{2}{13} = \dfrac{P}{169}$
$\quad P = \textbf{26 pigs}$

$C = 169 - 26 = \textbf{143 chickens}$

4. $R_DT_D + 10 = R_WT_W;\ R_D = 40;$
$R_W = 70;\ T_D = T_W + 2$

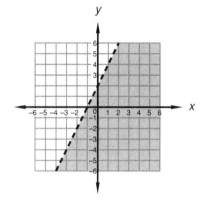

$40(T_W + 2) + 10 = 70T_W$
$40T_W + 80 + 10 = 70T_W$
$\qquad\qquad 90 = 30T_W$
$\qquad\qquad T_W = 3 \text{ hr}$

$T_W = 11 \text{ a.m.} + 3 \text{ hr} = \textbf{2 p.m.}$

5. (a) $N_P + 5N_N = 680$
(b) $N_P + N_N = 280$

$\qquad$ (a) $\quad N_P + 5N_N = 680$
$(-1)(b)\ -N_P - N_N = -280$
$\qquad\qquad\qquad\overline{\qquad 4N_N = 400}$
$\qquad\qquad\qquad\quad N_N = \textbf{100}$

6. $y < 2x + 2$
Test: try $(2, 0)$
$0 < 2(2) + 2$
$0 < 6 \quad$ true

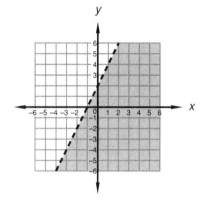

7. $-14 + 3x^2 - 19x = 3x^2 - 19x - 14$
try $(3x + 2)(x - 7)$, middle term is $-19x$
$\textbf{(3\textit{x} + 2)(\textit{x} -- 7)}$

8. $-14 + 19x + 3x^2 = 3x^2 + 19x - 14$
try $(3x - 2)(x + 7)$, middle term is $19x$
$\textbf{(3\textit{x} -- 2)(\textit{x} + 7)}$

9. $2x^2 - 15 + 7x = 2x^2 + 7x - 15$
try $(2x - 3)(x + 5)$, middle term is $7x$
$\textbf{(2\textit{x} -- 3)(\textit{x} + 5)}$

10. $2x^2 - 18 + 9x = 2x^2 + 9x - 18$
try $(2x - 3)(x + 6)$, middle term is $9x$
$\textbf{(2\textit{x} -- 3)(\textit{x} + 6)}$

11. $3x^2 + 14 + 23x = 3x^2 + 23x + 14$
try $(3x + 2)(x + 7)$, middle term is $23x$
$(3x + 2)(x + 7)$

12. $2x^2 - 17x + 21$
try $(2x - 3)(x - 7)$, middle term is $-17x$
$(2x - 3)(x - 7)$

13. $3x^2 + 16 - 26x = 3x^2 - 26x + 16$
try $(3x - 2)(x - 8)$, middle term is $-26x$
$(3x - 2)(x - 8)$

14. $18 + 15x + 2x^2 = 2x^2 + 15x + 18$
try $(2x + 3)(x + 6)$, middle term is $15x$
$(2x + 3)(x + 6)$

15. $3x^2 + 13x + 14$
try $(3x + 7)(x + 2)$, middle term is $13x$
$(3x + 7)(x + 2)$

16. $m = \dfrac{-6 - (-3)}{-3 - 2} = \dfrac{3}{5}$

$y = \dfrac{3}{5}x + b$

Use the point $(2, -3)$ for x and y.

$-3 = \dfrac{3}{5}(2) + b$

$b = -\dfrac{21}{5}$

$\mathbf{y = \dfrac{3}{5}x - \dfrac{21}{5}}$

17. Convert 4,000,000 square miles to square kilometers:

$4{,}000{,}000 \ \cancel{mi}^2 \times \dfrac{5280 \ \cancel{ft}}{1 \ \cancel{mi}} \times \dfrac{5280 \ \cancel{ft}}{1 \ \cancel{mi}} \times \dfrac{12 \ \cancel{in.}}{1 \ \cancel{ft}}$

$\times \dfrac{12 \ \cancel{in.}}{1 \ \cancel{ft}} \times \dfrac{2.54 \ \cancel{cm}}{1 \ \cancel{in.}} \times \dfrac{2.54 \ \cancel{cm}}{1 \ \cancel{in.}} \times \dfrac{1 \ \cancel{m}}{100 \ \cancel{cm}}$

$\times \dfrac{1 \ \cancel{m}}{100 \ \cancel{cm}} \times \dfrac{1 \ km}{1000 \ \cancel{m}} \times \dfrac{1 \ km}{1000 \ \cancel{m}}$

$= \mathbf{\dfrac{4{,}000{,}000(5280)(5280)(12)(12)(2.54)(2.54)}{(100)(100)(1000)(1000)} \ km^2}$

18. $ac - ad + bc - bd = a(c - d) + b(c - d)$
$= \mathbf{(a + b)(c - d)}$

19. $ab + 4a + 2b + 8 = a(b + 4) + 2(b + 4)$
$= \mathbf{(a + 2)(b + 4)}$

20. $ab + ac + xb + xc = a(b + c) + x(b + c)$
$= \mathbf{(a + x)(b + c)}$

21. $2mx - 3m + 2pcx - 3pc$
$= m(2x - 3) + pc(2x - 3) = \mathbf{(m + pc)(2x - 3)}$

22. $4k - kxy + 4pc - pcxy$
$= k(4 - xy) + pc(4 - xy) = \mathbf{(k + pc)(4 - xy)}$

23. $ac - axy + dc - dxy = a(c - xy) + d(c - xy)$
$= \mathbf{(a + d)(c - xy)}$

24. $\sqrt{\dfrac{3}{11}} = \dfrac{\sqrt{3}}{\sqrt{11}} \cdot \dfrac{\sqrt{11}}{\sqrt{11}} = \mathbf{\dfrac{\sqrt{33}}{11}}$

25. $\dfrac{2\sqrt{3} + 2}{\sqrt{5}} \cdot \dfrac{\sqrt{5}}{\sqrt{5}} = \mathbf{\dfrac{2\sqrt{15} + 2\sqrt{5}}{5}}$

26. $-2 < x + 2 \le 3$; $D = \{\text{Positive integers}\}$
$-4 < x \le 1$

27. $m = 3\left(-\dfrac{2}{3}\right)^2 + 20\left(-\dfrac{2}{3}\right) + 12$

$= \dfrac{4}{3} - \dfrac{40}{3} + \dfrac{36}{3} = \mathbf{0}$

28. $x = \dfrac{-b \pm \sqrt{b^2 - 4ac}}{2a}$

$= \dfrac{-20 \pm \sqrt{20^2 - 4(3)(12)}}{2(3)}$

$= \dfrac{-20 \pm 16}{6} = \mathbf{-6, -\dfrac{2}{3}}$

29. $V_{\text{Prism}} = A_{\text{Base}} \times \text{height}$

$= \left[31(5) + 15(13) + \dfrac{18(10)}{2}\right](12) \ \text{in.}^3$

$= [440](12) \ \text{in.}^3$

$= \mathbf{5280 \ \text{in.}^3}$

S.A. $= 2A_{\text{Base}} + (P \times \text{height})$

$= 2[440] \ \text{in.}^2 + [(110 + 2\sqrt{106}) \times 12] \ \text{in.}^2$

$= (880 + 1567.10) \ \text{in.}^2$

$= \mathbf{2447.10 \ \text{in.}^2}$

30. Convert 12,000 cubic feet to cubic meters:

$12{,}000 \ \cancel{ft}^3 \times \dfrac{12 \ \cancel{in.}}{1 \ \cancel{ft}} \times \dfrac{12 \ \cancel{in.}}{1 \ \cancel{ft}} \times \dfrac{12 \ \cancel{in.}}{1 \ \cancel{ft}} \times \dfrac{2.54 \ \cancel{cm}}{1 \ \cancel{in.}}$

$\times \dfrac{2.54 \ \cancel{cm}}{1 \ \cancel{in.}} \times \dfrac{2.54 \ \cancel{cm}}{1 \ \cancel{in.}} \times \dfrac{1 \ m}{100 \ \cancel{cm}} \times \dfrac{1 \ m}{100 \ \cancel{cm}}$

$\times \dfrac{1 \ m}{100 \ \cancel{cm}}$

$= \mathbf{\dfrac{12{,}000(12)(12)(12)(2.54)(2.54)(2.54)}{(100)(100)(100)} \ m^3}$

PROBLEM SET 129

1. $D = kV^2$

$1800 = k(30)^2$

$k = 2$

$D = 2V^2$

$D = 2(28)^2$

$D = \textbf{1568 meters}$

2. $D = kT^2$

$256 = k(3)^2$

$k = 28\frac{4}{9}$

$D = \left(28\frac{4}{9}\right)T^2$

$D = \left(28\frac{4}{9}\right)(8)^2$

$D = \textbf{1820}\frac{\textbf{4}}{\textbf{9}}$ **ft**

3. $G = kP^2$

$4 = k(2)^2$

$k = 1$

$G = P^2$

$G = (6)^2$

$G = \textbf{36}$

4. $R = \dfrac{k}{B^2}$

$4 = \dfrac{k}{(20)^2}$

$k = 1600$

$R = \dfrac{1600}{B^2}$

$R = \dfrac{1600}{(4)^2}$

$R = \textbf{100}$

5. $\dfrac{7}{12} = \dfrac{R}{16,800}$

$R = \textbf{9800 rabbits}$

$S = 16,800 - 9800 = \textbf{7000 squirrels}$

6. $y \geq \dfrac{1}{2}x - 2$

Test: try $(-2, 0)$

$0 \geq \dfrac{1}{2}(-2) - 2$

$0 \geq -3$ true

7. $\dfrac{a}{b} + \dfrac{c}{x} = m$

$\dfrac{a}{b}(bx) + \dfrac{c}{x}(bx) = m(bx)$

$ax + cb = mbx$

$cb = mbx - ax$

$cb = x(mb - a)$

$x = \dfrac{cb}{mb - a}$

8. $3x^2 + 25x - 18$

try $(3x - 2)(x + 9)$, middle term is $25x$

$\textbf{(3x - 2)(x + 9)}$

9. $3x^2 - 4 - x = 3x^2 - x - 4$

try $(3x - 4)(x + 1)$, middle term is $-x$

$\textbf{(3x - 4)(x + 1)}$

10. $2x^2 - 6 - 4x = 2x^2 - 4x - 6$

$= 2(x^2 - 2x - 3)$

try $2(x + 1)(x - 3)$, middle term is $-2x$

$\textbf{2(x + 1)(x - 3)}$

11. $3x^2 + 28x - 20$

try $(3x - 2)(x + 10)$, middle term is $28x$

$\textbf{(3x - 2)(x + 10)}$

12. $2x^2 + 15x + 25$

try $(2x + 5)(x + 5)$, middle term is $15x$

$\textbf{(2x + 5)(x + 5)}$

13. $2x^2 - 5x - 25$

try $(2x + 5)(x - 5)$, middle term is $-5x$

$\textbf{(2x + 5)(x - 5)}$

14. $ab + 15 + 5a + 3b = ab + 3b + 5a + 15$

$= b(a + 3) + 5(a + 3) = \textbf{(b + 5)(a + 3)}$

15. $ay + xy + ac + xc = y(a + x) + c(a + x)$

$= \textbf{(y + c)(a + x)}$

16. $3mx - 2p + 3px - 2m$

$= 3mx - 2m + 3px - 2p$

$= m(3x - 2) + p(3x - 2) = \textbf{(m + p)(3x - 2)}$

17. $kx - 15 - 5k + 3x = kx + 3x - 5k - 15$
$= x(k + 3) - 5(k + 3) = (x - 5)(k + 3)$

18. $xpc + pc^2 + 4x + 4c = pc(x + c) + 4(x + c)$
$= (pc + 4)(x + c)$

19. $acb - ack + 2b - 2k = ac(b - k) + 2(b - k)$
$= (ac + 2)(b - k)$

20. $-2 - |x| > -4;\ D = \{\text{Reals}\}$
$\quad\quad 2 > |x|$

21. $4 \le x + 2 < 7;\ D = \{\text{Integers}\}$
$\quad 2 \le x < 5$

22. $x \le 2$ or $x > 5;\ D = \{\text{Reals}\}$

23. $\sqrt{x + 2} - 4 = 1$
$\quad\quad \sqrt{x + 2} = 5$
$\quad\quad\quad x + 2 = 25$
$\quad\quad\quad\quad x = \mathbf{23}$

Check: $\sqrt{23 + 2} - 4 = 1$
$\quad\quad\quad\quad 5 - 4 = 1$
$\quad\quad\quad\quad\quad 1 = 1$

24. $\sqrt{x - 3} - 5 = 3$
$\quad\quad \sqrt{x - 3} = 8$
$\quad\quad\quad x - 3 = 64$
$\quad\quad\quad\quad x = \mathbf{67}$

Check: $\sqrt{67 - 3} - 5 = 3$
$\quad\quad\quad\quad 8 - 5 = 3$
$\quad\quad\quad\quad 3 = 3$

25. $m = \dfrac{-2 - 5}{3 - (-2)} = -\dfrac{7}{5}$

$y = -\dfrac{7}{5}x + b$

Use the point $(-2, 5)$ for x and y.

$5 = -\dfrac{7}{5}(-2) + b$

$b = \dfrac{11}{5}$

$y = -\dfrac{7}{5}x + \dfrac{11}{5}$

26. $y = -\dfrac{1}{4}x + b$

Use the point $(-2, 5)$ for x and y.

$5 = -\dfrac{1}{4}(-2) + b$

$b = \dfrac{18}{4} = \dfrac{9}{2}$

$y = -\dfrac{1}{4}x + \dfrac{9}{2}$

27. Since parallel lines have the same slope:

$y = -\dfrac{1}{3}x + b$

Use the point $(-2, 5)$ for x and y.

$5 = -\dfrac{1}{3}(-2) + b$

$b = \dfrac{13}{3}$

$y = -\dfrac{1}{3}x + \dfrac{13}{3}$

28. $\sqrt{\dfrac{3}{5}} = \dfrac{\sqrt{3}}{\sqrt{5}} \cdot \dfrac{\sqrt{5}}{\sqrt{5}} = \dfrac{\sqrt{15}}{5}$

29. $\sqrt{\dfrac{7}{3}} = \dfrac{\sqrt{7}}{\sqrt{3}} \cdot \dfrac{\sqrt{3}}{\sqrt{3}} = \dfrac{\sqrt{21}}{3}$

30. $\dfrac{2\sqrt{2} + \sqrt{2}}{\sqrt{2}} = \dfrac{2\sqrt{2} + \sqrt{2}}{\sqrt{2}} \cdot \dfrac{\sqrt{2}}{\sqrt{2}}$
$= \dfrac{4 + 2}{2} = 3$

PROBLEM SET 130

1. $R_F T_F + R_E T_E = 420;\ T_F = 6;$
$T_E = 3;\ R_E = 20 + R_F$

$6R_F + 3(20 + R_F) = 420$
$6R_F + 60 + 3R_F = 420$
$\quad\quad\quad 9R_F = 360$
$\quad\quad\quad\quad R_F = \mathbf{40\ mph}$

$R_E = 20 + (40) = \mathbf{60\ mph}$

2. $\dfrac{2}{13} = \dfrac{G}{2340}$
$\quad G = \mathbf{360\ greens}$

$W = 2340 - 360$
$W = \mathbf{1980\ whites}$

3. $\dfrac{2}{100}(N_C) = 480$
$\quad\quad\quad N_C = \mathbf{24{,}000}$

4. (a) $N_O + 10N_T = 2900$

(b) $N_O = N_T + 293$

Substitute (b) into (a) and get:

(a') $(N_T + 293) + 10N_T = 2900$

$$11N_T = 2607$$
$$N_T = \mathbf{237}$$

(b) $N_O = (237) + 293 = \mathbf{530}$

5. $R = \dfrac{k}{Y^2}$

$10 = \dfrac{k}{(100)^2}$

$k = 100{,}000$

$R = \dfrac{100{,}000}{(5)^2}$

$R = \mathbf{4000}$

6. $N \quad N + 2 \quad N + 4 \quad N + 6$

$-12(N + N + 6) + 6 = 19(-N - 4)$

$-24N - 72 + 6 = -19N - 76$

$10 = 5N$

$N = 2$

The desired integers are **2, 4, 6,** and **8.**

7. (a) $m = 2(2)^2 - 2(2) - 4 = 8 - 4 - 4 = \mathbf{0}$

(b) $m = 2(-1)^2 - 2(-1) - 4 = 2 + 2 - 4 = \mathbf{0}$

8. $V_{\text{Prism}} = A_{\text{Base}} \times \text{height}$

$\quad = \left[(36)(10) + \dfrac{(36)(10)}{2}\right](2)(3) \text{ ft}^3$

$\quad = [540](6) \text{ ft}^3$

$\quad = \mathbf{3240 \text{ ft}^3}$

9. $x^2 + 2x - 4 = 0$

$(x^2 + 2x \quad) - 4 = 0$

$(x^2 + 2x \quad) = 4$

$(x^2 + 2x + 1) = 4 + 1$

$(x + 1)^2 = 5$

$x + 1 = \pm\sqrt{5}$

$x = \mathbf{-1 \pm \sqrt{5}}$

10. $x^2 + 3x - 8 = 0$

$(x^2 + 3x \quad) - 8 = 0$

$(x^2 + 3x \quad) = 8$

$\left(x^2 + 3x + \dfrac{9}{4}\right) = 8 + \dfrac{9}{4}$

$\left(x + \dfrac{3}{2}\right)^2 = \dfrac{41}{4}$

$x + \dfrac{3}{2} = \pm\sqrt{\dfrac{41}{4}}$

$x = \mathbf{-\dfrac{3}{2} \pm \dfrac{\sqrt{41}}{2}}$

11. $x^2 + 2x - 5 = 0$

$(x^2 + 2x \quad) - 5 = 0$

$(x^2 + 2x \quad) = 5$

$(x^2 + 2x + 1) = 5 + 1$

$(x + 1)^2 = 6$

$x + 1 = \pm\sqrt{6}$

$x = \mathbf{-1 \pm \sqrt{6}}$

12. $x^2 + 4x - 7 = 0$

$(x^2 + 4x \quad) - 7 = 0$

$(x^2 + 4x \quad) = 7$

$(x^2 + 4x + 4) = 7 + 4$

$(x + 2)^2 = 11$

$x + 2 = \pm\sqrt{11}$

$x = \mathbf{-2 \pm \sqrt{11}}$

13. $3x^2 - 35 - 16x = 3x^2 - 16x - 35$

try $(3x + 5)(x - 7)$, middle term is $-16x$

$\mathbf{(3x + 5)(x - 7)}$

14. $-2x + 3x^2 - 5 = 3x^2 - 2x - 5$

try $(3x - 5)(x + 1)$, middle term is $-2x$

$\mathbf{(3x - 5)(x + 1)}$

15. $2x^2 - 5x - 12$

try $(2x + 3)(x - 4)$, middle term is $-5x$

$\mathbf{(2x + 3)(x - 4)}$

16. $p^2c - ab + p^2b - ac = p^2c + p^2b - ac - ab$

$= p^2(c + b) - a(c + b) = \mathbf{(p^2 - a)(c + b)}$

17. $ax^2 - ca + cx^2 - c^2 = ax^2 + cx^2 - ca - c^2$

$= x^2(a + c) - c(a + c) = \mathbf{(x^2 - c)(a + c)}$

18. $2y + mx^3 + my + 2x^3 = 2x^3 + 2y + mx^3 + my$

$= 2(x^3 + y) + m(x^3 + y) = \mathbf{(2 + m)(x^3 + y)}$

19. $4ab + 4x + abc + cx = 4(ab + x) + c(ab + x)$

$= \mathbf{(4 + c)(ab + x)}$

20. $4 \le x - 2 \le 8$; $D = \{\text{Reals}\}$

$6 \le x \le 10$

21. $3 - |x| > 2$; $D = \{\text{Integers}\}$

$1 > |x|$

22. $x < -2$ or $x \geq 4$; $D = \{$Integers$\}$

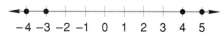

23. $m = \dfrac{-3 - 2}{5 - (-3)} = -\dfrac{5}{8}$

$y = -\dfrac{5}{8}x + b$

Use the point $(-3, 2)$ for x and y.

$2 = -\dfrac{5}{8}(-3) + b$

$b = \dfrac{1}{8}$

$y = -\dfrac{5}{8}x + \dfrac{1}{8}$

24. $\sqrt{4x + 1} - 1 = 2$

$\sqrt{4x + 1} = 3$

$4x + 1 = 9$

$4x = 8$

$x = \mathbf{2}$

Check: $\sqrt{4(2) + 1} - 1 = 2$

$\sqrt{9} - 1 = 2$

$3 - 1 = 2$

$2 = 2$

25. $\sqrt{5m - 5} + 6 = 7$

$\sqrt{5m - 5} = 1$

$5m - 5 = 1$

$5m = 6$

$m = \dfrac{\mathbf{6}}{\mathbf{5}}$

Check: $\sqrt{5\left(\dfrac{6}{5}\right) - 5} + 6 = 7$

$\sqrt{6 - 5} + 6 = 7$

$7 = 7$

26. Since parallel lines have the same slope:

$y = \dfrac{1}{5}x + b$

Use the point $(2, 4)$ for x and y.

$4 = \dfrac{1}{5}(2) + b$

$b = \dfrac{18}{5}$

$y = \dfrac{1}{5}x + \dfrac{18}{5}$

27. (a) $y \leq -x + 2$; Test: $(-2, 0)$ $0 \leq -(-2) + 2$

true $0 \leq 4$

(b) $y \geq x$; Test: $(-2, 0)$

$0 \geq -2$ true

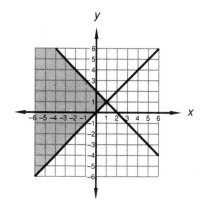

28. $\sqrt{\dfrac{2}{7}} = \dfrac{\sqrt{2}}{\sqrt{7}} \cdot \dfrac{\sqrt{7}}{\sqrt{7}} = \dfrac{\sqrt{14}}{7}$

29. $\sqrt{\dfrac{5}{12}} = \dfrac{\sqrt{5}}{2\sqrt{3}} \cdot \dfrac{\sqrt{3}}{\sqrt{3}} = \dfrac{\sqrt{15}}{6}$

30. $\dfrac{4 + \sqrt{3}}{\sqrt{6}} \cdot \dfrac{\sqrt{6}}{\sqrt{6}} = \dfrac{4\sqrt{6} + 3\sqrt{2}}{6}$

$= \dfrac{\mathbf{2\sqrt{6}}}{\mathbf{3}} + \dfrac{\mathbf{\sqrt{2}}}{\mathbf{2}}$

PROBLEM SET 131

1. $R_E T_E = R_F T_F$; $T_E = 20$; $T_F = 25$;

$R_E = R_F + 10$

$20(R_F + 10) = 25R_F$

$20R_F + 200 = 25R_F$

$200 = 5R_F$

$R_F = \mathbf{40\ mph}$

$R_E = (40) + 10 = \mathbf{50\ mph}$

2. $\$156 = P_P + \dfrac{30}{100}P_P$

$\$156 = \dfrac{130}{100}P_P$

$P_P = \mathbf{\$120}$

3. $G = \dfrac{k}{B^2}$

$5 = \dfrac{k}{(50)^2}$

$k = 12{,}500$

$G = \dfrac{12{,}500}{B^2}$

$G = \dfrac{12{,}500}{(10)^2}$

$G = \mathbf{125}$

4. $\dfrac{11}{16} = \dfrac{F}{800}$

$F = \mathbf{550}$

5. (a) $7N_G + 3N_S = 414$

(b) $N_G = N_S + 2$

Substitute (b) into (a) and get:

(a') $7(N_S + 2) + 3N_S = 414$

$10N_S + 14 = 414$

$10N_S = 400$

$N_S = \mathbf{40}$

(b) $N_G = (40) + 2$

$N_G = \mathbf{42}$

6. $N \qquad N + 2 \qquad N + 4$

$-3(N + N + 4) = 8(-N - 2) + 50$

$-6N - 12 = -8N + 34$

$2N = 46$

$N = 23$

The desired integers are **23, 25,** and **27.**

7. $\dfrac{x + \dfrac{4x}{3y}}{\dfrac{2ax}{y} + 4} = \dfrac{\dfrac{3xy + 4x}{3y}}{\dfrac{2ax + 4y}{y}} \cdot \dfrac{\dfrac{y}{2ax + 4y}}{\dfrac{y}{2ax + 4y}}$

$= \dfrac{\mathbf{3xy + 4x}}{\mathbf{6ax + 12y}}$

8. (a) $R_E T_E = R_W T_W$

(b) $R_E = 145$

(c) $R_W = 200$

(d) $T_E + T_W = 6$

$T_E = 6 - T_W$

Substitute (b) and (c) into (a) and get:

(a') $145T_E = 200T_W$

Substitute (d) into (a') and get:

(a'') $145(6 - T_W) = 200T_W$

$870 = 345T_W$

$T_W = \dfrac{\mathbf{58}}{\mathbf{23}}$

(d) $T_E = 6 - \dfrac{58}{23} = \dfrac{\mathbf{80}}{\mathbf{23}}$

9. $-3x = -2x^2 + 10$

$2x^2 - 3x - 10 = 0$

$x = \dfrac{-b \pm \sqrt{b^2 - 4ac}}{2a}$

$= \dfrac{-(-3) \pm \sqrt{(-3)^2 - 4(2)(-10)}}{2(2)}$

$= \dfrac{3 \pm \sqrt{9 + 80}}{4} = \dfrac{\mathbf{3 \pm \sqrt{89}}}{\mathbf{4}}$

10. $-2x = 5 - x^2$

$x^2 - 2x - 5 = 0$

$x = \dfrac{-b \pm \sqrt{b^2 - 4ac}}{2a}$

$= \dfrac{-(-2) \pm \sqrt{(-2)^2 - 4(1)(-5)}}{2(1)}$

$= \dfrac{2 \pm \sqrt{24}}{2} = \mathbf{1 \pm \sqrt{6}}$

11. $x^2 + 2x - 11 = 0$

$x = \dfrac{-b \pm \sqrt{b^2 - 4ac}}{2a}$

$= \dfrac{-2 \pm \sqrt{2^2 - 4(1)(-11)}}{2(1)}$

$= \dfrac{-2 \pm \sqrt{48}}{2} = \mathbf{-1 \pm 2\sqrt{3}}$

12. $5x^2 - 6x - 4 = 0$

$x = \dfrac{-b \pm \sqrt{b^2 - 4ac}}{2a}$

$= \dfrac{-(-6) \pm \sqrt{(-6)^2 - 4(5)(-4)}}{2(5)}$

$= \dfrac{6 \pm \sqrt{116}}{10} = \dfrac{\mathbf{3 \pm \sqrt{29}}}{\mathbf{5}}$

13. $-3x = -x^2 + 10$

$x^2 - 3x - 10 = 0$

$(x^2 - 3x \quad) = 10$

$\left(x^2 - 3x + \dfrac{9}{4}\right) = 10 + \dfrac{9}{4}$

$\left(x - \dfrac{3}{2}\right)^2 = \dfrac{49}{4}$

$x - \dfrac{3}{2} = \pm\sqrt{\dfrac{49}{4}}$

$x = \dfrac{3}{2} \pm \dfrac{7}{2} = \mathbf{5, -2}$

14. $-2x = 5 - x^2$

$x^2 - 2x - 5 = 0$

$(x^2 - 2x \quad) = 5$

$(x^2 - 2x + 1) = 5 + 1$

$(x - 1)^2 = 6$

$x - 1 = \pm\sqrt{6}$

$x = \mathbf{1 \pm \sqrt{6}}$

15. $x^2 + 2x - 11 = 0$

$(x^2 + 2x \quad) = 11$

$(x^2 + 2x + 1) = 11 + 1$

$(x + 1)^2 = 12$

$x + 1 = \pm\sqrt{12}$

$\boldsymbol{x = -1 \pm 2\sqrt{3}}$

16. $3x^2 - 5 + 14x = 3x^2 + 14x - 5$

try $(3x - 1)(x + 5)$, middle term is $14x$

$\boldsymbol{(3x - 1)(x + 5)}$

17. $-27 + 24x + 3x^2 = 3x^2 + 24x - 27$

$= 3(x^2 + 8x - 9)$

try $3(x - 1)(x + 9)$, middle term is $8x$

$\boldsymbol{3(x - 1)(x + 9)}$

18. $9x - 5 + 2x^2 = 2x^2 + 9x - 5$

try $(2x - 1)(x + 5)$, middle term is $9x$

$\boldsymbol{(2x - 1)(x + 5)}$

19. $km^2 + 2c - 2m^2 - kc = km^2 - 2m^2 - kc + 2c$

$= m^2(k - 2) - c(k - 2) = \boldsymbol{(m^2 - c)(k - 2)}$

20. $6a - xya - xyb + 6b = 6a + 6b - xya - xyb$

$= 6(a + b) - xy(a + b) = \boldsymbol{(6 - xy)(a + b)}$

21. $abx - 2yc + xc - 2yab$

$= abx + xc - 2yab - 2yc$

$= x(ab + c) - 2y(ab + c)$

$= \boldsymbol{(x - 2y)(ab + c)}$

22. $4xn + abn - abm - 4xm$

$= 4xn - 4xm + abn - abm$

$= 4x(n - m) + ab(n - m)$

$= \boldsymbol{(4x + ab)(n - m)}$

23. $m = \dfrac{-4 - 5}{-3 - 2} = \dfrac{9}{5}$

$y = \dfrac{9}{5}x + b$

Use the point $(2, 5)$ for x and y.

$5 = \dfrac{9}{5}(2) + b$

$b = \dfrac{7}{5}$

$\boldsymbol{y = \dfrac{9}{5}x + \dfrac{7}{5}}$

24. Since parallel lines have the same slope:

$y = \dfrac{2}{5}x + b$

Use the point $(-2, 5)$ for x and y.

$5 = \dfrac{2}{5}(-2) + b$

$b = \dfrac{29}{5}$

$\boldsymbol{y = \dfrac{2}{5}x + \dfrac{29}{5}}$

25. (a) $y \geq x$

Test: $(-3, 0)$;

$0 \geq -3$ true

(b) $y \leq -x + 2$

Test: $(-3, 0)$;

$0 \leq 5$ true

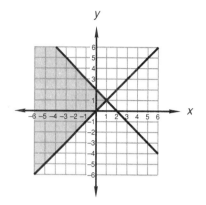

26. $(4 + 2\sqrt{2})(\sqrt{2} + 2)$

$= 4\sqrt{2} + 4 + 8 + 4\sqrt{2}$

$= \boldsymbol{12 + 8\sqrt{2}}$

27. $\sqrt{\dfrac{3}{8}} = \dfrac{\sqrt{3}}{2\sqrt{2}} \cdot \dfrac{\sqrt{2}}{\sqrt{2}} = \dfrac{\boldsymbol{\sqrt{6}}}{\boldsymbol{4}}$

28. $\dfrac{\sqrt{2} + 1}{\sqrt{2}} \cdot \dfrac{\sqrt{2}}{\sqrt{2}} = \dfrac{2 + \sqrt{2}}{2}$

$= \boldsymbol{1 + \dfrac{\sqrt{2}}{2}}$

29. $V_{\text{Cyl.}} = A_{\text{Base}} \times \text{height}$

$= \left[\dfrac{(8)(12)}{2} - \dfrac{\pi(2)^2}{2}\right](8)(12)(12)(12) \text{ in.}^3$

$\approx [41.72](13{,}824) \text{ in.}^3$

$\approx \boldsymbol{576{,}737.28 \text{ in.}^3}$

S.A. $= 2A_{\text{Base}} + (P \times \text{height})$

$= \{2[41.72] + (16 + 4\sqrt{13} + 2\pi)(8)\}(144)$

$\approx \boldsymbol{54{,}296.30 \text{ in.}^2}$

30. $4(2N + 7) = N + 69$

$8N + 28 = N + 69$

$7N = 41$

$N = \boldsymbol{\dfrac{41}{7}}$

PROBLEM SET 132

1. $R_P T_P = R_B T_B$; $R_P = R_B + 11$;
$T_P = 6$; $T_B = 72$

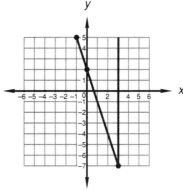

$6(R_B + 11) = 72R_B$
$66 = 66R_B$
$R_B = 1$

$R_P = (1) + 11 = $ **12 kilometers per hour**
$D_P = R_P T_P = 12(6) = $ **72 kilometers**

2. $W = \dfrac{k}{D^2}$

$25,000 = \dfrac{k}{(100,000)^2}$

$k = 2.5 \times 10^{14}$

$W = \dfrac{2.5 \times 10^{14}}{D^2}$

$W = \dfrac{2.5 \times 10^{14}}{(5000)^2}$

$W = $ **10,000,000 pounds**

3. (a) $400N_H + 100N_P = 4500$
(b) $N_H = N_P + 5$
Substitute (b) into (a) and get:
(a′) $400(N_P + 5) + 100N_P = 4500$
$ 500N_P = 2500$
$ N_P = 5$

(b) $N_H = (5) + 5 = $ **10**

4. $\dfrac{35}{100}P_P = 1351$
$P_P = $ **3860**

5. $\dfrac{17}{19} = \dfrac{N_S}{38,000}$
$N_S = $ **34,000**

6. (a) $P(2) = \dfrac{1}{4}$

(b) $P(3, 2) = P(3) \times P(2) = \dfrac{1}{4} \times \dfrac{1}{4} = \dfrac{1}{16}$
(c) $P(4, 3, 1) = P(4) \times P(3) \times P(1)$
$ = \dfrac{1}{4} \times \dfrac{1}{4} \times \dfrac{1}{4} = \dfrac{1}{64}$

7. $4 \leq x < 10$; $D = \{\text{Integers}\}$

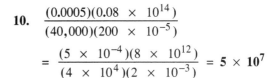

8. (a) $y = -3x + 2 = \dfrac{-3}{+1}x + 2$

(b) $x = 3$
The first step is to graph each of these lines.

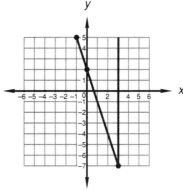

It appears that the lines cross at $x = 3$ and $y = -7$, so $(\mathbf{3, -7})$ is the solution.

9. (a) $4x - 5y = -3$
(b) $2x + y = 9$

 (a) $ 4x - 5y = -3$
$(-2)\text{(b)} -4x - 2y = -18$
$ -7y = -21$
$ y = 3$
(b) $2x + (3) = 9$
$ x = 3$

$(\mathbf{3, 3})$

10. $\dfrac{(0.0005)(0.08 \times 10^{14})}{(40,000)(200 \times 10^{-5})}$

$= \dfrac{(5 \times 10^{-4})(8 \times 10^{12})}{(4 \times 10^4)(2 \times 10^{-3})} = \mathbf{5 \times 10^7}$

11. (a) horizontal line: $y = \pm k$; $\mathbf{y = 4}$
(b) The desired equation is $y = mx + b$.
By inspection, $b = -2$.
By inspection, the sign for m is $-$.

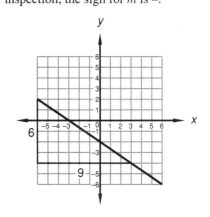

$|m| = \dfrac{6}{9} = \dfrac{2}{3}$

Since $b = -2$ and $m = -\dfrac{2}{3}$:

$y = -\dfrac{2}{3}x - 2$

12. $(3x^3 - 5) \div (x + 3)$

$$
\begin{array}{r}
3x^2 - 9x + 27 \\
x + 3 \overline{)\ 3x^3 + 0x^2 + \ 0x - \ 5} \\
\underline{3x^3 + 9x^2} \\
-9x^2 + \ 0x \\
\underline{-9x^2 - 27x} \\
27x - \ 5 \\
\underline{27x + 81} \\
-86
\end{array}
$$

$$3x^2 - 9x + 27 - \frac{86}{x + 3}$$

13. $-3\sqrt{12}(2\sqrt{6} - 5\sqrt{8})$

$= -3 \cdot 2\sqrt{2}\sqrt{2}\sqrt{3}\sqrt{2}\sqrt{3} + 3 \cdot 5\sqrt{2}\sqrt{2}\sqrt{3}\sqrt{2}\sqrt{2}\sqrt{2}$

$= \mathbf{-36\sqrt{2} + 60\sqrt{6}}$

14. $-2 = x^2 + 6x$

$0 = x^2 + 6x + 2$

$x = \dfrac{-b \pm \sqrt{b^2 - 4ac}}{2a}$

$x = \dfrac{-6 \pm \sqrt{6^2 - 4(1)(2)}}{2(1)}$

$x = \dfrac{-6 \pm \sqrt{28}}{2} = \mathbf{-3 \pm \sqrt{7}}$

15. $-7x = 4 - 2x^2$

$2x^2 - 7x - 4 = 0$

$x = \dfrac{-b \pm \sqrt{b^2 - 4ac}}{2a}$

$x = \dfrac{-(-7) \pm \sqrt{(-7)^2 - 4(2)(-4)}}{2(2)}$

$x = \dfrac{7 \pm \sqrt{81}}{4} = \mathbf{4, -\dfrac{1}{2}}$

16. $-4 + 9x^2 = 0$

$9x^2 - 4 = 0$

$(3x - 2)(3x + 2) = 0$

If $3x - 2 = 0$, $x = \mathbf{\dfrac{2}{3}}$

$-4 + 9\left(\dfrac{2}{3}\right)^2 = 0$

$0 = 0$ check

If $3x + 2 = 0$, $x = \mathbf{-\dfrac{2}{3}}$

$-4 + 9\left(-\dfrac{2}{3}\right)^2 = 0$

$0 = 0$ check

17. $5 = -x^2 - 6x$

$x^2 + 6x + 5 = 0$

$(x + 5)(x + 1) = 0$

If $(x + 1) = 0$, $x = \mathbf{-1}$

$5 = -(-1)^2 - 6(-1)$

$5 = 5$ check

If $(x + 5) = 0$, $x = \mathbf{-5}$

$5 = -(-5)^2 - 6(-5)$

$5 = 5$ check

18. $\dfrac{4x}{3} - \dfrac{2x + 4}{2} = 5$

$\dfrac{4x}{3}(6) - \dfrac{(2x + 4)}{2}(6) = 5(6)$

$8x - 6x - 12 = 30$

$2x - 12 = 30$

$2x = 42$

$x = \mathbf{21}$

19. $4 \in$ **Naturals, wholes, integers, rationals, and reals**

20. $\dfrac{1}{2}x - 2\dfrac{3}{5} = \dfrac{1}{10}$

$\dfrac{1}{2}x = \dfrac{1}{10} + \dfrac{13}{5}$

$\dfrac{1}{2}x = \dfrac{1}{10} + \dfrac{26}{10}$

$x = \dfrac{27}{10} \cdot \dfrac{2}{1}$

$x = \mathbf{\dfrac{27}{5}}$

21. (a) $R_H T_H = R_R T_R$

(b) $R_H = 2$

(c) $R_R = 12$

(d) $T_H = T_R + 5$

Substitute (b) and (c) into (a) and get:

(a′) $2T_H = 12T_R$

Substitute (d) into (a′) and get:

(a″) $2(T_R + 5) = 12T_R$

$2T_R + 10 = 12T_R$

$10T_R = 10$

$T_R = \mathbf{1}$

(d) $T_H = (1) + 5 = \mathbf{6}$

22.
$$-5 = x^2 - 7x$$
$$x^2 - 7x + 5 = 0$$
$$(x^2 - 7x \quad) = -5$$
$$\left(x^2 - 7x + \frac{49}{4}\right) = -5 + \frac{49}{4}$$
$$\left(x + \frac{7}{2}\right)^2 = \frac{29}{4}$$
$$x - \frac{7}{2} = \pm\frac{\sqrt{29}}{2}$$
$$x = \frac{7}{2} \pm \frac{\sqrt{29}}{2}$$

23.
$$-3x = 4 - x^2$$
$$x^2 - 3x - 4 = 0$$
$$(x^2 - 3x \quad) = 4$$
$$\left(x^2 - 3x + \frac{9}{4}\right) = 4 + \frac{9}{4}$$
$$\left(x - \frac{3}{2}\right)^2 = \frac{25}{4}$$
$$x - \frac{3}{2} = \pm\sqrt{\frac{25}{4}}$$
$$x = \frac{3}{2} \pm \sqrt{\frac{25}{4}}$$
$$x = \frac{3}{2} \pm \frac{5}{2}$$
$$x = \mathbf{4, -1}$$

24. $0 \not\le -x - 3 \not\le 2$; $D = \{\text{Integers}\}$
$0 \not\le -x - 3$ or $-x - 3 \not\le 2$
$0 > -x - 3$ or $-x - 3 > 2$
$x > -3$ or $x < -5$

$$-7 \ -6 \ -5 \ -4 \ -3 \ -2 \ -1$$

25. Since parallel lines have the same slope:
$$y = -\frac{2}{5}x + b$$
Use the point $(-3, 4)$ for x and y.
$$4 = -\frac{2}{5}(-3) + b$$
$$b = \frac{14}{5}$$
$$y = -\frac{2}{5}x + \frac{14}{5}$$

26. In general $a + 0 = a$, specifically $8 + 0 = 8$.

27. (a) $\sqrt{\dfrac{5}{8}} = \dfrac{\sqrt{5}}{2\sqrt{2}} \cdot \dfrac{\sqrt{2}}{\sqrt{2}} = \dfrac{\sqrt{10}}{4}$

    (b) $\dfrac{\sqrt{5} + 3}{\sqrt{5}} \cdot \dfrac{\sqrt{5}}{\sqrt{5}} = \dfrac{5 + 3\sqrt{5}}{5}$

$$= \mathbf{1 + \frac{3\sqrt{5}}{5}}$$

28. $\dfrac{(x^0)^{-2}(xx^2)^3(y^{-2})^4 y}{(xyy)^{-2}(yx^{-2})^4} = \dfrac{x^9 y^{-8} y}{x^{-2} y^{-4} y^4 x^{-8}}$
$$= \mathbf{x^{19} y^{-7}}$$

29. $x^2 y^{-2} - \dfrac{3x^2}{y^2} + \dfrac{12x^4 xy^{-2}}{x^3} - \dfrac{3x^2 y^2}{x^{-4}}$
$$= x^2 y^{-2} - 3x^2 y^{-2} + 12x^2 y^{-2} - 3x^6 y^2$$
$$= \mathbf{10x^2 y^{-2} - 3x^6 y^2}$$

30. $V_{\text{Solid}} = V_{\text{Prism}} - V_{\text{Cylinder}}$
$$= [A_{\text{Prism base}} - A_{\text{Cylinder base}}] \times \text{length}$$
$$= \left[\frac{3\sqrt{3}(6)}{2} - \pi(1)^2\right](10) \text{ m}^3$$
$$\approx \mathbf{124.48 \text{ m}^3}$$

PRACTICE SET 1

1. $R_E T_E = R_F T_F$; $T_E = 25$; $T_F = 30$;
$R_F = R_E - 15$

$$25 R_E = 30(R_E - 15)$$
$$5 R_E = 450$$
$$R_E = \mathbf{90 \text{ kilometers per hour}}$$
$$R_F = (90) - 15 = \mathbf{75 \text{ kilometers per hour}}$$

2. $\$275 = P_P - \dfrac{45}{100}P_P$
$$\$275 = \frac{55}{100}P_P$$
$$\mathbf{\$500} = P_P$$

3. $R = \dfrac{k}{B^2}$
$$7 = \frac{k}{(60)^2}$$
$$k = 25{,}200$$

$$R = \frac{25{,}200}{B^2}$$
$$R = \frac{25{,}200}{(20)^2}$$
$$R = \mathbf{63}$$

4. $H = 13, M = 8, T = 21$
$$\frac{13}{21} = \frac{H}{420}$$
$$H = \frac{13 \cdot 420}{21}$$
$$H = \mathbf{260}$$

5. $A_5 = \$22{,}000(1 + 0.11)^5$
$$A_5 = \$22{,}000(1.6850582)$$
$$A_5 = \mathbf{\$37{,}071.30}$$
$$\text{Interest} = \mathbf{\$15{,}071.30}$$

6. $\quad N \qquad N + 2 \qquad N + 4 \qquad N + 6$

$\quad -5(N + N + 4) = 6(-N - 6) + 40$

$\qquad -10N - 20 = -6N + 4$

$\qquad\qquad\qquad -24 = 4N$

$\qquad\qquad\qquad -6 = N$

The desired integers are $-6, -4, -2,$ and $0.$

7. $\quad \dfrac{3a + \dfrac{x}{2z}}{\dfrac{4am}{y} + 2} = \dfrac{\dfrac{6az + x}{2z}}{\dfrac{4am + 2y}{y}} \cdot \dfrac{\dfrac{y}{4am + 2y}}{\dfrac{y}{4am + 2y}}$

$\quad = \dfrac{6azy + xy}{8amz + 4zy}$

8. (a) $R_E T_E = R_W T_W$

(b) $R_E = 16$

(c) $R_W = 60$

(d) $T_E + T_W = 5$

$\qquad\qquad T_W = 5 - T_E$

Substitute (b) and (c) into (a) and get:

(a') $16T_E = 60T_W$

Substitute (d) into (a') and get:

(a'') $16T_E = 60(5 - T_E)$

$\qquad 16T_E = 300 - 60T_E$

$\qquad 76T_E = 300$

$\qquad\quad T_E = \dfrac{75}{19}$

(d) $T_W = \dfrac{95}{19} - \left(\dfrac{75}{19}\right) = \dfrac{20}{19}$

9. $\qquad\qquad -5 = -3x^2 - x$

$\quad 3x^2 + x - 5 = 0$

$\quad x = \dfrac{-b \pm \sqrt{b^2 - 4ac}}{2a}$

$\quad = \dfrac{-1 \pm \sqrt{1^2 - 4(3)(-5)}}{2(3)}$

$\quad = \dfrac{-1 \pm \sqrt{61}}{6}$

10. $\quad 4x = 2x^2 - 2$

$\qquad 0 = 2x^2 - 4x - 2$

$\quad x = \dfrac{-b \pm \sqrt{b^2 - 4ac}}{2a}$

$\quad = \dfrac{4 \pm \sqrt{(-4)^2 - 4(2)(-2)}}{2(2)}$

$\quad = \dfrac{4 \pm \sqrt{32}}{4}$

$\quad = 1 \pm \sqrt{2}$

11. $\quad 3x^2 + 3x - 8 = 0$

$\quad x = \dfrac{-b \pm \sqrt{b^2 - 4ac}}{2a}$

$\quad = \dfrac{-3 \pm \sqrt{3^2 - 4(3)(-8)}}{2(3)}$

$\quad = \dfrac{-3 \pm \sqrt{105}}{6}$

12. $\quad 4x^2 - 5x - 3 = 0$

$\quad x = \dfrac{-b \pm \sqrt{b^2 - 4ac}}{2a}$

$\quad = \dfrac{5 \pm \sqrt{(-5)^2 - 4(4)(-3)}}{2(4)}$

$\quad = \dfrac{5 \pm \sqrt{73}}{8}$

13. $\qquad\qquad\quad 4x = x^2 - 2$

$\qquad x^2 - 4x - 2 = 0$

$\qquad (x^2 - 4x \quad) = 2$

$\qquad (x^2 - 4x + 4) = 2 + 4$

$\qquad\qquad (x - 2)^2 = 6$

$\qquad\qquad x - 2 = \pm\sqrt{6}$

$\qquad\qquad\qquad x = 2 \pm \sqrt{6}$

14. $\qquad\qquad x^2 + 3x - 8 = 0$

$\qquad (x^2 + 3x \quad) = 8$

$\qquad \left(x^2 + 3x + \dfrac{9}{4}\right) = 8 + \dfrac{9}{4}$

$\qquad\qquad \left(x + \dfrac{3}{2}\right)^2 = \dfrac{41}{4}$

$\qquad\qquad x + \dfrac{3}{2} = \pm\dfrac{\sqrt{41}}{2}$

$\qquad\qquad\qquad x = -\dfrac{3}{2} \pm \dfrac{\sqrt{41}}{2}$

15. $\qquad\qquad -5 = -x^2 - x$

$\qquad x^2 + x - 5 = 0$

$\qquad (x^2 + x \quad) = 5$

$\qquad \left(x^2 + x + \dfrac{1}{4}\right) = 5 + \dfrac{1}{4}$

$\qquad\qquad \left(x + \dfrac{1}{2}\right)^2 = \dfrac{21}{4}$

$\qquad\qquad x + \dfrac{1}{2} = \pm\dfrac{\sqrt{21}}{2}$

$\qquad\qquad\qquad x = -\dfrac{1}{2} \pm \dfrac{\sqrt{21}}{2}$

16. $\quad 2x^2 - 6 + 11x = 2x^2 + 11x - 6$

$\quad = (2x - 1)(x + 6)$

17. $-33 + 30x + 3x^2 = 3x^2 + 30x - 33$
$= 3(x^2 + 10x - 11) = \mathbf{3(x - 1)(x + 11)}$

18. $-20x - 7 + 3x^2 = 3x^2 - 20x - 7$
$= \mathbf{(3x + 1)(x - 7)}$

19. $ax^3 + 5a - 4x^3 - 20 = a(x^3 + 5) - 4(x^3 + 5)$
$= \mathbf{(a - 4)(x^3 + 5)}$

20. $7z + cmz - cmx - 7x = 7z - 7x + cmz - cmx$
$= 7(z - x) + cm(z - x) = \mathbf{(7 + cm)(z - x)}$

21. $5a - mna - mnb + 5b$
$= 5a + 5b - mna - mnb$
$= 5(a + b) - mn(a + b)$
$= \mathbf{(5 - mn)(a + b)}$

22. $7ys + zfs - zfx - 7yx = 7ys - 7yx + zfs - zfx$
$= 7y(s - x) + zf(s - x) = \mathbf{(7y + zf)(s - x)}$

23. $m = \dfrac{-5 - 6}{-2 - 3} = \dfrac{11}{5}$

$y = \dfrac{11}{5}x + b$

Use the point $(3, 6)$ for x and y.

$6 = \dfrac{11}{5}(3) + b$

$b = -\dfrac{3}{5}$

$\mathbf{y = \dfrac{11}{5}x - \dfrac{3}{5}}$

24. Since parallel lines have the same slope:

$y = \dfrac{1}{5}x + b$

Use the point $(-3, 4)$ for x and y.

$4 = \dfrac{1}{5}(-3) + b$

$b = \dfrac{23}{5}$

$\mathbf{y = \dfrac{1}{5}x + \dfrac{23}{5}}$

25. (a) $y \leq x$
Test: $(2, 1)$
$1 \leq 2$

(b) $y \geq -x - 1$
Test: $(2, 1)$
$1 \geq -2 - 1$

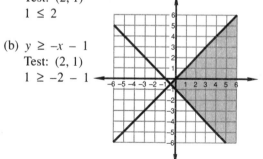

26. $(5 + 3\sqrt{3})(\sqrt{3} + 4) = 5\sqrt{3} + 9 + 20 + 12\sqrt{3}$
$= \mathbf{29 + 17\sqrt{3}}$

27. $\sqrt{\dfrac{5}{7}} = \dfrac{\sqrt{5}}{\sqrt{7}} \cdot \dfrac{\sqrt{7}}{\sqrt{7}} = \dfrac{\sqrt{35}}{7}$

28. $\dfrac{2\sqrt{3} + 2}{\sqrt{3}} \cdot \dfrac{\sqrt{3}}{\sqrt{3}} = \dfrac{6 + 2\sqrt{3}}{3}$

29. $(9x^2 - 4z^2)^2 = (9x^2 - 4z^2)(9x^2 - 4z^2)$
$= 81x^4 - 36x^2z^2 - 36x^2z^2 + 16z^4$
$= \mathbf{81x^4 - 72x^2z^2 + 16z^4}$

30. radius $= \dfrac{\text{diameter}}{2} = \dfrac{6\sqrt{2} \text{ in.}}{2} = 3\sqrt{2} \text{ in.}$

$V_{\text{Cylinder}} = A_{\text{Base}} \times \text{height}$
$= \pi(3\sqrt{2} \text{ in.})^2 \times 5 \text{ in.}$
$\approx \mathbf{282.6 \text{ in.}^3}$

PRACTICE SET 2

1. $R_R T_R = R_G T_G$; $T_R = 7$; $T_G = 63$;
$R_R = R_G + 16$

$7(R_G + 16) = 63R_G$
$7R_G + 112 = 63R_G$
$-56R_G = -112$
$R_G = 2$

$R_R = (2) + 16 = \mathbf{18 \text{ kilometers per hour}}$
$R_R T_R = 18(7) = \mathbf{126 \text{ kilometers}}$

2. $W = \dfrac{k}{D^2}$

$6000 = \dfrac{k}{(1000)^2}$

$k = 6{,}000{,}000{,}000$

$W = \dfrac{6{,}000{,}000{,}000}{D^2}$

$W = \dfrac{6{,}000{,}000{,}000}{(7000)^2}$

$W = \mathbf{122 \text{ pounds}}$

3. (a) $125N_B + 25N_G = 3500$
(b) $N_G = N_B + 8$
Substitute (b) into (a) and get:
(a$'$) $125N_B + 25(N_B + 8) = 3500$
$125N_B + 25N_B + 200 = 3500$
$150N_B = 3300$
$N_B = \mathbf{22}$

4. $\dfrac{30}{100}P_I = 1653$
$P_I = \mathbf{5510}$

5. $E = 7$, $D = 3$, $T = 10$

$$\frac{7}{10} = \frac{E}{26,000}$$

$$E = \frac{7 \cdot 26,000}{10}$$

$$E = \textbf{18,200}$$

6. $P(2, 5) = P(2) \cdot P(5) = \dfrac{1}{6} \cdot \dfrac{1}{6} = \dfrac{\mathbf{1}}{\mathbf{36}}$

7. $-6 \leq x < 4$; $D = \{\text{Reals}\}$

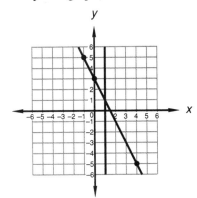

8. (a) $y = -2x + 3$

$$y = \frac{-2}{+1}x + 3$$

(b) $x = 1$

The first step is to graph each of these lines.

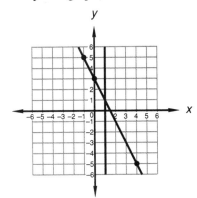

It appears that the lines cross at $x = 1$ and $y = 1$, so
(1, 1) is the solution.

9. (a) $2x - 3y = -1$
(b) $-3x + y = 5$

(a) $\quad 2x - 3y = -1$
(3)(b) $\underline{-9x + 3y = 15}$
$\qquad -7x \qquad\quad = 14$
$\qquad\qquad\quad x = -2$

(a) $2(-2) - 3y = -1$
$\qquad\quad -3 = 3y$
$\qquad\quad -1 = y$

(−2, −1)

10. $\dfrac{(0.000006)(0.03 \times 10^{16})}{(30,000)(600 \times 10^{-11})}$

$= \dfrac{(6 \times 10^{-6})(3 \times 10^{14})}{(3 \times 10^{4})(6 \times 10^{-9})} = \mathbf{1 \times 10^{13}}$

11. (a) The desired equation is $y = mx + b$.
By inspection, $b = 2$.
By inspection, the sign for m is +.

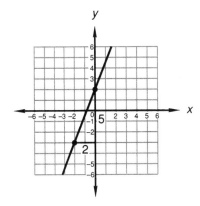

$$|m| = \frac{5}{2}$$

Since $b = 2$ and $m = \dfrac{5}{2}$: $\mathbf{y = \dfrac{5}{2}x + 2}$

(b) horizontal line: $y = \pm k$; $\mathbf{y = -2}$

12. $(5x^3 - 2) \div (x + 4)$

$$
\begin{array}{r}
5x^2 - 20x + 80 \\
x + 4 \overline{)\, 5x^3 + 0x^2 + 0x - 2} \\
\underline{5x^3 + 20x^2} \\
-20x^2 + 0x \\
\underline{-20x^2 - 80x} \\
80x - 2 \\
\underline{80x + 320} \\
-322
\end{array}
$$

$$\mathbf{5x^2 - 20x + 80 - \dfrac{322}{x + 4}}$$

13. $-3\sqrt{18}(5\sqrt{16} - \sqrt{27})$
$= -3 \cdot 5 \cdot 4 \cdot 3\sqrt{2} + 3\sqrt{9}\sqrt{9}\sqrt{2}\sqrt{3}$
$= \mathbf{-180\sqrt{2} + 27\sqrt{6}}$

14. $-3 = x^2 + 5x$
$\quad 0 = x^2 + 5x + 3$

$$x = \frac{-b \pm \sqrt{b^2 - 4ac}}{2a}$$

$$= \frac{-5 \pm \sqrt{5^2 - 4(1)(3)}}{2(1)}$$

$$= \frac{-5 \pm \sqrt{13}}{2}$$

15.
$$-4x = 7 - 3x^2$$
$$3x^2 - 4x - 7 = 0$$
$$(3x - 7)(x + 1) = 0$$

If $(3x - 7) = 0$, $x = \dfrac{7}{3}$

$$-4\left(\dfrac{7}{3}\right) = 7 - 3\left(\dfrac{7}{3}\right)^2$$
$$-\dfrac{28}{3} = 7 - \dfrac{49}{3}$$
$$-\dfrac{28}{3} = -\dfrac{28}{3}$$

If $(x + 1) = 0$, $x = -1$
$$-4(-1) = 7 - 3(-1)^2$$
$$4 = 4$$

16.
$$-9 + 25z^2 = 0$$
$$25z^2 - 9 = 0$$
$$(5z - 3)(5z + 3) = 0$$

If $(5z - 3) = 0$, $z = \dfrac{3}{5}$

$$-9 + 25\left(\dfrac{3}{5}\right)^2 = 0$$
$$-9 + 9 = 0$$

If $(5z + 3) = 0$, $z = -\dfrac{3}{5}$

$$-9 + 25\left(-\dfrac{3}{5}\right)^2 = 0$$
$$-9 + 9 = 0$$

17.
$$5 = -2x^2 - 11x$$
$$2x^2 + 11x + 5 = 0$$
$$(2x + 1)(x + 5) = 0$$

If $(2x + 1) = 0$, $x = -\dfrac{1}{2}$

$$5 = -2\left(-\dfrac{1}{2}\right)^2 - 11\left(-\dfrac{1}{2}\right)$$
$$5 = 5$$

If $(x + 5) = 0$, $x = -5$
$$5 = -2(-5)^2 - 11(-5)$$
$$5 = 5$$

18.
$$\dfrac{4x}{5} - \dfrac{3x + 3}{4} = 6$$
$$\dfrac{4x}{5}(20) - \dfrac{(3x + 3)}{4}(20) = 6(20)$$
$$16x - 15x - 15 = 120$$
$$x = 135$$

19. $\dfrac{\sqrt{2}}{3} \in$ **Irrationals and reals**

20.
$$\dfrac{b^2 + \dfrac{3}{b^3}}{4 - \dfrac{1}{b^2}} = \dfrac{\dfrac{b^5 + 3}{b^3}}{\dfrac{4b^2 - 1}{b^2}} \cdot \dfrac{\dfrac{4b^2 - 1}{b^2}}{\dfrac{4b^2 - 1}{b^2}}$$

$$= \dfrac{b^5 + 3}{4b^3 - b}$$

21. (a) $R_H T_H = R_X T_X$
(b) $R_H = 3$
(c) $R_X = 7$
(d) $T_X = T_H - 3$
Substitute (b) and (c) into (a) and get:
(a′) $3T_H = 7T_X$
Substitute (d) into (a′) and get:
(a″) $3T_H = 7(T_H - 3)$
$$4T_H = 21$$
$$T_H = \dfrac{21}{4}$$

(d) $T_X = \left(\dfrac{21}{4}\right) - 3 = \dfrac{9}{4}$

22.
$$-4 = -x^2 - 5x$$
$$x^2 + 5x - 4 = 0$$
$$(x^2 + 5x \quad) = 4$$
$$\left(x^2 + 5x + \dfrac{25}{4}\right) = 4 + \dfrac{25}{4}$$
$$\left(x + \dfrac{5}{2}\right)^2 = \dfrac{41}{4}$$
$$x + \dfrac{5}{2} = \pm\dfrac{\sqrt{41}}{2}$$
$$x = -\dfrac{5}{2} \pm \dfrac{\sqrt{41}}{2}$$

23.
$$-4x = 5 - x^2$$
$$x^2 - 4x - 5 = 0$$
$$(x^2 - 4x \quad) = 5$$
$$(x^2 - 4x + 4) = 5 + 4$$
$$(x - 2)^2 = 9$$
$$x - 2 = \pm\sqrt{9}$$
$$x = 2 \pm 3$$
$$x = -1, 5$$

24. $-4 \ngtr x + 4 \ngtr 5$; $D = \{\text{Reals}\}$
$$-4 < x + 4 < 5$$
$$-8 < x < 1$$

$$-9\ -8\ -7\ -6\ -5\ -4\ -3\ -2\ -1\ \ 0\ \ 1\ \ 2$$

25. Since parallel lines have the same slope:

$$y = -\frac{3}{4}x + b$$

Use the point $(-1, -1)$ for x and y.

$$-1 = -\frac{3}{4}(-1) + b$$

$$b = -\frac{7}{4}$$

$$y = -\frac{3}{4}x - \frac{7}{4}$$

26. $2(3 + 4) = 2 \cdot 3 + 2 \cdot 4$

27. $\sqrt{\dfrac{3}{2}} = \dfrac{\sqrt{3}}{\sqrt{2}} \cdot \dfrac{\sqrt{2}}{\sqrt{2}} = \dfrac{\sqrt{6}}{2}$

28. $\dfrac{\sqrt{2} + 7}{\sqrt{2}} \cdot \dfrac{\sqrt{2}}{\sqrt{2}} = \dfrac{2 + 7\sqrt{2}}{2}$

29. $\dfrac{(k^2)^{-3}(kk^{-1})^2(z^{-3})^3 z}{(kzz^2)^{-3}(zk^{-1})^4} = \dfrac{k^{-6}z^{-9}z}{k^{-3}z^{-9}z^4 k^{-4}} = kz^{-3}$

30. $V_{\text{Cylinder}} = A_{\text{Base}} \times \text{height}$

$$= [(12)(8) + \pi(4)^2](3)(3) \text{ ft}^3$$

$$\approx [146.24](9) \text{ ft}^3$$

$$\approx 1316.16 \text{ ft}^3$$

$$\approx \dfrac{(1316.16)(12)^3(2.54)^3}{(100)^3} \text{ m}^3$$

$$\approx \mathbf{37.27 \ m^3}$$

S.A. $= 2A_{\text{Base}} + (P \times \text{height})$

$$= 2[146.24] \text{ ft}^2 + [(24 + 2\pi(4))(3)(3)] \text{ ft}^2$$

$$\approx 292.48 \text{ ft}^2 + [442.08] \text{ ft}^2$$

$$\approx 734.56 \text{ ft}^2$$

$$\approx \dfrac{(734.56)(12)^2(2.54)^2}{(100)^2} \text{ m}^2$$

$$\approx \mathbf{68.24 \ m^2}$$

$V_{\text{Cone}} = \dfrac{1}{3}V_{\text{Cylinder}}$

$$= \dfrac{1}{3}\left[\dfrac{(1316.16)(12)^3(2.54)^3}{(100)^3}\right] \text{ m}^3$$

$$= \mathbf{12.42 \ m^3}$$

PRACTICE SET 3

1. $R_C T_C + R_P T_P = 3500$; $T_C = 9$;
$T_P = 4$; $R_C = R_P + 100$

$$\begin{array}{|c@{\ }c@{\ }c|} \hline D_P & & D_C \\ \hline \end{array}$$

$$9(R_P + 100) + 4R_P = 3500$$

$$9R_P + 900 + 4R_P = 3500$$

$$13R_P = 2600$$

$$R_P = \mathbf{200 \ mph}$$

$$R_C = (200) + 100 = \mathbf{300 \ mph}$$

2. $P = 11, U = 5, T = 16$

$$\dfrac{11}{16} = \dfrac{P}{16,800}$$

$$P = \mathbf{11{,}550}$$

$$U = 16{,}800 - (11{,}550) = \mathbf{5250}$$

3. $\dfrac{14}{100}(T) = 1197$

$$T = 8550$$

$$\text{Voted} = (8550) - 1197 = \mathbf{7353}$$

4. (a) $N_O + 5N_F = 3600$
(b) $N_O = N_F + 354$
Substitute (b) into (a) and get:
(a′) $(N_F + 354) + 5N_F = 3600$

$$6N_F = 3246$$

$$N_F = \mathbf{541}$$

(b) $N_O = (541) + 354 = \mathbf{895}$

5. $A_{10} = \$19{,}000(1 + 0.12)^{10}$
$A_{10} = \$19{,}000(3.1058482)$
$A_{10} = \mathbf{\$59{,}011.10}$
Interest $= \mathbf{\$40{,}011.10}$

6. $N \qquad N + 2 \qquad N + 4 \qquad N + 6$

$$-8(N + 2 + N + 4) = 14(-N - 6) - 6$$

$$-16N - 48 = -14N - 90$$

$$42 = 2N$$

$$21 = N$$

The desired integers are **21, 23, 25,** and **27.**

7. $5 = 3x^2 + 5x$

$$0 = 3x^2 + 5x - 5$$

$$x = \dfrac{-b \pm \sqrt{b^2 - 4ac}}{2a}$$

$$= \dfrac{-5 \pm \sqrt{5^2 - 4(3)(-5)}}{2(3)}$$

$$= \dfrac{-5 \pm \sqrt{85}}{6}$$

8.
$$-5x = 8 - 3x^2$$
$$3x^2 - 5x - 8 = 0$$

$$x = \frac{-b \pm \sqrt{b^2 - 4ac}}{2a}$$

$$= \frac{5 \pm \sqrt{(-5)^2 - 4(3)(-8)}}{2(3)}$$

$$= \frac{5 \pm \sqrt{121}}{6} = -1, \frac{8}{3}$$

9.
$$x^2 + 8x - 2 = 0$$
$$(x^2 + 8x \quad) = 2$$
$$(x^2 + 8x + 16) = 2 + 16$$
$$(x + 4)^2 = 18$$
$$x + 4 = \pm\sqrt{18}$$
$$x = -4 \pm 3\sqrt{2}$$

10.
$$x^2 + 6x - 3 = 0$$
$$(x^2 + 6x \quad) = 3$$
$$(x^2 + 6x + 9) = 3 + 9$$
$$(x + 3)^2 = 12$$
$$x + 3 = \pm\sqrt{12}$$
$$x = -3 \pm 2\sqrt{3}$$

11.
$$-36y^6 = -121x^2$$
$$121x^2 - 36y^6 = 0$$
$$(11x - 6y^3)(11x + 6y^3) = 0$$

12.
$$-41x = 6 - 7x^2$$
$$7x^2 - 41x - 6 = 0$$
$$(7x + 1)(x - 6) = 0$$

13.
$$a^2b - 2c^3m + mb - 2a^2c^3$$
$$= a^2b + mb - 2a^2c^3 - 2c^3m$$
$$= b(a^2 + m) - 2c^3(a^2 + m)$$
$$= (b - 2c^3)(a^2 + m)$$

14.
$$6ax + 7am^3 + 12d^3x + 14m^3d^3$$
$$= a(6x + 7m^3) + 2d^3(6x + 7m^3)$$
$$= (a + 2d^3)(6x + 7m^3)$$

15.
$$P(bj, j) = P(bj) \cdot P(j) = \frac{2}{52} \cdot \frac{4}{52} = \frac{1}{26} \cdot \frac{1}{13}$$
$$= \frac{1}{338}$$

16. $5 \geq x \geq -9$; $D = \{\text{Reals}\}$

17. $-2 - |x| > 2$; $D = \{\text{Integers}\}$
$$-4 > |x|$$
No integers

18. $m = \dfrac{-1 - 3}{3 - (-1)} = \dfrac{-4}{4} = -1$

$y = -x + b$

Use the point $(-1, 3)$ for x and y.

$3 = -1(-1) + b$

$b = 2$

$\mathbf{y = -x + 2}$

19. Since parallel lines have the same slope:

$y = \dfrac{2}{3}x + b$

Use the point $(3, 3)$ for x and y.

$3 = \dfrac{2}{3}(3) + b$

$b = 1$

$\mathbf{y = \dfrac{2}{3}x + 1}$

20.
$$\frac{2m + \dfrac{x}{3z}}{\dfrac{3mc}{z} + 1} = \frac{\dfrac{6mz + x}{3z}}{\dfrac{3mc + z}{z}} \cdot \frac{\dfrac{z}{3mc + z}}{\dfrac{z}{3mc + z}}$$

$$= \frac{6mz + x}{9mc + 3z}$$

21. (a) $R_E T_E + R_W T_W = 688$

(b) $R_E = 44$

(c) $R_W = 100$

(d) $T_E + T_W = 8$
$$T_W = 8 - T_E$$

Substitute (b) and (c) into (a) and get:

(a′) $44T_E + 100T_W = 688$

Substitute (d) into (a′) and get:

(a″) $44T_E + 100(8 - T_E) = 688$
$$44T_E + 800 - 100T_E = 688$$
$$112 = 56T_E$$
$$\mathbf{2 = T_E}$$

(d) $T_W = 8 - (2) = \mathbf{6}$

22. $-3\sqrt[3]{-27} = 9 \in$ **Naturals, wholes, integers, rationals, and reals**

23.
$$\sqrt{5x + 2} - 5 = 2$$
$$\sqrt{5x + 2} = 7$$
$$5x + 2 = 49$$
$$5x = 47$$
$$x = \frac{47}{5}$$

Check: $\sqrt{5\left(\dfrac{47}{5}\right) + 2} - 5 = 2$

$$\sqrt{49} - 5 = 2$$
$$7 - 5 = 2$$
$$2 = 2$$

24. $\sqrt{4c-7}+6=-3$
$$\sqrt{4c-7}=-9$$
$$4c-7=81$$
$$4c=88$$
$$c=22$$

Check: $\sqrt{4(22)-7}+6=-3$
$$\sqrt{81}+6=-3$$
$$9+6=-3 \ \text{not true}$$

No real number solution

25. $\sqrt{\dfrac{3}{8}}=\dfrac{\sqrt{3}}{2\sqrt{2}}\cdot\dfrac{\sqrt{2}}{\sqrt{2}}=\dfrac{\sqrt{6}}{4}$

26. $\dfrac{5+\sqrt{10}}{\sqrt{5}}\cdot\dfrac{\sqrt{5}}{\sqrt{5}}=\dfrac{5\sqrt{5}+5\sqrt{2}}{5}$
$$=\mathbf{\sqrt{5}+\sqrt{2}}$$

27. $(5+3\sqrt{3})(\sqrt{3}+3)=5\sqrt{3}+9+15+9\sqrt{3}$
$$=\mathbf{24+14\sqrt{3}}$$

28. $\left(y-\dfrac{1}{2}p\right)^2=\left(y-\dfrac{1}{2}p\right)\left(y-\dfrac{1}{2}p\right)$
$$=y^2-\dfrac{1}{2}py-\dfrac{1}{2}py+\dfrac{1}{4}p^2$$
$$=\mathbf{y^2-py+\dfrac{1}{4}p^2}$$

29. $4z^{-4}x^2-\dfrac{1}{x^{-2}z^4}+\dfrac{14z^5x^6}{yx^{-8}z^2z^7}$
$$=4z^{-4}x^2-z^{-4}x^2+14z^{-4}x^{14}y^{-1}$$
$$=\dfrac{\mathbf{3x^2y+14x^{14}}}{\mathbf{z^4y}}$$

30. $V=A_{\text{Base}}\times\text{height}$
$$=\left[(20)(20)-\dfrac{\pi(7)^2}{2}+\dfrac{(5)(20)}{2}\right](10)\ \text{ft}^3$$
$$\approx[373.07](10)\ \text{ft}^3$$
$$\approx\dfrac{(3730.7)(12)^3(2.54)^3}{(100)^3}\ \text{m}^3$$
$$\approx\mathbf{105.64\ m^3}$$

1. $P=\dfrac{k}{V}$
$$20=\dfrac{k}{30}$$
$$k=600$$

$$P=\dfrac{600}{V}$$
$$P=\dfrac{600}{5}$$
$$P=\mathbf{120\dfrac{lb}{in.^2}}$$

2. $P=kT$
$$4000=k(125)$$
$$k=32$$

$$P=32T$$
$$P=32(1000)$$
$$P=\mathbf{32,000\dfrac{lb}{in.^2}}$$

3. $R_{30}=(200)(3)^{30}$
$$R_{30}=\mathbf{4.118\times10^{16}}$$

4. $R_DT_D+15=R_RT_R;\ R_D=55;$
$R_R=65;\ T_D=T_R+3$

$$55(T_R+3)+15=65T_R$$
$$180=10T_R$$
$$18=T_R$$

$T=9\ \text{a.m.}+18\ \text{hrs}=\mathbf{3\ a.m.}$

5. (a) $N_D+N_Q=330$
(b) $10N_D+25N_Q=3885$

$(-10)(\text{a})\ -10N_D-10N_Q=-3300$
$\underline{\ (\text{b})\qquad 10N_D+25N_Q=\quad 3885\ }$
$$15N_Q=\quad585$$
$$N_Q=\mathbf{39}$$

6. $y \geq 3x + 4$
   Test: $(-2, 2)$
   $2 \geq 3(-2) + 4$
   $2 \geq -2$ true

7. $2x^2 + 13x + 21 = (2x + 7)(x + 3)$

8. $5x^2 - 34x - 7 = (5x + 1)(x - 7)$

9. $4m - sam + 4xy - saxy$
   $= m(4 - sa) + xy(4 - sa) = (m + xy)(4 - sa)$

10. $5cx + 3x - 5czx - 3xz$
    $= x(5c + 3) - xz(5c + 3) = x(1 - z)(5c + 3)$

11. $(7x - \sqrt{13})^2 = (7x - \sqrt{13})(7x - \sqrt{13})$
    $= 49x^2 - 7\sqrt{13}x - 7\sqrt{13}x + 13$
    $= 49x^2 - 14\sqrt{13}x + 13$

12. $(\sqrt{3}x + \sqrt{3})^2 = (\sqrt{3}x + \sqrt{3})(\sqrt{3}x + \sqrt{3})$
    $= 3x^2 + 3x + 3x + 3 = 3x^2 + 6x + 3$

13. $\sqrt{\dfrac{7}{12}} = \dfrac{\sqrt{7}}{2\sqrt{3}} \cdot \dfrac{\sqrt{3}}{\sqrt{3}} = \dfrac{\sqrt{21}}{6}$

14. $\dfrac{7\sqrt{11} + 3}{\sqrt{11}} \cdot \dfrac{\sqrt{11}}{\sqrt{11}} = \dfrac{77 + 3\sqrt{11}}{11}$

15. $\dfrac{6p + \dfrac{3m}{p}}{\dfrac{3mp}{z} + 5} = \dfrac{\dfrac{6p^2 + 3m}{p}}{\dfrac{3mp + 5z}{z}} \cdot \dfrac{z}{\dfrac{3mp + 5z}{3mp + 5z}}$

    $= \dfrac{6p^2z + 3mz}{3mp^2 + 5pz}$

16. $(4 + 3\sqrt{2})(\sqrt{2} + 3) = 4\sqrt{2} + 6 + 12 + 9\sqrt{2}$
    $= 18 + 13\sqrt{2}$

17. $0.00361 \in$ **Rationals and reals**

18. $-3 = x^2 + 7x$
    $0 = x^2 + 7x + 3$

    $x = \dfrac{-b \pm \sqrt{b^2 - 4ac}}{2a}$

    $= \dfrac{-7 \pm \sqrt{7^2 - 4(1)(3)}}{2(1)}$

    $= \dfrac{-7 \pm \sqrt{37}}{2}$

19. $-5x + 3 = 4x^2$
    $ 0 = 4x^2 + 5x - 3$

    $x = \dfrac{-b \pm \sqrt{b^2 - 4ac}}{2a}$

    $= \dfrac{-5 \pm \sqrt{5^2 - 4(4)(-3)}}{2(4)}$

    $= \dfrac{-5 \pm \sqrt{73}}{8}$

20. $ -3 = -x^2 - 9x$
    $ x^2 + 9x - 3 = 0$
    $ (x^2 + 9x) = 3$
    $\left(x^2 + 9x + \dfrac{81}{4} \right) = 3 + \dfrac{81}{4}$
    $ \left(x + \dfrac{9}{2} \right)^2 = \dfrac{93}{4}$
    $ \left(x + \dfrac{9}{2} \right) = \pm \dfrac{\sqrt{93}}{2}$
    $ x = -\dfrac{9}{2} \pm \dfrac{\sqrt{93}}{2}$

21. $ -5x = 1 - x^2$
    $ x^2 - 5x - 1 = 0$
    $ (x^2 - 5x) = 1$
    $\left(x^2 - 5x + \dfrac{25}{4} \right) = 1 + \dfrac{25}{4}$
    $ \left(x - \dfrac{5}{2} \right)^2 = \dfrac{29}{4}$
    $ \left(x - \dfrac{5}{2} \right) = \pm \dfrac{\sqrt{29}}{2}$
    $ x = \dfrac{5}{2} \pm \dfrac{\sqrt{29}}{2}$

22. $m = \dfrac{3 - 4}{-2 - 1} = \dfrac{-1}{-3} = \dfrac{1}{3}$

$y = \dfrac{1}{3}x + b$

Use the point $(1, 4)$ for x and y.

$4 = \dfrac{1}{3}(1) + b$

$b = \dfrac{11}{3}$

$y = \dfrac{1}{3}x + \dfrac{11}{3}$

23. Since parallel lines have the same slope:

$y = -\dfrac{1}{4}x + b$

Use the point $(-3, 3)$ for x and y.

$3 = -\dfrac{1}{4}(-3) + b$

$b = \dfrac{9}{4}$

$y = -\dfrac{1}{4}x + \dfrac{9}{4}$

24. (a) $R_E T_E + R_X T_X = 1100$
(b) $R_E = 50$
(c) $R_X = 200$
(d) $T_E + T_X = 10$
$\qquad T_E = 10 - T_X$

Substitute (b) and (c) into (a) and get:
(a') $50T_E + 200T_X = 1100$

Substitute (d) into (a') and get:
(a'') $50(10 - T_X) + 200T_X = 1100$
$\qquad 500 - 50T_X + 200T_X = 1100$
$\qquad\qquad\qquad 150T_X = 600$
$\qquad\qquad\qquad\quad T_X = \mathbf{4}$

(d) $T_E = 10 - (4) = \mathbf{6}$

25. (a) $y = -\dfrac{1}{2}x + 1 = \dfrac{-1}{+2}x + 1$
(b) $x = 1$

The first step is to graph each of these lines.

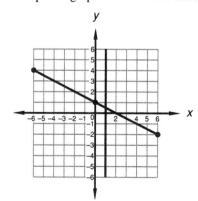

It appears that the lines cross at $x = 1$ and $y = \dfrac{1}{2}$,

so $\left(1, \dfrac{1}{2}\right)$ is the solution.

26. (a) $x - y = -5$
(b) $3x + y = 25$

$\begin{array}{rl} \text{(a)} & x - y = -5 \\ \text{(b)} & 3x + y = 25 \\ \hline & 4x = 20 \\ & x = 5 \end{array}$

(a) $(5) - y = -5$
$\qquad\qquad y = 10$

(5, 10)

27. $\dfrac{(0.00006)(0.09 \times 10^{11})}{(70,000)(500 \times 10^{-9})}$

$= \dfrac{(6 \times 10^{-5})(9 \times 10^{9})}{(7 \times 10^{4})(5 \times 10^{-7})} = \mathbf{1.54 \times 10^{7}}$

28. $\dfrac{x^{-4}(xx^{-1})^{3}(y^{-5})^{4}y}{x^{2}y^{-10}x^{-5}x^{-1}} = \dfrac{x^{-4}y^{-19}}{x^{-4}y^{-10}} = \boldsymbol{y^{-9}}$

29. $3x^{4}y^{-6} - \dfrac{x^{6}}{3^{-1}y^{6}x^{2}} - \dfrac{9y^{-9}x^{-3}x^{12}}{x^{5}y^{-3}}$

$= 3x^{4}y^{-6} - 3x^{4}y^{-6} - 9x^{4}y^{-6} = \boldsymbol{-9x^{4}y^{-6}}$

30. $V = A_{\text{Base}} \times \text{height}$

$= \left[9(9) - \dfrac{\pi(9)}{2} + \dfrac{9(2)}{2}\right](3)(12) \text{ in.}^{3}$

$\approx [75.87](36) \text{ in.}^{3}$

$\approx 2731.32 \text{ in.}^{3}$

$\approx (2731.32)(2.54)(2.54)(2.54) \text{ cm}^{3}$

$\approx \mathbf{44{,}758.32 \text{ cm}^{3}}$

PRACTICE SET 5

1. $D = kV^{2}$
$1600 = k(40)^{2}$
$\qquad k = 1$

$D = V^{2}$
$D = (32)^{2}$
$D = \mathbf{1024 \text{ meters}}$

2. $D = kT^{2}$
$432 = k(6)^{2}$
$\qquad k = 12$

$D = 12T^{2}$
$D = 12(11)^{2}$
$D = \mathbf{1452 \text{ feet}}$

3. $P = \dfrac{k}{M^2}$

$15 = \dfrac{k}{6^2}$

$k = 540$

$P = \dfrac{540}{M^2}$

$P = \dfrac{540}{2^2}$

$P = \mathbf{135}$

4. $B = 9, P = 7, T = 16$

$\dfrac{9}{16} = \dfrac{B}{33,920}$

$B = \mathbf{19,080}$

$P = 33,920 - (19,080) = \mathbf{14,840}$

5. $R_C T_C = R_H T_H;\ R_C = 3;\ R_H = 8;$

$T_C + T_H = 11$

$\quad\quad T_H = 11 - T_C$

$3T_C = 8(11 - T_C)$

$11T_C = 88$

$\quad T_C = 8$

$R_C T_C = 3(8) = \mathbf{24\ km}$

6. (a) The desired equation is $y = mx + b$.
By inspection, $b = -2$.
By inspection, the sign for m is +.

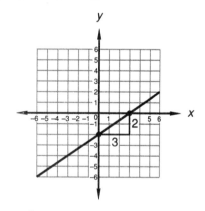

$|m| = \dfrac{2}{3}$

So $b = -2$ and $m = \dfrac{2}{3}$: $\mathbf{y = \dfrac{2}{3}x - 2}$

(b) horizontal line: $y = \pm k$; $\mathbf{y = 5}$

7. (b), (d)
(a) is not a function because 4 has 3 images.
(c) is not a function because -4 has 2 images.

8. $\sqrt{x + 4} - 4 = 6$

$\sqrt{x + 4} = 10$

$x + 4 = 100$

$x = \mathbf{96}$

Check: $\sqrt{96 + 4} - 4 = 6$

$\quad\quad\quad 10 - 4 = 6$

$\quad\quad\quad\quad\quad 6 = 6$

9. $x + 3 > 5$ or $x \le -4$; $D = \{\text{Reals}\}$

$\quad\quad x > 2$ or $x \le -4$

```
◄——●——+——+——+——+——+——○——►
  -6 -5 -4 -3 -2 -1  0  1  2  3  4
```

10. $(3\sqrt{5} + \sqrt{3})(\sqrt{5} + \sqrt{3}) = 15 + \sqrt{15} + 3\sqrt{15} + 3$

$= \mathbf{18 + 4\sqrt{15}}$

11. $(4 + 2\sqrt{11})(4 - \sqrt{11})$

$= 16 + 8\sqrt{11} - 4\sqrt{11} - 22 = \mathbf{-6 + 4\sqrt{11}}$

12. $(2a^2 + 4b^2)^2 = (2a^2 + 4b^2)(2a^2 + 4b^2)$

$= \mathbf{4a^4 + 16a^2b^2 + 16b^4}$

13. $(b^2 - \sqrt{2})^2 = (b^2 - \sqrt{2})(b^2 - \sqrt{2})$

$= \mathbf{b^4 - 2\sqrt{2}b^2 + 2}$

14. $\sqrt{\dfrac{7}{8}} = \dfrac{\sqrt{7}}{2\sqrt{2}} \cdot \dfrac{\sqrt{2}}{\sqrt{2}} = \dfrac{\mathbf{\sqrt{14}}}{\mathbf{4}}$

15. $\dfrac{4 + 2\sqrt{3}}{3\sqrt{5}} \cdot \dfrac{\sqrt{5}}{\sqrt{5}} = \dfrac{\mathbf{4\sqrt{5} + 2\sqrt{15}}}{\mathbf{15}}$

16. $\dfrac{5 + 2\sqrt{8}}{\sqrt{3}} \cdot \dfrac{\sqrt{3}}{\sqrt{3}} = \dfrac{\mathbf{5\sqrt{3} + 4\sqrt{6}}}{\mathbf{3}}$

17. radius $= \dfrac{\text{diameter}}{2} = \dfrac{2\sqrt{5}\ \text{m}}{2} = \sqrt{5}\ \text{m}$

$V_{\text{Cylinder}} = A_{\text{Base}} \times \text{height}$

$= \pi(\sqrt{5})^2\ \text{m}^2 \times 3\ \text{m}$

$\approx \dfrac{(47.1)(100)^3}{(2.54)^3(12)^3}\ \text{ft}^3$

$\approx \mathbf{1663.32\ ft^3}$

18. $10{,}000{,}000\ \cancel{\text{ft}}^3 \cdot \dfrac{12\ \cancel{\text{in.}}}{1\ \cancel{\text{ft}}} \cdot \dfrac{12\ \cancel{\text{in.}}}{1\ \cancel{\text{ft}}} \cdot \dfrac{12\ \cancel{\text{in.}}}{1\ \cancel{\text{ft}}}$

$\cdot \dfrac{2.54\ \text{cm}}{1\ \cancel{\text{in.}}} \cdot \dfrac{2.54\ \text{cm}}{1\ \cancel{\text{in.}}} \cdot \dfrac{2.54\ \text{cm}}{1\ \cancel{\text{in.}}}$

$= \mathbf{10{,}000{,}000(12)^3(2.54)^3\ cm^3}$

19. $\dfrac{x + 3}{3x} = \dfrac{5}{x} + \dfrac{1}{4}$

$\dfrac{(x + 3)}{3x}(12x) = \dfrac{5}{x}(12x) + \dfrac{1}{4}(12x)$

$4x + 12 = 60 + 3x$

$x = \mathbf{48}$

20. $\dfrac{2b}{y} - \dfrac{x}{4z} + m = s$

$\dfrac{2b}{y}(4zy) - \dfrac{x}{4z}(4zy) + m(4zy) = s(4zy)$

$8bz - xy + 4mzy = 4szy$

$\qquad\qquad 8bz = 4szy + xy - 4mzy$

$\qquad\qquad 8bz = y(4sz + x - 4mz)$

$\qquad\qquad\qquad y = \dfrac{\boldsymbol{8bz}}{\boldsymbol{4sz + x - 4mz}}$

21. $\dfrac{\dfrac{my^2}{x^2} - \dfrac{y}{x^3}}{\dfrac{z}{2x} - \dfrac{3m}{x^2}} = \dfrac{\dfrac{mxy^2 - y}{x^3}}{\dfrac{xz - 6m}{2x^2}} \cdot \dfrac{\dfrac{2x^2}{xz - 6m}}{\dfrac{xz - 6m}{2x^2}}$

$\qquad = \dfrac{\boldsymbol{2mxy^2 - 2y}}{\boldsymbol{x^2z - 6mx}}$

22. $(6x^4 - 6) \div (x + 1)$

$$
\begin{array}{r}
6x^3 - 6x^2 + 6x - 6 \\
x + 1 \overline{\smash{\big)}\, 6x^4 + 0x^3 + 0x^2 + 0x - 6} \\
\underline{6x^4 + 6x^3} \\
-6x^3 + 0x^2 \\
\underline{-6x^3 - 6x^2} \\
6x^2 + 0x \\
\underline{6x^2 + 6x} \\
-6x - 6 \\
\underline{-6x - 6} \\
0
\end{array}
$$

$\boldsymbol{6x^3 - 6x^2 + 6x - 6}$

23. $-4[(-1^2 - 2^0)(-3^3 - 2^2) + (-5)][-(-1)(-7^0)]$

$= -4[(-2)(-31) - 5][-1] = \boldsymbol{228}$

24. Since parallel lines have the same slope:

$y = -2x + b$

Use the point $(-2, 4)$ for x and y.

$4 = -2(-2) + b$

$b = 0$

$\boldsymbol{y = -2x}$

25. $m = \dfrac{-2 - 1}{1 - (-2)} = \dfrac{-3}{3} = -1$

$y = -x + b$

Use the point $(-2, 1)$ for x and y.

$1 = -1(-2) + b$

$b = -1$

$\boldsymbol{y = -x - 1}$

26. $y = -\dfrac{1}{4}x + b$

Use the point $(-1, -2)$ for x and y.

$-2 = -\dfrac{1}{4}(-1) + b$

$b = -\dfrac{9}{4}$

$\boldsymbol{y = -\dfrac{1}{4}x - \dfrac{9}{4}}$

27. $y \le -x + 5$

Test: $(0, 0)$

$0 \le 0 + 5$

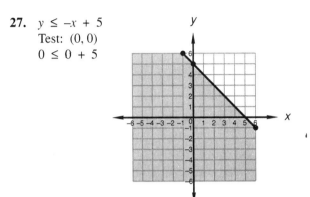

28. $\dfrac{(8 \times 10^{-17})(9{,}000{,}000)}{(3 \times 10^{-5})(4 \times 10^6)}$

$= \dfrac{(8 \times 10^{-17})(9 \times 10^6)}{(3 \times 10^{-5})(4 \times 10^6)} = \boldsymbol{6 \times 10^{-12}}$

29. $\qquad -3x^2 + 12x = 3$

$\qquad -3x^2 + 12x - 3 = 0$

$x = \dfrac{-b \pm \sqrt{b^2 - 4ac}}{2a}$

$\quad = \dfrac{-12 \pm \sqrt{12^2 - 4(-3)(-3)}}{2(-3)}$

$\quad = \dfrac{-12 \pm \sqrt{108}}{-6}$

$\quad = \boldsymbol{2 \pm \sqrt{3}}$

30. $\qquad\qquad -9x + 2 = x^2$

$\qquad\qquad x^2 + 9x - 2 = 0$

$\qquad\qquad (x^2 + 9x\quad) = 2$

$\left(x^2 + 9x + \dfrac{81}{4}\right) = 2 + \dfrac{81}{4}$

$\left(x + \dfrac{9}{2}\right)^2 = \dfrac{89}{4}$

$\left(x + \dfrac{9}{2}\right) = \pm\dfrac{\sqrt{89}}{2}$

$\qquad x = \boldsymbol{-\dfrac{9}{2} \pm \dfrac{\sqrt{89}}{2}}$

PRACTICE SET 6

1. (a) $350N_C + 500N_H = 6400$

(b) $N_H = N_C + 6$

Substitute (b) into (a) and get:

(a') $350N_C + 500(N_C + 6) = 6400$

$$850N_C = 3400$$

$$N_C = 4$$

(b) $N_H = (4) + 6 = \mathbf{10}$

2. $R_K T_K = R_R T_R$; $T_K = 3$; $T_R = 23$;

$R_K = R_R + 200$

$$3(R_R + 200) = 23R_R$$

$$600 = 20R_R$$

$$30 = R_R$$

$R_K = (30) + 200 = \mathbf{230}$ **miles per hour**

$R_K T_K = 3(230) = \mathbf{690}$ **miles**

3. $\dfrac{3}{11} = \dfrac{S}{8800}$

$S = \dfrac{3 \cdot 8800}{11}$

$S = \mathbf{2400}$

4. $Y = \dfrac{k}{A^2}$

$4000 = \dfrac{k}{8^2}$

$k = 256{,}000$

$Y = \dfrac{256{,}000}{A^2}$

$Y = \dfrac{256{,}000}{(10)^2}$

$Y = \mathbf{2560}$ **tons**

5. $N \qquad N + 2 \qquad N + 4 \qquad N + 6$

$6(N + N + 2) = 9(N + 6) + 9$

$12N + 12 = 9N + 63$

$3N = 51$

$N = 17$

The desired integers are **17, 19, 21,** and **23**.

6. $R_6 = 50{,}000(5)^6$

$R_6 = \mathbf{781{,}250{,}000}$

7. $4 = -5x - x^2$

$x^2 + 5x + 4 = 0$

$x = \dfrac{-b \pm \sqrt{b^2 - 4ac}}{2a}$

$= \dfrac{-5 \pm \sqrt{5^2 - 4(1)(4)}}{2(1)}$

$= \dfrac{-5 \pm \sqrt{9}}{2} = \mathbf{-1, -4}$

8. $3x^2 - 2 = 5x$

$3x^2 - 5x - 2 = 0$

$x = \dfrac{-b \pm \sqrt{b^2 - 4ac}}{2a}$

$= \dfrac{5 \pm \sqrt{(-5)^2 - 4(3)(-2)}}{2(3)}$

$= \dfrac{5 \pm \sqrt{49}}{6} = \mathbf{2, -\dfrac{1}{3}}$

9. $-3x = x^2 + 2$

$x^2 + 3x + 2 = 0$

$(x^2 + 3x \quad) = -2$

$\left(x^2 + 3x + \dfrac{9}{4}\right) = -2 + \dfrac{9}{4}$

$\left(x + \dfrac{3}{2}\right)^2 = \dfrac{1}{4}$

$\left(x + \dfrac{3}{2}\right) = \pm\dfrac{1}{2}$

$x = -\dfrac{3}{2} \pm \dfrac{1}{2}$

$x = \mathbf{-2, -1}$

10. $-5x = 4 - x^2$

$x^2 - 5x - 4 = 0$

$(x^2 - 5x \quad) = 4$

$\left(x^2 - 5x + \dfrac{25}{4}\right) = 4 + \dfrac{25}{4}$

$\left(x - \dfrac{5}{2}\right)^2 = \dfrac{41}{4}$

$\left(x - \dfrac{5}{2}\right) = \pm\dfrac{\sqrt{41}}{2}$

$x = \mathbf{\dfrac{5}{2} \pm \dfrac{\sqrt{41}}{2}}$

11. $x^2 = -5x - 6$

$x^2 + 5x + 6 = 0$

$(x^2 + 5x \quad) = -6$

$\left(x^2 + 5x + \dfrac{25}{4}\right) = -6 + \dfrac{25}{4}$

$\left(x + \dfrac{5}{2}\right)^2 = \dfrac{1}{4}$

$\left(x + \dfrac{5}{2}\right) = \pm\dfrac{1}{2}$

$x = -\dfrac{5}{2} \pm \dfrac{1}{2}$

$x = \mathbf{-2, -3}$

12. $y \not\leq \dfrac{1}{5}x - 3$

$y > \dfrac{1}{5}x - 3$

test: try $(3, 3)$

$3 > -\dfrac{12}{5}$

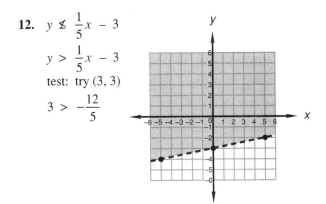

13.

$$\dfrac{m}{p} + \dfrac{x}{z} = y$$

$$\dfrac{m}{p}(pz) + \dfrac{x}{z}(pz) = y(pz)$$

$$mz + xp = ypz$$

$$mz = ypz - xp$$

$$mz = p(yz - x)$$

$$p = \dfrac{mz}{yz - x}$$

14. $5x^2 + 6x - 11 = (5x + 11)(x - 1)$

15. $6x^2 + 25x + 25 = (2x + 5)(3x + 5)$

16. $6x^2 - 149x - 25 = (6x + 1)(x - 25)$

17. $4ma + 6 + 24m + a = 4ma + a + 24m + 6$
$= a(4m + 1) + 6(4m + 1) = (a + 6)(4m + 1)$

18. $xyz + xy^2 + 6z + 6y = xy(z + y) + 6(z + y)$
$= (xy + 6)(z + y)$

19. $-5 + |-x| < -3$; $D = \{\text{Reals}\}$
$|-x| < 2$

```
     o———————————o
 -3 -2 -1  0  1  2  3
```

20. $6 \leq x + 3 < 8$; $D = \{\text{Integers}\}$
$3 \leq x < 5$

```
       •  •
    2  3  4  5  6
```

21. $x \leq -3$ or $x > 0$; $D = \{\text{Reals}\}$

```
◄——————•———————o————————►
  -5 -4 -3 -2 -1  0  1  2
```

22. $\sqrt{x + 5} - 6 = -1$
$\sqrt{x + 5} = 5$
$x + 5 = 25$
$x = \mathbf{20}$

Check: $\sqrt{20 + 5} - 6 = -1$
$\sqrt{25} - 6 = -1$
$5 - 6 = -1$
$-1 = -1$

23. $\sqrt{2x - 3} - 2 = 4$
$\sqrt{2x - 3} = 6$
$2x - 3 = 36$
$2x = 39$
$x = \dfrac{\mathbf{39}}{\mathbf{2}}$

Check: $\sqrt{2\left(\dfrac{39}{2}\right) - 3} - 2 = 4$
$\sqrt{36} - 2 = 4$
$6 - 2 = 4$
$4 = 4$

24. $m = \dfrac{3 - (-2)}{0 - (-4)} = \dfrac{5}{4}$

$y = \dfrac{5}{4}x + b$

Use the point $(-4, -2)$ for x and y.

$-2 = \dfrac{5}{4}(-4) + b$

$b = 3$

$y = \dfrac{5}{4}x + 3$

25. $y = -\dfrac{2}{3}x + b$

Use the point $(-3, 2)$ for x and y.

$2 = -\dfrac{2}{3}(-3) + b$

$b = 0$

$y = -\dfrac{2}{3}x$

26. Since parallel lines have the same slope:

$y = -\dfrac{3}{5}x + b$

Use the point $(3, -1)$ for x and y.

$-1 = -\dfrac{3}{5}(3) + b$

$b = \dfrac{4}{5}$

$y = -\dfrac{3}{5}x + \dfrac{4}{5}$

27. $\sqrt{\dfrac{4}{7}} = \dfrac{2}{\sqrt{7}} \cdot \dfrac{\sqrt{7}}{\sqrt{7}} = \dfrac{2\sqrt{7}}{7}$

28. $\dfrac{3\sqrt{5} + \sqrt{5}}{\sqrt{5}} \cdot \dfrac{\sqrt{5}}{\sqrt{5}} = \dfrac{15 + 5}{5} = \dfrac{20}{5} = \mathbf{4}$

29. $\dfrac{(0.003 \times 10^{-11})(700 \times 10^{20})}{(0.00009 \times 10^{-10})(8 \times 10^{25})}$

$= \dfrac{(3 \times 10^{-14})(7 \times 10^{22})}{(9 \times 10^{-15})(8 \times 10^{25})} = \mathbf{2.9 \times 10^{-3}}$

30. $V_{\text{Solid}} = A_{\text{Base}} \times \text{height}$

$= \left[\dfrac{(2)(2)}{2} + (5)(2) + \dfrac{\pi(2)^2}{2} \right](8)$ in.^{3}

$\approx [18.28](8)$ in.^{3}

$\approx (146.24)(2.54)(2.54)(2.54)$ cm^3

$\approx \mathbf{2396.44 \text{ cm}^3}$

PRACTICE SET 7

1. $B = 5;\ Q = 13;\ T = 18$

$\dfrac{5}{18} = \dfrac{B}{810}$

$B = \mathbf{225}$

$Q = 810 - (225) = \mathbf{585}$

2. $R_E T_E = R_e T_e;\ T_E = 3;\ T_e = 4;$
$R_E = R_e + 20$

$3(R_e + 20) = 4R_e$
$60 = R_e$

$R_e T_e = 60(4) = \mathbf{240 \text{ km}}$

3. $p(h, t, t, h) = p(h) \times p(t) \times p(t) \times p(h)$

$= \dfrac{1}{2} \times \dfrac{1}{2} \times \dfrac{1}{2} \times \dfrac{1}{2} = \dfrac{1}{16}$

4. $R = \dfrac{k}{B^2}$

$2 = \dfrac{k}{(40)^2}$

$k = 3200$

$R = \dfrac{3200}{B^2}$

$R = \dfrac{3200}{(10)^2}$

$R = \mathbf{32}$

5. $N \qquad N + 2 \qquad N + 4 \qquad N + 6$
$2(N + 2 + N + 4) = 10N - 2 + 20$
$4N + 12 = 10N + 18$
$-6 = 6N$
$-1 = N$
The desired integers are **−1, 1, 3, and 5.**

6. $78 = \dfrac{325}{100}(W_P)$
$\mathbf{\$24} = W_P$

7. $\dfrac{5a + \dfrac{3m}{x}}{\dfrac{4ma}{x} + 7} = \dfrac{\dfrac{5ax + 3m}{x}}{\dfrac{4ma + 7x}{x}} \cdot \dfrac{x}{4ma + 7x}$

$= \dfrac{\mathbf{5ax + 3m}}{\mathbf{4ma + 7x}}$

8. (a) $R_E T_E + 8 = R_W T_W$
(b) $R_E = 7$
(c) $R_W = 23$
(d) $T_E + T_W = 60$
$\qquad T_E = 60 - T_W$
Substitute (b) and (c) into (a) and get:
(a′) $7T_E + 8 = 23T_W$
Substitute (d) into (a′) and get:
(a″) $7(60 - T_W) + 8 = 23T_W$
$428 = 30T_W$

$\dfrac{214}{15} = T_W$

(d) $T_E = 60 - \left(\dfrac{214}{15}\right) = \dfrac{686}{15}$

9. $4 = 11x^2 + x$
$0 = 11x^2 + x - 4$

$x = \dfrac{-b \pm \sqrt{b^2 - 4ac}}{2a}$

$= \dfrac{-1 \pm \sqrt{1^2 - 4(11)(-4)}}{2(11)}$

$= \dfrac{-1 \pm \sqrt{177}}{22}$

10. $3x = 4x^2 - 5$
$0 = 4x^2 - 3x - 5$

$x = \dfrac{-b \pm \sqrt{b^2 - 4ac}}{2a}$

$= \dfrac{3 \pm \sqrt{(-3)^2 - 4(4)(-5)}}{2(4)}$

$= \dfrac{3 \pm \sqrt{89}}{8}$

11.
$$-9 = -x^2 - 13x$$
$$x^2 + 13x - 9 = 0$$
$$(x^2 + 13x \quad) = 9$$
$$\left(x^2 + 13x + \frac{169}{4}\right) = 9 + \frac{169}{4}$$
$$\left(x + \frac{13}{2}\right)^2 = \frac{205}{4}$$
$$\left(x + \frac{13}{2}\right) = \pm\frac{\sqrt{205}}{2}$$
$$x = -\frac{\mathbf{13}}{\mathbf{2}} \pm \frac{\sqrt{\mathbf{205}}}{\mathbf{2}}$$

12.
$$x^2 + 3 = 7x$$
$$x^2 - 7x + 3 = 0$$
$$(x^2 - 7x \quad) = -3$$
$$\left(x^2 - 7x + \frac{49}{4}\right) = -3 + \frac{49}{4}$$
$$\left(x - \frac{7}{2}\right)^2 = \frac{37}{4}$$
$$\left(x - \frac{7}{2}\right) = \pm\frac{\sqrt{37}}{2}$$
$$x = \frac{\mathbf{7} \pm \sqrt{\mathbf{37}}}{\mathbf{2}}$$

13. $-42x + 49 + 8x^2 = 8x^2 - 42x + 49$
$= \mathbf{(4x - 7)(2x - 7)}$

14. $-8x - 13 + 5x^2 = 5x^2 - 8x - 13$
$= \mathbf{(5x - 13)(x + 1)}$

15. $mnf + p^2af - 4mn - 4p^2a$
$= f(mn + p^2a) - 4(mn + p^2a)$
$= \mathbf{(f - 4)(mn + p^2a)}$

16. $5pa^4 - 7a + 25pa^3 - 35$
$= a(5pa^3 - 7) + 5(5pa^3 - 7)$
$= \mathbf{(a + 5)(5pa^3 - 7)}$

17. $y > 4x + 2$
Test: try $(-3, 0)$
$0 > 4(-3) + 2$
$0 > -10$

18. $V_{Cylinder} = A_{Base} \times \text{height}$
$= \pi(\sqrt{2})^2 \text{ cm}^2 \times 10 \text{ cm}$
$\approx 62.8 \text{ cm}^3$
$\approx \frac{(62.8)}{(2.54)^3(12)^3} \text{ ft}^3$
$\approx \mathbf{2.22 \times 10^{-3} \text{ ft}^3}$

S.A. $= 2A_{Base} + (C \times \text{height})$
$= 2\pi(\sqrt{2})^2 \text{ cm}^2 + \left[(2\pi\sqrt{2}) \times 10\right] \text{ cm}^2$
$\approx (12.56 + 88.81) \text{ cm}^2$
$\approx 101.37 \text{ cm}^2$
$\approx \frac{(101.37)}{(2.54)(2.54)(12)(12)} \text{ ft}^2$
$\approx \mathbf{0.11 \text{ ft}^2}$

19.
$$\frac{p + 4}{3p} = \frac{5}{p} + \frac{1}{4}$$
$$\frac{(p + 4)}{3p}(12p) = \frac{5}{p}(12p) + \frac{1}{4}(12p)$$
$$4p + 16 = 60 + 3p$$
$$p = \mathbf{44}$$

20.
$$\frac{(0.00014)(0.07 \times 10^{-12})}{(5000)(300 \times 10^8)}$$
$$= \frac{(1.4 \times 10^{-4})(7 \times 10^{-14})}{(5 \times 10^3)(3 \times 10^{10})} = \mathbf{6.53 \times 10^{-32}}$$

21. $\dfrac{3\sqrt{7} + 7}{\sqrt{7}} \cdot \dfrac{\sqrt{7}}{\sqrt{7}} = \dfrac{21 + 7\sqrt{7}}{7} = \mathbf{3 + \sqrt{7}}$

22. $(5 + 3\sqrt{5})(\sqrt{5} + 2) = 5\sqrt{5} + 15 + 10 + 6\sqrt{5}$
$= \mathbf{25 + 11\sqrt{5}}$

23. $\dfrac{3mp^{-2}}{m^{-5}} - \dfrac{5m^4}{p^2} + \dfrac{m^5p^{-4}}{mp^{-2}}$
$= 3m^6p^{-2} - 5m^4p^{-2} + m^4p^{-2}$
$= \mathbf{3m^6p^{-2} - 4m^4p^{-2}}$

24. $\sqrt{3x + 4} - 5 = 3$
$\sqrt{3x + 4} = 8$
$3x + 4 = 64$
$3x = 60$
$x = \mathbf{20}$

Check: $\sqrt{3(20) + 4} - 5 = 3$
$\sqrt{64} - 5 = 3$
$8 - 5 = 3$
$3 = 3$

25. $\dfrac{2x + 3}{my} + \dfrac{y}{p} = x + 4$

$\dfrac{(2x + 3)}{my}(pmy) + \dfrac{y}{p}(pmy) = (x + 4)pmy$

$2xp + 3p + my^2 = pmxy + 4pmy$

$my^2 = pmxy + 4pmy - 2xp - 3p$

$my^2 = p(mxy + 4my - 2x - 3)$

$p = \dfrac{my^2}{mxy + 4my - 2x - 3}$

26. $8 \le x + 5 \le 10;\ D = \{\text{Integers}\}$
$3 \le x \le 5$

27. $m = \dfrac{1 - (-1)}{1 - (-3)} = \dfrac{2}{4} = \dfrac{1}{2}$

$y = \dfrac{1}{2}x + b$

Use the point $(1, 1)$ for x and y.

$1 = \dfrac{1}{2}(1) + b$

$b = \dfrac{1}{2}$

$y = \dfrac{1}{2}x + \dfrac{1}{2}$

28. $y = \dfrac{3}{4}x + b$

Use the point $(-2, 2)$ for x and y.

$2 = \dfrac{3}{4}(-2) + b$

$b = \dfrac{7}{2}$

$y = \dfrac{3}{4}x + \dfrac{7}{2}$

29. Since parallel lines have the same slope:

$y = -\dfrac{3}{8}x + b$

Use the point $(2, -1)$ for x and y.

$-1 = -\dfrac{3}{8}(2) + b$

$b = -\dfrac{1}{4}$

$y = -\dfrac{3}{8}x - \dfrac{1}{4}$

30. $V_{\text{Solid}} = \left[(8)(6) - \dfrac{\pi(2)^2}{2}\right]\left(\dfrac{16}{12}\right) \text{ft}^3$

$\approx 55.63 \text{ ft}^3$

$\approx \dfrac{(55.63)(12)^3(2.54)^3}{(100)^3} \text{ m}^3$

$\approx \mathbf{1.58 \text{ m}^3}$

Practice Set 8

1. $E = 2;\ P = 61;\ T = 63$

$\dfrac{2}{63} = \dfrac{E}{7686}$

$E = \mathbf{244}$

$P = 7686 - (244) = \mathbf{7442}$

2. $N_O = \dfrac{k}{A^2}$

$5 = \dfrac{k}{(1000)^2}$

$k = 5{,}000{,}000$

$N_O = \dfrac{5{,}000{,}000}{A^2}$

$N_O = \dfrac{5{,}000{,}000}{(20)^2}$

$N_O = \mathbf{12{,}500}$

3. $R_W T_W = R_R T_R;\ R_W = 4;\ R_R = 10;$
$T_W + T_R = 14$
$\qquad T_R = 14 - T_W$

$4T_W = 10(14 - T_W)$
$14T_W = 140$
$\quad T_W = 10$

$R_W T_W = 4(10) = \mathbf{40 \text{ miles}}$

4.
N	$N + 2$	$N + 4$	$N + 6$

$-5(N + 2 + N + 4) = -7(N + 6) + 45$
$\qquad -10N - 30 = -7N + 3$
$\qquad\qquad -33 = 3N$
$\qquad\qquad -11 = N$

The desired integers are **-11, -9, -7,** and **-5.**

5. $\qquad -12x = -x^2 - 4$
$\qquad x^2 - 12x + 4 = 0$
$\qquad (x^2 - 12x\quad) = -4$
$\qquad (x^2 - 12x + 36) = -4 + 36$
$\qquad\qquad (x - 6)^2 = 32$
$\qquad\qquad (x - 6) = \pm\sqrt{32}$
$\qquad\qquad\qquad x = \mathbf{6 \pm 4\sqrt{2}}$

6.
$$x^2 = 11x - 2$$
$$x^2 - 11x + 2 = 0$$
$$(x^2 - 11x \quad) = -2$$
$$\left(x^2 - 11x + \frac{121}{4}\right) = -2 + \frac{121}{4}$$
$$\left(x - \frac{11}{2}\right)^2 = \frac{113}{4}$$
$$\left(x - \frac{11}{2}\right) = \pm\frac{\sqrt{113}}{2}$$
$$x = \frac{11 \pm \sqrt{113}}{2}$$

7.
$$-9x = 7x^2 + 2$$
$$0 = 7x^2 + 9x + 2$$
$$x = \frac{-b \pm \sqrt{b^2 - 4ac}}{2a}$$
$$= \frac{-9 \pm \sqrt{9^2 - 4(7)(2)}}{2(7)}$$
$$= \frac{-9 \pm \sqrt{25}}{14} = -\frac{2}{7}, -1$$

8.
$$-3 - 12x = 4x^2$$
$$0 = 4x^2 + 12x + 3$$
$$x = \frac{-b \pm \sqrt{b^2 - 4ac}}{2a}$$
$$= \frac{-12 \pm \sqrt{12^2 - 4(4)(3)}}{2(4)}$$
$$= \frac{-12 \pm \sqrt{96}}{8} = \frac{-3 \pm \sqrt{6}}{2}$$

9. (a) horizontal line: $y = \pm k$; $y = 3$
(b) The desired equation is $y = mx + b$.
By inspection, $b = -2$.
By inspection, the sign for m is $-$.

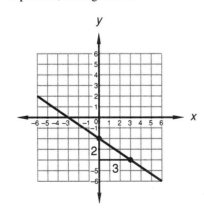

$$|m| = \frac{2}{3}$$

So $b = -2$ and $m = -\frac{2}{3}$: $y = -\frac{2}{3}x - 2$

10. $p(2, 5, 3) = p(2) \times p(5) \times p(3) = \frac{1}{5} \times \frac{1}{5} \times \frac{1}{5}$
$$= \frac{1}{125}$$

11. $y \leq -4x - 5$
Test: try $(-2, 0)$
$0 \leq -4(-2) - 5$
$0 \leq 3$

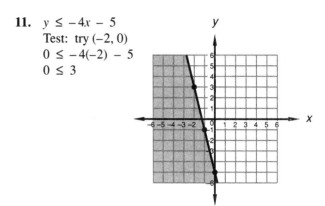

12. $x - 3 \leq y \leq -x$
Test: try $(-2, 0)$
$-2 - 3 \leq 0 \leq -(-2)$
$-5 \leq 0 \leq 2$

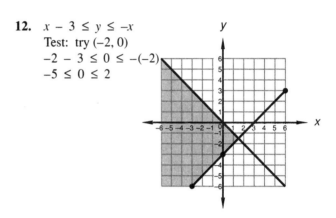

13. $x - 3 > 7$ or $x + 2 \leq 8$; $D = \{\text{Reals}\}$
$x > 10$ or $x \leq 6$

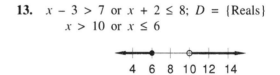

14. (a) $R_S T_S + 4 = R_B T_B$
(b) $R_S = 4$
(c) $R_B = 32$
(d) $T_S + T_B = 200$
$$T_S = 200 - T_B$$
Substitute (b) and (c) into (a) and get:
(a′) $4T_S + 4 = 32T_B$
Substitute (d) into (a′) and get:
(a″) $4(200 - T_B) + 4 = 32T_B$
$$800 - 4T_B + 4 = 32T_B$$
$$804 = 36T_B$$
$$\frac{67}{3} = T_B$$

(d) $T_S = 200 - \left(\frac{67}{3}\right) = \frac{533}{3}$

15. $\dfrac{m + \dfrac{x}{y}}{3mx + \dfrac{7}{4}} = \dfrac{\dfrac{my + x}{y}}{\dfrac{12mx + 7}{4}} \cdot \dfrac{\dfrac{12mx + 7}{4}}{\dfrac{12mx + 7}{4}}$

$= \dfrac{4my + 4x}{12mxy + 7y}$

16. $\dfrac{(7 \times 10^{-11})(5000)(3 \times 10^4)}{(2 \times 10^{-8})(100{,}000)}$

$= \dfrac{(7 \times 10^{-11})(5 \times 10^3)(3 \times 10^4)}{(2 \times 10^{-8})(1 \times 10^5)} = 5.25$

17. $(6 + 3\sqrt{2})(2\sqrt{2} + 2) = 12\sqrt{2} + 12 + 12 + 6\sqrt{2}$

$= 24 + 18\sqrt{2}$

18. $\dfrac{\sqrt{5} + 7}{3\sqrt{5}} \cdot \dfrac{\sqrt{5}}{\sqrt{5}} = \dfrac{5 + 7\sqrt{5}}{15}$

19. $\sqrt{\dfrac{3}{7}} = \dfrac{\sqrt{3}}{\sqrt{7}} \cdot \dfrac{\sqrt{7}}{\sqrt{7}} = \dfrac{\sqrt{21}}{7}$

20. $-3\big[(-4^2 - 4^0)(-3^2 - 3) + (-104)\big]$

$= -3\big[(-17)(-12) - 104\big] = -300$

21. $\dfrac{m}{3a} + \dfrac{p}{x} + k = z$

$\dfrac{m}{3a}(3ax) + \dfrac{p}{x}(3ax) + k(3ax) = z(3ax)$

$mx + 3ap + 3akx = 3axz$

$mx = 3axz - 3akx - 3ap$

$mx = a(3xz - 3kx - 3p)$

$a = \dfrac{mx}{3xz - 3kx - 3p}$

22. $(5a^2 + 2b^2)^2 = (5a^2 + 2b^2)(5a^2 + 2b^2)$

$= 25a^4 + 20a^2b^2 + 4b^4$

23. $(5a^2 + 2b^2)(5a^2 - 2b^2) = 25a^4 - 4b^4$

24. $\sqrt{4x + 4} + 6 = 12$

$\sqrt{4x + 4} = 6$

$4x + 4 = 36$

$4x = 32$

$x = 8$

Check: $\sqrt{4(8) + 4} + 6 = 12$

$\sqrt{36} + 6 = 12$

$6 + 6 = 12$

$12 = 12$

25. $3\dfrac{3}{8}m + \dfrac{1}{2} = 2\dfrac{3}{7}$

$\dfrac{27}{8}m = \dfrac{17}{7} - \dfrac{1}{2}$

$\dfrac{27}{8}m = \dfrac{34}{14} - \dfrac{7}{14}$

$m = \dfrac{27}{14} \cdot \dfrac{8}{27}$

$m = \dfrac{4}{7}$

26. $10\ \text{mi}^2 \cdot \dfrac{5280\ \text{ft}}{1\ \text{mi}} \cdot \dfrac{5280\ \text{ft}}{1\ \text{mi}} \cdot \dfrac{12\ \text{in.}}{1\ \text{ft}} \cdot \dfrac{12\ \text{in.}}{1\ \text{ft}}$

$\cdot \dfrac{2.54\ \text{cm}}{1\ \text{in.}} \cdot \dfrac{2.54\ \text{cm}}{1\ \text{in.}} \cdot \dfrac{1\ \text{m}}{100\ \text{cm}} \cdot \dfrac{1\ \text{m}}{100\ \text{cm}}$

$\cdot \dfrac{1\ \text{km}}{1000\ \text{m}} \cdot \dfrac{1\ \text{km}}{1000\ \text{m}}$

$= \dfrac{10(5280)(5280)(12)(12)(2.54)(2.54)}{(100)(100)(1000)(1000)}\ \text{km}^2$

27. Since parallel lines have the same slope:

$y = \dfrac{1}{3}x + b$

Use the point $(3, -3)$ for x and y.

$-3 = \dfrac{1}{3}(3) + b$

$b = -4$

$y = \dfrac{1}{3}x - 4$

28. $m = \dfrac{-1 - 4}{-1 - 2} = \dfrac{-5}{-3} = \dfrac{5}{3}$

$y = \dfrac{5}{3}x + b$

Use the point $(-1, -1)$ for x and y.

$-1 = \dfrac{5}{3}(-1) + b$

$b = \dfrac{2}{3}$

$y = \dfrac{5}{3}x + \dfrac{2}{3}$

29. $y = -3x + b$

Use the point $(2, -3)$ for x and y.

$-3 = (-3)2 + b$

$b = 3$

$y = -3x + 3$

30. $V = A_{\text{Base}} \times \text{height}$

$= \left[(18)(18) - \dfrac{\pi(2)^2}{2} - \dfrac{(4)(4)}{2}\right](2)(12)\ \text{in.}^3$

$\approx [309.72](24)\ \text{in.}^3$

$\approx 7433.28\ \text{in.}^3$

$\approx \dfrac{(7433.28)(2.54)(2.54)(2.54)}{(100)(100)(100)}\ \text{m}^3$

$\approx 0.12\ \text{m}^3$

PRACTICE SET 9

1. $\$265,000 = \dfrac{128}{100} P_P$

$\$207,031.25 = P_P$

2. $A_{20} = \$1500(1 + 0.09)^{20}$

$A_{20} = \$1500(5.6044108)$

$A_{20} = \mathbf{\$8406.62}$

Interest $= \mathbf{\$6906.62}$

3. $B = \dfrac{k}{G^2}$

$12 = \dfrac{k}{5^2}$

$k = 300$

$B = \dfrac{300}{G^2}$

$B = \dfrac{300}{(10)^2}$

$B = \mathbf{3}$

4. $E = 3; \ I = 14; \ T = 17$

$\dfrac{3}{17} = \dfrac{E}{71,400}$

$E = \mathbf{12,600}$

5. $R_E T_E = R_F T_F; \ T_E = 24; \ T_F = 30;$

$R_E = R_F + 17$

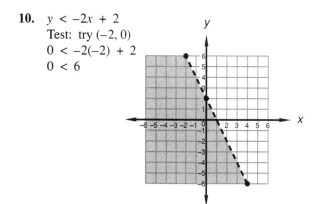

$24(R_F + 17) = 30R_F$

$408 = 6R_F$

$\mathbf{68 \ mph} = R_F$

$R_E = (68) + 17 = \mathbf{85 \ mph}$

6. $p(8, 4) = p(8) \times p(4) = \dfrac{1}{13} \times \dfrac{1}{13} = \dfrac{\mathbf{1}}{\mathbf{169}}$

7. $-2 \le x + 1 \le 4; \ D = \{\text{Reals}\}$

$-3 \le x \le 3$

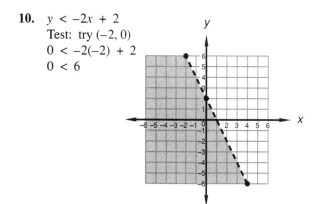

8. (a) vertical line: $x = \pm .k; \ \mathbf{x = -5}$

(b) The desired equation is $y = mx + b$.

By inspection, $b = -2$.

By inspection the sign for m is +.

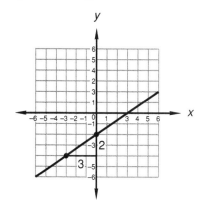

$|m| = \dfrac{2}{3}$

So $b = -2$ and $m = \dfrac{2}{3}; \ \mathbf{y = \dfrac{2}{3}x - 2}$

9. (a) $y = 2x - 3$

$y = \dfrac{+2}{+1}x - 3$

(b) $x = 1$

The first step is to graph each of these lines.

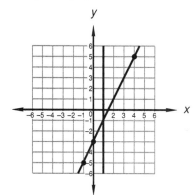

It appears that the lines cross at $x = 1$ and $y = -1$, so $\mathbf{(1, -1)}$ is the solution.

10. $y < -2x + 2$

Test: try $(-2, 0)$

$0 < -2(-2) + 2$

$0 < 6$

11. $(4 + 3\sqrt{5})(2 + \sqrt{5}) = 8 + 6\sqrt{5} + 4\sqrt{5} + 15$

$= \mathbf{23 + 10\sqrt{5}}$

12. $(4a^2 + 4b^2)^2 = (4a^2 + 4b^2)(4a^2 + 4b^2)$
$= 16a^4 + 32a^2b^2 + 16b^4$

13. $\dfrac{(36{,}000 \times 10^{-22})(4000 \times 10^{-4})}{(0.000009 \times 10^6)(0.0007 \times 10^{-3})}$

$= \dfrac{(3.6 \times 10^{-18})(4 \times 10^{-1})}{(9 \times 10^0)(7 \times 10^{-7})} = 2.29 \times 10^{-13}$

14. $\dfrac{6x^5y^{-3}(x^6)^{-2}y^3x^2y}{(3x^0)^2x^2y^{-2}(xy)^2} = \dfrac{6x^{-5}y}{9x^4} = \dfrac{2y}{3x^9}$

15. $\dfrac{3 + \sqrt{5}}{\sqrt{3}} \cdot \dfrac{\sqrt{3}}{\sqrt{3}} = \dfrac{3\sqrt{3} + \sqrt{15}}{3}$

16. $-2[(-2^3 - 2^0)(2^3 - 3^2)][-(-2)(1^0)]$
$= -2[(-9)(-1)][2] = -36$

17. $3\sqrt{m + 6} - 5 = 2$
$\qquad 3\sqrt{m + 6} = 7$
$\qquad\quad \sqrt{m + 6} = \dfrac{7}{3}$
$\qquad\qquad m + 6 = \dfrac{49}{9}$
$\qquad\qquad\quad m = -\dfrac{5}{9}$

Check: $3\sqrt{-\dfrac{5}{9} + 6} - 5 = 2$

$\qquad\qquad 3\sqrt{\dfrac{49}{9}} - 5 = 2$

$\qquad\qquad\qquad 7 - 5 = 2$

$\qquad\qquad\qquad\qquad 2 = 2$

18. $\dfrac{x + 6}{4x} = \dfrac{4}{3x} + \dfrac{3}{4}$

$\dfrac{(x + 6)}{4x}(12x) = \dfrac{4}{3x}(12x) + \dfrac{3}{4}(12x)$

$\qquad 3x + 18 = 16 + 9x$

$\qquad\qquad 2 = 6x$

$\qquad\qquad \dfrac{1}{3} = x$

19. $V_{\text{Solid}} = A_{\text{Base}} \times \text{height}$

$= \left[7(4) + \dfrac{2(2)}{2} + \dfrac{3(4)}{2}\right](3)(3) \text{ ft}^3$

$= [36](9) \text{ ft}^3$

$= 324 \text{ ft}^3$

$= \dfrac{(324)(12)^3(2.54)^3}{(100)^3} \text{ m}^3$

$= 9.17 \text{ m}^3$

20. $5 = 4x^2 + 3x$
$0 = 4x^2 + 3x - 5$

$x = \dfrac{-b \pm \sqrt{b^2 - 4ac}}{2a}$

$= \dfrac{-3 \pm \sqrt{3^2 - 4(4)(-5)}}{2(4)} = \dfrac{-3 \pm \sqrt{89}}{8}$

21. $\qquad\qquad -3x = 9 - 2x^2$
$2x^2 - 3x - 9 = 0$

$x = \dfrac{-b \pm \sqrt{b^2 - 4ac}}{2a}$

$= \dfrac{3 \pm \sqrt{(-3)^2 - 4(2)(-9)}}{2(2)}$

$= \dfrac{3 \pm \sqrt{81}}{4} = 3, -\dfrac{3}{2}$

22. $\qquad\qquad\qquad -3 = -x^2 + 5x$
$\qquad\qquad x^2 - 5x - 3 = 0$
$\qquad\qquad (x^2 - 5x \quad) = 3$

$\left(x^2 - 5x + \dfrac{25}{4}\right) = 3 + \dfrac{25}{4}$

$\qquad \left(x - \dfrac{5}{2}\right)^2 = \dfrac{37}{4}$

$\qquad \left(x - \dfrac{5}{2}\right) = \pm\dfrac{\sqrt{37}}{2}$

$\qquad\qquad x = \dfrac{5 \pm \sqrt{37}}{2}$

23. $\qquad\quad -4x = 3 - x^2$
$x^2 - 4x - 3 = 0$
$(x^2 - 4x \quad) = 3$
$(x^2 - 4x + 4) = 3 + 4$
$\quad (x - 2)^2 = 7$
$\quad (x - 2) = \pm\sqrt{7}$
$\qquad\qquad x = 2 \pm \sqrt{7}$

24. (a) $R_C T_C = R_B T_B$
(b) $R_C = 12$
(c) $R_B = 4$
(d) $T_C + T_B = 60$
$\qquad T_B = 60 - T_C$
Substitute (b) and (c) into (a) and get:
(a′) $12T_C = 4T_B$
Substitute (d) into (a′) and get:
(a″) $12T_C = 4(60 - T_C)$
$\qquad 16T_C = 240$
$\qquad\quad T_C = 15$

(d) $T_B = 60 - (15) = 45$

25. **(a), (c), (d)**
(b) is not a function because -4 has 2 images.

26. $(7x^4 - x^2 + 1) \div (x - 1)$

$$
\begin{array}{r}
7x^3 + 7x^2 + 6x + 6 \\
x - 1 \overline{\smash{)}\; 7x^4 + 0x^3 - x^2 + 0x + 1} \\
\underline{7x^4 - 7x^3} \\
7x^3 - x^2 \\
\underline{7x^3 - 7x^2} \\
6x^2 + 0x \\
\underline{6x^2 - 6x} \\
6x + 1 \\
\underline{6x - 6} \\
7
\end{array}
$$

$7x^3 + 7x^2 + 6x + 6 + \dfrac{7}{x - 1}$

27. S.A. $= 2A_{\text{Base}} + (\text{C} \times \text{height})$
$= 2\pi(\sqrt{3})^2 \text{ in.}^2 + (2\pi\sqrt{3})(13) \text{ in.}^2$
$\approx \mathbf{160.24 \text{ in.}^2}$

28. $1000 \text{ mi}^3 \cdot \dfrac{5280 \text{ ft}}{1 \text{ mi}} \cdot \dfrac{5280 \text{ ft}}{1 \text{ mi}} \cdot \dfrac{5280 \text{ ft}}{1 \text{ mi}}$

$\cdot \dfrac{12 \text{ in.}}{1 \text{ ft}} \cdot \dfrac{12 \text{ in.}}{1 \text{ ft}} \cdot \dfrac{12 \text{ in.}}{1 \text{ ft}} \cdot \dfrac{2.54 \text{ cm}}{1 \text{ in.}} \cdot \dfrac{2.54 \text{ cm}}{1 \text{ in.}}$

$\cdot \dfrac{2.54 \text{ cm}}{1 \text{ in.}} \cdot \dfrac{1 \text{ m}}{100 \text{ cm}} \cdot \dfrac{1 \text{ m}}{100 \text{ cm}} \cdot \dfrac{1 \text{ m}}{100 \text{ cm}}$

$\cdot \dfrac{1 \text{ km}}{1000 \text{ m}} \cdot \dfrac{1 \text{ km}}{1000 \text{ m}} \cdot \dfrac{1 \text{ km}}{1000 \text{ m}}$

$= \dfrac{1000(5280)^3(12)^3(2.54)^3}{(100)^3(1000)^3} \text{ km}^3$

29. $m = \dfrac{3 - (-4)}{3 - (-1)} = \dfrac{7}{4}$

$y = \dfrac{7}{4}x + b$

Use the point $(3, 3)$ for x and y.

$3 = \dfrac{7}{4}(3) + b$

$b = -\dfrac{9}{4}$

$y = \dfrac{7}{4}x - \dfrac{9}{4}$

30. Since parallel lines have the same slope:
$y = -4x + b$
Use the point $(3, 3)$ for x and y.
$3 = -4(3) + b$
$b = 15$
$y = -4x + 15$

Practice Set 10

1. $N \qquad N + 2 \qquad N + 4 \qquad N + 6$
$6(N + N + 6) = 9(N + 2) + 42$
$\qquad 12N + 36 = 9N + 60$
$\qquad\qquad 3N = 24$
$\qquad\qquad\ N = 8$
The desired integers are **8, 10, 12,** and **14.**

2. $R_R T_R = R_r T_r;\ T_R = 9;\ R_r = R_R - 16;$
$T_r = 81$
$\qquad 9R_R = 81(R_R - 16)$
$\qquad 1296 = 72R_R$

$18\dfrac{\text{km}}{\text{hr}} = R_R$

$R_R T_R = 9(18) = \mathbf{162 \text{ km}}$

3. $R_7 = 10(3)^7$
$R_7 = \mathbf{21,870}$

4. $p(5, 3, 6) = \dfrac{1}{6} \times \dfrac{1}{6} \times \dfrac{1}{6} = \dfrac{\mathbf{1}}{\mathbf{216}}$

5. $z = \dfrac{k}{p^2}$

$200 = \dfrac{k}{(30)^2}$

$\quad k = 180,000$

$z = \dfrac{180,000}{p^2}$

$z = \dfrac{180,000}{(50)^2}$

$z = \mathbf{72}$

6. (a) $5N_N + 10N_D = 2800$
(b) $N_N + N_D = 500$

$\qquad\quad \text{(a)} \quad 5N_N + 10N_D = \ \ 2800$
$(-5)\text{(b)} \ \ \underline{-5N_N - 5N_D = -2500}$
$\qquad\qquad\qquad\quad 5N_D = \ \ \ \ 300$
$\qquad\qquad\qquad\quad\ N_D = 60$

(b) $N_N + (60) = 500$
$\qquad\quad N_N = \mathbf{440}$

7. $6x^2 + 15x - 9 = 3(2x^2 + 5x - 3)$
$= \mathbf{3(2x - 1)(x + 3)}$

8. $3mn + 4yn - 3mo - 4yo$
$= n(3m + 4y) - o(3m + 4y)$
$= \mathbf{(n - o)(3m + 4y)}$

9. $\sqrt{\dfrac{3}{11}} = \dfrac{\sqrt{3}}{\sqrt{11}} \cdot \dfrac{\sqrt{11}}{\sqrt{11}} = \dfrac{\sqrt{33}}{11}$

10. $\dfrac{5\sqrt{11} + 3}{\sqrt{11}} \cdot \dfrac{\sqrt{11}}{\sqrt{11}} = \dfrac{\mathbf{55 + 3\sqrt{11}}}{\mathbf{11}}$

11. $\dfrac{8x + \dfrac{2p}{c}}{\dfrac{3cx}{z} - 4} = \dfrac{\dfrac{8xc + 2p}{c}}{\dfrac{3cx - 4z}{z}} \cdot \dfrac{\dfrac{z}{3cx - 4z}}{\dfrac{z}{3cx - 4z}}$

$= \dfrac{\mathbf{8xcz + 2pz}}{\mathbf{3c^2x - 4cz}}$

12. $(5\sqrt{2} + 3)(2\sqrt{2} - \sqrt{2}) = 20 + 6\sqrt{2} - 10 - 3\sqrt{2}$
$= \mathbf{10 + 3\sqrt{2}}$

13. $\dfrac{(0.0006 \times 10^{-4})(6 \times 10^{20})}{(1,000,000)(300 \times 10^{-22})}$

$= \dfrac{(6 \times 10^{-8})(6 \times 10^{20})}{(1 \times 10^{6})(3 \times 10^{-20})} = \mathbf{1.2 \times 10^{27}}$

14. $11x^{10}y^{-8} - \dfrac{xy^5 x}{y^{10}y^3 x^{-12}} - \dfrac{8x^{14}y^{10}}{3x^{-3}y^7 xx^{-2}y^{11}}$

$= 11x^{10}y^{-8} - x^{14}y^{-8} - \dfrac{8x^{18}y^{-8}}{3}$

$= \dfrac{\mathbf{33x^{10} - 3x^{14} - 8x^{18}}}{\mathbf{3y^8}}$

15. $\sqrt{2} \in$ **Irrationals and reals**

16. $(8x^4 + 3p^2)^2 = (8x^4 + 3p^2)(8x^4 + 3p^2)$
$= \mathbf{64x^8 + 48x^4p^2 + 9p^4}$

17. $x - 11 > -16$ or $x + 5 \le 8$; $D = \{\text{Integers}\}$
$\quad x > -5$ or $x \le 3$
All integers

18. (a) The desired equation is $y = mx + b$.
By inspection, $b = -4$.
By inspection, the sign for m is $-$.

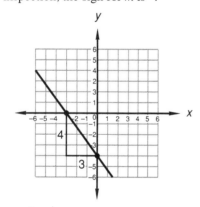

$|m| = \dfrac{4}{3}$

So $b = -4$ and $m = -\dfrac{4}{3}$: $\mathbf{y = -\dfrac{4}{3}x - 4}$

(b) vertical line: $x = \pm k$; $\mathbf{x = 5}$

19. $\dfrac{z + 4}{z} = \dfrac{2}{z} + \dfrac{1}{9}$

$\dfrac{(z + 4)}{z}(9z) = \dfrac{2}{z}(9z) + \dfrac{1}{9}(9z)$

$9z + 36 = 18 + z$
$8z = -18$
$z = -\dfrac{\mathbf{9}}{\mathbf{4}}$

20. $\dfrac{3c}{m} - \dfrac{y}{4p} + z = 5$

$\dfrac{3c}{m}(4pm) - \dfrac{y}{4p}(4pm) + z(4pm) = 5(4pm)$

$12cp - my + 4pmz = 20pm$
$12cp + 4mpz - 20pm = my$
$p(12c + 4mz - 20m) = my$

$p = \dfrac{\mathbf{my}}{\mathbf{12c + 4mz - 20m}}$

21. $3\sqrt{m + 5} - 2 = 9$
$\quad 3\sqrt{m + 5} = 11$
$\quad\quad \sqrt{m + 5} = \dfrac{11}{3}$
$\quad\quad\quad m + 5 = \dfrac{121}{9}$
$\quad\quad\quad\quad m = \dfrac{\mathbf{76}}{\mathbf{9}}$

Check: $3\sqrt{\dfrac{76}{9} + 5} - 2 = 9$

$\quad\quad 3\sqrt{\dfrac{121}{9}} - 2 = 9$

$\quad\quad\quad 11 - 2 = 9$
$\quad\quad\quad\quad 9 = 9$

22. $y \le -3x + \dfrac{1}{2}$
Test: try $(0, 0)$

$0 \le -3(0) + \dfrac{1}{2}$

$0 \le \dfrac{1}{2}$

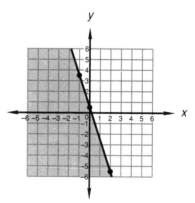

23.
$$-5x = -x^2 - 4$$
$$x^2 - 5x + 4 = 0$$
$$(x^2 - 5x \quad) = -4$$
$$\left(x^2 - 5x + \frac{25}{4}\right) = -4 + \frac{25}{4}$$
$$\left(x - \frac{5}{2}\right)^2 = \frac{9}{4}$$
$$\left(x - \frac{5}{2}\right) = \pm\sqrt{\frac{9}{4}}$$
$$x = \frac{5}{2} \pm \frac{3}{2}$$
$$x = \mathbf{1, 4}$$

24.
$$-x^2 = -9x + 2$$
$$x^2 - 9x + 2 = 0$$
$$(x^2 - 9x \quad) = -2$$
$$\left(x^2 - 9x + \frac{81}{4}\right) = -2 + \frac{81}{4}$$
$$\left(x - \frac{9}{2}\right)^2 = \frac{73}{4}$$
$$\left(x - \frac{9}{2}\right) = \pm\frac{\sqrt{73}}{2}$$
$$x = \mathbf{\frac{9 \pm \sqrt{73}}{2}}$$

25.
$$-6x = -3x^2 + 2$$
$$3x^2 - 6x - 2 = 0$$

$$x = \frac{-b \pm \sqrt{b^2 - 4ac}}{2a}$$
$$= \frac{6 \pm \sqrt{(-6)^2 - 4(3)(-2)}}{2(3)}$$
$$= \frac{6 \pm \sqrt{60}}{6} = \mathbf{\frac{3 \pm \sqrt{15}}{3}}$$

26.
$$5x^2 - 3 = 11x$$
$$5x^2 - 11x - 3 = 0$$

$$x = \frac{-b \pm \sqrt{b^2 - 4ac}}{2a}$$
$$= \frac{11 \pm \sqrt{(-11)^2 - 4(5)(-3)}}{2(5)}$$
$$= \mathbf{\frac{11 \pm \sqrt{181}}{10}}$$

27. $V_{\text{Solid}} = A_{\text{Base}} \times \text{height}$

$$= \left[\frac{\pi(4)^2}{2} + 4(8) + \frac{4(8)}{2}\right](1)(100) \text{ cm}^3$$

$$\approx [73.12](100) \text{ cm}^3$$

$$\approx 7312 \text{ cm}^3$$

$$\approx \frac{(7312)}{(2.54)(2.54)(2.54)} \text{ in.}^3$$

$$\approx \mathbf{446.21 \text{ in.}^3}$$

28. $m = \dfrac{4 - (-2)}{1 - (-2)} = \dfrac{6}{3} = 2$

$y = 2x + b$

Use the point $(-2, -2)$ for x and y.

$-2 = 2(-2) + b$

$b = 2$

$\mathbf{y = 2x + 2}$

29. Since parallel lines have the same slope:

$$y = -\frac{2}{5}x + b$$

Use the point $(1, 4)$ for x and y.

$$4 = -\frac{2}{5}(1) + b$$

$$b = \frac{22}{5}$$

$$\mathbf{y = -\frac{2}{5}x + \frac{22}{5}}$$

30. $y = -\dfrac{2}{3}x + b$

Use the point $(3, 3)$ for x and y.

$$3 = -\frac{2}{3}(3) + b$$

$$b = 5$$

$$\mathbf{y = -\frac{2}{3}x + 5}$$